Invertebrate Zoology

INVERTEBRATE ZOOLOGY

Second Edition

Robert W. Hegner

Late Professor of Protozoology, The Johns Hopkins University

Joseph G. Engemann

Assistant Professor of Biology, Western Michigan University

THE MACMILLAN COMPANY

COLLIER-MACMILLAN LIMITED, LONDON

To *Sister Marie Celeste*
and the many other teachers
who introduced me to that
grand flowering of creation,
the invertebrates

Second Printing, 1969

Earlier edition by Robert W. Hegner copyright 1933 by The Macmillan Company.

Library of Congress catalog card number: 68–10240

The Macmillan Company

Collier-Macmillan Canada, Ltd., Toronto, Ontario

Printed in the United States of America

Preface

TWENTY-FIVE printings of the previous edition of this text in a period of three decades attest to the value of Hegner's approach to invertebrate zoology. I was one of many satisfied students who received their initiation into the world of the invertebrates through the pages of the late author's book.

The philosophy of the first edition is retained: the *type approach* is used to give specific examples as a base for understanding adaptation and variation within the phyla. This approach also provides a more flexible text with greater usefulness in both lecture and laboratory. The topical treatment used permits the combination of theory and application to specific groups, so that the student is not overwhelmed with conceptual knowledge before he knows about the organisms to which it is pertinent.

Among the topics included in this edition that are new to invertebrate zoology since the appearance of the first edition in 1933 are ultrastructure, especially of protozoa; *Neopilina*; the Pogonophora; and facets of classical biology revitalized by the methods and findings of molecular biology.

Some references from the previous edition are retained, and new references have been added that purposely emphasize recent articles in *Science* and *Transactions of the American Microscopical Society*. A small college library can readily provide these journals in a minimal core of science references.

Although the recent progress made in the field of invertebrate zoology is enormous and wide ranging, I hope that the small sample presented in this book will convey some idea of the range and excitement of recent research trends as well as most of the more important concepts of invertebrate zoology.

I am grateful to the many zoologists upon whose work textbooks such as this one are dependent. I am especially grateful to those who so generously provided illustrations or gave their permission for reproducing such material. Mr. and Mrs. Sam Rizzetta receive my thanks for copying and improving many of the drawings retained from the first edition as well as for executing a number of original ones. For critical reading of portions of the manuscript, suggestions, and other help I have many people to thank, especially Dr. Milton A. Miller, Dr. Edgar Inselberg, Dr. Edwin Steen, Mr. Frank Hinds, Dr. Richard Brewer, Dr. Karl Stiles, and Dr. T. Wayne Porter. For omissions and errors I bear sole responsibility. Special thanks go to my wife, Nancy, for the help she has been.

J. G. E.

Contents

List of Tables   xiii

Introduction   xv

General References xvii

Chapter I. Phylum Protozoa   1

Superclass Mastigophora 2
Euglena / Other Mastigophora

Superclass Opalinata 23

Superclass Sarcodina 24
Amoeba proteus / Other Sarcodina

Superclass Sporozoa 48
Monocystis / Plasmodium vivax / Other Sporozoa

Superclass Ciliata 61
Tetrahymena pyriformis / Paramecium / Other Ciliata

Protozoa in General 101

References to Literature on the Protozoa 117

Chapter II. Phylum Porifera 121

Class Calcarea 122
Leucosolenia / Scypha

Class Demospongiae 129
Spongilla

Other Porifera 132
Calcarea / Hexactinellida / Demospongia

Sponges in General 138

References to Literature on the Porifera 146

Chapter III. Phylum Coelenterata 148

Class Hydrozoa 148
Hydra / Obelia / Gonionemus / Other Hydrozoa

Class Scyphozoa 180
Aurelia / Other Scyphozoa

Class Anthozoa 186
Metridium / Astrangia / Other Anthozoa

Coelenterata in General 197

References to Literature on the Coelenterata 204

Chapter IV. Phylum Ctenophora 206

References to Literature on the Ctenophora 211

Chapter V. Phylum Platyhelminthes 212

Class Turbellaria 213
Dugesia / Other Turbellaria

Class Trematoda 224
Opisthorchis sinensis / Other Trematoda

Class Cestoda 238
Taenia / Other Cestoda

Platyhelminthes in General 244

References to Literature on the Platyhelminthes 250

Chapter VI. Phylum Aschelminthes 252

Class Gastrotricha 253
Chaetonotus / Other Gastrotricha

Class Rotifera 255
Epiphanes senta / Other Rotifera

Class Kinorhyncha 262

Class Nematoda 263
Turbatrix aceti / Ascaris lumbricoides / Other Nematoda

Class Nematomorpha 281

Aschelminthes in General 282

References to Literature on the Aschelminthes 284

Chapter VII. Minor Phyla 286

Phylum Mesozoa 289

Phylum Acanthocephala 290

Phylum Rhynchocoela 293

Phylum Priapulida 296

Phylum Entoprocta 297

Phylum Ectoprocta 298
Phylactolaemata / Gymnolaemata

Phylum Brachiopoda 302
Inarticulata or Ecardines / Testicardines or Articulata

Phylum Phoronidea 303

Phylum Sipunculida 304

Phylum Chaetognatha 305

Phylum Pogonophora 307

Phylum Hemichordata 310

References to Literature on the Minor Phyla 311

Chapter VIII. Phylum Annelida   313

Class Polychaeta 314
Nereis virens / Other Polychaeta

Class Oligochaeta 325
Lumbricus terrestris / Other Oligochaeta

Class Archiannelida 338

Class Hirudinea 339
Hirudo medicinalis / Other Hirudinea

Class Echiuroidea 345

Annelids in General 346

References to Literature on the Annelida 349

Chapter IX. Phylum Mollusca   350

Class Amphineura 351
Neopilina galatheae / Other Amphineura

Class Gastropoda 355
Helix pomatia / Other Gastropoda

Class Scaphopoda 367

Class Cephalopoda 368
Loligo pealii / Other Cephalopoda

Class Pelecypoda 377
Anodonta / Other Pelecypoda

Mollusks in General 390

References to Literature on the Mollusca 393

Chapter X. Phylum Arthropoda   395

Class Crustacea 396
The Crayfish / Asellus / Other Crustacea

Class Insecta 437

Class Chilopoda 437

Class Diplopoda 440

Class Pauropoda 441

Class Symphyla 442

Class Onychophora 443

Class Merostomata 446

Class Arachnida 448
The Spider / Other Arachnida

Class Pycnogonida 461

Class Tardigrada 461

Class Pentastomida 462

Arthropods in General 463

References to Literature on the Arthropoda 468

Chapter XI. Class Insecta   471

Dissosteira carolina 471

Other Insecta 485
Subclass Apterygota / Subclass Exopterygota
/ Subclass Endopterygota

Insects in General 535

References to Literature on the Insecta 538

Chapter XII. Phylum Echinodermata   541

Class Asteroidea 542
Asterias / Other Asteroidea

Class Ophiuroidea 550

Class Echinoidea 553
Arbacia / Other Echinoidea

Class Holothuroidea 561
Thyone / Other Holothuroidea

Class Crinoidea 565

Fossil Echinoderms 568

Echinoderms in General 569

References to Literature on the Echinodermata 572

Chapter XIII. Phylum Chordata 574

Subphylum Urochordata 574
Ciona intestinalis / Other Urochordata

Subphylum Cephalochordata 577

Chordates in General 578

References to Literature on the Chordata 578

Chapter XIV. Invertebrates—An Overview 579

References 584

Index 589

List of Tables

Some Common Trematodes of Man   237

Some Common Cestodes of Man   243

An Outline of the Invertebrate Phyla   288

Descriptive Table of the Appendages of the Crayfish   400

The Number and Position of the Gills of the Crayfish   407

The Characteristics of *Peripatus* Arranged so as to Show the Similarity to and Differences from Arthropods and Annelids   446

Segments and Appendages of Arthropoda   464

Introduction

MOST ANIMALS are invertebrates. However, most of the time spent on the study of animals in introductory courses is on the study of vertebrates. Many fundamental principles of physiology, genetics, ecology, and taxonomy apply equally well to invertebrates and vertebrates. Biochemical pathways common to all living things can frequently be studied with greater ease in invertebrates. A knowledge of the invertebrates can simplify the selection of an organism that can be used to greater advantage in molecular biology. Invertebrates, with small size and short life cycles, are excellent organisms for investigations of population dynamics and other ecological phenomena. Perhaps more important is the direct effect of many invertebrates on man and his possessions. Of growing importance is the use of invertebrates in the biological control of pests now being held in check with poisons which may accumulate in our soils and waters.

Beneficial and detrimental effects of invertebrates are an important factor in modern living. Of utmost importance is the pollination of many crops by insects. Other benefits include the production of commercially valuable substances (e.g., waxes, honey, and silk), the use of some invertebrates as food animals, service as scavengers and for aeration of the soil, and an important role as intermediate forms in the food chain. Their value more than offsets the harm done as disease organisms, carriers of disease, and destroyers of food and other valuable substances.

As man's utilization of space on earth increases, knowledge of the exact role of the various invertebrates must increase if we are to manage our resources in a way that will not be disastrous.

Molecular biology is important to—and has benefitted from—invertebrate zoology. An attempt has been made in this book to show the relationship between the invertebrates and the advances in molecular biology with which they are most closely associated. For the complete story of macromolecules, their formation, and degradation, replete with alphabetic abbreviations such as DNA, RNA, and ATP, one must turn to genetics, physiology, and biochemistry. This is not because molecular biology is an unimportant part of invertebrate zoology, but because the vast numbers and varieties of invertebrates make it impossible to adequately cover both the classical aspects of invertebrate zoology and the molecular aspects. Thus the emphasis here is on a balanced approach with as many guideposts as possible added to connect this subject with other areas of biology.

Since all biologists are ultimately involved with organisms, and organisms that are closely related may differ markedly in their molecular, ecological, and genetic aspects, it is important to be able to distinguish organisms in a systematic way. That is one reason why invertebrate zoology is an important subject early in the career of a biologist.

The last chapter of this book is intended to serve as a summary to connect some of the unifying threads of invertebrate zoology; it may also be read as an introduction, along with the beginning of Chapter VII, for those who have not had a recent course in general zoology or general biology.

The information and theories accumulated about invertebrates are too extensive to be contained in one text. Morphological, ecological, and to a lesser extent taxonomic and physiological studies reported in the older literature retain much of their usefulness today. Thus the person who would become an invertebrate zoologist must become familiar with the accumulated literature or know how to tap the wealth of information there.

References from this and other texts will provide one entry into the literature. Two of the most important bibliographic tools are *Biological Abstracts* and the *Zoological Record*. Each provides an index of most pertinent information published before or during the year that they are dated. Through them one can learn of useful literature found in an increasing array of journals, museum reports, and government publications. Use of literature cited in such papers is an efficient way of locating additional information on the subject. Of equal importance to the researcher is communication with his colleagues, either informally or at society meetings.

Two important recent treatises on the invertebrates are the still incompleted works of Hyman (1940–) and Grasse (1948–). Among recent texts that students will find useful is that of Barnes (1963) for phylogenetic discussions, Hickman (1967) for general features of the major groups, and Meglitsch (1967) for the classical biology of invertebrates. Books especially useful for identification include those of Edmondson (1959), Pennak (1953; also contains many valuable general discussions), Light and others (1954), Pratt (1935), and the *How to Know* series of the Brown Publishing Company. Titles of the general references listed below indicate their content.

General References

ALLEE, W. C., A. E. EMERSON, O. PARK, and K. P. SCHMIDT. 1949. *Principles of Animal Ecology*. Saunders, Philadelphia.

BARNES, R. D. 1963. *Invertebrate Zoology*. Saunders, Philadelphia.

BLACKWELDER, R. E. 1963. *Classification of the Animal Kingdom*. Southern Illinois Univ. Press, Carbondale.

BORRADAILE, L. A., F. A. POTTS, L. E. S. EASTHAM, J. T. SAUNDERS, and G. A. KERKUT. 1959. *The Invertebrata*. Cambridge Univ. Press.

BRONN, H. G. (Ed.) 1880– . *Klassen und Ordnungen des Tier-reichs*. Leipzig.

BROWN, F. A. (Ed.) 1950. *Selected Invertebrate Types*. Wiley, New York.

BULLOCK, T. H., and G. A. HORRIDGE. 1965. *Structure and Function in the Nervous System of Invertebrates*. Freeman, San Francisco.

BULLOUGH, W. S. 1960. *Practical Invertebrate Anatomy*. Macmillan, London.

BYKHOVSKAYA-PAVLOVSKAYA, I. E., *et al.* 1962. *Key to Parasites of Freshwater Fish of the U.S.S.R.* Translated by A. Birron and Z. S. Cole. 1964. U.S. Dept. Comm.

HARMER, S. F., and A. E. SHIPLEY. (Eds.) 1891–1909. *The Cambridge Natural History*. London.

CARTHY, J. D. 1958. *An Introduction to the Behavior of Invertebrates*. Macmillan, New York.

CHANDLER, A. C. 1955. *Introduction to Parasitology*. Wiley, New York.

CHENG, T. C. 1964. *The Biology of Animal Parasites*. Saunders, Philadelphia.

DAWYDOFF, C. 1928. *Embryologie comparée des invertébrés*. Masson et Cie, Paris.

DOUGHERTY, E. (Ed.) 1963. *The Lower Metazoa*. Univ. of California Press, Berkeley.

EDMONDSON, W. T. (Ed.) 1959. *Fresh-Water Biology*. 2nd Ed. Wiley, New York.

GRASSE, P. (Ed.) 1948– . *Traité de Zoologie*. (Tomes I–XI on invertebrates.) Masson et Cie, Paris.

HALSTEAD, B. W. 1965. *Poisonous and Venomous Marine Animals of the World*. G.P.O., Washington.

HESSE, R., W. C. ALLEE, and K. P. SCHMIDT. 1937. *Ecological Animal Geography*. Wiley, New York.

HICKMAN, C. P. 1967. *Biology of the Invertebrates*. Mosby, Saint Louis.

HYMAN, L. H. 1940– . *The Invertebrates*. McGraw-Hill, New York.

HYNES, H. B. N. 1960. *The Biology of Polluted Waters*. Liverpool Univ. Press, Liverpool.

KEVAN, D. K. 1962. *Soil Animals*. Philosophical Library, New York.

KUKENTHAL, W., and T. KRUMBACH. (Eds.) 1923. *Handbuch der Zoologie*. Berlin.

LANKESTER, R. (Ed.) 1909– . *A Treatise on Zoology*. Black, London.

LIGHT, S. F., R. I. SMITH, F. H. PITELKA, D. P. ABBOTT, and F. M. WEESNER. 1954. *Intertidal Invertebrates of the Central California Coast*. Univ. of California Press, Berkeley.

MacGINITIE, G. E., and N. MacGINITIE. 1949. *Natural History of Marine Animals*. McGraw-Hill, New York.

MALLIS. 1960. *Handbook of Pest Control*. MacNair Dorland, New York.

MAYR, E., E. G. LINSLEY, and R. L. USINGER. 1953. *Methods and Principles of Systematic Zoology*. McGraw-Hill, New York.

MEGLITSCH, P. A. 1967. *Invertebrate Zoology*. Oxford Univ. Press, New York.

MOORE, R. C. (Ed.) 1953– *Treatise on Invertebrate Paleontology*. Geol. Soc. Am., New York.

MORGAN, A. H. 1930. *Field Book of Ponds and Streams*. Putnam, New York.

NOBLE, E. R., and G. A. NOBLE. 1964. *Parasitology*. Lea and Febiger, Philadelphia.

PENNAK, R. W. 1953. *Fresh-Water Invertebrates of the United States*. Ronald Press, New York.

PRATT, H. S. 1935. *A Manual of the Common Invertebrate Animals*. McGraw-Hill, New York.

RICKETTS, E. F., and J. CALVIN. 1939. *Between Pacific Tides*. Stanford Univ. Press.

ROGERS, W. P. 1962. *The Nature of Parasitism*. Academic Press, New York.

SHROCK, R. R., and W. H. TWENHOFEL. 1953. *Principles of Invertebrate Paleontology*. McGraw-Hill, New York.

SMITH, R. C. 1962. *Guide to the Literature of the Zoological Sciences*. Burgess, Minneapolis.

SWEETMAN, H. L. 1958. *The Principles of Biological Control*. Brown, Dubuque.

WHIPPLE, H. E. (Ed.) 1963. Some Biochemical and Immunological Aspects of Host-Parasite Relationships. *Ann. N.Y. Acad. Sci.* **113** (1).

ZWEIFEL, F. W. 1961. *A Handbook of Biological Illustration*. Univ. of Chicago Press.

Chapter I

Phylum Protozoa

W ITHIN the phylum Protozoa are animals with a great diversity of complexity, size, and behavior. Although not subdivided into cells of differing functions, as the other phyla are, the protozoan carries on all the life processes with one cell. They range from simple cells, containing little more than cytoplasm and nucleus, to complex cells with variation in vacuoles, fibrils, and other organelles. Some are so small as to be barely visible with the light microscope. Others are large enough to be seen with the unaided eye. All require the microscope as an aid to study of their structure. In recent years the electron microscope has revealed much about their ultrastructure to many researchers. Many protozoa are economically important parasites, which live in or upon the bodies of other animals or plants. Free-living protozoa are found performing a variety of functions in fresh water, salt water, and soil communities. Whether parasitic or free-living, all protozoans require the presence of sufficient moisture to prevent drying for activity and growth to occur. Only the resistant spores or cysts of some species of protozoa are able to withstand dessication.

Protozoa are of increasing importance in the study of molecular biology for the following reasons. Many of the biochemical pathways used by protozoans are used by all animals, including man. Some protozoans can be cultured in chemically defined media, in which no other species are present, to rapidly produce large populations of essentially identical cells for use as experimental and control organisms. They are sometimes used for bio-assay because of their sensitive growth responses to various nutrients.

Free-living protozoa are not distributed among bodies of water in a haphazard fashion; each species is more or less restricted to a definite type of habitat just as are higher animals. Some species live in fresh water; others, only in salt water; some live in contact with the bottom; others, float about suspended in the water; some are known to live only in the soil, and others, only in sphagnum swamps. Free-living protozoa are to be found almost everywhere on the surface of the earth where moisture exists.

Parasitic protozoa are likewise rather definitely restricted in their habitats. Every higher animal that has been carefully studied has been found to harbor parasitic protozoa. Each species of animal, as a rule, is parasitized by its own peculiar species of protozoa. For example, 28 different species of protozoa are known to live in man. Many of these appear to occur in monkeys also, but only a few of them have been recorded from other animals. The parasitic species are usually separated into two groups; those that live in the digestive tract are known as intestinal protozoa and those that live principally in the blood, as blood-inhabiting protozoa.

The number and variety of protozoa is very great. About 46,000 species have been named, although over 20,000 of them are fossil forms. Thousands of species of free-living protozoa have been described, and each kind of higher animal seems to possess one or more types of protozoa peculiar to itself, hence the number of parasitic protozoa is probably at least as great as that of all other animals combined. The number of individuals is also enormous. Billions of a free-living species may exist in a single pond. Among parasitic varieties we need only refer to the millions of ciliates that occur in the stomach of cattle and the millions of flagellates that live in the cecum of almost every rat.

These immense numbers of protozoa have traditionally been separated by their means of locomotion into four classes: Sarcodina with pseudopodia, Mastigophora with flagella, Ciliata with cilia, and Sporozoa with no organelles for locomotion. Recently, the Committee on Taxonomy and Taxonomic Problems of the Society of Protozoologists published a revised classification of the Protozoa (Honigberg *et al.*, 1964). Their classification attempts to show phylogeny and reflects recent discoveries. Although it is less simple than an artificial classification, it is followed here, with some modification, as the classification most likely to have some stability in future years. Classes of Sarcodina follow Bovee and Jahn (1965).

1 / Superclass Mastigophora: The Flagellated Protozoa

(1) Euglena

The genus *Euglena* contains over a dozen species. Two commonly found in algae-choked ponds are *E. viridis* and *E. gracilis*. They are green, and—although a single animal cannot be seen with the naked eye—a great many massed together impart a green tint to the water.

Cytology.   (Fig. 1–1.) *Euglena* is a single elongated cell pointed at the posterior, and blunt at the anterior end. Two kinds of cytoplasm can be distinguished in *Euglena* as in *Amoeba* and *Paramecium*, a dense outer layer, the

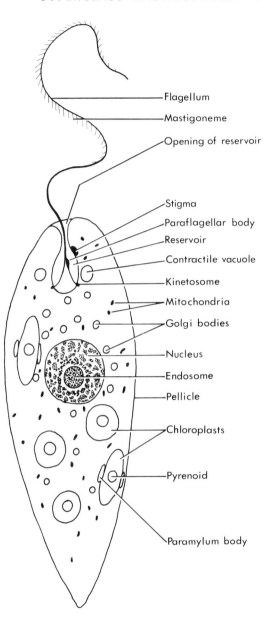

Fig. 1-1. *Euglena*. Diagram of main cytological features. (Modified after several sources.)

Flagellum
Mastigoneme
Opening of reservoir
Stigma
Paraflagellar body
Reservoir
Contractile vacuole
Kinetosome
Mitochondria
Golgi bodies
Nucleus
Endosome
Pellicle
Chloroplasts
Pyrenoid
Paramylum body

ectoplasm, and a central mass, the *endoplasm*, which is more fluid. A thin cuticle is present, as in *Paramecium*, covering the entire surface of the body. Parallel ridges of this cuticle spiral around the animal, making it appear striated. A little to one side of the center of the anterior blunt end of the body is a funnel-shaped depression known as the *cytostome*. At the bottom of this depression is an opening that leads into a short duct called the *gullet*. This, in turn, enters a large spherical vesicle, the *reservoir*, into which several minute *contractile vacuoles* discharge their contents. The mouth (cytostome) and gullet are not used for the ingestion of food but as a canal for the escape of fluid from the reservoir.

A conspicuous structure in *Euglena* is the red eye spot or *stigma*. This is placed near the inner end of the gullet close to the reservoir. It consists of protoplasm in which are embedded a number of granules of red pigment. It is thought that the *paraflagellar body* is a light-sensitive structure, which is enabled to give a directional light response because of the one-sided light filtering action of the stigma.

Euglena has a single oval *nucleus* lying in a definite position near the center of the body. There is a distinct nuclear membrane, which electron microscope studies have shown to consist of a double layer penetrated by numerous pores. The nucleus contains a central body known as the *endosome* (syn. *nucleolus*, *karyosome*).

Euglena derives its green color from a number of oval disks suspended in the protoplasm. These are known as *chromatophores*. Located in the center of each chromatophore is a collection of granules, the *pyrenoid*. The protoplasm of the chromatophore contains chlorophyll, which enables *Euglena* to produce food by the process of photosynthesis. This plantlike characteristic has caused botanists to classify *Euglena* as an alga.

Other structures within *Euglena* appear when properly stained. Numerous small granules, termed *mitochondria*, are scattered throughout the cell. The mitochondria are important as a location of many of the biochemical reactions of the cell during respiration. *Golgi bodies* are abundant but of unknown function.

A long, whiplike *flagellum* extends from the opening of the reservoir. It comes from one of the two flagella that originate from *kinetosomes* located in the wall of the reservoir. The electron-microscopic structure of a flagellum is similar to that of a cilium (Fig. 1–2) in that each has 11 electron dense fibers arranged in a pattern of two central fibers and nine peripheral fibers. Only the peripheral fibers extend into the kinetosome. The distal portion of the flagellum contains numerous minute fibers, known as *mastigonemes*, which project laterally.

Nutrition. Although *Euglena* has a mouth (cytostome) and gullet, it is doubtful, as noted above, if any food is ingested. Food is manufactured photosynthetically, as in plants, with the aid of light and the chlorophyll in the chromatophores. This mode of nutrition is known as *holophytic*, or *autotrophic*. Photosynthesis enables the oxygen of a water molecule to be released, while the hydrogen of the water molecule reduces the carbon dioxide present through a series of steps to form carbohydrates and more water. Light of blue and red wavelengths is utilized with greatest efficiency. The carbohydrates are stored as a starchlike substance called *paramylum*. The conversion of the simple sugars

Fig. 1-2. Cilia. Electron micrograph of several *Didinium nasutum* cilia. × 64,000. The nine, double, peripheral fibers and two central fibers visible in the cross-sections are common to both cilia and flagella. (Photo courtesy of Dorothy R. Pitelka, Cancer Research Genetics Laboratory, University of California.)

produced by photosynthesis to paramylum is presumed to occur due to the action of the pyrenoid. Both pyrenoids and chromatophores are permanent cell structures and increase in number by division and not by the origin of new ones from other parts of the body. All the food necessary for the life of *Euglena* need not be produced by photosynthesis. When the chlorophyll is destroyed by treatment with certain drugs, the colorless *Euglena* resulting can continue to live if provided with a medium rich in organic nutrients. This seems to indicate that organic substances in solution are absorbed through the surface of the body, that is, *saprophytic* nutrition can occur and may supplement the normal holophytic nutrition. The nutrition of *Euglena* differs from that of the majority of animals, since the latter live by ingesting solid particles of food and are said to be *holozoic*, or *heterotrophic*.

Locomotion.   *Euglena* changes its shape frequently, becoming shorter and thicker, and shows certain squirming movements. These prove that it possesses considerable elasticity, because the normal shape is regained if enough water is present. Often in a favorable specimen, the threadlike flagellum may be seen projecting from the anterior end of the body and bending to and fro, drawing the animal after it. Pitelka and Schooley (1955) have found that when the flagellum is fixed at a pH near that of the culture medium the mastigonemes are closely applied to the flagellum. Under other conditions, the mastigonemes (Fig. 1–3) may extend laterally from one side of the flagellum. Jahn and co-workers (1964) have shown that the presence of a sufficient number of laterally

Fig. 1-3. Mastigonemes. Lateral view of *Ochromonas malhamensis* flagellum showing numerous pantoneme mastigonemes. × 25,300. (From Pitelka and Schooley, 1955, *Univ. Calif. Publ. Zool.*, **61**:79–128. Electron micrograph courtesy of Dorothy R. Pitelka, Cancer Research Genetics Laboratory, University of California.)

projecting mastigonemes can reverse the direction of the propulsive force (Fig. 1-4) provided by the flagellum of *Ochromonas* although the undulations of the flagellum are the same. Some workers think that the propulsive force comes from the sculling action of the tapered *Euglena* as it vibrates due to the movement of the flagellum.*

Behavior. *Euglena* swims through the water in a spiral path. The effect of this is the production of a perfectly straight course through the trackless water. When stimulated by a change in the intensity of the light, *Euglena*, in the

---

* If the flagellum cannot be seen in the living animal, a little iodine placed under the cover glass will help to make it visible.

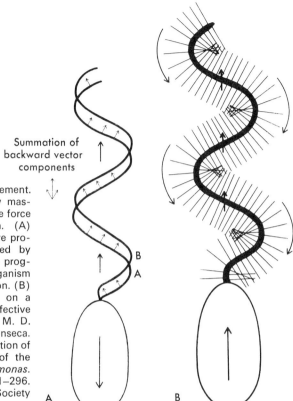

Summation of
backward vector
components

Fig. 1-4. Flagellar movement. Diagram to indicate how mastigonemes may reverse the force exerted by a flagellum. (A) Distally directed sine wave produces the force indicated by small arrows as the wave progresses from *A* to *B*. Organism moves in opposite direction. (B) Action of mastigonemes on a similar wave reverses effective force. (From T. L. Jahn, M. D. Landman, and J. R. Fonseca. The mechanism of locomotion of flagellates. II. Function of the mastigonemes of *Ochromonas*. *J. Protozool.,* **11**(3):291–296. Copyright 1964 by the Society of Protozoologists.)

majority of cases, stops or moves backward, turns strongly toward the dorsal surface, but continues to revolve on its long axis. The posterior end then acts as a pivot, while the anterior end traces a circle of wide diameter in the water. The animal may swim forward in a new direction from any point in this circle. This is the *avoiding reaction*.

Euglena is very sensitive to light. It swims toward an ordinary light such as that from a window, and if a culture containing euglenae is examined, most of the animals will be found on the side toward the brightest light. This is of distinct advantage to the animal, because light is necessary for the assimilation of carbon dioxide by means of its chlorophyll. *Euglena* will swim away from the direct rays of the sun. Direct sunlight will kill the organism if allowed to act for a long time. The ultraviolet portion of the solar spectrum is probably the most injurious portion, because large amounts of ultraviolet light are lethal for many organisms. If a drop of water containing euglenae is placed in the direct sunlight and then one half of it is shaded, the animals will avoid the shady part and also the direct sunlight, both of which are unfavorable to them, and will remain in a small band between the two in the light best suited for

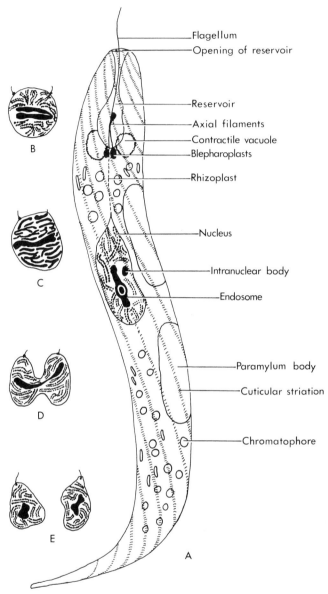

Flagellum
Opening of reservoir

Reservoir
Axial filaments
Contractile vacuole
Blepharoplasts
Rhizoplast

Nucleus

Intranuclear body
Endosome

Paramylum body
Cuticular striation

Chromatophore

B
C
D
E
A

Fig. 1-5, A. *Euglena spirogyra:* nuclear division. *(A) Vegetative form* with nuclear chromatin in the form of paired rows of chromomeres. Only the proximal portion of the flagellum is included. *(B) Prophase nucleus.* The chromosomes are in pairs; the endosome has elongated and divided into two; the axial filaments are attached to two blepharoplasts on the nuclear membrane that have arisen from the intranuclear body. *(C) Metaphase nucleus.* The chromosomes separate and the endosome elongates. *(D) Anaphase nucleus.* The nuclear membrane constricts; the chromosomes divide longitudinally and become granular; and the endosome constricts. *(E) Nuclear division completed.* The nuclei next assume the appearance indicated in *A.* (After Ratcliffe.)

them, that is, their optimum. By shading various portions of the body of a *Euglena*, it has been found that the region in front of the eye spot is more sensitive than any other part. It should be noted that when *Euglena* is swimming through the water it is this anterior end which first reaches an injurious environment; the animals give the avoiding reaction at once, and are thus carried out of danger.

Reproduction. Reproduction in *Euglena* takes place by binary longitudinal fission. Nuclear division takes place within the nuclear membrane. The chromatin, which is in the form of paired strands of chromomeres in the vegetative stage, forms pairs of chromosomes each of which divides longitudinally into two (Fig. 1–5, A). The endosome becomes constricted into two approximately equal parts. The intranuclear body also divides into two. The body begins to divide at the anterior end. The old flagellum is retained by one half, whereas a new flagellum is developed by the other. Often division takes place while the animals are in the encysted condition. Occasionally euglenae are found which have become almost spherical and are surrounded by a rather thick gelatinous covering which they have secreted. Such an animal is said to be encysted. In this condition periods of drought are successfully passed; the animals become active when water is again encountered. Usually in cultures brought into the laboratory many cysts are found on the sides of the dish. Encystment frequently takes place without any apparent cause; the animal rests in this condition for a time and then emerges to its free-swimming habit.

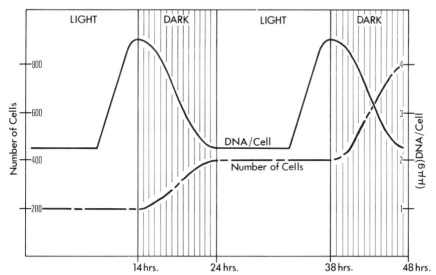

Fig. 1-5, B. DNA in *Euglena*. Dotted line indicates relative numbers of *Euglena* which undergo a doubling in numbers during the dark period. Solid line indicates DNA per cell with the amount doubling during the last of the light period. (Adapted from Edmunds, 1964.)

Before encystment the flagellum is thrown off, a new one being produced when activity is again resumed. One cyst usually produces two euglenae, although these may divide while still within the old cyst wall to make four in all. Certain observers have recorded as many as 32 young flagellated euglenae that escaped from a single cyst. Fission occurs only during the hours of darkness in ordinary circumstances (Fig. 1–5, B); however, synthesis of protoplasmic constituents occurs only during hours of light with replication of DNA limited to the latter part of those hours.

(2) Other Mastigophora

The superclass Mastigophora includes a very large number of minute Protozoa that are rather difficult to classify. It is convenient to separate them into two classes: (1) plantlike species or Phytomastigophorea, and (2) animal-like species or Zoomastigophorea. Certain of the more common and interesting species will be referred to under some of the orders recognized in these two subclasses.

Phytomastigophorea

Order Chrysomonadida.   This order includes a number of small forms that contain typically one or two brownish chromatophores and one to three flagella. The body is often amoeboid and food may even be taken in by pseudopodia. Nutrition is either holophytic, holozoic, or both.

Protozoa of Drinking Water.   Several species of Chrysomonadida are of particular interest because they sometimes become very numerous in water confined in reservoirs and render it unfit for drinking purposes. They are all colonial in habit. *Uroglenopsis americana* (Fig. 1–6, A) forms spherical colonies the individuals of which are embedded in the periphery of a gelatinous matrix.

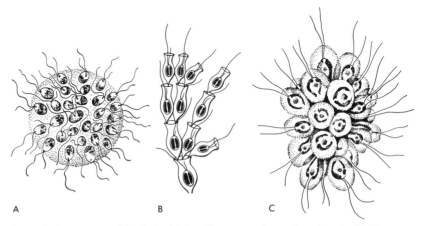

Fig. 1-6. Chrysomonadida. Colonial flagellates sometimes obnoxious in drinking water. (A) *Uroglenopsis americana.* (B) *Dinobryon sertularia.* (C) *Synura uvella.* (After various authors.)

A stigma and a platelike chromatophore are present. *Dinobryon sertularia* (Fig. 1–6, B) has a vaselike, hyaline, or yellowish cellulose test, usually a stigma, and one or two brownish chromatophores. *Synura uvella* (Fig. 1–6, C) consists of from 2 to 50 individuals arranged in radial fashion; each has a stigma and two brown chromatophores. *Uroglenopsis* is said to be the worst of the species, giving rise to a fishy odor; when large numbers are present an odor resembling cod liver oil results. *Dinobryon* also produces a fishy odor. *Synura* is responsible for an odor resembling ripe cucumbers and a bitter and spicy taste. These odors are due to aromatic oils elaborated by the organisms during growth and liberated when they die and disintegrate. They are recognizable when present in minute amounts; for example, the oil of *Synura* produces a perceptible odor in a dilution of 1 part oil to 25 million parts water. Treating water with copper sulphate kills these Protozoa so that the odors eventually disappear.

Order Cryptomonadida.   *Chilomonas paramecium* (Fig. 1–7, B) is a common species belonging to this order, one that frequently occurs in laboratory cultures. It is about 35 microns in length, without chromatophores and hence colorless, with two anteriorly directed flagella, a contractile vacuole on one side near the anterior end, a spherical nucleus posterior to the center, and a mass of endoplasm that is distinctly alveolar in structure. No solid food particles are ingested, but nutritive substances are absorbed through the surface of the body.

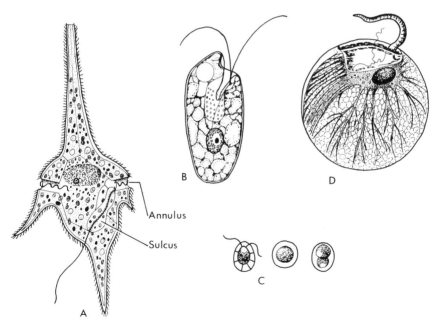

Annulus

Sulcus

A   B   C   D

Fig. 1-7. Phytomastigophorea. (A) Dinoflagellida; *Ceratium macroceras*. (B) Cryptomonadida; *Chilomonas paramecium*. (C) Volvocida; *Haematococcus lacustris*. Causes red rain and red snow when present in large numbers. Active, resting, and division stages. (D) Dinoflagellida; *Noctiluca scintillans*. (After various authors.)

Order Dinoflagellida (Figs. 1–7, A and 1–7, D). The most characteristic features of the Dinoflagellida are their shell and flagellar apparatus. The shell or *lorica* is a rigid structure, sometimes very bizarrre in form, composed of cellulose, or an allied substance, which usually has a longitudinal groove, the *sulcus,* and a circular groove, the *girdle* (annulus). Two flagella are present which issue from pores in the lorica and lie within these grooves. The flagellum in the sulcus extends beyond it and provides much of the motive force. The undulations of the flagellum in the girdle rise enough above the surface of the organism to provide part of the forward thrust.

The majority of the Dinoflagellida are holophytic and possess chromatophores, which may be brown, pale green, or yellow. A few species, however, have taken on a holozoic method of nutrition and may even ingest their food by pseudopodia. Frequently a stigma is present. Asexual reproduction by fission takes place.

Ecology of the Dinoflagellates. Most of the dinoflagellates are salt-water species; a large number are parasites, and many live in fresh water. *Ceratium hirundinella* (Fig. 1–7, A) has a distinctive appearance and is found in both fresh water and salt water. An interesting marine species is *Noctiluca scintillans* (Fig. 1–7, D). It is spherical in shape, bilaterally symmetrical, and usually from 500 to 1,000 microns in diameter. It possesses a small flagellum, a tentacle, and cytoplasm that is much vacuolated. Sometimes noctilucas are so abundant in the Atlantic and Pacific as to color the water red by day and render it phosphorescent by night. The "red tide" coincides with the abundance of some species of dinoflagellate, often *Gymnodinium brevis*. The oils, which are stored as food by the dinoflagellates causing the "red tide," are thought to be toxic to many other marine animals when they are liberated in large amounts by the natural death of many of the dinoflagellates. The Gulf of Mexico has been the site of many of the "red tide" fish kills. Dinoflagellates are the symbiotic protozoan present in the cells of many marine invertebrates, such as corals and mollusks. Such symbiotic dinoflagellates, which are presumed to provide a nutritional advantage to their host, are known by the term *Zooanthellae*. In such a mutualistic association, the dinoflagellates are not recognizable as such, but they regain their dinoflagellate characteristics when removed from the host.

Order Euglenida. Euglenida contains those flagellates that store their food reserve as paramylum. All Euglenida can undergo the squirming undulations known as *metaboly*; such metabolic movements are not amoeboid movements. *Euglena* is a rather typical genus and presents the principal characteristics of the group. A number of interesting species are common in fresh water. *Euglena pisciformis* is a highly active spindle-shaped species. *E. spirogyra* is large and sluggish. *E. sanguinea* has a hematochrome. *E. deses* has a very short flagellum and is highly metabolic. The genus *Phacus* (Fig. 1–8, A) is represented by several fresh-water species. The body is much flattened, and the cuticle has conspicuous striations. Green chromatophores are present. *Peranema tricho-*

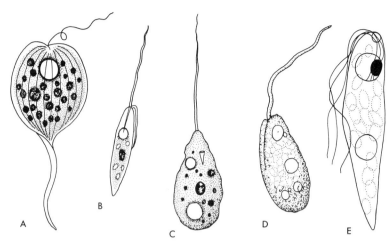

Fig. 1-8. Euglenida. (A) *Phacus longicaudus*. (B) *Heteronema acus*. (C) *Peranema trichophorum*. (D) *Copromonas subtilis*. (E) *Euglenamorpha hegneri*. (After various authors.)

phorum (Fig. 1–8, C) is a common species. The body is broad and truncated at the posterior end when in locomotion, and a long flagellum with vibrating tip extends out from the pointed anterior end. The body is very metabolic when stationary. *Heteronema acus* (Fig. 1–8, B) occurs in fresh water and in the soil. Two flagella arise from the anterior end: one directed forward and the other backward. The body is colorless, metabolic, and pointed at both ends.

Copromonas subtilis (Fig. 1–8, D) is an interesting species because it is coprozoic, that is, it occurs in the feces of higher animals which it finds a favorable environment. It has been recorded from the feces of frogs, toads, pigs, and man. A parasitic species, *Euglenamorpha hegneri* (Fig. 1–8, E), that occurs commonly in the intestine of frog and toad tadpoles probably belongs to this group, and, if so, is the only representative that possesses three flagella. It lives between the food mass and the wall of the intestine or rectum of tadpoles and can be transferred from one tadpole to another of the same or different species either by association of infected tadpoles with clean tadpoles or by feeding clean tadpoles with the rectum from infected animals.

Order Volvocida.   The Volvocida are undoubtedly closely allied to the algae. The body is covered with a rigid cellulose membrane. Biflagellate forms are typical, the flagella being inserted through pores in the cellulose wall. Most species are exclusively holophytic and possess a large cup-shaped green chromatophore. A few colorless forms that live saprophytically are referred to this order, but in no case do any of the forms ingest solid food. A red stigma or eye spot is also present. Asexual reproduction takes place giving rise to numbers of small flagellated swarmers. Sexual phenomena are definitely known for a

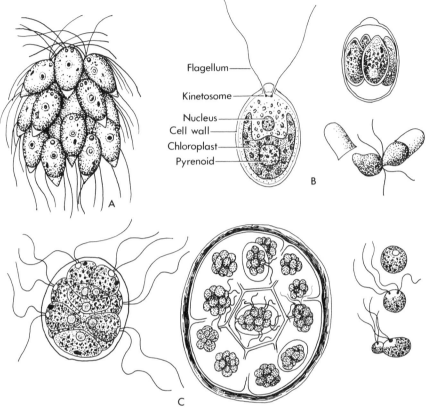

Flagellum
Kinetosome
Nucleus
Cell wall
Chloroplast
Pyrenoid

A

B

C

Fig. 1-9. Colonial Volvocida. (A) *Spondylomorum quaternarium.* (B) *Chlamydomonas monadina;* active, dividing, and fusion of gametes. (C) *Pandorina morum;* active, dividing, and fusion of gametes into a zygote. (After Oltmanns and others.)

large number of species. Colony formation is quite frequent. An interesting group of genera belonging mostly to the family Volvocidae can be arranged to illustrate the evolution of multicellular from unicellular organisms and also the evolution of sex as indicated in the following paragraphs and in Figures 1–9 and 1–10.

Spondylomorum (Fig. 1–9, A) is colonial in habit with 16 cells in each colony. These cells are practically independent. Each of them reproduces by fission to form a colony like the parent colony. No gamete formation is known.

Chlamydomonas (Fig. 1–9, B) is a unicellular type that reproduces vegetatively by fission into two, four, or eight daughter cells and also produces gametes, all of one size, that fuse together in pairs forming zygotes. The zygotes undergo fission resulting in a number of vegetative unicellular individuals. After vegetative fission, cells may be retained in irregularly shaped groups by an abundance of gelatinous material that ordinarily separates as the coating of the individual cells. Such a grouping of cells, which is not truly colonial, is known as a *palmella* formation.

Pandorina (Fig. 1–9, C) is a colonial form of 16 cells embedded in a gelatinous matrix, each independent of the others. New colonies are produced by each cell by fission. Gametes are also formed, some being larger than others. The larger gametes appear to fuse with the smaller ones to form zygotes. Because sexual reproduction usually includes the fusion of a larger female gamete with a smaller male gamete, the process in *Pandorina* seems to furnish an early stage in the evolution of sex.

Eudorina is a colonial type with 32 cells. Each cell may reproduce a colony vegetatively by fission. At times the cells of certain colonies become large; this is characteristic of female colonies and the large cells are macrogametes. In male colonies, each cell divides to form 16 or 32 microgametes. The microgametes fuse with the macrogametes in pairs to form zygotes. In this genus there is no doubt about the difference in size between the conjugating gametes.

Pleodorina is a somewhat spherical colony, like *Eudorina*, with the cells arranged at the surface with their flagella out. However, some of the cells are small *somatic* cells that do not have a reproductive capacity. The somatic cells

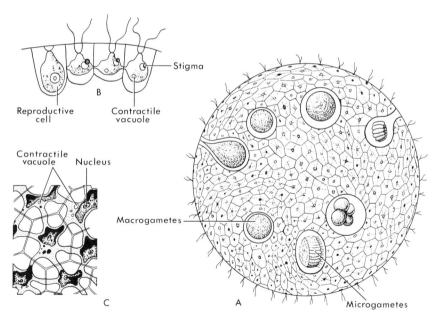

Fig. 1-10. *Volvox globator:* a large colonial flagellate. (A) A sexually ripe colony, showing microgametes and macrogametes in various stages of development, surface detail is omitted over the internal gametes. (B) A portion of the edge of the colony highly magnified, showing three flagellate cells united by protoplasmic strands, and a single reproductive cell. (C) A single cell connected with surrounding cells by protoplasmic strands. (After Kölliker, from Bourne.)

are located at one end; the larger generative cells complete the majority of the spherical arrangement.

Volvox globator (Fig. 1–10) represents the final stage in the series. The thousands of vegetative cells in a colony are united by protoplasmic strands; physiological continuity is thus established between the cells, a condition not found in the colonies previously described. Most of the cells contain an eye spot, chlorophyll, a contractile vacuole, and two flagella. These are the somatic cells. The production of daughter colonies is accomplished by special reproductive cells that are set aside for this purpose. The asexual method proceeds as follows. Certain cells of the colony are larger than others and lack flagella; a number of these in one colony increase in size and divide by simple fission into a great number of cells, producing new colonies without being fertilized. The cells that act in this way are named parthenogonidia. The sexual method of reproduction may be observed in colonies that contain as many as 50 of the larger nonflagellated cells. Some of these grow larger and may be recognized as female cells or macrogametes; others produce by simple division a flat plate, containing about 128 spindle-shaped male cells or microgametes. These fuse with the macrogametes. The zygote thus formed secretes a surrounding wall and in this condition the winter is passed. The following spring the zygote breaks out of the wall and by division produces a new colony. The smaller somatic cells contained in the mother colony fall to the bottom and disintegrate as soon as the new colonies produced by the fertilized germ cells have escaped.

In *Pleodorina* and *Volvox*, true somatic cells are encountered for the first time, that is, cells that function only vegetatively and are unable to reproduce the colony. In the other forms described every cell is capable of reproducing the whole. *Volvox* also contains true germ cells, that is, cells that have given up nutritive functions to carry on reproduction. Furthermore, a clear case of natural death occurs in the somatic cells when they fall to the bottom of the pond and disintegrate. The bodies of higher animals consist of many cells that may be separated into somatic and germ cells. The latter are either male or female. In most cases the fusion of a male cell with a female cell is necessary before a new animal can be reproduced. At any rate, some of these germ cells maintain the continuation of the species by producing new individuals, whereas the somatic cells perish when the animal dies.

Zoomastigophorea

Order Choanoflagellida. The order Choanoflagellida contains a small number of free-living species having a single flagellum surrounded at the base with a delicate collar. A fresh-water species is *Monosiga brevipes* (Fig. 1–11, B). Collared, flagellated cells occur in this order of protozoa, in the sponges, and in some echinoderms.

Order Rhizomastigida. The order Rhizomastigida is characterized by the fact that the organisms ingest their food at any point on the body by means of

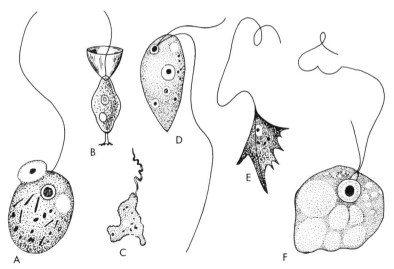

Fig. 1-11. Zoomastigophorea. (A) *Oikomonas termo*. (B) *Monosiga brevipes*. (C) *Mastigamoeba invertens*. (D) *Bodo saltans*. (E) *Cercomonas longicauda*. (F) *Monas vulgaris*. (After various authors.)

pseudopodia. They exhibit so many transitional characters between the true Sarcodina on the one hand and the Mastigophora on the other that it is exceedingly difficult to define their exact relationships. A common species in fresh water and soil is *Mastigamoeba aspera*. This species has a single long flagellum and pushes out finger-like pseudopodia. *Mastigamoeba hylae* is a parasitic species that occurs in the large intestine of frog tadpoles. A short, inactive flagellum arises from the nucleus at the anterior end. *Histomonas meleagridis* causes a liver infection in turkeys and other fowl. No cyst stage is known, but the amoeboid flagellate is able to get from one host to the next in the eggs of a different parasite of fowl, the nematode *Heterakis gallinae*.

Order Kinetoplastida.   The order Kinetoplastida comprises a number of flagellates generally of small size, and only one to four flagella. Most species are parasitic. The order is of particular interest because it includes the flagellates living in the blood and tissues of man.

Of the free-living Kinetoplastida, *Oikomonas termo* (Fig. 1–11, A) is a simple type that is often common in fresh water and soil. It is very small (4 to 5 microns in diameter), spherical in shape, and has a single long flagellum. *Bodo caudatus*, *Cercomonas longicauda* (Fig. 1–11, E), and *Monas vulgaris* (Fig. 1–11, F) are very common in stagnant water and infusions, and the first two are often coprozoic. *Bodo* (Fig. 1–11, D) is ovoid and plastic with two anterior flagella, one directed forward, the other trailing behind, and a spherical nucleus near or anterior to the center of the body. *Cercomonas* is similar to *Bodo*, but the trailing flagellum is attached to the side of the body and the nucleus is pyriform.

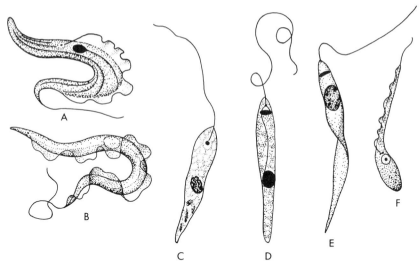

Fig. 1-12. Kinetoplastida. (A) *Trypanosoma rotatorium*, from the frog. (B) *Trypanosoma diemyctyli*, from the newt. (C) *Leishmania donovani*, from man. (D) *Herpetomonas muscarum*, from the house fly. (E) *Phytomonas elmassiani*, from the milkweed plant. (F) *Crithidia gerridis*, from the water strider. Some Kinetoplastida have several stages: the trypanosome stage has an undulating membrane extending past the nucleus; the crithidial stage has a shorter undulating membrane; the herpetomonad stage has no undulating membrane; and the leishmania stage has neither undulating membrane nor external flagellum. (After various authors.)

Monas has two anterior flagella directed forward, one a longer primary flagellum and the other a shorter secondary flagellum.

The six genera of parasitic species described in the following paragraphs are obviously closely related. They include those usually grouped together as blood-inhabiting flagellates to distinguish them from another group that live in the digestive tract, called intestinal flagellates. During its life cycle *Trypanosoma* may assume trypanosome, crithidial, herpetomonad, and leishmania stages (see Fig. 1–12); *Herpetomonas* may appear in trypanosome, crithidial, herpetomonad, and leishmania stages; *Crithidia* in crithidial, herpetomonad, and leishmania stages; and *Leishmania* in herpetomonad and leishmania stages. This phenomena of a single species having different shapes at different times is known as *polymorphism*.

The Genus Trypanosoma. The trypanosomes are widely spread among animals. They occur in man, many other mammals, birds, reptiles, amphibians, and fish. The type species, *T. rotatorium* (Fig. 1–12, A), occurs in the blood of frogs and is not uncommon in this country. Another species, *T. diemyctyli**

---

* Specimens may be obtained by snipping off the end of the newt's tail and mounting a drop of blood on a slide. Permanent preparations are made by spreading the blood on the slide as a film, allowing it to dry, and staining it with Wright's Stain or by the Romanowsky method.

(Fig. 1–12, B), is present in the blood of the common crimson-spotted newt, *Triturus viridescens*, in certain localities. Three species are known from man: *Trypanosoma gambiense* the organism of Gambian sleeping sickness and *T. rhodesiense* of Rhodesian sleeping sickness occur in Africa; and *T. cruzi* of Chagas' disease is localized in South and Central America. The African types live also in wild game, such as antelope, and are transmitted by tsetse flies; the American type occurs especially in armadillos, which serve as reservoirs from which the transmitting agents, the triatoma kissing bugs, may acquire their infection. All human trypanosomes are pathogenic and frequently bring about the death of the host.

Animal trypanosomes are mostly nonpathogenic. *T. lewisi* of the wild rat is a good example of this type. The rat is thought to produce a substance, called *ablastin*, by some unknown method. Ablastin inhibits division of *T. lewisi* but does not destroy them. Among the more important trypanosomes that cause disease in lower animals are *T. equiperdum*, the organism of the disease of horses known as dourine; *T. brucei*, the organism of nagana in various domesticated animals; *T. evansi*, of surra in domesticated animals; *T. equinum*, of mal-de-caderas in horses and mules; and *T. hippicum*, of murrina in horses and mules. Trypanosomes are often local in their distribution, that is, many species are limited to the animals in certain definite geographical areas. This is due primarily to the fact that the transmitting agents are geographically restricted. For the most part, the transmitting agents of trypanosomes of terrestial animals are blood-sucking insects and those of aquatic animals are blood-sucking leeches. The transmitting agents are usually active carriers, that is, the trypanosomes pass through part of their life cycle within their bodies and are not merely transferred mechanically by them as typhoid fever germs are spread by house flies which are passive carriers.

The Genus Leishmania.   The leishmanias are probably transmitted from man to man by sand flies. Kala-azar, a disease widely distributed in Asia, is due to *Leishmania donovani* (Fig. 1–12, C), a species that attacks especially the endothelial cells and macrophages. Also localized in the Far and Near East is *L. tropica*, the organism of oriental sore or cutaneous leishmaniasis. One attack by this species gives immunity to further infection. The type of cutaneous leishmaniasis that occurs in South and Central America is due to *L. braziliensis*, a species that resembles *L. tropica* morphologically but differs from it in its serological reactions.

The genus *Crithidia* is parasitic in anthropods and other invertebrates. A species that may easily be obtained for study is *C. gerridis* (Fig. 1–12, F) from the intestine of water striders of the genus *Gerris*.

The genus *Herpetomonas* also lives in invertebrates. The species that can most readily be secured for examination is *H. muscarum* (Fig. 1–12, D), which lives in the intestine of the common house fly and other flies.

The genus *Leptomonas* is similar to *Herpetomonas* in structure and also only parasitizes invertebrates. A rare species, *Leptomonas karyophilus*, is the only

known zooflagellate parasitic in another protozoan. It is found in the macronucleus of *Paramecium*.

The genus *Phytomonas* (Fig. 1–12, E) is of peculiar interest because it occurs
in the latex of plants, such as milkweeds and euphorbias, and is transmitted
by hemipterous insects.

Order Diplomonadida.   Diplomonadida are protozoans with a definite
bilateral symmetry. They include one of the more common intestinal flagellates of man, *Giardia lamblia* (Fig. 1–13, E). *G. lamblia* lives in the duodenum
where it maintains itself against the force of peristalsis by clinging to the
intestinal wall by means of its sucking disk. It multiplies by binary fission and
forms cysts that pass out of the body in the feces and are infective to other
human beings whose food or drink may become contaminated by them.
Giardias occur in many other vertebrates and can best be obtained for study
from the duodenum of laboratory rats and frog tadpoles. Dogs, cats, mice,

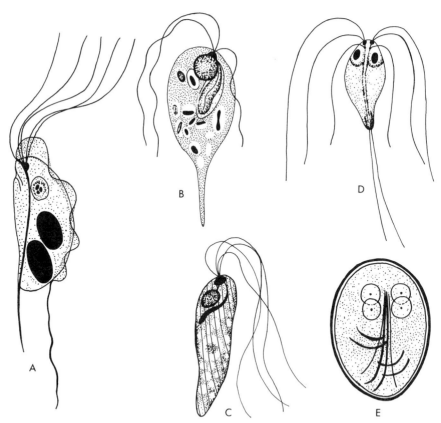

Fig. 1-13. Intestinal flagellates. (A) *Trichomonas hominis*, from man. (B) *Chilomastix
mesnili*, from man. (C) *Polymastix bufonis*, from the toad. (D) *Hexamita salmonis*, from
the salmon. (E) *Giardia lamblia*, cyst, from man. (After various authors.)

rabbits, guinea-pigs, herons, and many other animals are parasitized by their own peculiar species of giardias.

Hexamita (Fig. 1–13, D) is a diplomonad with six anterior and two posterior flagella, with species living in a wide variety of animals including the laboratory rat, turkeys, salmon, and cockroaches.

Order Trichomonadida. The order Trichomonadida contains several intestinal flagellates of man. Trichomonads have three to five anteriorly directed flagella and one recurrent flagellum often associated with an undulating membrane. They also have a longitudinal supporting structure known as an *axostyle*. Trichomonads live in the mouth, large intestine, and vagina and a large percentage of the general population is infected by them. It is not certain that more than one species exists in man, but they have been given different specific names. Thus, the mouth form is known as *Trichomonas tenax*; that in the intestine, *T. hominis* (Fig. 1–13, A); and the vaginal form, *T. vaginalis.* No cysts are formed by trichomonads; hence, they must be transmitted in the active, trophozoite stage. Trichomonads* are abundant in lower animals.

Many other flagellates that live in the digestive tract of various animals are in the Trichomonadida or closely related orders. Among them are species of the genera *Chilomastix* and *Polymastix. Chilomastix mesnili* (Fig. 1–13, B) lives in the large intestine of man. Other species occur in rats, rabbits, and other common animals. *Polymastix* lives in many lower animals but not in man. *P. melolonthae* is found in the cockchafer. *P. bufonis* (Fig. 1–13, C) lives in frogs and toads.

The intestinal flagellates of man are thought to be nonpathogenic in most cases of infection.

Order Hypermastigida. The order Hypermastigida includes a number of peculiar flagellates that live in the gut of certain insects and possess some very complex structures. All of the forms bear many flagella, which may be arranged in bunches or may be distributed over the entire body. This is the only order of zooflagellates in which sexual reproduction has been demonstrated. In addition to finding sexuality in them, Cleveland has demonstrated that a correlation exists between reproductive processes of some of these protozoans and the hormonal cycles of their wood roach host.

Intestinal Flagellates of Termites. The flagellate inhabitants of the intestine of termites are of special interest because of the number of species, the number of individuals in a single termite, their complexity, the large number of flagella possessed by many of them, and the symbiotic relations between some of them and their hosts. Species from at least 11 families and 40 genera of flagellates have been reported from termites. A species that well illustrates the enormous development of flagella and the complexity of the body is *Trichonympha*

---

* The best way to secure trichomonads for study is to examine in 0.7 per cent NaCl solution material from the rectum of the frog or cecum of laboratory rats.

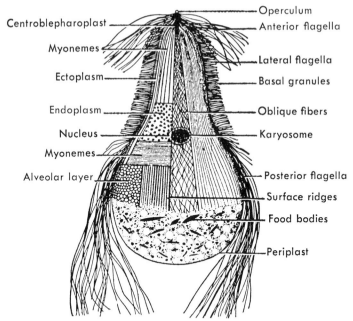

Fig. 1-14. Hypermastigida. *Trichonympha campanula*. Sections of the body show the structures found at different levels. Surface ridges form the outer layer with their rows of flagella; beneath are successively oblique fibers, alveolar layer and transverse myonemes. In the endoplasm are longitudinal myonemes. (From Kofoid and Swezy.)

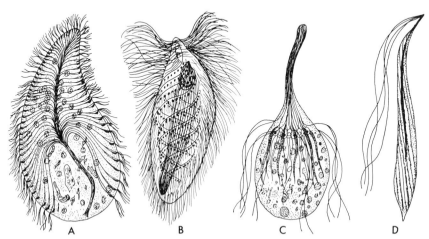

Fig. 1-15. Intestinal flagellates of termites. (A) *Sunderella tabogae*, from *Lobitermes longicollis*. (B) *Spirotrichonympha flagellata*, from *Reticulitermes lucifugus*. (C) *Proboscidiella kofoidi*, from *Cryptotermes dudleyi*. (D) *Streblomastix strix*, from *Termopsis laticeps*. (A, C, D, after Kirby; B, after Grassi.)

campanula (Fig. 1–14). An excellent example of symbiotic relations is furnished by certain of these flagellates and their hosts. The flagellates render the cellulose (in wood) eaten by termites digestible by the insects; without the aid of the flagellates the wood eaten is not digested and the termites starve to death. Some of the characteristics of these termite protozoa are illustrated in Figure 1–15.

The genus *Lophomonas* contains species that are common in the intestine of cockroaches. *L. blattarum* has a pyriform body and bears a tuft of flagella at the anterior end. *L. striata* is spindle-shaped and is characterized by rodlike bodies obliquely arranged at the periphery of the body.

2 / Superclass Opalinata

The Opalinata in the past have been known as the Protociliata, a name which implied a primitive ciliate nature. Recent workers have decided they are a specialized group intermediate between ciliates and flagellates. The Opalinata contains a single order, Opalinida, and a single family, Opalinidae, with species that are common in the rectum of frogs, toads, and tadpoles. There are four genera: *Protoopalina* (Fig. 1–16, A), with a cylindrical binucleate form;

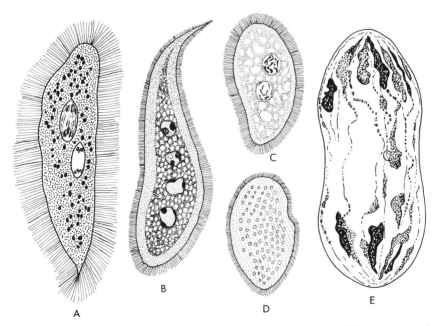

Fig. 1-16. Opalinidae. (A) *Protoopalina*, a binucleate species; nuclei in anaphase of mitosis. (B) *Cepedea lanceolata*, a quadrinucleate species. (C) *Zelleriella macronucleata*, a binucleate species; nuclei in prophase of mitosis. (D) *Opalina ranarum*, a multinucleate species. (E) Nucleus of *Opalina* in anaphase of mitosis showing large, flat, "trophic" chromosomes, and small, linear, "reproductive" chromosomes. (After Metcalf.)

Zelleriella (Fig. 1–16, C), with a flattened binucleate form; *Cepedea* (Fig. 1–16, B), with a cylindrical multinucleate form; and *Opalina* (Fig. 1–16, D), with a flattened multinucleate form. These genera are all characterized by a covering of cilia of equal length arranged in parallel rows, by the absence of a cytostome, and by the presence of only one type of nucleus. The nuclei, however, are of considerable interest because in some species, during mitosis, two types of chromosomes have been observed. Large chromosomes lie near the surface of the mitotic spindle and smaller chromosomes, in the form of slender rows of granules, are in the center of the mitotic figure (Fig. 1–16, E). These two types of chromosomes may represent the material of the macronucleus and micronucleus, respectively, of the ciliates. Another interesting characteristic of the Opanlinidae is the fact that in many species the nuclei come to rest in some stage of mitosis. The number of nuclei in the individuals of various species ranges from two to several thousand.

Opalina ranarum (Fig. 1–16, D), which lives in the rectum of the frog, is the commonest and best-known species. When alive it is opalescent in appearance. Some specimens reach a length of about a millimeter and may be seen with the naked eye. The body contains a large number of spherical nuclei evenly distributed throughout the cytoplasm. Many small spindle-shaped bodies of unknown character are present in the endoplasm. Reproduction is by binary division during most of the year, but in the spring rapid division results in the production of many small individuals, which encyst and pass out in the feces of the frog. When these cysts are ingested by tadpoles, they hatch in the rectum and give rise either to macrogametocytes or microgametocytes. The gametocytes, which contain from three to six nuclei, divide into uninucleate macrogametes or microgametes. These conjugate forming zygotes from each of which a young opalina develops. *Opalina ranarum* may be kept alive outside of the body of the frog for as long as three days in Locke's solution.

3 / Superclass Sarcodina

(1) Amoeba proteus

Amoeba proteus (Fig. 1–17) is a one-celled animal about 250 microns (0.25 mm) in diameter and so transparent that it is invisible to the naked eye. Under the compound microscope, it appears as an irregular colorless or light blue particle of animated jelly that is constantly changing its shape by thrusting out finger-like processes.

Habitat. *Amoeba proteus* lives in fresh-water ponds and streams. It may be obtained for laboratory use from a variety of places, such as the organic ooze from decaying vegetation or the lower surface of lily pads. About two weeks before the specimens are needed, a mass of pond weed (*Ceratophyllum* is the best) should be gathered, placed in flat dishes, and immersed in water. The

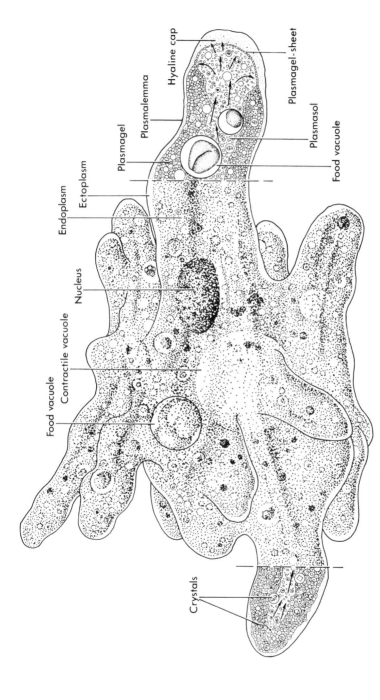

Fig. 1-17. *Amoeba proteus*: cytology. Horizontal optical section through portions of an advancing pseudopodium and a retreating pseudopodium. (Modified from Mast and Woodruff.)

Hyaline cap

Plasmalemma

Plasmagel

Plasmagel-sheet

Plasmasol

Plasmagel

Ectoplasm

Endoplasm

Food vacuole

Nucleus

Contractile vacuole

Food vacuole

Crystals

vegetation soon decays, and a brown scum appears on the surface. In this scum amoeba may be found.

The fact that amoebae appear in large numbers in cultures, such as just described, indicates that decaying pond weed furnishes a good habitat for them. Here they find their food, which consists of algae, other protozoa, bacteria, and other animal and vegetable matter.

General Cytology (Fig. 1–17).   Two regions are distinguishable in the body of amoeba: an outer colorless layer of clear cytoplasm, the *ectoplasm*, and a comparatively large central mass of granular cytoplasm, the *endoplasm*. A single clear spherical body, usually lying near the end of the animal away from the direction of motion, and disappearing at more or less regular intervals, is the *contractile vacuole*. Suspended in the endoplasm is a nucleus, usually one or more *food vacuoles*, material ready for excretion, foreign substances such as grains of sand, and undigested particles, the amount of the latter depending upon the feeding activity of the specimen at the time of examination.

The *nucleus* is not easily seen in living specimens. In animals that have been properly killed and stained, it appears as a biconcave disk in young specimens but it is often folded and convoluted in older specimens. Electron microscope studies show a honeycomb layer under a double-layered nuclear envelope. Nuclei of some genera of amoebae are distinct enough to be used for identification of the genus. The position of the nucleus in the endoplasm is not definite, but changes during the movements of the amoeba. Within the nucleus are many small, spherical chromosomes said to number over 500. During the life of an amoeba, before the period of reproduction, the nucleus plays an important role in the metabolic activity of the cell. This has been proved by experiments in which the animal was cut in two. The streaming of the cytoplasm ceases within a few minutes in the piece without a nucleus but is resumed after a few hours. The enucleated amoeba may attach itself to the substratum and exhibits irritability although its responses to stimuli are modified. Food bodies are engulfed and digested in an apparently normal manner but death finally ensues. The part with the nucleus continues its life as a normal amoeba. Other studies have shown that nuclei transferred to the cytoplasm of another amoeba from which the nucleus has been removed will produce characteristics in the hybrid amoeba resembling those of the cell donating the nucleus. The characteristics of the cell donating the cytoplasm are retained to varying degrees in different experiments. Because such blends of characteristics are maintained through successive generations, it is clear that both nucleus and cytoplasm have an important role in determining cell characteristics and inheritance. Division of the nucleus during reproduction will be described later.

The *contractile vacuole* is thought to be a water regulatory organelle, because its rate of activity is inversely proportional to the osmotic concentration of the media. Further evidence comes from a recent study that found the fluid in the vacuole is hypoosmotic to the protoplasm. It derives its name from the fact that at more or less regular intervals it suddenly disappears, its walls having collapsed or contracted, its contents leaving the cell. That energy is required for its activity is indicated by the ring of mitochondria surrounding it. Because no contractile elements have been demonstrated, it is thought that the energy is used in filling it against a diffusion gradient. It is located posterior to the nucleus (i.e., away from the direction of the advancing pseudopodia). The water that diffuses into the cell and is expelled by the contractile vacuole may have an important function in transporting oxygen in and waste products out of the cell, although diffusion through the cell membrane is adequate in marine and parasitic forms that lack contractile vacuoles.

Food vacuoles, mitochondria, oil droplets, various crystals, and small granules are also found in the endoplasm.

Physiology.   Although extremely simple in structure, amoeba carries on practically all of the vital activities characteristic of the higher animals. It is capable of automatic movement, of reacting to various stimuli, of carrying on metabolic processes, of growth, and of reproduction. These are all fundamental properties of protoplasm and are here exhibited in simple form.

Locomotion.   Amoeba moves from place to place by means of finger-like protrusions of the body, known as *pseudopodia*. Four basic types of pseudopodia exist based on their structure (Fig. 1–18). (1) *Lobopodia* (Fig. 1–18, A) are broad and blunt and contain both an outer layer of ectoplasm and an inner portion of endoplasm. They are the type of pseudopodia found in *Amoeba proteus*. (2) *Filopodia* (Fig. 1–18, B) are narrow and contain only ectoplasm. (3) *Axopodia* (Fig. 1–18, C) have a fine coating of cytoplasm over an axial

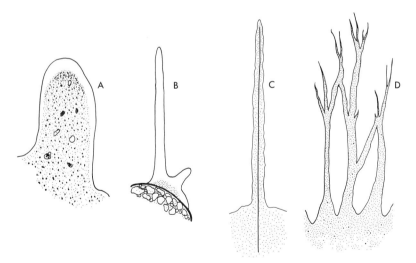

Fig. 1-18. Types of pseudopodia. (A) Lobopodium of *Amoeba proteus*. (B) Filopodium of *Difflugia oblonga*. (C) Axopodium of *Actinosphaerium eichhorni*. (D) Rhizopodia of *Gromia*.

filament. Although the coating is of ectoplasm, it is more granular than the ectoplasm of the previous types. Axopodia are capable of retraction and bending even though they have an axial structure. (4) *Rhizopodia* (Fig. 1–18, D) are thin, branching pseudopodia that produce a network by fusion of the branches. Axopodia and rhizopodia may have the cytoplasm streaming in opposite directions on opposite sides of the same pseudopodium, a condition never observed in lobopodia. Thus, there may be more than one explanation for pseudopodial movement. Even in lobopodia, the most intensively studied type, protozoologists do not agree on the explanation for their method of formation. All have observed a rather fluid endoplasm flowing into or against the enlarging ectoplasmic front of the pseudopodium. Allen (1962) proposes that the explanation involves a contraction of contractile elements at the anterior, thus drawing the endoplasm into the advancing pseudopodium. Mast (1931), Goldacre and Lorch (1950), and Rinaldi and Jahn (1963) have proposed that the contraction occurs at the posterior in the gelated endoplasm, that at the same time solation is occurring where it is in contact with the solated endoplasm and flows up with the endoplasm to be again gelated at the anterior of the advancing pseudopodium. Most protozoologists have supported the latter view. Unfortunately, electron microscopy has been unable to contribute to the solution with present techniques. Rinaldi and Jahn (1963) have analyzed motion pictures of granule movements in advancing pseudopodia as well as the various concepts and observations given in support of the two theories and concluded that the concept of amoeboid movement as given by Mast is essentially correct.

According to Mast, the body of an amoeba is divided into four parts (Fig. 1–19). (1) The *plasmasol* is a central elongated portion of colloidal substances in the sol phase. These substances move toward the direction of lowest pressure. (2) The *plasmagel* is a colloidal substance of protoplasm in the gel phase that forms a tube around the plasmasol. The plasmagel contracts at the posterior and undergoes a change to the sol phase at its junction with the plasmasol. (3) The *plasmalemma* is a very thin elastic surface layer or membrane (in some

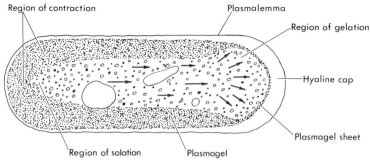

Fig. 1-19. Diagram of regions involved in amoeboid movement according to the contraction-hydraulic theory. (Modified from Mast.)

Fig. 1-20. *Difflugia oblonga* in locomotion. Pseudopodia, numbered in the sequence formed, are extended, attached, and contracted to pull the amoeba forward.

amoebas it is actually a thick and rigid structure). (4) A *hyaline layer* exists between the plasmagel and the plasmalemma. The plasmasol and plasmagel constitute the endoplasm, and the hyaline layer and the plasmalemma constitute the ectoplasm. The contraction of the posterior plasmagel produces a hydraulic pressure on the plasmasol. The resistance to the pressure is least at the anterior where the thin sheet of plasmagel is continually stretched and occasionally broken, but continually reformed by gelation of plasmasol. The plasmagel is strongest at the sides and of intermediate strength at the posterior. Thus, a pressure at the anterior causes a reversal of flow, or a pressure at the side of the anterior causes a deflection away from the pressure. The plasmagel is under continuous tension and any localized reduction in elastic strength will cause the formation of a pseudopodium.

Pseudopodial movement in *Difflugia* (Fig. 1–20), a shelled amoeba, is interesting when compared with that of *Amoeba*. The pseudopodia are extended through the opening of the shell one after another and attached to the substratum at the tip. The pseudopodium then contracts and the shell containing the body is drawn forward. The action is thought to be due to the same contraction-hydraulic system that functions in the previously described lobopodia.

Forms having axopodia and rhizopodia (or reticulopodia) have a flow of protoplasm in both directions on opposite sides of narrow pseudopodia. Jahn and Bovee (1965) have proposed that a different mechanism is involved with an active shearing or sliding that warrants revision of the classification of the Sarcodina. Their classification is followed here (Jahn and Bovee, 1965) because the differences in pseudopodial movement seem to provide a better basis for reflecting a major phylogenetic difference than the presence or absence of axial structures in the pseudopodia used in earlier systems. A genetic change resulting in the loss of the ability to produce a structure such as an axial filament is not considered reason to place the shorted relative in a different class if other characteristics indicate a close relationship.

Metabolism. Growth in *Amoeba*, as in any living thing, involves a complex series of changes. The chemical compounds that make up the bodies of animals are extremely labile; they are constantly breaking down into simpler substances or becoming more complex by the addition of new materials. The changes are accomplished through the aide of enzymes, which are thought to be produced by an interaction of substrate, nucleic acids, proteins, and other substances. *Metabolism* is the term used to include this great complex of incessant changes. Some processes use energy, releasing it from high-energy phosphate compounds such as adenosine triphosphate (ATP), to build up compounds; others break down substances to produce energy, usually in the form of high-energy phosphate compounds. These changes occur within the cell, for the most part, so that the term *cellular metabolism* is sometimes applied. They also occur after substances such as oxygen and amino acids have been received in the cell and before the ultimate breakdown products of carbon dioxide, water, and nitrogenous wastes are eliminated so that the term *intermediate metabolism* is applied also. Because some substances are produced from other substances via a long sequence of particular changes such sequences are referred to as *metabolic pathways.*

One of the principle sources of energy for cellular activity comes from the *cellular respiration* of glucose. A reversible series of reactions result in the break-down of glucose and the net production of ATP. The first part of the series of reactions is known as *glycolysis.* The last part of the series is known as the *citric acid cycle,* because the oxaloacetate that combines with the acetyl group left from glycolysis to form citric acid is eventually reformed by the degradation of citric acid. The citric acid cycle has been localized in the mitochondria. Although these metabolic pathways have not been demonstrated in

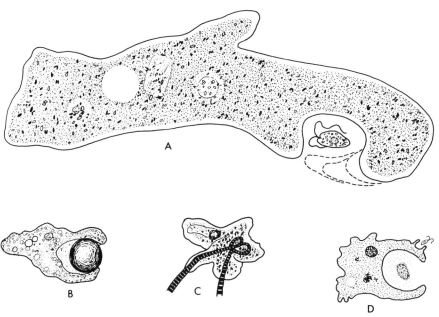

Fig. 1-21. *Amoeba.* Ingestion of food. (A) Successive positions of a pseudopodium of an amoeba capturing a flagellate, *Chilomonas.* (B) Ingesting a cyst of a flagellate, *Euglena.* (C) Ingesting a filament of *Ocillatoria.* (D) A food cup for ingesting a flagellate superimposed on a food cup containing a ciliate. (A, after Kepner and Taliaferro; B, after Jennings; C, after Rhumbler; D, after Becker.)

their entirety in any protozoan, enough has been demonstrated in many to make their occurrence in most very likely.

A portion of the energy stored in fats and proteins can also be released by some of the same pathways by which glucose and other carbohydrates are metabolized. However, protein metabolism results in the formation of ammonia, which may diffuse out of a simple aquatic animal like *Amoeba*. Ammonia is toxic in large concentrations and does not readily diffuse from water to air so that terrestrial animals tend to have a large part of their nitrogenous wastes accumulated as compounds of low solubility or low toxicity such as in uric acid and urea. Urea has been identified in the contractile vacuoles of *Amoeba*.

Ingestion. The ingestion, or taking in of food (Fig. 1–21), occurs without the aid of a mouth. Other protozoans, algae, or other particulate organic matter serving as food may be engulfed at any point on the surface of the body, but is usually taken in at what may be called the temporary anterior end, that is, the part of the body toward the direction of locomotion. Jennings describes ingestion as follows. The amoeba flows against the food particle, which does not adhere but tends to be pushed forward away from the animal. That part of the body directly back of the food ceases its forward movements while, on either side and above, pseudopodia are extended which gradually form a concavity in which the food lies, and finally bend around the particle until their ends meet and fuse. A small amount of water is taken in with the food, so that there is formed a vacuole whose sides were formerly the outside of the body, and whose contents consist of a particle of nutritive material suspended in water. The whole process of food-taking occupies one or more minutes, depending on the character of the food. Amoeba is not always successful in accomplishing what it undertakes, but when it does not capture its prey at once, it seems to show a persistence usually only attributed to higher organisms. No doubt the reactions in food-taking depend upon both mechanical and chemical stimuli.

A somewhat similar process occurs on a smaller scale with no particles actually ingested. Small pockets may form on the surface, their openings then close to pinch off a small vacuole of water, and the enclosed water vacuole is said to have been formed by the process of *pinocytosis*. Such a process may be important in nutrition of higher forms by providing a way in which large molecules can pass the barrier of the cell membrane.

Digestion. Food vacuoles serve as temporary digestive organelles. After a food vacuole has become embedded in the endoplasm, its walls pour into it a secretion of some acid, probably HCl. Various enzymes are also part of the digestive fluid, which breaks down protein substances, and perhaps also fats and sugars, but not starch.

Egestion. Indigestible particles are egested at any point on the surface of the amoeba, there being no special opening to the exterior for this waste matter. Usually such particles are heavier than the protoplasm, and as the

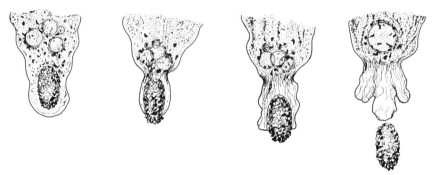

Fig. 1-22. *Amoeba verrucosa.* Four stages in the ejection of a waste pellet. Note the rigidity of the pellicle. (After Howland.)

animal moves forward they lag behind, finally passing out at the end away from the direction of movement; that is, amoeba flows away, leaving the indigestible solids behind. This process is not so simple in such a species as *Amoeba verrucosa*, which possesses an ectoplasmic pellicle that is a thick, tough membrane. Waste pellets are extruded as shown in Figure 1–22; a new pellicle, which prevents the outflow of the endoplasm, is formed at the point of exit.

Assimilation. The peptones and amino acids, derived from the digestion of protein substances, together with the water and mineral matter taken in when the gastric vacuole was formed, are absorbed by the surrounding protoplasm and pass directly into the body substance of the animal. These particles of organic and inorganic matter are then assimilated; that is, they are rearranged to form new particles of living protoplasm that are deposited among the previously existing particles. The ability to thus manufacture protoplasm from unorganized matter is one of the fundamental properties of living substance. Nucleic acids are thought to have an important role in the process.

Dissimilation. The energy for the work done by amoeba comes from the breaking down of complex molecules by oxidation or "physiological burning." This is the cellular respiration previously mentioned. The products of this slow combustion are the energy of movement, heat, and residual matter. Ordinarily the residual matter consists of solids and fluids, mainly water, some mineral substances, urea, and CO_2. Secretions, excretions, and the products of respiration are included in this list.

Secretion. We have already noted that an acid is poured into the gastric vacuoles by the surrounding protoplasm. Such a product of dissimilation, which is of use in the economy of the animal, is known as a secretion.

Excretion. Materials representing the final reduction of substances in the process of metabolism are called excretions. These are deposited either within or outside of the body. A large part of the excretory matter, including urea and CO_2, passes through the general surface of the body. The fluid content of the contractile vacuole is known to contain urea; therefore, this organ has an excretory function in addition to its osmoregulatory action.

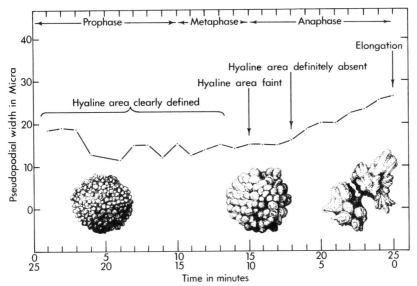

Fig. 1-23. *Amoeba proteus.* Binary fission. Graph showing pseudopodial width during phases of mitosis. Drawings show the appearance during late prophase, early anaphase, and late telophase. (Modified from Chalkley and Daniel.)

Respiration. The contractile vacuole is also respiratory, because CO_2 probably makes its way to the exterior by way of this organ. Oxygen dissolved in water is taken in through the surface of the body. This gas is necessary for the life of the animal; if replaced by hydrogen, movements cease after 24 hours; if air is then introduced, movements begin again; if not, death ensues.

Growth. If food is plentiful, more substance is added to the living protoplasm of the amoeba than is used up in its various physical activities. The result is an increase in the volume of the animal. This is growth, and, as in all other living organisms, growth by the addition of new particles among the preexisting particles.

Reproduction (Fig. 1–23). , There is, however, a limit with regard to the size that may be attained by *Amoeba proteus*, as it rarely exceeds 0.25 mm ($\frac{1}{100}$ inch) in diameter. When this limit is reached, the animal divides into two parts. It is supposed that this division is inaugurated through some unknown change in the relations between the nucleus and the cytoplasm.

We are certain of only one type of reproduction in *Amoeba proteus*: binary fission. Sporulation and other types of reproduction have been described by investigators but have never been satisfactorily established. A description of the binary fission of *Amoeba proteus* (Fig. 1–23) is as follows. Nuclear division is mitotic, with multiple spindles forming while the nuclear membrane is disappearing at metaphase.

The average time for the division process at a temperature of 24°C is 33 minutes, with an average deviation of about 2 minutes. The *prophase* lasts about 10 minutes, the *metaphase* not over 5 minutes, probably less, the *anaphase* about 10 minutes, and the *telophase* about 8 minutes. The nuclear phases are accompanied by typical changes in cell form that are readily distinguishable under a magnification of 30 diameters. During prophase the cell is spherical, studded with fine pseudopodia and exhibits under reflected light a clearly defined hyaline area at its center. During metaphase the picture is similar, except that the hyaline area is very faint. During anaphase the pseudopodia become rapidly coarser, and the hyaline area is no longer visible. The telophase is accompanied by elongation of the cell and cleft formation.

Under the cultural conditions used, the average measured width of the pseudopodia in early prophase was 18 micra; from mid prophase to metaphase it was 13 to 14 micra. At anaphase the average width began to increase and at the beginning of telophase attained a value of 26 micra. It is possible merely from observation of the external appearance of the living cell to select from culture under a magnification as low as 30 diameters cells showing any desired stage of *nuclear* division except actual metaphase. Such selection can readily be made with 97 per cent accuracy, thus making possible the study of the effect of reagents upon the separate nuclear phases in cell division. The modal volume of *Amoeba proteus* at division under the cultural conditions employed is 0.0027 cubic millimeters. Binucleate forms are produced in culture by failure of cytoplasmic fission. Evidence is presented that the contractile vacuole ceases to function during division from the time that the nucleus enters the metaphase stage until cell division is completed. The close correlation of the disappearance of the nuclear membrane with the cessation of the activity of the contractile vacuole and the beginning of the rapid increase in average width of the pseudopodia during the nuclear anaphase, suggests a causative relation between these phenomena (Chalkley and Daniel).

The *development* of amoeba is simply a matter of growth; the daughter cells resulting from binary division become full-grown specimens by means of a gradual increase in volume.

Behavior.   The sum total of all the various movements of an animal constitute what is known as its behavior. In amoeba these movements may be separated into those connected with locomotion and those resulting from external stimuli. We have already given an account of the locomotion of amoeba, and so shall confine ourselves now to a discussion of its responses to different kinds of stimuli. The reactions of amoeba to stimuli have been grouped by Jennings into positive, negative, and food-taking. The last named were discussed under ingestion. The following account, then, will deal with positive and negative reactions of *Amoeba proteus* to external stimulation.

Reactions to Stimuli.   Amoebae react to various kinds of stimuli including contact, chemicals, heat, light, and electricity.

If the animal reacts by a movement toward the stimulus, such as light, it is said to react *positively*; if away from the stimulus, *negatively*.

Amoeba reacts negatively when touched at any point with a solid object; the part affected contracts and the animal moves away (Fig. 1–24). When

Fig. 1-24. *Amoeba:* reaction to contact. A specimen moves away from a mechanical stimulus. (From Jennings.)

however, an amoeba is floating freely in the water and a pseudopodium comes in contact with the substratum, the animal moves in the direction of that pseudopodium until the normal creeping position has been attained (Fig. 1–25). Contact with food also results in positive reactions. Amoeba, therefore, reacts negatively to a strong mechanical stimulus and positively to a weak one.

Reactions to chemicals prove that amoeba is sensitive to changes in the chemical composition of the water surrounding it. *Amoeba* reacts negatively to many chemicals (Fig. 1–26) and changes in culture water. Experimental studies indicate that amoebae are able to "sense" food some distance away; this is probably the result of chemical stimuli.

Fig. 1-25. *Amoeba:* reaction to contact. Changes in shape when a floating amoeba encounters a solid. (From Jennings.)

Changes in the environment have a profound influence on the shape of amoeba. When an organism is transferred from culture fluid to pure water it becomes radiate in form. If it is then placed in the proper concentration of any one of a number of salts it changes its form as indicated in Figure 1–27. The

Fig. 1-26. *Amoeba:* reaction to a chemical. Methyl green results in a negative reaction. (From Jennings.)

Fig. 1-27. Changes in the shape of an amoeba when transferred from pure water to an *N*/1000 solution of NaCl. The numbers indicate the time of day and the arrows the direction of protoplasmic streaming in the pseudopodia. (After Mast.)

form assumed by the organism appears to depend directly upon its water content.

Negative reactions result if amoeba is locally affected by heat, since the animal will move away from heat stimuli. Cold and excessive heat retard its activities, which cease altogether between 30 and 35°C.

Amoeba will orient itself in the direction of the rays of a strong light and move away from it (Fig. 1–28), but may react positively to a very weak light. The light causes gelation of the plasmasol adjoining the plasmagel, making it thicker and increasing the elastic strength of the portion illuminated. The response to light is thus due to the contraction of the plasmagel in the region stimulated, owing to the increase in the elastic strength of the plasmagel in this region. The evidence at present indicates that, while gelation or solation produced in a pseudopod of an amoeba by localized illumination is not followed by gelation or solation in other pseudopods, the effect of localized gelation and solation is transmitted, that *Amoeba* acts as an organized unit, and that its actions are, on the whole, adaptive. *Amoeba* responds to an electric current by moving toward the cathode; this results from the solation of the plasmagel on the cathodal side of the organism.

In amoeba there are no organs that can be compared with what we call sense organs in higher animals, and we must attribute its reactions to stimuli to that fundamental property of protoplasm called irritability. The superficial layer of

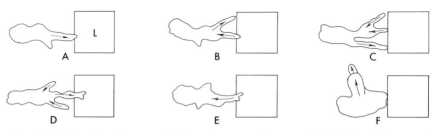

Fig. 1-28. Reaction of an amoeba toward an area of intense light (L), the light rays of which were perpendicular to the slide. The successive positions of the amoeba are indicated at intervals of about one half a minute. The arrows show the direction of protoplasmic streaming in the pseudopodia. (After Mast.)

cytoplasm receives the stimulus and transfers the effects to some other part of the body; thus may be shown the phenomenon of *internal irritability* or *conductivity*. The stimulus causing a reaction seems to be in most cases *a change in the environment*. The behavior of amoeba in the absence of external stimuli, for example when it is suspended freely in the water, shows that some of its activities are initiated by internal causes.

The reactions of amoeba to stimuli are of undoubted value to the individual and to the preservation of the race, for the negative reaction is in most cases produced by injurious agents such as strong chemicals, heat, and mechanical impacts, whereas positive reactions are produced usually by beneficial agents. The responses, therefore, in the former cases carry the animal out of danger; in the latter, to safety.

Amoeba is of interest to animal psychologists because it represents animal protoplasm at a very low level of structural organization that exhibits behavior. The potential of protoplasm lacking an organized nervous system can be studied here.

A review of the facts obtained thus far seems to show that factors are present in the behavior of amoeba "comparable to the habits, reflexes, and automatic activities of higher organisms," and "if amoeba were a large animal, so as to come within the everyday experience of human beings, its behavior would at once call forth the attribution to it of states of pleasure and pain, of hunger, desire, and the like, on precisely the same basis as we attribute these things to the dog" (Jennings).

(2) Other Sarcodina

The Sarcodina are divided into two classes, Hydraulea and Autotractea. In the Hydraulea all sides of a pseudopodium have the same direction of movement with respect to the axis of the pseudopodium. In the Autotractea the pseudopodia are slender and movement may occur in opposite directions on opposite sides of the same pseudopodium; the pseudopodia frequently have axial structures.

Hydraulea

Order Amoebida. The order Amoebida contains amoeboid Sarcodina with lobose pseudopodia; but there is neither skeleton nor shell.

Amoeba proteus is the type of the superclass Sarcodina usually selected for detailed study and probably no other member of this superclass is as satisfactory for this purpose. However, many species of both free-living and parasitic Sarcodina may easily be secured for observation that differ in various respects from the type. Some of these are described in the following paragraphs.

Free-Living Amoebae (Fig. 1–29). Several different species of amoeba have been grouped together in the past under the name *Amoeba proteus*. *Amoeba proteus* was described by Leidy in 1879. It is characterized by the possession,

Fig. 1-29. Amoebida. (A) *Amoeba dubia;* nucleus ovoidal. (B) *Amoeba discoides;* nucleus discoidal. (C) *Pelomyxa palustris;* many nuclei. (D) *Pelomyxa carolinensis;* many nuclei. (E) *Amoeba verrucosa;* the tough pellicle results in many pseudopodia. (A, B, after Schaeffer; C, after Doflein; D, after Kepner and Edwards; E, after Wang.)

in the younger forms, of a nucleus in the shape of a biconcave disk, which may become folded and convoluted in the older forms. It also has definite ectoplasmic ridges that are constant cell structures. A second form is much like the true *Amoeba proteus* except that it possesses a disklike nucleus that never becomes folded and its ectoplasm never shows the ridges constantly present in *Amoeba proteus*. The name *Amoeba discoides* has been given to this species (Fig. 1–29, B). A third form possesses an ovoid nucleus instead of a discoidal one and does not show any cytoplasmic ridges. Furthermore, it is characterized by a type of locomotion different from that of the other species. To this form the name *Amoeba dubia* (Fig. 1–29, A) has been given. By means of carefully pedigreed cultures, Schaeffer has been able to show that these three forms breed true and probably represent true species. Another fairly common species is *Amoeba verrucosa*, a sluggish form that has a tough pellicle and many short pseudopodia (Fig. 1–29, E).

To the genus *Pelomyxa* belong a number of very large fresh-water amoeba-like species that contain many nuclei (Fig. 1–29, C and D). A characteristic feature of this genus is that the cytoplasm usually contains a number of refringent bodies, which are of an albuminous nature and which are associated with a bacterium. Furthermore, the organisms generally load their cytoplasm with sand and debris of all kinds in addition to food material. *Pelomyxa* reproduces

Fig. 1-30. Drawings of electrophoretograms of amoebae. (A) Stained to show some water-soluble proteins. (B) Pattern of acid phosphatase activity. (C) Pattern of esterase activity. (1) *Amoeba proteus*, strain Bk. (2) *A. proteus*, strain T. (3) *A. discoides*. (4) *Chaos chaos*. Those marked with an ∗ were run at the same time and those marked with a # were run at different times to show the reproducibility of the method. (From J. R. Kates and L. Goldstein. A comparison of protein composition of three species of amoebae. *J. Protozool.* **11**(1):30–35. Copyright 1964 by the Society of Protozoologists.)

itself asexually by simple fission or by multiple fission. Encystment may occur in *Pelomyxa*.

Protein Differences of Species.   The availability of techniques for comparison of proteins by chromatographic, electrophoretic, and antigenic characteristics has made it possible to compare species for similarities of their protein composition. In general, species in the same genus have a greater similarity of proteins than species in different genera. Although these techniques have not enabled biologists to determine phylogenetic relationships as well as was hoped, they have provided much interesting information. Only slight differences, if any, have been detected in the spectrum of proteins of *Amoeba discoides* and two different strains of *Amoeba proteus* by electrophoretograms. However, the three differ markedly in comparison with proteins of a species of *Pelomyxa* (Fig. 1–30). The fact that the same bands of protein or protein-like compounds appear in electrophoretograms does not prove that the amoebae are identical, but it does indicate that they have a grouping of compounds with approximately the same properties of migration in electric fields. When one considers that a single gene may often have a profound effect on an organism, it seems reasonable to assume that organisms alike enough to be classified in the same species should have great similarity of protein composition. Considerable changes could probably be made in some protein molecules without markedly changing the size, weight, and charge, which would determine the electrophoretic properties. Similarly, changes may not affect the properties by which they are recognized chromatographically or antigenically. When more information on differences within the better known species and genera has been accumulated, taxonomists may be able to use such techniques for establishing generic boundaries.

Parasitic Amoebae.   Of special interest in the Superclass Sarcodina are the parasitic amoebae, particularly those that occur in man. Human beings may be infected by as many as six species. One, *Entamoeba gingivalis,** lives in the mouth in the tartar around the base of the teeth. Probably 50 per cent of the general population are infected. This amoeba feeds principally on bacteria and leucocytes and is probably harmless, although it is known to be present more frequently in diseased than in healthy mouths. Transmission occurs by contact during kissing.

The other five parasitic amoebae of man live in the large intestine. One of them, *Entamoeba histolytica* (Fig. 1–31, C) is pathogenic. The infective stage is a spherical cyst containing four nuclei. Encystment takes place in the large intestine and the cysts pass out in the feces. Cysts that are swallowed in contaminated food or drink hatch in the small intestine giving rise to amoebae with four nuclei, which subsequently divide into uninucleate amoebae. This species infects about 10 per cent of the general population, but most of the

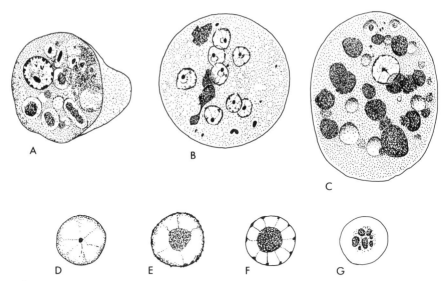

Fig. 1-31. Amoebae parasitic in the large intestine of man. (A) *Entamoeba coli*, a harmless species showing pseudopodium, nucleus and food vacuoles. (B) *Entamoeba coli*, cyst containing 8 nuclei and a few chromatoid bodies (in black). (C) *Entamoeba histolytica*, the organism of amoebic dysentery, containing a nucleus and many red blood corpuscles (in black). (D) Nucleus of *Entamoeba*. (E) Nucleus of *Endolimax*. (F) Nucleus of *Iodamoeba*. (G) Nucleus of *Dientamoeba*. (A–C after Stabler; D–G after various authors.)

* Specimens may be observed by scraping material from the base of the teeth and mounting it in 0.7 per cent NaCl solution.

infected persons are carriers, that is, the amoebae live and multiply in their large intestine and produce cysts but do not injure them. In a few persons, however, the amoebae attack the wall of the intestine producing ulcers and giving rise to amoebic dysentery. Several races exist which vary in size and pathogenicity. They seem to be particularly fond of red blood cells as a food supply. From the intestinal wall, the amoebae may be carried in the blood stream to the liver, lungs, brain, etc., where they sometimes produce abscesses. Compounds containing iodine are used successfully to cure amoebiasis.

The remaining four species of human amoebae are supposed to be harmless. They are *Entamoeba coli, Endolimax nana, Iodamoeba bütschlii,* and *Dientamoeba fragilis.* These amoebae differ from one another especially in their nuclear structure (Fig. 1–31). The last named frequently possesses two nuclei. The parasitic amoebae resemble in general the free-living amoebae but do not possess contractile vacuoles.

Practically every lower animal that has been carefully examined has been found to be infected with parasitic amoebae. For example, *Hydramoeba hydroxena* (Fig. 1–32) is an amoeba that occurs on the external surface and in the gastrovascular cavity of *Hydra.* It dies in from 4 to 10 days if removed from

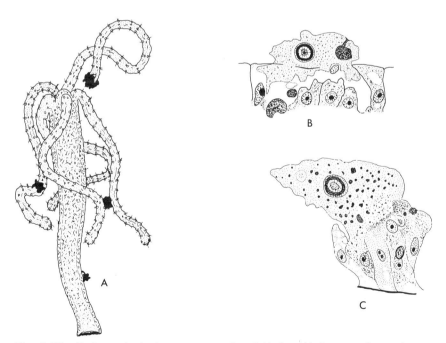

Fig. 1-32. *Hydramoeba hydroxena:* a parasite of *Hydra.* (A) Four specimens (represented in black) on the surface of a hydra. (B) An amoeba destroying ectodermal cells. (C) An amoeba ingesting endodermal cells. (After Reynolds and Looper).

its host and is hence an obligate parasite. The hydras are injured by the amoebae and usually are killed by them in about a week. Perhaps the parasitic amoebae most easily obtained for study are those that occur in the intestine of the frog, frog tadpole, cockroach, and rat. Material containing parasitic Protozoa should always be diluted for study with a 0.7 per cent solution of NaCl instead of with water.

Order Arcellinida. A number of common fresh-water genera belong to this order, including *Arcella, Difflugia, Centropyxis, Lecquereusia,* and *Euglypha.*

The arcellas possess a shell secreted entirely by the organism. This shell is arched above and has an opening in the center of the lower, flattened surface through which lobose pseudopodia are extended. *Arcella vulgaris* (Fig. 1–33, A) possesses two nuclei. *A. dentata* (Fig. 1–33, B) also has two nuclei, and a shell with dentate projections around the periphery (Fig. 1–33). *A. polypora* may contain as many as 15 nuclei. In prepared specimens a large granular ring

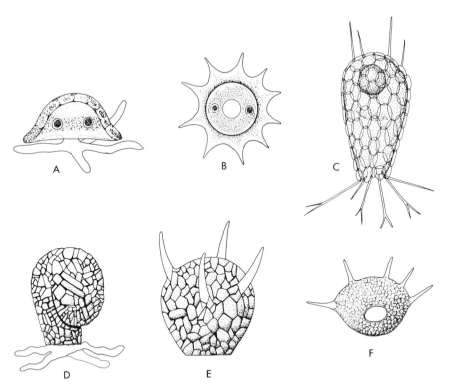

Fig. 1-33. Order Arcellinida. Common species of shelled Sarcodina. (A) *Arcella vulgaris.* (B) *Arcella dentata.* (C) *Euglypha acanthophora.* (D) *Lecquereusia modesta.* (E) *Difflugia corona.* (F) *Centropyxis aculeata.* (A, B, D, E, F, after Wang; C, after Calkins.)

of protoplasm appears that stains deeply in haematoxylin; this is known as the chromidial body.*

The commonest species of the genus *Difflugia* are *D. oblonga*, *D. lobostoma*, and *D. corona*. *D. oblonga* has a bottle-shaped shell with a more or less distinct cylindrical neck (Fig. 1–20). *D. lobostoma* has a spherical or ovate shell with a lobed mouth opening. *D. corona* has a spherical shell with a variable number of spines at the end opposite the mouth opening (Fig. 1–33, E). A single nucleus is present. The shell is made of cemented sandgrains.

The genus *Euglypha* contains several common species with a membranous shell composed of secreted chitinous or siliceous plates, and teeth around the mouth opening. The pseudopodia are filiform. *E. acanthophora* usually has a few long spines (Fig. 1–31, C). *E. ciliata* has numerous smaller spines and is common in sphagnum moss.

Asexual reproduction in the Arcellinda takes place by binary fission, just as in the Amoebida but is complicated by the presence of a shell. For example, in the case of *Difflugia corona* the organism prior to division accumulates a number of sand grains within its interior. At the time of reproduction the protoplasm absorbs water, swells, and projects through the mouth of the shell. The projecting mass finally attains the size and assumes the shape of another *Difflugia*. The sand grains then rise to the surface, spread over it, and become embedded in a chitinous secretion which hardens and completes the formation of a new shell. By the time the new shell is formed, the nucleus has already divided and one of the daughter nuclei migrates into the newly protruded mass of protoplasm. Finally, the protoplasmic masses separate and two difflugias are formed, one inhabiting the old shell and the other the new shell.

Order Mycetozoida.   The order Mycetozoida includes those organisms known as *slime molds*. They have cellulose cyst walls and fungus-like fruiting bodies and have been studied as much by botanists as by zoologists. Amoeboid and flagellated stages occur during portions of their life cycles when they are most protozoan-like. The knowledge of groups such as these and the plantlike flagellates has been significant in the increased use of the Kingdom Protista as a classification of forms not differentiated into tissues. The amoeboid stage has lobopodia and many may fuse together and form a *plasmodium* (a multi-nucleate, amoeboid mass, which is spelled the same as the generic name of malaria). In some species flagellated gametes fuse in pairs and then become multinucleated plasmodia by mitotic division of the nucleus. The plasmodium eventually produces the fruiting body, which is named a *sporangium* (Fig. 1–34). In the sporangium, usually atop a stalk, are produced many haploid, cellulose-walled spores following meiotic division of the nuclei.

* Arcellas can be reared in the laboratory quite easily. Pond weeds to which they are attached should be shaken vigorously in a large-mouthed bottle half full of water. The water should then be distributed to Syracuse watch glasses or petri dishes and kept covered at room temperature. Within a day or two, young arcellas may be found. Their shells are almost transparent, and nuclei, food bodies, and vacuoles can be seen clearly.

Fig. 1-34. Order Mycetozoida. Sporangia of *Stemonitis*.

Autotractea

Order Proteomyxida. The order Proteomyxida contains a number of forms of very doubtful relationships; the only common characteristics are the absence of a shell and the formation of filose or reticulose pseudopodia.

An example of the Proteomyxida is *Pseudospora volvocis* (Fig. 1–35), which often parasitizes colonies of *Volvox*. It occurs in amoeboid, flagellated, and heliozoan stages. In infected colonies of *Volvox* the amoeboid stages can be seen creeping about and devouring the cell-individuals of its host. Another genus is *Vampyrella*. *V. lateritia* (Fig. 1–35, B) has a spherical body and is orange-red in color. It feeds on *Spirogyra* and other algae.

Labrinthula macrocystis are small spindle shaped protozoans that move with a poorly understood gliding movement. It has been a serious parasite of eel grass along the eastern coast of the United States.

Order Heliozoida. The characteristics of this group may be stated as follows. The body is generally divided into two regions: (1) a cortical layer, which is alveolar in appearance, contains the contractile vacuole and gives rise to the pseudopodia, and (2) a medullary layer, which contains the nuclear

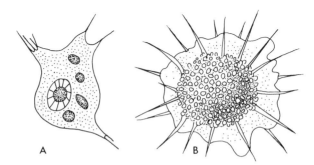

Fig. 1-35. Proteomyxida. (A) *Pseudospora volvocis;* amoeboid stage of a parasite of *Volvox*. (B) *Vampyrella lateritia*. (A, after Robertson; B, after Conn.)

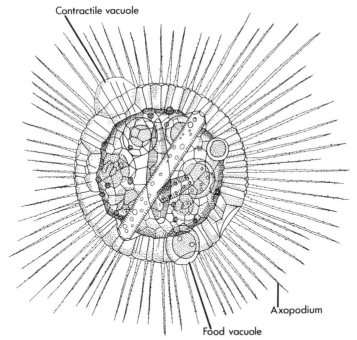

Contractile vacuole

Axopodium

Food vacuole

Fig. 1-36. Heliozoida. *Actinosphaerium eichhorni*. The endoplasm is crowded with food vacuoles containing diatoms, and nuclei are represented in the figure by the dark areas. (After Leidy.)

apparatus, food vacuoles, and, in some cases, symbiotic algae. Many Helio-zoida possess skeletons, which may be either simple or complex in structure and may be composed of various materials. Asexual reproduction is effected by either binary fission or gemmation.

Two of the best-known species of Heliozoida are *Actinophrys sol* and *Actinosphaerium eichhorni*. The former occurs among the vegetation in quiet, fresh water. It is spherical and small (about 50 microns in diameter); has a large central nucleus; and possesses many large vacuoles in the ectoplasm. *Actino-sphaerium eichhorni* (Fig. 1–36) is large, reaching one millimeter in diameter; has many nuclei in the outer layer of endoplasm and several contractile vacu-oles. It is common among the plants in fresh-water ponds.

Order Radiolarida (Fig. 1–37). The Radiolarida are exclusively marine and possess a central capsule, which is a membranous structure that divides the protoplasm of the body into an intra- and extracapsular region. The extra-capsular region is itself divided into three layers. (1) The assimilative layer con-tains the food, which is taken in by the axopodia, and various metaplastic granules. (2) The calymma contains a large number of vacuoles and is supposed to have a hydrostatic function. In some species this layer also contains a

Fig. 1-37. Radiolarida. Siliceous skeletons of several species.

number of yellow symbiotic dinoflagellates. (3) The external layer surrounds the body and from it the axopodia arise. In the majority of species reproduction is associated with the formation of flagellated swarm spores, which arise by a process of multiple fission within the intracapsular region. Several thousand species are planktonic in the ocean. Most have skeletons or spicules of siliceous material or else strontium sulphate. Because the skeletons are not dissolved by dilute acid, they selectively accumulate in some of the deeper parts of the ocean where acids have removed the calcareous parts of other organisms.

Order Foraminiferida. All the Foraminiferida possess shells, which may be chitinous, calcareous, or of foreign materials cemented together. Few have siliceous shells. Shells, or tests, usually have many chambers formed by addition of new and larger chambers to the old following division. Two structural types commonly exist in the same species, (1) a microspheric form, identifiable by a small first chamber, which gives rise asexually to numerous individuals of the next form, (2) a megalospheric form, identifiable by a large first chamber, which gives rise to numerous flagellated gametes that fuse to produce more of the microspheric form. If the test has only the main opening, or aperture, from which the reticulopodia are protruded it is said to be imperforate. Perforate species have numerous small openings, through which the reticulopodia extend, in addition to the aperture. Many types of shells are formed in different species (Fig. 1–38) with the coiled arrangement of chambers being one of the most common. The majority of the Foraminiferida are marine

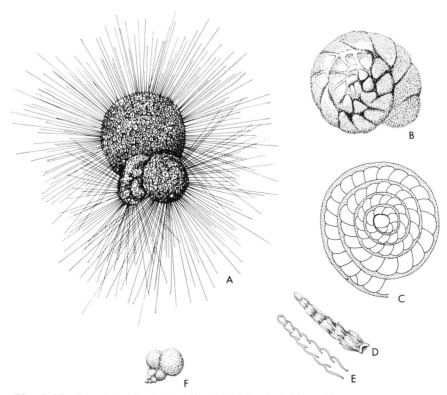

Fig. 1-38. Foraminiferida shells. (A) *Globigerina bulloides*, with globular chambers and long spines. (B) *Rotalia beccari*, upper surface showing chambers arranged in a helicoid spiral. (C) *Nummulites laevigatus*, cross-section of megalospheric form showing chambers in a spiral plane. (D) *Nodosaria*, with chambers in a linear arrangement. (E) *Nodosaria*, diagram of longitudinal section. (F) *Gumbelina*, with chambers added on alternate sides along the plane of growth. (A–C, after several authors; D–F, original.)

forms, although a few such as *Allogromia* (Fig. 1–39) occur in fresh water. Most of them live in the mud of the sea bottom and large areas in the Atlantic Ocean consist of globigerina ooze. So abundant are their shells that they form a large part of the white chalk laid down during the Cretaceous period and the nummulitic limestone of the Eocene. *Globigerina bulloides* (Fig. 1–38) is a cosmopolitan species that is pelagic in habit and also lives in the mud at the bottom of the sea to depths of 3,000 fathoms. Because the pelagic species of the past showered ancient sea beds with their skeletons, which are small enough to be brought up with well drillings, the identification of distinctive species from different aged sedimentary rocks is now important to geologists for stratigraphic correlation. The Pliocene-Pleistocene boundary in deep-sea sediments is marked by abrupt changes in the Foraminiferida fauna (Ericson, 1963). The abundance and variety of species in the geological record, with some in existence for long periods of time and others for shorter periods, makes them one of the more useful groups of fossils for aging rocks.

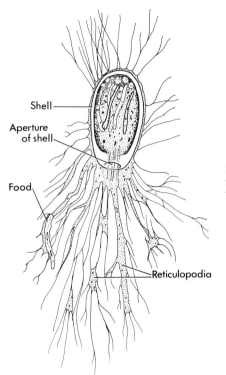

Shell

Aperture
of shell

Food

Reticulopodia

Fig. 1-39. *Foraminiferida. Allogromia*, a fresh-water species, showing capture of food. (From Woodruff.)

4 / Superclass Sporozoa

(1) Monocystis

Monocystis is selected as a type of the superclass Sporozoa because it illustrates many of the characteristics of this group and is easily obtained for study.* It is a parasite in the seminal vesicles of the common earthworm. The stages that are usually present are the trophozoite (Fig. 1–40, A), cysts containing two specimens (B), or gametes and spores in various phases of development (C, D, E), and isolated spores (F, G).

The life cycle of *Monocystis* is briefly as follows. *Spores* (Fig. 1–40, G), are probably released from the seminal vesicles of the earthworm by the death and decay of the earthworm. Each spore contains eight *sporozoites*, which are released from the spore following ingestion by another worm and action of its digestive juices on the spore. Each sporozoite penetrates a bundle of sperm mother cells (I) of the earthworm, and is then termed a *trophozoite*. Here it lives at the expense of the cells among which it lies. The spermatozoa of the

* To obtain living *Monocystis* a living earthworm should be pinned down and a slit made in the body wall from about the tenth to the fifteenth segments. The whitish bodies that extrude are the seminal vesicles that contain male gametes and, usually, *Monocystis*; parts of these should be pinched off with a forceps and stirred up in a drop of 0.7 per cent NaCl solution on a slide and covered.

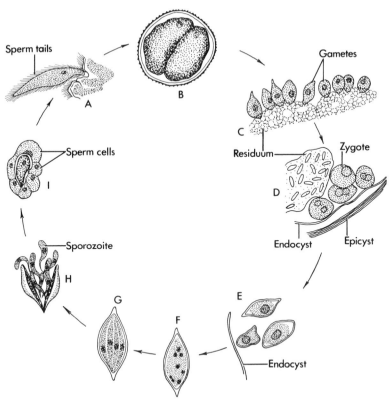

Fig. 1-40. Gregarinida. Life cycle of *Monocystis*, parasitic in the seminal vesicle of the earthworm. (A) A mature individual attached to the sperm-funnel of the earthworm. (B) Two mature individuals joined side by side. (C) Gametes formed within the cyst. (D) Conjugation of gametes to form zygotes. (E) Zygotes that have become spores. (F) A single spore containing eight nuclei. (G) A fully developed spore containing eight sporozoites. (H) The eight sporozoites escaping from the sporocyst. (I) Young trophozoite among sperm-mother cells. (After various authors.)

earthworm which are deprived of nourishment by the parasite, slowly shrivel up finally becoming tiny filaments on the surface of the trophozite (A).

When this stage is reached, two trophozoites come together (B) and are surrounded by a common two-layered cyst wall (D). Each then divides, producing a number of small cells called *gametes* (C). The gametes unite in pairs (D) to form *zygotes*. It is probable that the gametes produced by one of the trophozoites do not fuse with each other, but with gametes produced by the other trophozoite enclosed in the cyst. Each zygote becomes lemon-shaped, and secretes a thin hard wall about itself. It is now known as a *sporoblast* (E). The nucleus of the sporoblast divides successively into two, four, and finally eight daughter nuclei (F); each of these, together with a portion of the cytoplasm, becomes a sporozoite (G, H).

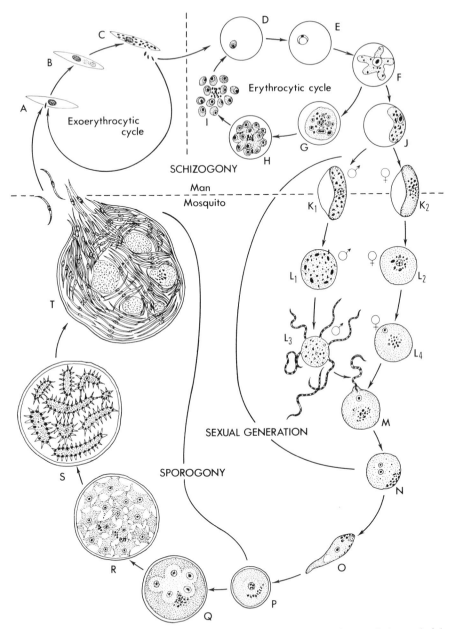

Fig. 1-41. *Plasmodium* of man. Diagram illustrating the life history of the malarial fever parasite. (A–C) Cycle of schizogony in the endothelial cells of the liver. (D–I) Cycle of schizogony in the red blood cells; the duration of this schizogonous cycle is similar to the duration of a cycle of symptoms. (J–N) Sexual generation. (O) Ookinete. (P–T) Sporogony; occurs in the wall of the mosquito alimentary tract. (From Minchin after various authors, modified.)

(2) Plasmodium vivax

One of the best known of all the Sporozoa is *Plasmodium vivax*, which causes tertian malarial fever. This minute animal was discovered in 1880 in the blood of malaria patients by a French military doctor, Laveran. It is transmitted from man to man by the bite of certain species of diseased mosquitoes belonging to the genus *Anopheles*. The two most common genera of mosquitoes are *Culex* and *Anopheles*. One of the easiest methods of distinguishing one from the other is by observing their position when at rest. It will be found that the harmless *Culex* holds its abdomen approximately parallel to the surface on which it alights, whereas the abdomen of *Anopheles* is held at an angle.

There are three well-known types of malaria; these may be recognized by the intervals between successive chills. (1) Tertian fever, caused by *Plasmodium vivax*, is characterized by an attack every 48 hours; (2) quartan fever, caused by *Plasmodium malariae*, with an attack every 72 hours, and (3) estivo-autumnal or subtertian fever, caused by *Plasmodium falciparum*, produces attacks daily, or more or less constant fever. The life histories of these three species of *Plasmodium* differ very slightly one from another.

Malarial fever is transmitted by diseased female mosquitoes only. The mouth parts of these insects are adapted for piercing (Fig. 11–20). When they have been thrust into the skin of the victim, a little saliva is forced into the wound. This saliva contains a weak poison, which is supposed to prevent the coagulation of the blood and, thus, the clogging of the puncture. Blood is sucked up by the mouth parts into the alimentary canal of the mosquito; this process occupies from two to three and a half minutes. With the saliva a number of parasites, which were stored in the salivary glands of the insect, find their way into the wound. These are known as *sporozoites* (Fig. 1–41, A). Each sporozoite penetrates an endothelial cell of the liver (B) where it becomes a trophozoite feeding at the expense of the host cell. The fully grown trophozoite divides by multiple fission into many *merozoites*. The merozoites are released and penetrate other endothelial cells to become trophozoites as before to continue the *exoerythrocytic cycle*. The *erythrocytic cycle* starts when merozoites formed in the exoerythrocytic cycle in the liver cells eventually enter red blood cells to develop as trophozoites. In the red blood corpuscle the trophozoite feeds and grows at the expense of the protoplasm of the red blood corpuscle. The trophozoite reaches its full size in about 50 hours and is then known as a *schizont*; this undergoes a type of multiple division, thus producing from 15 to 24 daughter cells which are also called *merozoites*. The merozoites are liberated into the blood stream in about 8 hours and immediately attack fresh red blood corpuscles. Some of the merozoites develop into schizonts, but others become sexual cells called *gametocytes*.

When a mosquito bites a malaria patient it sucks up blood containing gametocytes. If the mosquito is of the genus *Culex* or of some genus other than *Anopheles*, the parasites are, in the course of time, destroyed in its stomach; but if the mosquito is a female belonging to the proper species of *Anopheles*, development is completed. The female gametocyte produces a mature *macrogamete*, and within the male gametocyte six to eight flagella-like bodies develop which are *microgametes* comparable to spermatozoa. Fertilization then ensues and the zygote thus formed changes into a motile, wormlike *ookinete* (some sources attribute the wormlike shape to aberrant individuals), which enters the wall of the mosquito's stomach. Here it rounds up into an *oocyst*, which grows at the expense of the surrounding tissue, and after six or seven days undergoes *sporulation* during which hundreds of spindle-shaped sporozoites are produced. These break out into the body cavity of the mosquito and some of them find their way into its salivary glands; here they remain ready to be injected into the next human being the mosquito bites.

Development in the blood of a man does not go beyond the macrogamete and microgamete stage of the sexual cycle. The factor limiting further development seems to be the temperature of man since further development will occur if blood with gametes is removed to lower temperatures. Although the exoerythrocytic and erythrocytic cycles continue in untreated individuals, the infection in the mosquito disappears in a few months.

Until recent years, malaria was the most important of all human diseases, especially in tropical and subtropical regions. Although destruction of the vector with DDT and other means as well as treatment of infected humans with antimalarial drugs has markedly reduced the dangers from malaria, cases still number in the millions each year. Quinine remains one of the most effective therapeutic agents, but numerous synthetic drugs also capable of destroying the parasites in the human body have been discovered. Widespread use of some of the newer antimalarial drugs has been followed with the increase of a few resistant strains of malaria, which must then be treated with one of the other antimalarial drugs. Of interest is the resistance to malaria possessed by some men with a modified hemoglobin due to the presence in the heterozygous condition of the gene for sickle cell anemia.

(3) Other Sporozoa

The Sporozoa are all parasitic Protozoa, which usually pass from one host to another in the spore stage. The spore is generally a seedlike body with a covering called the *sporocyst* (Fig. 1–40, F and G). In species whose spores are subjected to air, water, or other agents in their passage from one host to another, these bodies are very resistant, but in other species which are propagated from one host to another directly, either by being inoculated into the new host by a blood-sucking animal or by being eaten by the new host, the spores do not always have such a resistant covering (Fig. 1–41).

Sporozoa are among the most widely distributed of all parasitic animals; members of almost every large group of animals in the animal kingdom are parasitized by one or more species. Infection is very common among the vertebrates, anthropods, mollusks, and worms, and less common among echinoderms, coelenterates, and Protozoa. Comparatively few species are lethal and only a small number seem to be very harmful to their hosts.

The life cycles of the Sporozoa are often very complicated. Frequently there is an alternation of hosts, certain stages being passed in a vertebrate and other stages in an invertebrate which serves as a transmitting agent from one vertebrate host to another. Two types of reproduction are characteristic of the life cycles of most species, (1) multiplicative reproduction or *schizogony* during which many organisms are formed in a single host, and (2) *sporogony*, a propagative reproduction involving sexual processes and ending in the formation of spores which are usually transferred to another host.

As compared with the other Protozoa, the Sporozoa are greatly modified by their parasitic existence. These modifications are represented by the absence of locomotor organs, a mouth, anal opening, excretory pore, and vacuoles. There is usually a single nucleus present. Nutrition is by absorption or by ingestion of host cytoplasm. Many organs of the host may be parasitized, especially the alimentary tract, kidneys, blood, muscle, and connective tissues. When the parasites live inside of cells they are said to be *cytozoic*; when among the cells, *histozoic*; and when in cavities, *coelozoic*.

Classification of the Sporozoa. The groups that are brought together in the superclass Sporozoa have certain characteristics in common but are not necessarily closely related. They are combined in one superclass largely for convenience. It seems best to separate them into three classes—Telosporea, Cnidosporea, and Acnidosporea—and to divide these into orders.

Telosporea

The class Telosporea contains three orders: (1) Gregarinida, (2) Coccida, and (3) Haemosporida. The members of these orders produce spores that have neither polar capsule nor polar filament and that are produced at the termination of the life of the trophozoite.

Order Gregarinida. The gregarines are common parasites of insects, especially in the digestive tract and body cavity, and less common in other groups of vertebrates and invertebrates. They are, at first, intracellular but later often become free in cavities of the body. Here they sometimes grow to a comparatively enormous size. *Monocystis* has already been described (Fig. 1–40). Another type easily obtained for study is *Gregarina* (Fig. 1–42, B) which occurs in the intestine of grasshoppers, cockroaches, and meal-worms. The sporozoites penetrate the epithelial cells of the intestinal wall and the trophozoites that develop from them are at first intracellular; later the trophozoites break out of the epithelial cell to which they are attached for a time by the head or *epimerite*; this, the *cephalont* stage, consists of two parts, the posterior *deutomerite* which contains the nucleus, and an anterior *protomerite* and *epimerite* (Fig. 1–42, A). When the cephalont becomes detached from the cell, it loses its epimerite and is then known as a *sporont*. Sporonts are motile by an

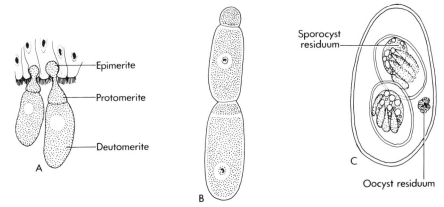

Fig. 1-42. Telosporea. (A) Gregarinida. *Leidyana erratica* attached to intestinal cells of cricket. (B) Gregarinida. *Gregarina blattarum* of the cockroach; two animals attached end to end in syzygy. (C) Coccida. *Isospora hominis* of man; oocyst containing two spores, each with four sporozoites. (After various authors.)

unknown gliding mechanism. The sporonts within the intestine unite end to end, a condition known as *syzygy* (Fig. 1–42, B). Two sporonts conjugate and surround themselves with a wall thus forming a cyst; they are gametocytes, each of which produces a large number of gametes. The gametes copulate in pairs, thus becoming zygotes, and secrete sporocysts and hence are spores. Within each spore, eight sporozoites are produced. The sporozoites, that are liberated with the aid of digestive enzymes in the intestine of the hosts that have ingested the spores, bring about new infections.

Order Coccida. The Coccida are Sporozoa whose life cycle includes both schizogony and sporogony and is passed in a single host. They are parasitic in vertebrates, centipedes, mollusks, insects, annelids, and flatworms. The life cycle of a typical species, *Eimeria stiedae* of the rabbit is illustrated in Figure 1–43.

The sporozoites that escape from the spores in the intestine of the host (A) penetrate the intestinal wall to reach hepatic portal blood vessels and are swept with the blood to the liver where they enter the epithelial cells of the bile-ducts and become trophozoites (B); each trophozoite is a schizont, which produces a number of daughter merozoites asexually (C–D); this multiplicative process is known as schizogony. The merozoites may enter other epithelial cells becoming trophozoites and pass through another period of asexual reproduction (B, C, D), or, after the penetration of epithelial cells, may produce merozoites which are gametocytes; these penetrate other epithelial cells (E, F) where they develop into macrogametocytes (G, I) or microgametocytes (H, J). Each merozoite produces either one large macrogamete (I) or a large number of microgametes (J). One microgamete copulates with each macrogamete, a process that may be considered fertilization, thus

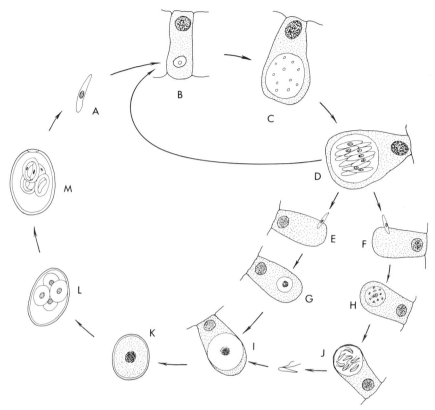

Fig. 1-43. Coccida. *Eimeria stiedae*, life cycle. (A) Sporozoite. (B–D) Cycle of schizogony in the epithelial cells of the bile ducts of the rabbit. (E–J) Gamete production. (K–M) Sporogony.

producing a zygote. A wall forms about the zygote, and the body is then known as an oocyst (K). The protoplasm within divides to form four sporoblasts (L), each of which forms a sporocyst about itself thus becoming a spore (M). Within each spore, two sporozoites develop.

Coccida in Man. Three species of Coccida have been found in man. *Isospora hominis* (Fig. 1–42, C) is the most common of the three species of *Isospora*, and all are more common in the tropics. They are apparently parasites of the intestinal mucosa and rarely produce serious disease. Knowledge of them is largely confined to the oocysts, which are present in the feces of infected individuals for a limited time. In most cases they produce a diarrhea of about two weeks duration.

Coccida in Lower Animals. The Coccida most easily obtained for study are those in the rabbit, *Eimeria stiedae* (Fig. 1–43). Oocysts of this species may be found in the feces of a large proportion of these animals. They are in an unsporulated stage when passed but sporulation may be observed if the material is placed in a 5 per cent aqueous solution of potassium bichromate to inhibit the growth of bacteria. Development into sporoblasts and the formation of sporozoites takes place in about three days.

Eimeria schubergi is a parasite of centipedes of the genus *Lithobius*. It occurs in the intestine and has a life cycle similar to *E. stiedae*.

Other species of *Eimeria* occur in various species of mammals, birds, reptiles, amphibians, and fish. All of these are pathogenic if their life cycles are similar to that of *E. stiedae* in the rabbit but most of them do not injure the host very severely. *E. stiedae* frequently brings about the death of rabbits, however, and *E. zurnii* is a cause of diarrhea in cattle. The *Eimeria* of birds, *E. tenella*, is likewise lethal under certain conditions, especially when epidemics occur among young chickens. Amoeboid host cells seem to aid the sporozoites in reaching the site where development occurs.

Coccidia of the genus *Isospora* also occur in vertebrates of all classes. Cats and dogs are commonly infected with *I. felis* and *I. rivolta*. Other species occur in birds and cold-blooded vertebrates.

Haemogregarines are Coccida that occur in the blood of frogs as well as other amphibians, reptiles, birds, and fish. Their life cycles involve a blood-sucking leech or arthropod as a second host. The species *Lankesterella minima* (Fig. 1–44, B) is transmitted to frogs by the leech, *Placobdella*. *L. minima* sporozoites, when first introduced, penetrate endothelial cells of the frog and produce a generation or more of merozoites followed by production of macrogametes and microgametes, which unite to form a zygote. The zygote

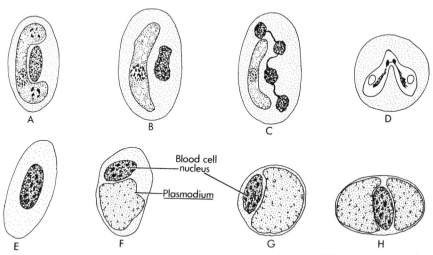

Fig. 1-44. Sporozoa of the blood. (A) *Haemoproteus* in the red blood corpuscle of a bird. (B) *Lankesterella* in the red blood corpuscle of a frog. (C) *Karyolysus* in the red blood corpuscle of a frog. (D) *Babesia canis* in the red blood corpuscle of a dog. (E) A normal red blood corpuscle of a bird. (F) (G) and (H) *Plasmodium relictum* in the red blood cells of a pigeon; (H) shows two parasites. (A, B, C, after Hegner; D after Nuttall; E, F, G, H, original.)

develops into an oocyst within which the sporozoites are formed. When the sporocysts are released, they enter the red blood cells. In the red blood cell the sporozoite develops into the trophozoite which, as it grows, pushes the host cell nucleus to one side (Fig. 1–44, B). *Karyolysus* (Fig. 1–44, C) causes the nucleus of the parasitized red cell to break up into several pieces. The invertebrate host is a mite as is the invertebrate host of *Hepatozoon muris. H. muris* gametocytes develop in white blood cells of the rat and complete the sexual phase of reproduction in a blood-feeding mite. The cycle is completed when a rat eats an infected mite.

Order Haemosporida. The Haemosporida, as the name implies, are Sporozoa that live in the blood. They penetrate the blood cells of vertebrates where they pass through schizogony and go through part of their life cycle in invertebrate hosts where sporogony occurs. The most important species are the malarial parasites of man. Representatives of a number of genera may be obtained from common lower animals, for example, *Haemoproteus* from birds; piroplasmas and anaplasmas from cattle suffering from Texas fever; and *Plasmodium* from birds.*

Haemoproteus (Fig. 1–44, A) is a genus common in birds, turtles, snakes, and lizards. The best-known species is *H. columbae,* a parasite of the common pigeon that has been reported from various parts of the world. The life cycle of this species includes asexual reproduction in the endothelial cells of the blood vessels of the pigeon's lungs and other organs, and the development of male and female gametocytes. The transmitting agent in which sporozoites are formed is a hippoboscid fly, *Lynchia.* Within the red cells the organism grows partly around the red-cell nucleus in the form of a halter, hence the term halteridium often applied to members of this genus.

Piroplasmas of the genus *Babesia* undergo sporogony after ingestion of the infected blood cells (Fig. 1–44, D) of a mammal by a tick. *B. bigemina* ookinetes penetrate the eggs of ticks where they develop along with the eggs to produce eventually ticks with infected salivary glands containing sporozoites which may infect cattle, the mammalian hosts, when they are bitten by ticks. Piroplasmas are sometimes classified with the Sarcodina or considered of uncertain relationship. Their life cycle is quite comparable to many of the other Haemosporida although budding or binary fission occurs rather than schizogony. Rudzinska and Trager (1962) have found that the cytoplasm, in electron micrographs, is similar to that of *Plasmodium berghei,* although only a single plasma membrane covers *Babesia* in contrast to two for *Plasmodium,* and ingestion of blood cell cytoplasm seems to be important in the nutrition of both.

Malarial parasites of the genus *Plasmodium* occur in lower animals as well

---

* Preparations are made by securing a drop of fresh blood from an infected individual, spreading it on a slide where it is allowed to dry, and then staining it by a Romanowsky method (e.g., using Wright's stain).

as in man. They have been recorded especially from birds, bats, squirrels, and lizards. The species in birds are of particular interest because they were used by Ross in working out the sexual cycle of malarial parasites in mosquitoes. They are also of great value for purposes of teaching and investigation since they can be transmitted easily from sparrows to captive canaries by blood inoculation, and when the latter are once infected they appear to remain infected throughout their lives. The method of procedure is to prick a vein in the leg and suck up a drop of blood into a syringe containing normal saline solution. This is then injected into the breast muscle or peritoneal cavity of a fresh bird. The average length of the prepatent period is about five days. The period of rise in the number of parasites is also about five days when from 10 to 5,000 parasites per 10,000 red cells are present. Then a rapid fall in the number of parasites occurs and no more can be found in the blood except after long search. That the birds remain infected is evident from the fact that they suffer relapses, much as human beings do, and also by the fact that blood from the birds is infective to fresh birds. Bird malaria is of value for the study of therapeutic agents. *Plasmodium berghei*, which can be maintained in the rat, has been found to ingest the cytoplasm of the host red blood cell in a manner much like food vacuole formation in amoebas.

Cnidosporea

The Cnidosporea contains Sporozoa that produce spores in each of which are one to four *polar capsules* and in each polar capsule a coiled *polar filament*. The two principal orders are the Myxosporida and Microsporida. Because of their complex structure some zoologists think they may represent degenerate metazoans. There are interesting parallels between the polar capsule and coelenterate nematocysts. Both have filaments that seem to be discharged by turning inside out.

Order Myxosporida.   The Myxosporida (Fig. 1–46, A and B) are principally parasites of fish. The life cycle is comparatively simple, since there is no

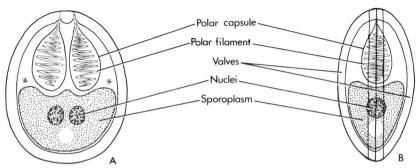

Fig. 1-45. Myxosporida. Diagram of a spore before fusion of the sporoplasm nuclei. (A) Front view. (B) Side view.

intermediate host. The principal organs of the host invaded by the parasite are the gall-bladder, gills, kidney, urinary bladder, muscle, integument, connective tissue, spleen, and ovary. The spores are complicated structures (Fig. 1–45). When swallowed by a new host, the polar filaments are thought to turn inside out and fix the spore to the intestinal wall. The two nuclei of the sporoplasm fuse before it hatches to invade the host tissue. Growth to a multinucleate mass occurs and new spores develop within this vegetative stage from portions termed *pansporoblasts* in which several nuclei develop, two of which form the nuclei of the gametes which will form the new sporoplasm. Cells formed by other nuclei of the pansporoblast and their associated cytoplasm are responsible for formation of the polar capsules and valves. The Myxosporida are often parasites with a mild effect on the host but severe infections may bring about the death of the host.

Order Microsporida. The Microsporida (Fig. 1–46, C and D) are characterized by the presence of spores that are extremely small and possess usually only one polar capsule. The hosts of most Microsporida are arthropods; the rest belong to other groups of invertebrates and to the cold-blooded vertebrates. Among the invertebrate hosts are included three species of Sporozoa and one ciliate. Certain of the Microsporida are of great economic importance because they bring about the death of animals of value to man. For example, the species *Nosema bombycis* causes a chronic disease in silkworms known as pebrine. This species is generally distributed throughout the tissues of the host, including the eggs developing in the ovary. These eggs are deposited by the silkworm moth and the larvae that hatch from them are thus infected by the so-called "hereditary" transmission. Pasteur was able to control silkworm disease, which once threatened to destroy the silk industry of France, by eliminating infected eggs which he was able to recognize with the aid of a microscope. Another important species economically is *Nosema apis* (Fig.

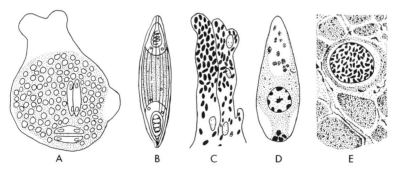

Fig. 1-46. Cnidosporea and Acnidosporea. (A) Myxosporida; *Myxidium lieberkuhni*, vegetative stage, from pike. (B) Myxosporida; *Myxidium lieberkuhni*, spore from pike. (C) Microsporida; *Nosema apis*, spores in the cells of the stomach of the honeybee. (D) Microsporida; *Thelohania magna*, young spore from a mosquito larva. (E) Toxoplasmida; spores of *Sarcocystis* in the muscle fibers of man. (After various authors.)

1–46, C), which causes nosema disease in honeybees. Infection is brought about by the ingestion of spores and is limited to the digestive tract. Other species of Microsporida are to a certain degree beneficial because they attack harmful insects, for example, the larvae of several species of anopheline mosquitoes that are carriers of human malaria may be infected.

Acnidosporea

The class Acnidosporea contains two orders of doubtful position, the Toxoplasmida and the Haplosporida.

Order Toxoplasmida. The spores of the Toxoplasmida do not contain polar capsules. Toxoplasmida are parasites of vertebrates, being especially common in sheep, cattle, and horses. They occur in reptiles and birds as well as mammals. The life cycle of the sarcosporidium of rats and mice, *Sarcocystis muris*, is the best known. Spores ingested by mice hatch in the intestine, and liberate amoebulae that penetrate the cells of the intestinal epithelium; here the trophozoites grow and multiply by schizogony. Apparently the merozoites migrate to the muscles where they become located in the fibers; here growth results in a multinucleate plasmodium which divides by plasmotomy. In the course of time the masses of parasites form long, slender, cylindrical bodies with pointed ends, known as "Miescher's tubes" within which immense numbers of sickle-shaped spores are formed. Very little is known regarding the method of transmission of Toxoplasmida.

A few cases of sarcosporidiosis have been reported from man; the organisms are found in the muscle usually at autopsy (Fig. 1–46, E). In most cases no serious results are brought about by the infection, although *S. muris*, which spreads throughout the entire body, brings about death in mice, and death sometimes also occurs in sheep as a result of heavy infections.

Toxoplasma gondii (Fig. 1–47) is an intracellular parasite found in man and many other animals. About a third of the people tested in some portions of the United States have antibodies indicating they have been infected with *T*.

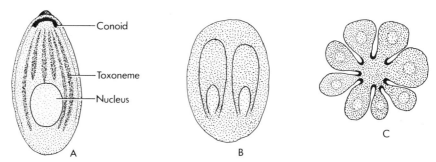

Fig. 1-47. *Toxoplasma gondii.* (A) Diagram of *Toxoplasma.* (B) Internal development of two filial cells. (C) Rosette formation of eight filial cells. (Adapted from electron micrographs by Gavin, Wanko, and Jacobs.)

gondii. Most infections are subclinical. Gavin, Wanko, and Jacobs (1962) have demonstrated what seem to be several methods of reproduction, two of which are indicated in Fig. 1–47. Reproduction is asexual and the method of infection is not certain.

The Toxoplasmida have been of doubtful protozoan status. One has been reported as becoming, under some conditions, a definite fungus. Perhaps this strengthens the Protista concept.

Order Haplosporida. The Haplosporida are parasites of lower vertebrates and invertebrates. The genus *Haplosporidium* occurs in marine and fresh-water annelids and mollusks. *Ichthyosporidium* is parasitic in fish. *Bertramia* parasitizes aquatic worms and rotifers.

5 / Superclass Ciliata

(1) Tetrahymena pyriformis

Tetrahymena pyriformis is an inhabitant of fresh-water in many parts of the world. It is easily cultured in the laboratory and can be grown in media containing only chemically defined nutrients. Cultures maintained in a nutrient media with no other living organisms are said to be maintained *axenically.* Because these ciliates can be grown in pure culture, and in chemically defined media, they have been very popular and useful in biological research at the cellular and molecular level. *Tetrahymena* was the first animal to be grown axenically.

General Morphology. *T. pyriformis* (Fig. 1–48) is an egg-shaped, uniformly ciliated, small, plastic protozoan. The *buccal cavity* is pyriform, much like the shape of the entire cell, and is located near the anterior end. About 20 rows of *cilia* run longitudinally the length of the animal with two of them originating postorally. The *cytoproct* (cell anus) is located near the posterior in one of the postoral ciliary rows. Two contractile vacuole pores are located several ciliary rows away near the level of the cytoproct. Three membranelles and an undulating membrane are in the buccal cavity. An ovoid *macronucleus* is centrally located. Near the macronucleus is usually a smaller nucleus, the *micronucleus,* which contains the genetic material involved in sexual phenomena. Only ciliates have a macronucleus and a micronucleus, that is, two sizes of nuclei in the same cell. A single *contractile vacuole* is located posterior to the nuclei. Various vacuoles and granules may be visible internally.

Cytology. Ciliates stained with silver stains show the granule at the base of a cilium as a darkly staining object, the *kinetosome.* The kinetosomes are said to be self-duplicating bodies from which the cilium develops. In *Tetrahymena,* the kinetosomes are arranged in longitudinal rows. A fiber arises

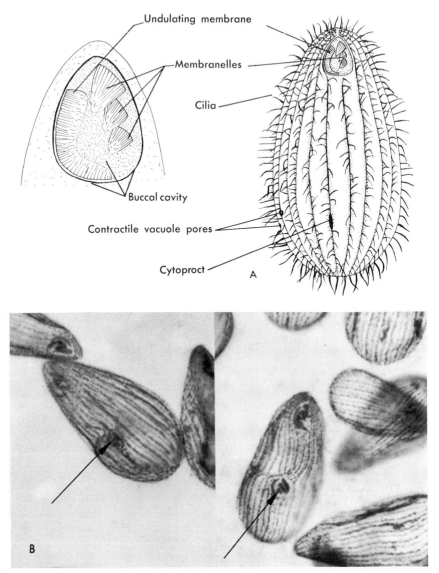

Fig. 1-48. *Tetrahymena pyriformis.* (A) Diagram of general anatomy. (B) Photos show organization of kinetosomes in new oral region prior to fission.

from each kinetosome and passes to the right and then anteriorly as it closely parallels other fibers from other kinetosomes in the row. This set of parallel fibers is known as the *kinetodesma*. The kinetodesma and the associated row of kinetosomes is a *kinety*. Additional fibers (Fig. 1–49) also embedded in the ectoplasm have been described by Pitelka (1961). The function of the various fibers is not known but most speculate that the kinetodesma is involved in

Fig. 1-49. Kineties of *Colpidium campylum*. Diagrammatic surface views of three kineties showing features similar to those of *Tetrahymena pyriformis*. Cilia are indicated as empty circles, with parasomal sacs shown as smaller circles anterior to them. Left kinety shows kinetodesmal fibers. Center kinety shows longitudinal, transverse, and postciliary fibers. Right kinety shows primary and secondary meridians of pellicle with small circles indicating protrichocyst attachments. (From D. R. Pitelka. Fine structure of the silverline and fibrillar systems of three tetrahymenid ciliates. *J. Protozool.* **8**(1):75–89. Copyright 1961 by the Society of Protozoologists.)

coordination or conduction of impulses. They may have a supporting function. Experimental evidence from microdissection of *Paramecium* indicates that some conducting system is located in a kinety, or associated with it. The cilium (Fig. 1–2) has an ultrastructure similar to the flagellum of the flagellates. Nine peripheral fibers surround two central fibers. These fibers are embedded in an electron transparent material and the surface of the cilium is a membrane continuous with the surface membrane of the cell. The peripheral fibers of the cilium, but not the central fibers, extend into the kinetosome (Fig. 1–50). The buccal cavity of *Tetrahymena* contains three *membranellae* on the left and an *undulating membrane* on the right. These are formed from closely associated sets of kinetosomes from which ciliary fibers that have undergone a degree of fusion arise. In the bottom of the buccal

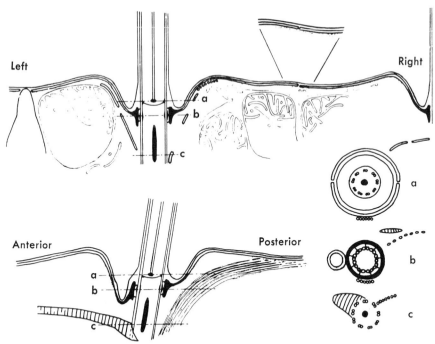

Fig. 1-50. Diagrams of cortical structure of *Colpidium campylum*. Top, transverse section; bottom left, longitudinal section; bottom right, three sections through ciliary base at points indicated. Section *a* shows transverse fibrils at bottom, section *b* shows parasomal sac at left, and section *c* shows kinetodesmal fiber to left with postciliary fibrils at right. (From Dorothy R. Pitelka. Fine structure of the silverline and fibrillar systems of three tetrahymenid ciliates. *J. Protozool.* **8**(1):75–89. Copyright 1961 by the Society of Protozoologists.)

cavity is the *cytostome*. Prior to division a new mouth arises posterior to, and some distance from, the old mouth but in association with the same kineties.

A *micronucleus*, when present, is usually closely associated with the *macronucleus*. Elliott and others have studied *Tetrahymena* from many parts of the world and found that those lacking a micronucleus are very common. Such *amicronucleate* strains are incapable of sexual reproduction. The macronucleus is centrally located and not visible in unstained specimens. Both nuclei stain with stains that are specific for DNA.

The *contractile vacuole*, located at the posterior, is a single structure, which apparently fills through a system of microtubules that extend into part of the cell (Fig. 1–51). Contractile vacuole pores have a well-defined structure in electron micrographs (Fig. 1–52).

Mitochondria (Figs. 1–51 and 1–53) are of the microtubular type and most abundant near the ectoplasm. *Food vacuoles* circulate throughout the endoplasm in those which are fed on particulate matter, but no food vacuoles are

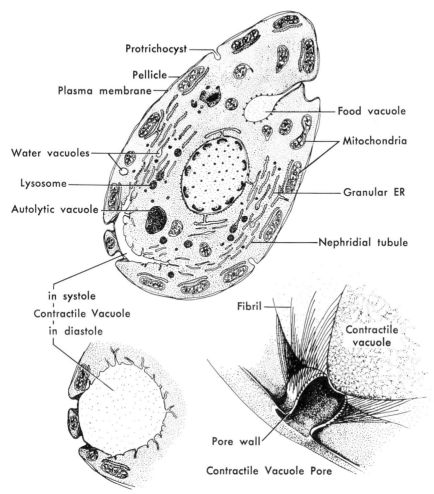

Fig. 1-51. A schematic representation of the nephridial system and related structures. The contractile vacuole is shown in systole and diastole. The pore with its associated fibrils and contractile vacuole is shown in three dimensions. Other structures such as protrichocysts and autolytic vacuoles are shown. (From A. M. Elliott and I. J. Bak. The contractile vacuole and related structures in *Tetrahymena pyriformis. J. Protozool.* **11**(2):250–261. Copyright 1964 by the Society of Protozoologists.)

known to be formed in those grown in nutrient solutions. Lipid droplets (Fig. 1–56, A) are most abundant in the anterior of the cell. Other inclusions are sometimes present, as well as sites of enzyme activity which can be localized by histochemical studies. Various studies such as those of Fennell and Marzke (1954) have shown that such enzymes as the phosphatases vary in abundance and distribution with age of cultures and different culture solutions.

Fig. 1-52. The contractile vacuole of *Tetrahymena*. (A) Electron micrograph of the vacuole in diastole, pore to upper end. × 11,250. (B) Vacuole in systole, below pore which is in center. × 18,000. (From A. M. Elliott and I. J. Bak. The contractile vacuole and related structures in *Tetrahymena pyriformis*. *J. Protozool.* **11**(2): 250–261. Copyright 1964 by the Society of Protozoologists. Courtesy of Dr. Alfred M. Elliott.)

Fig. 1-53. Electron micrograph of *Tetrahymena*. Sections of two microtubular type mitochondria are visible. The outer membrane of the macronucleus (upper right) is seen to be continuous with the granular endoplasmic reticulum. × 27,000. (From A. M. Elliott and I. J. Bak. The contractile vacuole and related structures in *Tetrahymena pyriformis*. *J. Protozool.* **11**(2):250–261. Copyright 1964 by the Society of Protozoologists. Courtesy of Dr. Alfred M. Elliott.)

Amino acids			Growth factors	
Arginine	150		Ca pantothenate	0.1
Histidine	110		Folic acid	0.01
Isoleucine	100		Niacin	0.1
Leucine	70		Pyridoxine HCl	2.0
Lysine	35		Riboflavin	0.1
Methionine	35		Thiamine HCl	1.0
Phenylalanine	100		Thioctic acid	0.001
Serine	180			
Threonine	180		**Carbon source**	
Tryptophane	40		Glucose	1000.
Valine	60		Sodium acetate	1000.

Nucleic Acids			Inorganic salts	
Adenylic acid	25		K_2HPO_4	100.
Cytidylic acid	25		$MgSO_4 \cdot 7H_2O$	10.
Guanylic acid	25		$Zn(NO_3)_2 \cdot 6H_2O$	5.
Uracil	25		$FeSO_4 \cdot 7H_2O$	0.5
			$CuCl_2 \cdot 2H_2O$	0.5

Fig. 1-54. Axenic culture. Growth of *Tetrahymena pyriformis* can be maintained in fortified peptone broth and a number of other bacteria free media. Chemically defined media will also support growth. The ingredients listed above are for Elliott's modification of Kidder and Dewey media. Numerical values are in mg/liter of aqueous solution. The diagrammatic culture indicates the honeycombed pattern frequently assumed by the ciliates as they move in constantly changing formation. Such formations are most noticeable at high population levels.

Physiology. *Tetrahymena* is of considerable value in physiological research, because it can be grown in pure culture in chemically defined media. The fact that it has a cellular metabolism similar in many ways to the cellular metabolism of man makes it a useful tool. It can utilize nutrients by glycolysis and the tricarboxylic acid cycle. It requires the same amino acids (Fig. 1–54) as man.

Gibbons and Rowe (1965) have isolated a protein from *Tetrahymena* cilia which has adenosine triphosphatase activity. It may be a contractile element of cilia, but it is different from contractile proteins such as actin and myosin. They have suggested the term *dynein* as a name for the protein.

Viable *Tetrahymena* have been recovered from cells frozen in a protective solution to −20°C, then stored three months at the temperature of liquid nitrogen.

Tetrahymena exhibits very sensitive growth responses, either an increase or decrease, to many treatments and substances. Such sensitivity makes them potentially valuable organisms for biological assay of nutrients and other substances.

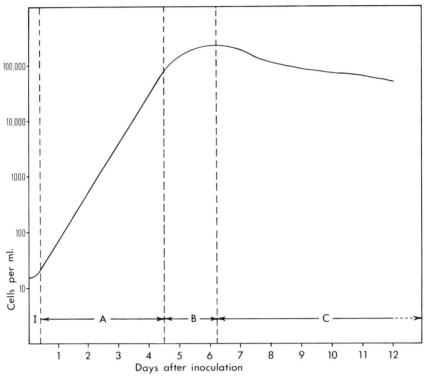

Fig. 1-55. Growth curve of *Tetrahymena* populations. *I*, lag phase following inoculation into fresh media. *A*, logarithmic growth phase. *B*, negative acceleration of growth. *C*, period of declining population size.

Growth in numbers of cells following inoculation into fresh media is very rapid (Fig. 1–55). Following a brief lag phase of adjustments to new culture conditions, a logarithmic growth phase occurs in which the population growth is very rapid until *limiting factors* such as depletion of nutrients, lack of oxygen, or accumulation of waste products slows the rate of increase. Eventually the population dies out after a long period in which the numbers decline because cell deaths exceed cell divisions. Such laboratory growth patterns show interesting parallels to growth phenomena in natural populations. However, the period of decline found in most laboratory situations would be a stable, but fluctuating, level of population size in natural environments due to continuing replenishment of the food supply. Evident in culture conditions is how the unchecked population growth of the logarithmic and following growth phase tends to overshoot the population level, which can be maintained by the culture conditions at that time. Such population growth without checks in the early phases would be rare under natural conditions.

Cells in the logarithmic growth phase can be induced to divide synchronously (Fig. 1–56) with the other cells in the population by a series of temperature shocks (Scherbaum and Zeuthen, 1954). This has simplified the problem of studying the biochemistry of dividing cells.

Taxonomy.   Corliss (1954) found that *Tetrahymena* was often referred to as *Glaucoma* or *Colpidium*. Using the infraciliature, especially distribution of kinetosomes, as well as other characteristics, many strains of *Tetrahymena* are referable to the species *T. pyriformis*. However, reproductive studies of mating types indicate that the species includes a number of reproductively isolated populations. These different populations have been designated as

Fig. 1-56. *Tetrahymena pyriformis.* Stained to show lipid droplets. (A) From a culture past the logarithmic phase of growth; (B) and (C) from a culture in the logarithmic growth phase subjected to temperature shocks to synchronize cell divisions. (B) Prior to onset of division. (C) During peak of cell divisions. The darkly stained lipid droplets visible in the anterior of cells in (A) are nearly absent in (B) and (C). Many other cytoplasmic materials not stained in these preparations also have a specific pattern of localization with abundance varying with culture conditions.

varieties and are comparable to species in other groups. Because they cannot be distinguished by morphological criteria, it is convenient to consider them all *T. pyriformis*, but because they do have physiological differences it is important that experimentalists designate the source of their material when reporting the results of experiments on *Tetrahymena* so that more meaningful comparisons can be made.

Genetics. *Tetrahymena* typically has a diploid micronucleus. X-rays have been used to induce the development of ones with a haploid micronucleus. *Conjugation* occurs in which micronuclear material is exchanged by two cells of different mating types. Mating types are similar to sexes although some varieties have numerous mating types. The phenomena of conjugation will be discussed in greater detail for *Paramecium*. Macronuclei are more important in determining phenotype of a cell than micronuclei although the latter determine the characteristics present in the macronucleus following conjugation. That is because the old macronucleus degenerates during conjugation and a new one is formed by the new micronuclei following conjugation. Varieties lacking a micronucleus are common but they only divide by binary fission. In binary fission the macronucleus is thought to divide by *amitosis*, pinching in two with half going to each of the new daughter cells. Because there are many sets of chromosomes in the macronucleus each daughter cell usually gets some of all the needed chromosomes so that more of the same can be formed.

Recently (Elliott, Addison, and Carey, 1962) there were one-third amicro-nucleate strains in 28 samples containing *Tetrahymena* from 188 samples of European fresh-water locations. Several different varieties were found, some of which also occur in America.

(2) Paramecium

Paramecium lives in fresh-water ponds and streams and is very easily obtained. Cultures prepared for *Amoeba* will in most cases sooner or later contain a host of paramecia.

General Morphology (Fig. 1–57). If a drop of water containing *Paramecium* is placed on a slide, the animals may be seen with the naked eye moving rapidly from place to place.* Under the microscope they appear cigar-shaped. Close inspection reveals a depression extending from the end directed forward in swimming, obliquely backward and toward the right, ending just posterior to the middle of the animal. This is the *oral groove*. The *vestibule* is a depression in the posterior part of the oral groove which opens into the curving, funnel-like *buccal cavity* (gullet). The oral groove and

---

* The movements of paramecia will be retarded for easier observation if the slide is first coated with a film of viscous methyl cellulose (available from most biological supply houses) before the paramecia are added.

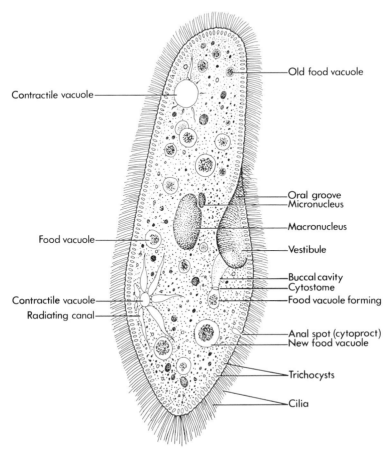

Contractile vacuole

Old food vacuole

Contractile vacuole

Food vacuole

Contractile vacuole

Radiating canal

Oral groove
Micronucleus

Macronucleus

Vestibule

Buccal cavity
Cytostome
Food vacuole forming

Anal spot (cytoproct)
New food vacuole

Trichocysts

Cilia

Fig. 1-57. *Paramecium* viewed from the side. (Modified after several authors.)

vestibule have cilia much like those covering the general surface of the cell. The buccal cavity contains organelles of modified cilia somewhat resembling the structures in the buccal cavity of *Tetrahymena*. The buccal cavity of *Paramecium* passes obliquely downward and posteriorly and opens through the *cytostome* into the endoplasm. The oral groove gives the animal an unsymmetrical appearance. Because *Paramecium* swims with the slender but blunt end foremost, we are able to distinguish this as the *anterior end*. The opposite end, which is thicker but more pointed, represents the *posterior end*, whereas the side containing the oral groove may be designated as *oral* or *ventral*, the opposite side *aboral* or *dorsal*. The motile organs are fine thread-like *cilia* regularly arranged over the surface. Two layers of cytoplasm are visible, as in *Amoeba*, an outer comparatively thin clear area, the *ectoplasm*, and a central granular mass, the *endoplasm*. Besides these a distinct *pellicle* is present outside of the ectoplasm. Lying in the ectoplasm are a great

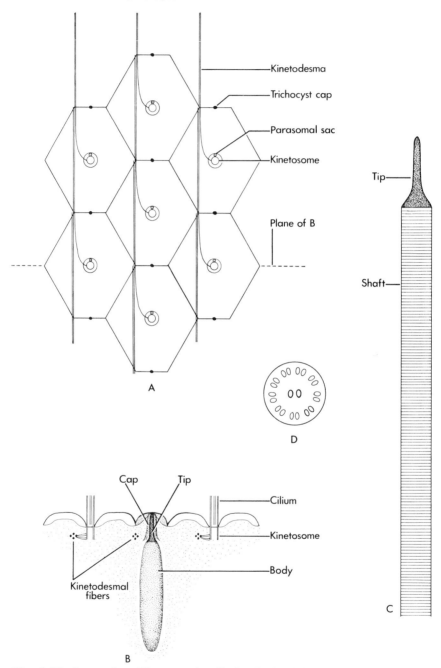

Fig. 1-58. *Paramecium.* Diagrams of pellicular details. (A) Relationship of surface hexagons to kineties and trichocysts. (B) Cross-section of pellicle showing undischarged trichocyst. (C) Discharged trichocyst. (D) Fiber pattern in cross-section of cilium. (Modified after several authors.)

number of minute sacs, the *trichocysts*, which discharge long threads to the exterior when properly stimulated. One large *contractile vacuole* is situated near either end of the body, close to the dorsal surface, and a variable number of *food vacuoles* may usually be seen. The *nuclei* are two in number, a large *macronucleus* and a smaller *micronucleus* (some species of *Paramecium* have more than one micronucleus); these are suspended in the cytoplasm near the mouth opening. The *anal spot*, or *cytoproct*, can be observed in living cells only when solid particles are discharged. It is situated just behind the posterior end of the oral groove.

Cytology. The *endoplasm* of *Paramecium* occupies the central part of the body. It appears granular and most of the larger granules are shown by cytochemical reactions to be reserve food particles; they flow from place to place, indicating that the protoplasm is quite fluid. The *ectoplasm* does not contain any of the large granules characteristic of the endoplasm, because its density prevents their entrance. In this respect the two kinds of cytoplasm resemble the ectoplasm and endoplasm of *Amoeba*. If a drop or two of 35 per cent alcohol is added to a drop of water containing paramecia, the pellicle will be raised in some of the specimens in the form of a blister. Under the higher powers of the microscope a great number of hexagonal areas can be seen on the surface. The hexagons (Fig. 1–58) are formed by the sides of raised areas around the cilia. The *cilia* (Figs. 1–58 and 1–60) arise from basal granules called *kinetosomes.** The kinetosomes have a regular distribution (Fig. 1–59), except in the buccal cavity where they are grouped at the bases of three long membranelles and an undulating membrane. From each body kinetosome a fiber passes to the right and anterior to partly parallel similar fibers from other kinetosomes in the same row. These fibers form the *kinetodesma* (Fig. 1–58, A). The kinetodesma and its associated kinetosomes are the *kinety*.

The cilium itself has an ultrastructure similar to the ultrastructure of the flagellum. A "nine plus two" pattern describes the nine double peripheral fibers and two central fibers, which are found in the ciliary cross-section (Fig. 1–58, D). The membranelles and undulating membranes of ciliates which have them differ a great deal from the undulating membrane of such flagellates as *Trypanosoma*. The undulating membrane of *Trypanosoma* is powered by the flagellum, which runs through the distal end of the membrane, whereas the undulating membrane of ciliates is formed by the close association and fusion of numerous cilia. Cilia develop from the kinetosomes, but the origin of the kinetosomes is uncertain. Some think they are self-duplicating bodies, others think they may arise from the nucleus.

* The kinetosomes can be stained in paramecia by drying specimens on a slide, soaking them in 2 per cent silver nitrate for a few minutes, rinsing most of the silver nitrate out with distilled water for about 2 minutes, then exposing the wet slide to an ultraviolet light source (about 5 minutes in bright sun) until a browning of the specimen occurs.

Oral
groove

Fig. 1-59. *Paramecium:* Silver-stained to show the pattern of kinetosomes in the pellicle. Note the transverse rows in the oral groove.

Contractile
vacuole pore

Fig. 1-60. Schematic representation of the beating of a row of cilia. (After Verworn.)

Interspersed with the kinetosomes of the cilia is a layer of elongate, sack-like bodies with their long axes extending about four microns perpendicular to the surface. These are *trichocysts* (Fig. 1–58). During development in a vesicle in the cytoplasm the trichocyst is filled with a layered material (Yusa, 1962). In the mature trichocyst the layering is lost and the structure is capped by an electron-dense part resembling an inverted tack. With proper stimulation trichocysts discharge a filament tipped by the trichocyst cap.* The filament is finely striated with the striations oriented across the filament in a direction opposite to that of the striations or layering of the immature trichocysts from which the filaments are formed. The filament extruded from the trichocyst is about eight times the length of the trichocyst. Trichocysts are supposed to function as organs of defense. In some instances they have been reported to provide anchorage to the substrate. Evidence that the

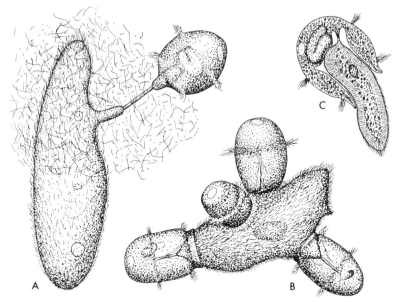

Fig. 1-61. *Paramecium* attacked by the ciliate *Didinium nasutum*. (A) *Paramecium* discharges its trichocysts thus forcing the attacking Didinium away. (B) Four small didinia attacking a *Paramecium*. (C) Section of a large *Didinium* swallowing a small *Paramecium*. (After Mast.)

* Paramecia may discharge trichocysts when a small amount of osmic or acetic acid is added to their water. Aqueous Bismark Brown stain may cause their discharge and stain them as well.

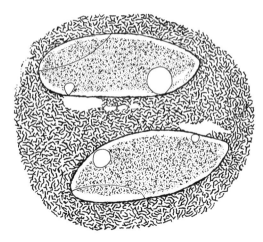

Fig. 1-62. *Paramecium:* discharge of contractile vacuoles. The organisms are represented swimming in a solution of India ink. (After Jennings.)

trichocysts are weapons of defense is furnished when *Paramecium* encounters another ciliate *Didinium*. If the seizing organ of this protozoan becomes fastened in the *Paramecium*, a great number of trichocysts near the place of the injury are discharged (Fig. 1–61). These produce a substance that becomes jelly-like on entering the water; this tends to force the two animals apart, and, if the *Paramecium* is a large one, it frequently succeeds in making its escape.

Two *contractile vacuoles* are present, occupying definite positions, one near either end of the body. They lie close to the dorsal surface and communicate with a large portion of the body through a system of *radiating canals*, six to ten in number, which connect with still smaller microtubules that have been demonstrated with the electron microscope. The vacuoles grow in size by the addition of liquid excreted by the protoplasm into the canals and then poured into them. When the full size is reached, the contents are discharged to the exterior through the contractile vacuole pore (Fig. 1–62).* The two vacuoles do not contract at the same time, but alternately; the interval between successive contractions is from 10 to 20 seconds.

In *Paramecium trichium* the two contractile vacuoles are permanent structures with vesicles that collect and pour fluids into them and with a long convoluted excretory tubule ending in an excretory pore opening on the aboral surface. The duration of the systole is long compared with that of the diastole due probably to the presence of the excretory tubule. What has been said of the function of the contractile vacuole in *Amoeba* applies as well to

---

*Expulsion of the fluid contents of the contractile vacuoles may be seen in the following way. Paramecia should be mounted in water into which has been rubbed up a stick of India or Chinese ink. They then appear white against a black background. Part of the water should be withdrawn from beneath the cover glass, thus slightly compressing them. If now a specimen in profile is found and watched, the discharge produces a bright spot outside in the opaque liquid; this lasts from 1 to 2 seconds, and is then driven off by the cilia (Fig. 1–62).

Fig. 1-63. *Paramecium:* spiral path; views 1, 2, 3, and 4, successive positions occupied. The dotted areas with small arrows show the currents of water drawn from the front. (From Jennings.)

that of *Paramecium*, i.e., it acts as an organelle of excretion and respiration, and is probably hydrostatic. Most of the nitrogen excreted by *Paramecium* is in the form of urea, and this substance has been detected in the contractile vacuole. However, the greater part of the excretory matter, including urea, apparently passes by dialysis directly to the exterior through the pellicle. That the primary function of the contractile vacuole is to regulate the water content of the protoplasm is indicated by the correlation between the frequency of pulsation and the rate water is taken in. For example, most long periods between pulsations, up to 6 minutes when actively swimming, occur when little water is ingested, and most short periods occur when the animals are at rest.

Paramecium is considered to have a neuromotor apparatus, which has been said to include transverse fibrils and internal neurofibrils in addition to the kinetodesma previously described. The various fibrils have been demonstrated, although some have been considered internally discharged trichocysts by some investigators. Whether the others are supporting or conducting fibrils is not known, although evidence indicates a kinety must remain intact for beating to remain coordinated along its length as illustrated in Fig. 1–60. The neuromotor apparatus is more highly developed in some of the more complex ciliates with its greatest concentration and a neuromotor center near the oral region.

Locomotion. The only movements of *Paramecium* that in any way resemble those of *Amoeba* are seen when the animal passes through a space smaller than its shorter diameter; it will then exhibit an elasticity which allows it to squirm through. In a free field *Paramecium* swims by means of its cilia. They produce a continuous rotation to the left and a simultaneous forward or backward movement. The movement is opposite to the direction that the cilia are inclined. The anterior end moves in an aboral direction due to the powerful beating of the oral cilia. The combination of this aboral swerving and the rotation to the left produces a spiral course of unchanging direction (Fig. 1–63). Rotation is thus effective in enabling an unsymmetrical animal to swim in a straight course through a medium which allows deviations to right or left, and up or down. It is well known that a human being cannot keep a straight course when lost in the woods, although he has a chance to err only to the right or left.

Nutrition. The *food* of *Paramecium* consists principally of bacteria and minute protozoa. The animal does not wait for the food to come within its reach, but by continually swimming from place to place is able to enter regions where favorable food conditions prevail. The cilia also aid in bringing in food particles, because a sort of vortex is formed by their arrangement about the oral groove which directs a steady stream of water toward the mouth.

Figure 1–64 illustrates the formation of a *food vacuole*. Food particles that are swept into the mouth are carried down into the buccal cavity by the undulating membrane and membranellae; they are then moved onward by the buccal ciliature and are finally gathered together at the end of the passageway into a vacuole which gradually forms in the endoplasm. When this vacuole has reached a certain size, it is swept away from the extremity of the cytostome by the surrounding protoplasm, and the formation of another vacuole is begun (Fig. 1–65). A food vacuole is a droplet of water with food particles suspended within it. As soon as one is separated from the cytostome, it is swept away by the rotary streaming movement of the endoplasm known as *cyclosis*. This carries the food vacuole around a definite course that begins

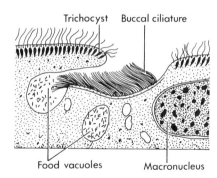

Trichocyst   Buccal ciliature

Food vacuoles   Macronucleus

Fig. 1-64. *Paramecium:* formation of food vacuole. Section through cytopharynx showing the manner in which bacteria are swept into the food vacuole in process of formation. (After Maier.)

behind the cytostome, passes backward to the posterior end, then forward near the dorsal surface to the anterior end, and finally downward and along the ventral surface toward the mouth. During this journey digestion takes place. At first the vacuole decreases in size as water is removed from it and the acidity in the vacuole increases. Before elimination the vacuole increases in size and the pH approaches the alkaline range. Undigested particles in the vacuole are discharged through the *cytoproct* (Fig. 1–57), a structure that is closed at other times in its location on a kinety posterior to the oral groove. The processes of digestion, excretion, respiration, growth, and other aspects of metabolism are so similar to those described for *Amoeba* that they will not

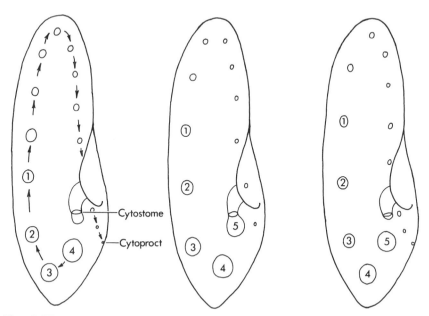

Fig. 1-65. *Paramecium:* successive stages in the formation and movement (cyclosis) of food vacuoles. Numbered vacuoles are numbered in the sequence in which they were formed.

be considered further here. Wichterman (1953) gives a complete account of many aspects of the biology of *Paramecium*.

Reproduction.   *Paramecium* reproduces by simple *binary fission*. This process is interrupted occasionally by a process of nuclear reorganization such as *conjugation, cytogamy,* or *autogamy.* Conjugation is a sexual process, which has been intensively studied.

Binary Fission.   In binary fission the animal divides transversely (Fig. 1-66). The first indication of a forthcoming division is seen in the micronucleus, which undergoes mitosis, its substance being equally divided between the two daughter nuclei; these separate and finally come to lie one near either end of the body. Figure 1-66 shows two dividing micronuclei, because there are two of these in *Paramecium aurelia.* The macronucleus elongates and then divides transversely. The buccal cavity produces a bud, which develops into another buccal cavity, these two structures move apart, the old buccal cavity advancing to the ventral middle line of the forepart of the body, and the new one to a similar position in the posterior half. The buccal ciliature remains with the old buccal cavity, whereas new membranellae and an undulating membrane arise in connection with the new buccal cavity. A new contractile

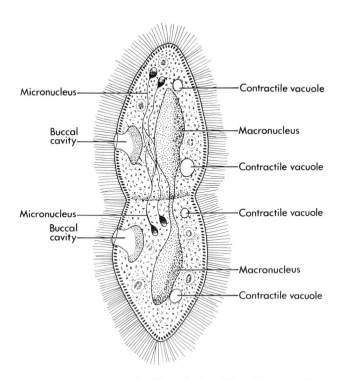

Fig. 1-66. *Paramecium aurelia:* binary fission. (From Newman after Lang.)

vacuole arises near the anterior end of the body, another just back of the middle line. While these events are taking place, a constriction appears near the middle of the longitudinal diameter of the body; this cleavage furrow becomes deeper and deeper until only a slender thread of protoplasm holds the two halves of the body together. This connection is finally severed and the two daughter *Paramecia* are freed from each other. Each contains both macro- and micronuclei, two contractile vacuoles, and a cytostome with cytopharynx. The entire process occupies about 2 hours. The time, however, varies considerably, depending upon the temperature of the water, the quality and quantity of food, and probably other factors. The daughter *Paramecia* increase rapidly in size, and at the end of 24 hours divide again if the temperature remains at from 15–17°C; if the temperature is raised to 17–20°C, two divisions may take place in one day.

Encystment of *Paramecium* has been described, but if it really occurs, it apparently is a rare phenomenon.

Conjugation. At a certain time in the life cycle of *Paramecium* conjugation occurs. Conjugation requires the presence of two paramecia of different mating types. Members of the same *mating type* do not ordinarily enter into conjugation together but can be induced to conjugate by various techniques. One of the most enlightening methods was used in a recent study where mating and conjugation were induced in those of the same mating type by the introduction of cilia from paramecia of a different mating type. It seems that the surfaces of cilia from similar mating types will not adhere to each other but will adhere to surfaces of cilia of different mating types. Thus, the addition of cilia from those of a different mating type can serve as the glue to hold those of similar mating type together for the process of conjugation to occur. The conjugating pair adhere to each other with their ventral (oral) surfaces in contact and a protoplasmic bridge is constructed between them. As soon as this union is effected, the nuclei pass through a series of stages which have been likened to the maturation processes of metazoan eggs.

Although considerable variation has been observed in different species and strains, some features of conjugation are quite constant in most reports. Reference to Figure 1–67 will help to make clear the following description. Two divisions of the micronuclei occur in each conjugant (1, 2, 3) during which time the old macronucleus starts to disintegrate. During these divisions the haploid number of chromosomes is produced in the micronuclei. One of the haploid micronuclei so formed undergoes another division (4) to form the gametic nuclei, while the remaining micronuclei eventually disintegrate. One of the gametic nuclei so formed becomes the migratory male nucleus, which passes to the other conjugant (5), which also has produced a male nucleus for exchange. The male nuclei fuse with the female nuclei (Fig. 1–68) remaining in the conjugants to produce the fusion nucleus of fertilization or *synkaryon* (6, 7). Each ex-conjugant or zygote then undergoes a series of nuclear divisions (7, 9). After two of these divisions, some of the nuclei

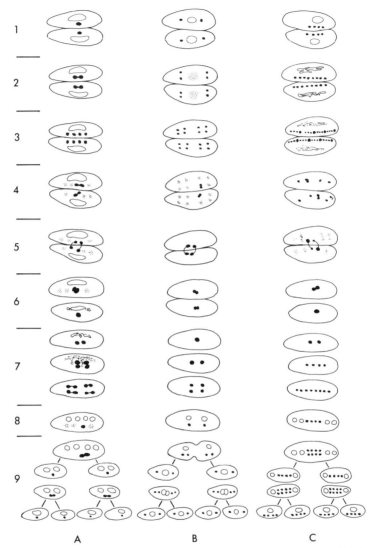

A   B   C

Fig. 1-67. *Paramecium:* conjugation. (A) *P. caudatum.* (B) *P. aurelia.* (C) *P. multimicronucleatum.* 1–3, first two prezygotic (meiotic) divisions, degeneration of macronucleus; 4, third prezygotic division (mitotic); 5, fertilization; 6, synkaryon (zygote) formation; 7–8, postzygotic divisions and formation of macronuclear anlagen; 8–9, last micronuclear divisions accompanied by cell division. (Modified: A, after Calkins from Wichterman; B, after Woodruff; C, after Barnett.)

formed begin to differentiate as macronuclei, while the others remain as micronuclei. Four macronuclei are formed during this process (7, 8, 9), while sufficient micronuclei are formed by division to reconstitute the original number of macronuclei and micronuclei in each of the four cells produced by the two cytoplasmic divisions of each ex-conjugant.

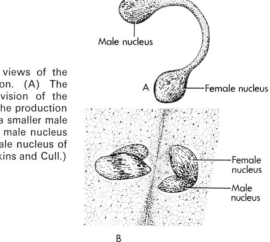

Male nucleus

A — Female nucleus

Fig. 1-68. *Paramecium:* two views of the micronuclei during conjugation. (A) The spindle formed during the division of the micronucleus which results in the production of a large female nucleus and a smaller male nucleus. (B) The fusion of the male nucleus of one conjugant with the female nucleus of the other conjugant. (From Calkins and Cull.)

Female nucleus

Male nucleus

B

The daughter cells resulting from this process of conjugation are considerably smaller than the original conjugant. They undergo growth and an indefinite number of generations are produced by the transverse division of the four daughter cells resulting from each conjugant.

Cytogamy and *autogamy* resemble conjugation in many respects. In cytogamy the process is nearly identical to conjugation except the synkaryon is formed by the male and female nucleus from the same cell; thus, no cross-fertilization is achieved. Autogamy is almost identical to cytogamy except there is no fusion of cells in pairs; self-fertilization occurs following nuclear events similar to those of conjugation and cytogamy. The events following synkaryon formation are similar in all three processes. Before autogamy was completely described as the meiotic and sexual phenomenon which occurred in *Paramecium aurelia* every 40 or 50 generations, it was known as endomixis and thought to be a simpler method of reorganization than it really is.

Macronuclear regeneration sometimes occurs after conjugation or autogamy. The fragments of the macronucleus do not disappear but grow and are distributed during successive divisions until only one fragment remains per cell as a regenerated and complete macronucleus. Because the fragments of the macronucleus were not formed by mitotic division, the resulting regenerated macronuclei have different genetic characteristics. Because as many as 40 fragments may produce macronuclei by regeneration and they can be functional in the absence of micronuclei, it seems probable that there are at least 40 complete sets of chromosomes in a macronucleus.

Genetics. A number of monohybrid crosses have been performed with paramecia and the results indicate typical Mendelian inheritance occurs in these protozoans. Artificial induction of autogamy or cytogamy has been a useful tool in these studies by supplying genetically homozygous individuals

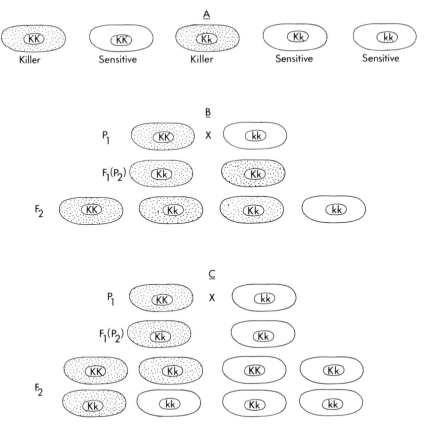

Fig. 1-69. *Paramecium:* transmission of Kappa. (A) Killer and sensitive phenotypes for various genotypes and particle combinations. (B) Phenotype ratios when cytoplasmic transfer of Kappa particles occurs. (C) Phenotypes when no cytoplasmic transfer occurs.

for use in test crosses and in detecting genes present in the progeny of such crosses. In testing progeny of crosses the heterozygous condition of the micronucleus will be indicated by the presence of all one characteristic after autogamy in about one half of the cases and the contrasting characteristic in the rest of the cases. No change or variability will be present after autogamy of homozygous individuals. Mating type is a characteristic following simple Mendelian inheritance. Expression of most characteristics is dependent on development of the macronucleus.

The most interesting genetic story in paramecia has come from the work of Sonneborn and others. Some paramecia have DNA-containing particles in their cytoplasm which produce a substance capable of killing other paramecia that lack the particles. The particles have been termed *Kappa particles*. The paramecia containing them are referred to as "killers" and the poison produced as *paramecin*. A genetic factor must be present in the macronucleus for kappa particles to be maintained in the cytoplasm (Fig. 1–69). The gene for maintenance of kappa may be present in the macronucleus, but cells will still be sensitive to paramecin if they lack kappa particles. At conjugation some cytoplasm containing kappa may be transferred to sensitive individuals turning them into "killers" if they have the necessary gene for maintenance of kappa. Because the particles must be present to be produced and they can be transferred with some of the cytoplasm during conjugation when cytoplasmic bridges exist, they are an example of cytoplasmic inheritance. Kappa particles are said to have some of the characteristics of viruses, but their dependance for self-duplication upon a nuclear gene makes them an interesting example of nuclear and cytoplasmic interaction.

Behavior. *Paramecium* is a more active animal than *Amoeba*, swimming across the field of the microscope so rapidly that careful observations are necessary to discover the details of its movements. As in *Amoeba*, its activities are either *spontaneous*, that is, initiated because of some internal influence, or result from some *external stimulus*. This stimulus is in all cases a *change in the environment*. For example, if a drop of distilled water is added to a drop of ordinary culture water containing a number of paramecia, all of the animals will enter and remain in the distilled water; they are stimulated to a certain kind of activity by the change in the composition of the water. They will soon become acclimated to their new surroundings and will behave themselves within the distilled water in a normal manner until another change in their environment stimulates them to further reactions.

Avoiding Reaction. *Paramecium* responds to stimuli either *negatively* or *positively*. The negative response is known as the "*avoiding reaction*"; it takes place in the following manner. When a *Paramecium* receives an injurious stimulus at its anterior end, it reverses its cilia and swims backward for a short distance out of the region of stimulation; then its rotation decreases in rapidity and it swerves toward the aboral side more strongly than under normal conditions. Its posterior end then becomes a sort of pivot upon which the animal swings about in a circle (Fig. 1–70). During this revolution samples of the surrounding medium are brought into the oral groove. When a sample no longer contains the stimulus, the cilia resume their normal beating and the animal moves forward again. If this once more brings it into the region of the stimulus, the avoiding reaction is repeated; this goes on as long as the animal receives the stimulus. The repetition of the avoiding reaction is very well shown when *Paramecium* enters a drop of $\frac{1}{50}$ per cent acetic acid. In attempting to get out of the drop the surrounding water is encountered; to this the avoiding reaction is given and a new direction is taken within the acid, which of course leads to the water and another negative reaction. Figure 1–71, B shows part of the pathway made by a single *Paramecium* under these conditions.

Positive Reaction to Chemicals. If a little acid is placed in the center of a

Fig. 1-70. *Paramecium:* diagram of the avoiding reaction. *A*, solid object or other source of stimulation. 1–6, successive positions occupied by the animal. (The rotation on the long axis is not shown.) (From Jennings.)

large drop of water containing a number of paramecia, all of the animals in the drop will sooner or later encounter the acid, and having once entered are unable to escape, just as in the case described above. A group is therefore formed in the acid, illustrating what is called a positive reaction (Fig. 1–71, A). This experiment may be repeated using a $\frac{1}{2}$ per cent solution of common salt in which are placed a number of specimens. If a drop of $\frac{1}{10}$ per cent solution of the same chemical is now added, the paramecia will swim into and directly across it, but on reaching the boundary between the two solutions on the other side of the drop, the avoiding reaction will be given. Soon the weaker solution will contain all of the animals which, having once entered, cannot escape. In many cases, as above, the passage from a strong solution to a weak solution causes no reaction. For certain substances, however, there is a definite strength which seems to suit the *Paramecium* better than any other, and no reaction takes place on entering it. Passage from such a solution to either a weaker or a stronger calls forth the avoiding reaction. The concentration is therefore called the "*optimum*." The optimum concentration depends on the chemical. Movement out of the zone of optimum concentration causes an avoiding reaction (Fig. 1–72). Thus, with the arrival of additional paramecia, there is an accumulation of animals in the optimal region.

Contact. Paramecia may give any one of three reactions to contact stimuli; the first two are negative, the third positive. (1) If *Paramecium* swims against an obstacle, or if the anterior end, which is more sensitive than the other parts of the body, is touched with a glass rod, the avoiding reaction is given. (2) When any other part of the body is stimulated in a like manner,

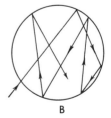

Fig. 1-71. *Paramecium:* positive reaction to acids. (A) Collection of paramecia in a drop of 1/50 per cent acetic acid. (B) Path followed by a single paramecium in a drop of acid showing mechanism of the collection shown in (A). Each time the organism comes to the boundary of the acid it gives an avoiding reaction. (From Jennings.)

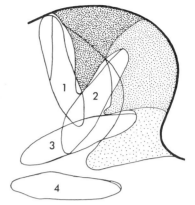

Fig. 1-72. *Paramecium:* weak avoiding reaction as a result of contact with acidified ink. 1, 2, 3, 4, successive positions and final escape. (After Mast and Lashley.)

the animal may simply swim forward. (3) Frequently a *Paramecium*, upon striking an object when swimming slowly, comes to rest with its cilia in contact with the object (Fig. 1–73). This positive reaction often brings the animals into an environment rich in food.

Light. Paramecia do not respond in any way to ordinary visible *light*, but give the avoiding reaction when ultraviolet rays are thrown upon them; if unable to escape, death ensues in from 10 to 50 seconds.

Temperature. The optimum temperature for *Paramecium* lies, under ordinary conditions, between 24° and 28°C. A number of animals placed on a slide, which is heated at one end, will swim about in all directions, giving the avoiding reaction where stimulated, until they become oriented so as to move toward the cooler end. This is the method of *trial and error*, that is, the animal tries all directions until the one is discovered which allows it to escape from the region of injurious stimulation.

Gravity. Gravity in some unknown way causes paramecia to orient themselves with their anterior ends pointed upward. This brings them near the surface of the water. If a number are equally distributed in a test tube of

Fig. 1-73. *Paramecium* at rest with anterior end against a mass of bacteria *A*, showing the currents produced by the cilia. (From Jennings.)

Fig. 1-74. Paramecia collected at the top of a vertical tube. (From Jennings after Jensen.)

water, they will gradually find their way to the top (Fig. 1–74). The most probable theory to account for this is that the substances within the body, being of different specific gravities, move about when the animal changes its position and act as stimuli, relief being obtained only when the animal has placed its body with its long diameter perpendicular to the earth's surface and its anterior end up. Under certain conditions *Paramecium* is positive to gravity.

Currents. If paramecia are placed in running water, they orient themselves with the anterior ends upstream and swim against the current. This is probably caused by the interference of the current with the beating of the cilia, for as soon as an animal reaches a position with anterior end upstream, the water no longer tends to reverse the cilia.

Electric Current. Paramecia may be subjected to an electric current in the laboratory. A weak current causes a movement toward the cathode; a strong current reverses the direction of the beating of the cilia and causes the animals to swim backward toward the anode. Many other interesting phenomena might be cited, but the entire subject is too complex for brief discussion.

Other Remarks. Frequently *Paramecium* may be stimulated in more than one way at the same time. For example, a specimen that is in contact with a solid is acted upon by gravity and may be acted upon by chemicals, heat, currents of water, and other stimuli. It has been found that gravity always gives way to other stimuli, and that if more than one other factor is at work the one first in the field exerts the greater influence.

Both the spontaneous activities and reactions due to external stimuli are due to changes in the internal condition of the animal. The *physiological condition* of *Paramecium*, therefore, determines the character of its response. This physiological state is a dynamic condition, changing continually with the processes of metabolism going on within the living substance of the animal. Thus, one physiological state resolves itself into another; this becomes easier and more rapid after it has taken place a number of times, giving us grounds for the belief that stimuli and reactions have a distinct effect upon succeeding responses.

Whether this represents learning may be questioned. Gelber (1958) found that paramecia fed with bacteria introduced on a needle continued to approach an introduced needle containing no bacteria although untrained paramecia did not.

We may sum up the external factors that produce or determine reactions as follows: (1) The organism may react to a *change*, even though neither beneficial nor injurious. (2) Anything that tends to interfere with the normal current of life activities produces reactions of a certain sort ("negative"). (3) Any change that tends to restore or favor the normal life processes *may* produce reactions of a different sort ("positive"). (4) Changes that in themselves neither interfere with nor assist the normal stream of life processes may produce negative or positive reactions, according as they are usually followed by changes that are injurious or beneficial. (5) Whether a given change shall produce reaction or not often depends on the completeness or incompleteness of the performance of the metabolic processes of the organism under the existing conditions. This makes the behavior fundamentally regulatory.

Although the preceding generally holds true for changes that the species have been exposed to in the past in their natural environment, it seems likely that their reactions to the many synthetic products (e.g., detergents and insecticides) which man now introduces into their environment may not yet have been through sufficient selection to have survival value.

(3) Other Ciliata

The Ciliata are characterized by the possession of cilia during a part or whole of their life cycle. In most Ciliata the nuclear material is separated into a large macronucleus and a smaller micronucleus. Most Ciliata are free-living in fresh water or the sea. Many of them, however, are ectoparasites or endoparasites of vertebrates and invertebrates. The Ciliata have been separated into four classes: Holotrichea, Peritrichea, Suctorea, and Spirotrichea. Typical Holotrichea have simple, uniform body ciliature, and the oral region is usually inconspicuous. Peritrichea have conspicuous oral ciliature and no body cilia on adults; the oral ciliature winds counterclockwise as it approaches the cytostome, and adults are frequently stalked. Suctorea have no ciliature on the adults; they feed by means of suctorial tentacles and are usually stalked. Spirotrichea have conspicuous buccal ciliature, which usually includes an adoral zone of membranelles, which winds clockwise to the cytostome.

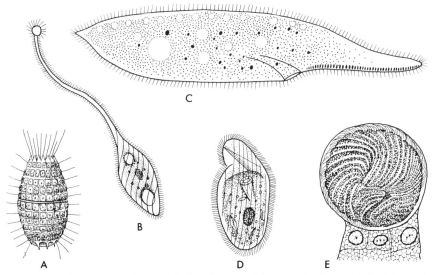

Fig. 1-75. Gymnostomatida. (A) *Coleps hirtus*. (B) *Lacrymaria olor*. (C) *Dileptus anser*. (D) *Chilodonella cucullus*. (E) *Amphileptus branchiarum*, rounded up in gill of a frog tadpole. *Dileptus* has many micronuclei (the larger black spherical bodies) and a macronucleus distributed in small granules throughout the endoplasm. (A, after Conn; B, D, after Wang; C, after Visscher, modified; E, after Wenrich.)

Holotrichea

Order Gymnostomatida.   A buccal cavity is absent in gymnostomes. The cytostome opens directly on the surface. In the more primitive gymnostomes, it opens at the anterior pole as in *Coleps hirtus* (Fig. 1–75, A), a barrel-shaped species covered with twenty longitudinal rows of platelets and with three posterior spines. *Lacrymaria olor* (Fig. 1–75, B) is slender, 400 microns in length, and possesses a long, highly flexible proboscis. *Didinium nasutum* (Fig. 1–61) is barrel-shaped, with cilia restricted to two girdles, and a very expansible cytostome at the end of a proboscis-like elevation. It feeds on *Paramecium* and other ciliates, which it engulfs whole. *Dileptus anser* (Fig. 1–75, C) has many micronuclei and the chromatin of the macronucleus distributed in granules throughout the endoplasm. *Chilodonella cucullulus* (Fig. 1–75, D) possesses a pharyngeal basket around the cytostome consisting of rod-shaped trichites.

Parasitic Gymnostomatida species are not as numerous as the widely distributed free-living species. *Buxtonella sulcata* lives in the cecum of cattle. *Amphileptus branchiarum* (Fig. 1–75, E) spends part of its life in the gills of frog tadpoles.

Order Trichostomatida.   A greater development of the mouth region occurs in the trichostomes. The cytostome is in the bottom of a ciliated

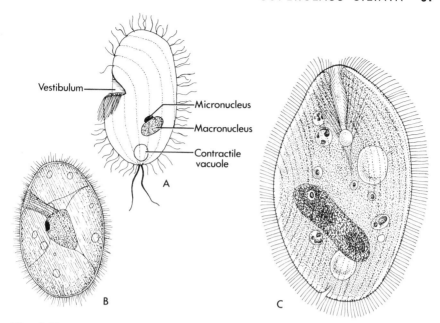

Vestibulum
Micronucleus
Macronucleus
Contractile vacuole
A
B
C

Fig. 1-76. Trichostomatida. (A) *Colpoda steini*, free-living. (B) *Isotricha intestinalis*, from the stomach of cattle. (C) *Balantidium coli* from the intestine of man. (A, after several authors; B, after Becker; C, after Wenyon.)

depression (vestibulum). *Colpoda* (Fig. 1–76, A) is a genus of usually free-living trichostomes commonly encountered and somewhat kidney-shaped. *Isotricha intestinalis* (Fig. 1–76, B) is an inhabitant of the stomach of cattle. *Balantidium* (Fig. 1–76, C) is an interesting genus of parasitic trichostomes recorded from many vertebrates and invertebrates. The species that lives in man, *B. coli* (Fig. 1–76, C), is of special importance, because it also lives in pigs and monkeys and is responsible for dysenteric conditions in its human host. *B. coli* is present in the majority of pigs in this country but does not cause symptoms in them. It forms cysts, which represent the infective stage, and human beings probably become infected by swallowing the cysts from pigs. The occurrence in man in the United States is very rare, and less than 1 per cent worldwide.

Order Astomatida. The order Astomatida contains uniformly ciliated, parasitic, and cytostomeless ciliates (Fig. 1–77), which have held a prominent position in phylogenetic speculation. Their similarity to the planula larvae of coelenterates and the acoelous flatworms may be overemphasized, because the absence of a mouth may be a secondary parasitic modification. They are primarily parasites of oligochaetes.

Order Hymenostomatida. Uniform body ciliation, (Fig. 1–78) as well as the possession of an undulating membrane and three membranelles in

Fig. 1-77. Astomatida. *Anoplophrya marylandensis*, from the intestine of the earthworm. (After Conkling.)

the buccal cavity, is typical of the species in the order Hymenostomatida. The most familiar genus is *Paramecium*. A number of species of *Paramecium* have been described: *P. aurelia* possesses two micronuclei; *P. multimicro-nucleatum* has four or more micronuclei; and *P. busaria* contains Zoochlorel-lae as symbionts. The eight species of *Paramecium* may be separated into two groups according to their general shape. Species in the Aurelia group, consisting of *P. caudatum*, *P. aurelia*, and *P. multimicronucleatum*, are spindle shaped and the body length is more than three times the width. The Bursaria group, consisting of *P. calkinsi*, *P. woodruffi*, *P. trichium*, *P. bursaria*, and *P. polycaryum*, have blunter ends and the body length is less than three times the width.

Other interesting hymenostomes include the much studied *Tetrahymena pyriformis*; *Frontonia leucas* (Fig. 1–78, A), a very large species about 300 microns in length; *Colpidium* (Fig. 1–78, B), common in infusions and with a somewhat concave oral surface; and the parasite, *Ichthyophthirius multi-filiis* (Fig. 1–78, D), a very large species that attacks the skin and gills of fresh-water fish, often causing their death.

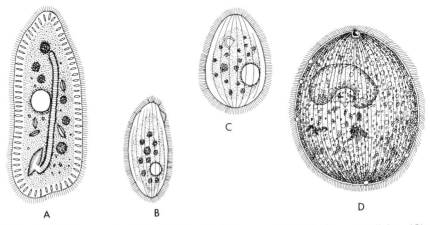

Fig. 1-78. Hymenostomatida. (A) *Frontonia leucas*. (B) *Colpidium cucullulus*. (C) *Glaucoma scintillans*. (D) *Ichthyophthirius multifiliis*. (A) (B) and (C) Free-living; (D) parasite from the skin of fish. (A–C, after Wang; D, after Butschli.)

Peritrichea

Order Peritrichida. Members of this order typically lack body cilia in the adult stage but their oral ciliature is conspicuously developed. Most are *sessile* (sedentary). Sessile animals are attached relatively permanently to other objects. Most peritrichs are attached by a stalk that is secreted by a region at the aboral end known as the *scopula*. The feeding apparatus is highly specialized. The adoral spiral zone is wound around the peristomial disk, which can be completely contracted over the cytostome by means of myonemes on the margin. These *myonemes* are strands of cytoplasm specialized as contractile organelles. The adoral cilia are generally modified to form two undulating membranes, which run parallel to each other. Instead of the adoral zone leading directly to the cytostome, it leads into a vestibule supplied with an undulating membrane and into which the cytoproct and contractile vacuole as well as the cytostome open. Stalked species produce a *telotroch* under certain conditions. The telotroch is important in dispersal of the peritrichs, because it is formed from a cell that grows a basal girdle of cilia, loses its mouth structures, and becomes detached from the stalk to swim free until a new place of attachment is found.

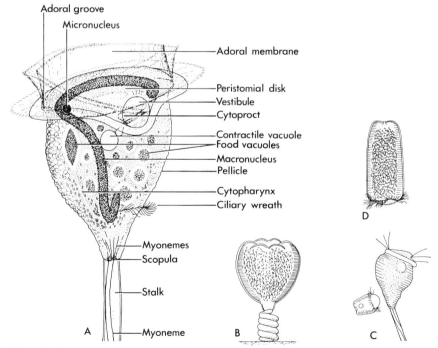

Fig. 1-79. *Vorticella.* (A) Diagram showing structure of a specimen. (B) *Vorticella campanula*, contracted. (C) *Vorticella striata* with sexual zooid. (D) *Vorticella campanula*, telotroch or free-swimming swarm stage. (After Noland and Finley.)

Species of the genus *Vorticella* (Fig. 1–79) are common in fresh water. *Vorticella campanula* has a body shaped like an inverted bell, has a contractile stalk, is always solitary, and is yellowish or greenish. *Carchesium polypinum* (Fig. 1–80, A) is a colonial species with branching stalks that contract independently of one another. *Epistylis flavicans* (Fig. 1–80, B) is also colonial; its stalks are dichotomous and not contractile. *Zoothamnium* resembles *Carchesium*, but the entire colony contracts simultaneously. Species from these and related genera occur commonly on the surface of crustaceans and the shells of mollusks in either fresh or salt water.

In addition to the sessile peritrichs there are a large number of free-swimming, but parasitic, ones. One of the common species is *Trichodina pediculus* (Fig. 1–80, C). It may be found gliding along the body surface of the fresh-water *Hydra*, tadpoles, and other aquatic animals. Other species are ectozoic on the fresh-water flatworms of the genus *Planaria* and on the gills of certain fishes and mollusks. *Trichodina* is short and hour-glass shaped, with a spiral band of adoral cilia leading into a cytopharynx, a ribbon-

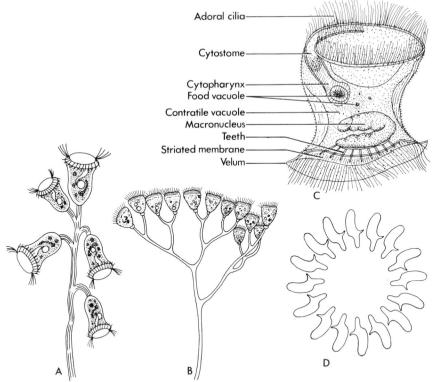

Fig. 1-80. Peritrichida. (A) *Carchesium polypinum.* (B) *Epistylis flavicans.* (C) *Trichodina pediculus*, an epizoic parasite that lives on *Hydra* and other aquatic animals. (D) Teeth from aboral disk of *Trichodina*. (A, B, after Wang; C, after Clark; D, modified after Shtein.)

shaped nucleus, and one contractile vacuole. The aboral surface is modified into a disklike organ of attachment consisting of an inner ring of radially arranged teeth, an outer band of cilia, and a peripheral fold, the *velum*.

Suctorea

Order Suctorida. The Suctorida are typically sedentary forms that are devoid of any ciliary mechanism in the "adult" stage and have no buccal cavity, but capture and ingest food by means of characteristic tentacles. They reveal their relationship to the Ciliata by the production of free-swimming ciliated larvae, and by the possession of a typical ciliate nuclear apparatus consisting of separate macronuclei and micronuclei. All species possess capitate or suctorial tentacles each of which, as a rule, ends in a suckerlike knob. When a small ciliate, upon which the suctorian feeds, strikes the end of the tentacle, it is held fast by this suckerlike organ, and the general body substance of the prey is sucked down the tentacle into the body. Reproduction takes place typically by the formation of ciliated embryos formed from buds

Fig. 1-81. Suctorea. (A) *Tokophrya lemnarum:* typical specimen. (B) *T. lemnarum:* larva with four bands of cilia around body and a tuft of cilia at one end. (C) *T. lemnarum:* larva after fixation, with pedicel and small tentacles. (D) *Sphaerophrya:* an endoparasitic species within a brood pouch in the body of a ciliate. (E) *Ophryodendron abietinum:* ciliated embryo. (A–C, after Noble; D, after Stein; E, after Martin.)

or processes constricted off, either externally or into an internal pouch, from the parent suctorian. After swimming around for a period of time, the ciliated embryos settle down, become attached, and are transformed into typical suctoria.

Free-living species (Fig. 1–81, A–C) belonging to this subclass are frequently encountered in vegetation gathered from ponds and in infusions. *Podophrya collini* is an American species with a stalk. *Sphaerophrya magna* has a spherical body without a stalk.

Large numbers of Suctoria may be regarded as parasites in the broad sense of the term. Among these are ectocommensals that attach themselves more or less regularly to some species of aquatic animal; for example, *Discophrya elongata* prefers the shells of gastropods. Endocommensals live in natural cavities in their hosts; for example, *Trichophrya salparum* lives in the pharyngeal cavities of certain tunicates. The true parasites also live both on the surface and in the interior of their hosts. *Ophryodendron abietinum* is an example of a true ectoparasite (Fig. 1–81, E). The genus *Sphaerophrya* includes endoparasites that live within the bodies of ciliates, such as *Stentor*, *Paramecium*, and *Stylonychia* (Fig. 1–81, D). A sort of brood pouch is formed within the host in which the "embryo" suctorian lives with tentacles retracted. Ciliated larvae are formed in the brood pouch, separate from the host, and develop into free-living individuals.

Spirotrichea

Order Heterotrichida.   The species of Heterotrichida may have cilia covering the entire body or portions of it, but there is an adoral zone of either large cilia or membranelles. Many of the large well-known ciliates living in fresh water and in the sea belong to this order. Both free-living and parasitic species are included. In several of the larger well-known ones such as *Stentor*, *Blepharisma*, and *Spirostomum* the macronucleus may take on a beaded appearance after division but returns to a more compact state prior to the next division (Fig. 1–82).

Stentor coeruleus (Figs. 1–82 and 1–83) is a large bluish ciliate, visible to the naked eye, that has been an especially useful subject for studying the developmental biology of organisms at the cellular level. Much of the research described in *The Biology of Stentor* (Tarter, 1961) is with *S. coeruleus.* The beaded, or nodular, macronucleus makes the removal and transplantation of portions simpler for studies of macronuclear function. The ready fusion of cut portions of cells makes grafting of portions of these large cells possible. Some phenomena demonstrated with micro-surgical techniques on these large cells are: a polarity in disoriented parts of the ectoderm; an axial gradient in regeneration of parts; induction of a different developmental stage in heteroplastic grafts; and interdependence of nucleus and cytoplasm. *Stentor* is often attached to solid objects, but can swim freely through the water. *Stentor polymorphus* lives either attached or free-swimming. When free-

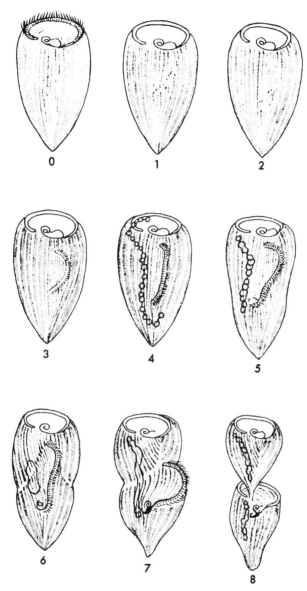

Fig. 1-82. Fission of *Stentor coeruleus*. Adoral membranelles omitted after the first drawing. (From V. Tartar. *The Biology of Stentor*. Copyright 1961 by Pergamon Press Inc., New York.)

swimming, it is oval or pyriform in shape; when attached, it assumes a trumpet shape. Its body is usually green because of the presence of Zoochlorellae. *Stentor* ingests a wide variety of food organisms of the proper size, sometimes including others of the same species.

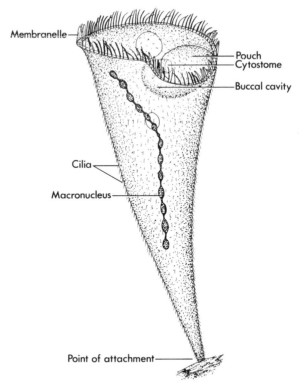

Membranelle

Pouch
Cytostome

Buccal cavity

Cilia

Macronucleus

Point of attachment

Fig. 1-83. *Stentor coeruleus* in normal extended position, as when attached to a solid object. (After Schaeffer, modified.)

Blepharisma lateritia (Fig. 1–84, A) is a free-living heterotrich that contains a pigment associated with the kinetosomes, which renders the body rose-red. *Spirostomum ambiguum* (Fig. 1–84, B) is a long slender species with a moniliform nucleus. *Bursaria truncatella* (Fig. 1–84, C) is a large broad species with a long curved, bandlike macronucleus and many micronuclei.

There are numerous parasitic species in addition to the many free-living Heterotrichida such as those just described. An interesting example is the genus *Nyctotherus*, which may easily be obtained for study from cockroaches and frogs. *N. ovalis* occurs in the intestine of cockroaches. The most common species in frogs is *N. cordiformis* (Fig. 1–84, D). This species has a long peristome extending from the anterior end to the center of the body and leading into a long curved buccal cavity. Other species occur in frogs, myriapods, water beetles, crustaceans, crinoids, and fish.

Order Entodiniomorphida. The order Entodiniomorphida is of special interest, because it contains the most complex of the protozoans. All are endocommensal in herbivores. Simple cilia are lacking, the ciliature being restricted to small zones of membranelles. The structure of *Epidinium*

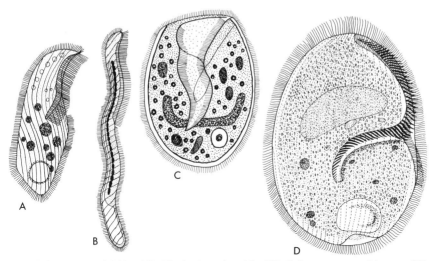

Fig. 1-84. Heterotrichida. (A) *Blepharisma lateritia*. (B) *Spirostomum ambiguum*. (C) *Bursaria truncatella*. (D) *Nyctotherus cordiformis*, a parasitic species from the rectum of the frog. (A, B, C, after Wang; D, after Wenyon.)

ecaudatum (Fig. 1–85) illustrates the complexity of the group. Of particular interest is the so-called neuromotor apparatus consisting of a central motorium connected with nerve rings and fibrils that make up a complicated system.

Ciliates of Cattle.   The first and second stomachs of cattle, that is the rumen and reticulum, are highly infected with Protozoa, mostly ciliates. In this habitat two species of amoebae, five species of flagellates, and about 60 species of ciliates have been reported. Fifty-four species of the ciliates are from the order Entodiniomorphida and most of these are in the genera *Diplodinium*, *Entodinium*, and *Ostracodinium*. The rumen ciliates are obligate anerobes that feed on bacteria, other Protozoa, and fragments of the host's food. Their exact relations to the host are not known. The host can live without them and does not appear to be harmed by them. They may constitute an important source of protein, because they are readily digested after they pass the upper chambers of the stomach. They do not form cysts, so that transmission to new hosts requires contamination of food with saliva or rumen juice from an infected individual.

Order Hypotrichida.   The hypotrichs are typically modified for a creeping mode of life and are strikingly dorso-ventrally flattened with the ventral surface usually supplied with cirri (groups of cilia fused together), which are used as "legs" for creeping over the substratum. Their movements are jerky and rapid on surfaces but comparable to other ciliates when swimming above the bottom. The peristomial groove is well developed and possesses a very

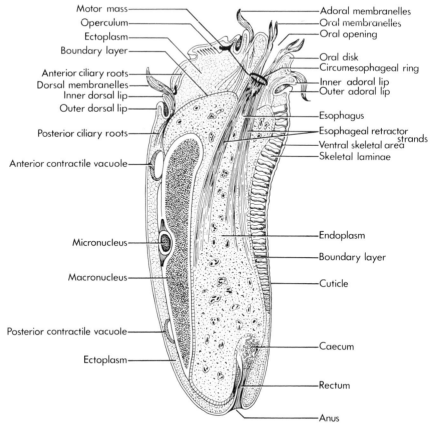

Motor mass
Operculum
Ectoplasm
Boundary layer
Anterior ciliary roots
Dorsal membranelles
Inner dorsal lip
Outer dorsal lip
Posterior ciliary roots
Anterior contractile vacuole
Micronucleus
Macronucleus
Posterior contractile vacuole
Ectoplasm

Adoral membranelles
Oral membranelles
Oral opening
Oral disk
Circumesophageal ring
Inner adoral lip
Outer adoral lip
Esophagus
Esophageal retractor strands
Ventral skeletal area
Skeletal laminae
Endoplasm
Boundary layer
Cuticle
Caecum
Rectum
Anus

Fig. 1-85. *Epidinium ecaudatum.* Diagram to illustrate the neuromotor apparatus and complex structure of one of the Entodiniomorphida. (After Sharp.)

highly differentiated adoral zone of membranelles. The buccal cavity is supplied with an undulating membrane.

There are a large number of free-living species of hypotrichs (Fig. 1–86). Many are common in infusions. Some of the species that may be encountered are as follows. *Stylonychia mytilus* (Fig. 1–86, A and B) occurs in both fresh and salt water; it has two macronuclei and three prominent caudal cirri. *Oxytricha bifaria* (Fig. 1–86, C) also occurs in both fresh and salt water; it has marginal cilia but no caudal cirri. *Uroleptus musculus* (Fig. 1–86, D) has two median rows of fine cirri, three anterior cirri, but no anal cirri. *Euplotes charon* (Fig. 1–86, E) is a marine species with an ovoidal body ventrally flattened, nine or more large cirri opposite the peristomial groove, and about nine cirri at the posterior end. *Euplotes* is a genus of ciliates that has been the object of much research. They are large and have a C-shaped macronucleus. The hypotrichs are thought to be the most highly evolved group of ciliates.

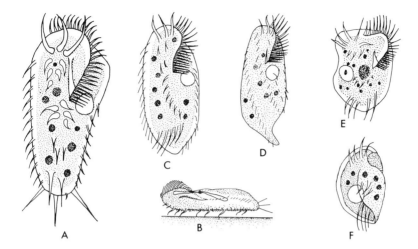

Fig. 1-86. Free-living Hypotrichida. (A) *Stylonychia mytilus.* (B) *Stylonychia mytilus.*
(C) *Oxytricha bifaria.* (D) *Uroleptus musculus.* (E) *Euplotes charon.* (F) *Aspidisca
costata.* (B, after Kent; others after Wang.)

An interesting ectoparasitic hypotrich is commonly encountered on *Hydra*,
the fresh-water polyp. *Kerona pediculus* creeps about on the surface of *Hydra*
with untiring activity. It is dependent upon its host for food, but, besides the
cells of the host, will ingest other Protozoa, especially euglenoids; the latter,
however, are not ingested if the *Kerona* is detached from its host.

6 / Protozoa in General

The knowledge of the morphology, physiology, and classification of
various types of Protozoa obtained from the study of the preceding pages
makes it possible for us at this point to discuss some of the characteristics
common to all Protozoa and to refer to some of the interesting biological
facts and principles illustrated by this phylum.

Ecology.   Protozoa live in almost every conceivable type of habitat, and
their relations to their surroundings provide a fascinating study in ecology.
As noted previously, moisture is absolutely necessary for the continued
existence of Protozoa; hence, we find them in fresh-water streams and bodies
of fresh and salt water of all sizes, in the soil to a depth of a foot or more,
within the bodies of other animals, and in moist places almost everywhere.

Each species plays some role in the trophic structure, or energy cycle, of
the community of organisms in which they occur. Some of the chlorophyll-
containing flagellates are *producers* capable of fixing and storing energy from
the sun. Most are not photosynthetic but, like all other animals, are *consumers.*
Consumers use the energy of compounds produced by photosynthetic

organisms and stored in organic compounds. If the organic compounds are still stored in the plant producing them, the animal using them is a *primary consumer* or *herbivore*. If they have been transferred and stored in another animal, the animal using them from this source is a *secondary consumer*; when use causes the death of the source animal the user is a *carnivore*, when death of the source is not immediate or follows use the user is a *parasite*.

Protozoa that live suspended in the water without access to the shore or bottom constitute a large part of the plankton. Prominent in the plankton are the Phytomastigophorea, some of which occasionally undergo sudden increases in abundance to produce a "bloom" visible to the eye. Sarcodinids of the class Autotractea are in many cases planktonic. Few ciliates are found in the plankton of fresh-water, although the marine plankton is nearly the only community occupied by the ciliate order Tintinnida. Many protozoans that are not truly planktonic may be found in the water near the bottom, near vegetation, or near floating debris where they have strayed from their source of food. Many Protozoa are temporarily or permanently attached to fixed or moving objects such as rocks or the bodies of aquatic animals. Shelled species are often unable to swim and must creep about on solid objects in the water. Each species is more or less restricted to a certain type of environment just as are higher animals. Factors limiting them to their environment are often complex interactions of biological and physical features. For more information on this aspect ecology texts and journals should be consulted. Some have broad tolerances to environmental conditions and are, for example, found in both fresh water and salt water. Most are much more specific in their requirements.

The Protozoa that are best known to students and teachers are those that appear when pond weed is brought into the laboratory and allowed to decay under fresh water. Less well known are the species included in fresh-water and marine plankton, those that live in the soil and other moist places, and those that parasitize plants and other animals. The small sizes of protozoans enable them to exist in minute spaces; hence, they are more ubiquitous than any other type of animal.

The number of species of Protozoa that one may expect to find is indicated by the observation that the surface water of a typical pond in the botanical gardens of the University of Pennsylvania during the period of one year contained 27 species of Sarcodina, 31 species of Mastigophora, and 109 species of Ciliata. The seasonal distribution of these organisms appeared to be influenced principally by temperature, the oxygen content and hydrogen-ion concentration of the water, and the relative amount of dissolved acids in the water at different times of the year. The greatest number of most of the species occurred during September and October.

Protozoa of the Soil. That Protozoa live in the soil is not generally realized. They appear, however, to be present in all soils, being most abundant at a depth of 6 inches and few in number at depths of from some 12 to

18 inches. Several hundred species have been recorded from soil; most of these occur in fresh water also. The types most commonly encountered in order of abundance are small flagellates, amoebae, shelled amoebae, and ciliates. Some of the common genera are the flagellates, *Cercomonas, Oikomonas, Heteromita,* and *Spiromonas*; the Sarcodina, *Naegleria, Hartmanella, Amoeba,* and *Difflugia*; and the ciliates, *Enchelys, Colpidium, Colpoda,* and *Gonostomum.* The number of Protozoa in the soil depends chiefly on the size of the soil particles and the amount of organic material present. Cutler reports in ten samples of soil, five from a manured plot and five from one that had not been manured for many years, 1,690 amoebae, 7,460 flagellates, and 15 ciliates per gram. There appears to be a definite relation between the number of Protozoa and bacteria present since the latter serve as food for the Protozoa. Soil Protozoa multiply readily in a medium rich in organic matter, such as a hay infusion, and can easily be cultivated in the laboratory by adding a few grams of soil to such a medium in a covered dish.

General Morphology. *Form and Size.* Every species of protozoan has a definite form and the size of the individuals vary within definite, usually narrow, limits. Even *Amoeba proteus,* which is often erroneously described as a shapeless mass of protoplasm, has size and form characteristics that separate it from other species of amoebae. Form is determined largely by the consistency of the cytoplasm, by the production of limiting membranes, shells, and skeletons, and by the character of the activities of the organisms. Thus, the changes in shape of amoebae are possible because of the absence of a cuticle, and the great elasticity of such species as *Euglena* is the result of a thin pleated cuticle. Shells and tests such as those of *Arcella* and *Difflugia* obviously determine the shape of those species that secrete them and are so constant in form as to furnish excellent criteria for taxonomic purposes. The skeletons of some species are very elaborate structures of calcium carbonate or silica. Form is also correlated with the organism's mode of life. Protozoa that are suspended in the water are often spherical; those that move in a definite direction, such as *Paramecium,* are ellipsoidal and the longer axis lies in the path of progression; attached species, like *Vorticella,* are more or less radial in symmetry; species that creep about on the surface of solid objects, such as *Oxytricha,* may be dorsoventrally flattened; and a few species, as in *Giardia,* are bilaterally symmetrical. Size is a characteristic that is extraordinarily constant. Anyone who has measured large numbers of individuals of a given species can appreciate this.

Cytoplasm. The cytoplasm of Protozoa is mostly colorless but some species are tinted, for example *Stentor coeruleus,* which is blue, and *Blepharisma lateritia,* which is rose-red. Two types of cytoplasm are usually distinguishable, the peripheral ectoplasm which is denser, hyaline, and homogeneous, and the central endoplasm which is more fluid and often granulated or alveolated. That these two types of cytoplasm may change from one to the other has been demonstrated in *Amoeba proteus*, but in many species they appear to be persistent.

Nuclei. Most Protozoa possess a single nucleus but many of them have two (*Arcella vulgaris*) or many (*Opalina ranarum*) of the same type, or two of different types (Ciliata in general). The characteristic shape of the nucleus is spherical, but many other forms are common; for example, the oval nucleus of *Paramecium*, the kidney-shaped nucleus of *Balantidium coli*, and the moniliform nucleus of *Spirostomum*. There are two principal types of nuclear structure: the vesicular type in which the chromatin is concentrated in a single mass or grain (*Arcella*), and the granular type in which the chromatin is distributed in grains throughout the entire nucleus (*Amoeba*). Although some protozoan nuclei may be described as strictly of the vesicular or granular type, the majority are intermediate in structure and partake of the characters of both types. The two types of nuclei possessed by ciliates are known as macronuclei and micronuclei; the former are polyploid and control the vegetative functions, and the latter are diploid and control the reproductive processes of the organism. Another peculiar nuclear condition exhibited by the Ciliata is the distributed nucleus of *Dileptus*, in which the chromatin granules are scattered throughout the cytoplasm. In the *Opalinata* the combination nucleus of *Opalina* contains a group of large chromosomes, trophic in function, and a second group of small chromosomes reproductive in function. As in higher animals the most important nuclear element is the DNA-containing chromatin. In some Protozoa chromatin occurs in the form of granules, called chromidia, located in the cytoplasm either scattered or in a ring, as in *Arcella*. These chromidia are probably of nuclear origin.

NUCLEAR DIVISION. The macronuclei of the Ciliata appear to divide usually by direct or amitotic division as in *Paramecium*. In a few species of Protozoa, for example in *Ephelota* among the Suctorida, the macronucleus branches and new nuclei arise by the pinching off of buds from these branches. But the majority of protozoan nuclei divide by some type of mitosis. Chromosomes arise, divide, and are equally distributed to the daughter cells as in metazoan cells. In some species, mitosis occurs within the nuclear membrane.

Vacuoles. Contractile vacuoles, food vacuoles, and stationary vacuoles containing fluid may be present in the bodies of Protozoa. As a rule, contractile vacuoles are found in fresh-water species and are absent in a great many parasitic and marine forms. Their function appears to be to regulate the osmotic pressure of the cell by the elimination of a portion of the water constantly being taken into the cell by imbibition and osmosis. They are also concerned with the elimination of nitrogenous wastes and possibly with the elimination of carbon dioxide (respiration).

Mitochondria. Aerobic respiration is associated with the mitochondria, which are of variable shape with a double membrane covering them and inner membranes shaped as either internal plates or tubules. Most protozoans have tubules in the interior of the mitochondria. Mitochondria seem to be closely associated with energy-using structures such as locomotor organelles and contractile vacuoles.

Membranes. In addition to the surface membranes of protozoan cells, internal membranes are frequently abundant in their electron micrographs. Some of the membranes are closely packed as in the golgi apparatus, others seem more scattered in arrangement as in the endoplasmic reticulum. Many of the membranes have small granules along their surface. Membranes are thought to be of great significance in carrying enzyme systems in orderly arrangement for efficient cellular metabolism.

Plastids and Other Inclusions. The principal inclusions that are of more or less constant occurrence in Protozoa are chromatophores, pyrenoids, stigmata, crystals, pigments, and symbiotic organisms. Chromatophores are characteristic of holophytic Protozoa. They vary in shape and number but are constant in these respects in the different species. They contain green chlorophyll but may be colored yellow, brown, or red by pigments. Pyrenoids are the centers around which are formed paramylum bodies or other starchlike substances. They may be free or embedded in chromatophores. Stigmata or eye spots are bodies colored red by pigment and often accompanied by a lenslike paramylum body. Pigments of various colors may be present in Protozoa. Thus, malarial organisms elaborate a brownish pigment (melanin) as a product of the digestion of hemoglobin. Crystals may also be constant inclusions in certain Protozoa. For example, several species of fresh-water amoebae contain crystals that differ in shape from one another but are constant in shape for each species. Oil droplets are elaborated by some species, such as *Uroglena.*

Organelles of Motion and Locomotion. The ectoplasm is the layer in most intimate contact with the environment and is the seat of the organelles of motion and locomotion. In the Sarcodina movement is effected by means of temporary extrusions of the protoplasm, called pseudopodia, which are always formed from the ectoplasm although the endoplasm may flow in later. They are of two functional types: hydraulic and autotracteous. In the hydraulic type, which may be either lobopodia or filopodia, the endoplasm flows into the region of weakest tensile strength when propelled hydraulically by contraction of other portions of the ectoplasm. In the autotracteous type, which may be axopodia or reticulopodia, the propulsive force is not known although movement may occur in both directions on opposite sides of the pseudopodium, and thus seems to be due to a different mechanism than in the contraction-hydraulic type.

Flagella and cilia, which characterize the Mastigophora, Opalinata, and Ciliata, have a fundamental similarity of ultrastructure. They are vibratile threadlike processes with an internal structure of two central fibers and nine peripheral fibers, which arise from a basal granule, the kinetosome. The mechanism from which they derive their movement is not known, but the way they impart movement to the organism or the surrounding material is known to follow the laws of hydrodynamics. Flagella are comparatively long and usually few in number. Flagella may be divided into two types: tractella and pulsella. The first type is situated at the end that is anterior when the organism is in motion and drags the body along; the latter is generally situated posteriorly and pushes or propels the body forward. In a number of the parasitic flagellates, frequently a thin layer of protoplasm connects a given flagellum, thoughout the greater part of its length, with the body and is known as an undulating membrane. Cilia, which are the organs of locomotion in the class Ciliata, are also slender threadlike processes, which differ from flagella chiefly in that they are very much smaller in comparison to the body of the protozoon, occur in much greater numbers, and differ in their type of movement. Cilia are generally arranged in rows, and there is a definite coordination between the beat of the individual cilia in each row. There are several modifications of the cilia, such as cirri, membranellae, and undulating membranes. These are all produced by the fusion of a number of cilia. Mention should also be made of certain contractile elements known as myonemes, which are muscle-like and occur in the body of certain of the Mastigophora, Ciliata, and Sporozoa.

Organelles for the Capture and Ingestion of Food.   The organelles of locomotion also play the principal rôle in the capture and ingestion of food. Thus, *Amoeba proteus* engulfs solid food bodies and is even able to capture other Protozoa and cut in two such organisms as *Paramecium* and *Frontonia* by means of its pseudopodia. Holozoic flagellates that ingest solid particles, in many cases use their flagella to drive them into the cytostome. The ciliates possess the most complicated mechanism for capturing and ingesting food; this consists of cilia modified in length and arrangement or fused together into cirri or undulating membranes which may extend down into the cytopharynx. In the Suctorea, tentacles are provided which paralyze organisms, usually ciliates, that come in contact with them and suck the protoplasm out of the prey and pass it down into the endoplasm leaving very little but the periplast behind. Many other specialized structures are present among the Protozoa that aid in the capture and ingestion of food, such as the trichocysts of *Paramecium* and the myonemes of *Vorticella*. Many free-living Protozoa and practically all of the parasitic Protozoa do not ingest solid particles and have no organelles for that purpose; they manufacture food by photosynthesis or absorb it through the surface of the body.

General Physiology.   *Nutrition.*   The principal types of nutrition exhibited by Protozoa are holozoic, holophytic, and saprozoic. Protozoa, such as *Amoeba* and *Paramecium*, that feed on solid particles are said to be holozoic. As a rule, each species is capable of food selection, for example, the holotrichous ciliate, *Actinobolina radians*, pays no attention to many small ciliates and flagellates but immediately captures *Halteria grandinella* whenever an opportunity is afforded; and *Didinium nasutum* has a predilection for *Para-*

mecium. The ingested food of holozoic Protozoa is confined in food vacuoles and digested and assimilated as described in *Amoeba* and *Paramecium*. Undigested material is cast out at any point on the surface (*Amoeba*) or through a definite cytoproct (*Paramecium*).

Holophytic nutrition is particularly common among the Phytomastigophorea. The exclusively holophytic forms (notably some Chloromonadida) require only the presence of sunlight, certain dissolved minerals, and CO_2 to build up and synthesize their complex food materials. Many of the other chromatophore-bearing species, however, live and reproduce much more readily in a medium containing some organic matter. Consequently they must, to a certain extent, be saprophytic. Certain species of Protozoa, such as *Paramecium bursaria* and *Stentor polymorphus*, may obtain nutriment from the green algae (*Zoochlorellae*) that live within them.

Saprozoic nutrition involves the absorption through the general body wall or through some specialized region of the body of dissolved organic material in the medium. Dissolved proteins and carbohydrates resulting from the disintegration of plants and animals, as in an infusion, probably furnish the food for this type of organism. Many parasites, such as *Entamoeba histolytica* and *Balantidium coli*, ingest solid particles and are thus holozoic, but they may also absorb through the body surface food digested by the host or the disintegrated protoplasm of the host. Other parasites, such as *Opalina* and *Giardia*, do not possess any structural modifications for the ingestion of solid particles and must obtain all their nutriment by absorption.

Secretion.   Various types of secretions are produced by Protozoa. Some of them are as follows. The endoplasm of holozoic species secretes digestive enzymes; Suctorea secrete a poison that paralyzes other Ciliata that come in contact with their tentacles; many species secrete shells (*Arcella*) or skeletons (*Radiolaria*); the pseudopodia of certain Sarcodina are mucilaginous (*Difflugia*) and enable the organisms to adhere to the substratum; arcellas secrete gas bubbles which lower their weight and bring them to the surface of the water; the parasite of amoebic dysentery (*Entamoeba histolytica*) secretes a proteolytic enzyme which dissolves the cells of the intestinal wall of its human host.

Excretion.   Soluble waste materials are excreted either by diffusion through the general body surface, or, after accumulation in the contractile vacuole, by emptying from it to the exterior. Another very effective method of eliminating waste materials from the body is to throw them out of solution by precipitation. The crystals described in *Amoeba proteus* and the pigment in *Actinosphaerium* may be of this nature. The melanin pigment of certain blood-inhabiting Sporozoa is an insoluble waste formed from the digestion of hemoglobin.

Respiration.   Respiration, in its broadest sense, includes any process by which an organism liberates the potential energy represented in the complex chemicals of its body. It may be effected either aerobically by oxidation or anaerobically by the splitting up of complex chemical substances into simple compounds. The end result, in either case, is the same. Most free-living Protozoa live in an environment containing more or less dissolved oxygen. Through the general body surface the animal absorbs the oxygen and eliminates the carbon dioxide and water which result from the oxidation. The contractile vacuole is probably also effective in eliminating these wastes. Many parasitic forms live in environments which are partially or totally lacking in oxygen. Here respiration must be of the anaerobic type.

Circulation. The protozoan body is so small that the circulation of nutritive material, secretions, excretions, etc., takes place by streaming movements of the cytoplasm and hence no circulatory system is necessary. Thus, food vacuoles are distributed through the body of *Paramecium* by cyclosis, and in a suctorian, the protoplasm of its prey passes through the tentacles and into the body.

Motion and Locomotion. Movements among the Protozoa are due to pseudopodia, flagella, cilia, and contractile elements such as myonemes. Amoebid movement has been described in *Amoeba proteus.* As noted, pseudopodia are of two chief types—lobopodia and axopodia. The former are the common type and occur in the amoebae. They consist of an extrusion of the body with no specific structural differentiation. Axopodia, on the other hand, found in such forms as *Actinophrys*, are capable of swinging or bending movements and possess a secreted axis, which is either rigid or elastic in nature. Mastigophora move by means of flagella. The commonest type of flagellum is the tractellum, i.e., a flagellum which drags rather than propels the organism. In some species the entire length of the flagellum is thrown into motion and the organism may progress very rapidly, as in the hemoflagellates; in other species only about one third of the distal end vibrates, often causing the organism to progress in a series of jumps. In certain species, like *Peranema*, almost the entire flagellum is held stiff and only a very small part of the distal end moves. Mastigophora with flagella may move by means of pseudopodia, and some of the highly developed Euglenida, such as *Euglena*, periodically lose their flagella and move about by crawling along the substratum with a kind of rocking movement. Forms with a semiresistant periplast, especially the Euglenida, often exhibit peristaltic waves of contraction which run down the length of the body. Such movements are termed metabolic, or euglenoid, because they are especially common in *Euglena*.

Movement among the Ciliata is effected by cilia. The action of cilia in locomotion has been described in *Paramecium*. As a rule, cilia are situated in rows, and their movement is concerted. Each cilium contracts a short interval after the one in front of it and before the one behind it. Thus, viewed from the side, a moving row of cilia looks as if successive waves were passing over it. Furthermore, adjacent cilia of different rows beat in unison. When seen from above a ciliated surface has the appearance of a wheat field in the wind, i.e., successive waves follow one another across the ciliated surface (Fig.

1–60). Hypotrichous ciliates are capable of swimming, but spend most of their time creeping on the substratum by means of cirri on the ventral surface which represent bunches of fused cilia and act practically as legs. In *Euplotes*, the cirri are aided in creeping by the peristomial membranelles.

Behavior. The reactions of Protozoa to stimuli, which taken together constitute what is known as their behavior, have attracted much study. Some of the results have already been noted in *Amoeba, Euglena,* and *Paramecium*. In general, the reaction of an animal to a stimulus involves three systems: first, a sense receptor; second, a conducting system; and third, an effector. Such structures are not visibly differentiated in forms like *Amoeba,* but the portion of the body that receives the stimulus is also the one that reacts so that conduction is probably little more than a general effect of the stimulus on a localized portion of the body.

The flagellates have progressed markedly in the development of a reflex type of behavior (receptor-conductor-effector), due largely to the presence of definite organs of locomotion and more or less permanent body form. This is evident from a comparison of the behavior of *Amoeba* and *Euglena*. Of special interest is the relation of the stigma to light stimulation.

The reflex type of reaction is developed to a much higher state in the Ciliata. The reactions of *Paramecium* to various stimuli have already been described. In *Stentor* there is fairly clear evidence that one portion of the body receives the stimulus, that this is transmitted to definite cilia, which in turn produce a definite motor response. Fibrillar systems are present in the ciliate ectoplasm, but little evidence is available to clarify their function. Definite neuromotor fibrils and centers are known in the more highly specialized ciliates such as *Euplotes*.

In conclusion, we can do no better than to insert a quotation from Jennings (1906).

All together, there is no evidence of the existence of differences of fundamental character between the behavior of the Protozoa and that of the lower Metazoa. The study of behavior lends no support to the view that the life activities are of an essentially different character in the Protozoa and the Metazoa. The behavior of the Protozoa appears to be no more and no less machine-like than that of the Metazoa; similar principles govern both.

Reproduction. *Asexual Reproduction.* The common method of reproduction in the Protozoa is that of simple or binary fission. During this process first the nucleus, then the cytoplasm divides. In some cases the nucleus undergoes a series of divisions after which the body divides into as many parts as there are nuclei. Such a process is known as multiple fission. In other cases the division of the cytoplasm only takes place at special periods in the life cycle so that, as a result, the typical condition of the organism is that of a plasmodium. When division of such a plasmodium does take place, it generally forms two or more multinucleate bodies. Such a process is known as plasmotomy.

Budding is a type of asexual reproduction that occurs regularly in certain species. A bud is a part of the cytoplasm of the parent containing a nucleus of parental origin. Buds cut off from the outside of the parent are exogenous. This occurs, for example, in certain amoebae (*Endamoeba patuxent* of the oyster), in the flagellate *Noctiluca*, in Sporozoa, and in *Ephelota* and most other Suctorea. Endogenous or internal budding is not as common as the exogenous type. It consists in the separation of a mass of cytoplasm, containing a nucleus, from the rest of the organism within the body. It occurs commonly in certain Sporozoa and a few Suctorea.

Sexual Reproduction. Conjugation, or the temporary union of two individuals of the same species involving an exchange of nuclear material, accompanies sexual reproduction in many Protozoa, especially Ciliata. This process has been described fully in *Paramecium*. When the conjugants are of the same size as in *Paramecium*, they are said to be isogamous; when of different sizes, as in *Chilodon cucullulus*, anisogamous. The permanent union of two protozoan individuals is called copulation. The organisms that unite are usually smaller than normal vegetative individuals and are known as gametes. The gametes may be of the same size (isogamous) as in *Monocystis*, or may differ in size (anisogamous) as in *Plasmodium vivax*. In the latter case they correspond to the egg cells and spermatozoa of the Metazoa. The body formed by the fusion of two gametes is a zygote. The life cycles of many of the Protozoa, especially the Sporozoa, are sometimes very complicated because of the sexual reproduction involved.

Special Morphology and Physiology. Various topics of interest in connection with Protozoa are referred to briefly here. Further information may be found in books on Protozoology or in scientific journals.

Colonial Protozoa and Metazoa. Although Protozoa are defined as unicellular animals, many of them are colonial in habit and others at certain stages in their life cycles consist of many cells. The colonial forms, as we have seen, may consist of a variable number of cells irregularly arranged (*Carchesium*) or of a definite number arranged in a definite way (Volvocidae). The members of the colony may be entirely independent, except for the common gelatinous matrix in which they are embedded (*Pandorina*), or may be connected by protoplasmic strands (*Volvox*). The cells may be of one kind (*Spondylomorum*) or may be differentiated into somatic cells and germ cells (*Volvox*). The somatic cells of Protozoa in general differ from somatic cells in the Metazoa, because there is no histological differentiation among them and they are comparatively independent. Multicellular stages occur regularly in the life cycles of certain Protozoa. For example, in the gregarine, *Ophryocystis*, each member of a pair at the time of copulation divides into two cells, a small uninucleate gamete and a larger binucleate cell which forms a protecting envelope. A theory favored by many zoologists is that the Metazoa evolved from the Protozoa through stages resembling somewhat the colonial Protozoa of today. Perhaps the most fundamental difference between protozoan and metazoan cells is the fact that the Protozoa are able with one cell to carry on all the life processes characteristic of the Metazoa; whereas metazoan cells are limited to special functions.

Neuromotor Apparatus. The term "neuromotor apparatus" has been applied to a system of connected fibrils centering in a differentiated mass of cytoplasm near the anterior end called the motorium. In a ciliate, *Epidinium ecaudatum*, that lives in the rumen of cattle, a fibril connects the motorium with a circumesophageal ring which encircles the gullet. From this, other fibrils lead posteriorly along the gullet. There are also fibrils running to the bases of the adoral membranelles and to the operculum. Similar systems of fibrils have been described in a number of other ciliates and in many flagellates. Special technical methods are necessary to reveal these fibrils. Microdissection experiments indicate that the activities of the organism are coordinated by the neuromotor system. For example, when the motorium is destroyed uncoordinated movements of the membranelles result.

Conjugation and Autogamy. The significance of conjugation cannot be definitely stated. Some investigators believe that *Paramecium* and other ciliates pass through a life cycle containing three distinct stages. The period of (1) youth is characterized by rapid cell multiplication and growth; (2) maturity, by less frequent cell division, sexual maturity, and the cessation of growth; and (3) old age, by degeneration and natural death. Death is avoided by conjugation, which rejuvenates the senescent animals.

The amitotic division of the macronucleus, which occurs during binary fission, may segregate into divided macronuclei unequal proportions of the various chromosomes. Succeeding divisions could further increase the imbalance to a point at which the macronucleus can no longer function properly, and the reconstitution of the macronucleus following conjugation or autogamy is essential to survival. Recent work of Dysart has shown that the macronuclei of various tetrahymenids contain from 15 to 900 times the amount of DNA (an important genetic material in the chromosomes) found in the haploid micronuclei. In view of the absence of a spindle for precise division of the chromosomes of the macronucleus, it is not unlikely that after many divisions the balance of chromosomes originally present would be lost in some cells.

A favorable balance may be restored by either conjugation or autogamy. It may be noted at this point that Weismann many years ago suggested that Protozoa do not die a natural death, because the two daughter cells resulting from binary division share the parental protoplasm between them and the parent does not die but simply loses her identity in her offspring.

Mutualism (Symbiosis). Symbiosis, which formerly was used to imply the permanent association of two specifically distinct organisms to their mutual advantage, has taken on a meaning to biologists of an intimate association of more than one kind of organism, which may be (1) disadvantageous to one (parasitism); (2) essential to one but of no advantage or disadvantage to the other (commensalism); or (3) essential or useful to both (mutualism). Mutualism occurs in many protozoans such as the ciliates *Paramecium busaria* and *Stentor polymorphus* and certain Radiolarida, which contain symbiotic algae (Zoochlorellae) or dinoflagellates (Zooanthellae). Some Protozoa are obligatory symbionts of higher organisms, e.g., flagellates in the intestine of termites.

Cellular Metabolism. Increased knowledge of culture methods for many protozoans has made possible the rapid advance in our understanding of their physiology at the molecular level. *Tetrahymena pyriformis* has been an outstanding species in revealing details of molecular biology. The presence of many metabolic pathways in common with man have made the Protozoa of practical value in experimental studies relating to the biology of man.

Ultrastructure. The electron microscope has contributed a great deal of information in recent years documenting the fundamental unity and diversity of cells and organisms. The prevalence of membranes in the cytoplasm of organisms was a feature not anticipated. The homology of cilia and flagella is of special interest. The recent text of Pitelka (1963) is a valuable contribution drawing the studies of protozoan ultrastructure together.

The History of Our Knowledge of Protozoa. Protozoa were unknown before microscopes were invented. They were first seen and described by Anton von Leeuwenhoek (1632–1723). About 30 species described by him are recognizable today. The first one was a *Vorticella* described in 1675. Later in 1681 he found in his own stools and described the first protozoan from man, now known as *Giardia lamblia.* Protozoa soon became favorite material for study and played a prominent role in the development of biology, but only a few names and discoveries can be included here. Joblot (1718) showed that no Protozoa appeared in a hay infusion unless exposed to the atmosphere, thus disproving the theory of the spontaneous generation of Protozoa. He likewise (1754) discovered the contractile vacuole and the importance of the arrangement of cilia. Part of the life history of the vorticellas was worked out by Trembley (1747). The nature of the Protozoa was being discussed at this time and was not conceded by Linnaeus to be of the animal type until 1767. Order was established for the Protozoa by O. F. Müller (1786), who adopted binomial nomenclature and named nearly 400 species, of which 150 remain in the group today. The term Infusoria was applied to the entire phylum. Ehrenberg's large monograph on *The Infusoria as Complete Organisms* appeared in 1836. He, like many other investigators at this time, believed Protozoa to possess eyes and various internal organs characteristic of higher animals. The Sarcodina were studied particularly by Dujardin (1801–1860) who called their protoplasm "sarcode." The term protoplasm was applied to the cell substance by Purkinje in 1840 and by von Mohl in 1846. The unicellular nature of the Protozoa was established by von Siebold in 1848.

From this time on many students of the Protozoa advanced our knowledge of the phylum and published large monographs on the various types. Some of the more important are included in the references at the end of this chapter. Parasitic Protozoa did not attract particular attention until it was discovered that certain species were pathogenic to lower animals or to man. The discovery of each new pathogenic species has been followed by a flood of literature representing the results of investigation by many students. Among the disease-producing parasitic Protozoa of man should be mentioned *Entamoeba histolytica* of amoebic dysentery and amoebic liver abscess, the trypanosomes of African sleeping sickness and of Chagas' disease in South America, the leishmanias of oriental sore and kala-azar, the intestinal flagellates, *Balantidium coli* of ciliate dysentery, and the malarial parasites. Important agents of animal diseases are the trypanosomes of dourine, nagana, surra, mal-de-caderas, and murrina in cattle, horses, and mules, the coccidia of birds and rabbits and the piroplasmas of Texas fever in cattle and other similar diseases.

Protozoa and Metazoa.   It is usually assumed by zoologists that Metazoa have evolved from Protozoa, and, granted the truth of evolution, the assumption that the many-celled animals developed from protozoan-like ancestors seems reasonable. How this took place during the remote ages in the history of life upon the earth is a difficult and unsolved problem. Among Protozoa, as already described, are species consisting of many cells forming colonies in some of which the cells have become differentiated into somatic cells and germ cells. In certain species the somatic cells are of several types that perform different functions. Such an organism is really a metazoan. It is impossible to state definitely, however, that the Metazoa have evolved by the aggregation of similar cells into colonies and their subsequent differentiation although this seems quite probable. The possibility has also been suggested that the Metazoa have arisen from multinucleate Protozoa in which each nucleus assumed control of that portion of the cytoplasm immediately surrounding it and the so-called energids thus formed developed different functions. The superficial resemblance of the astome ciliates to the planula larvae of coelenterates and the acoelous flatworms has led some to consider the ciliates as the protozoans from which the metazoans arose. The peculiar nuclear condition of the ciliates indicates that if such a hypothetical origin occurred it would have been from ciliates more primitive than the existing ones.

Protista.   Protozoa and algae are so closely related through the Phytomastigophorea that they seem to be the point of divergence of plants and animals. Because the position of other protozoans as animals or plants may be questionable (viz., the fungi-like Mycetozoida and some questionable

Sporozoa), the Protista concept has arisen. Those using the Kingdom Protista include in it all unicellular organisms and simpler organisms. Higher plants and animals are left in separate kingdoms as before. The point of the fundamental unity of organisms can be made without disrupting the conventional classification.

Classification of the Protozoa. The classification presented here is much abbreviated and arranged to be useful to one who is not specializing in protozoology. It includes particularly those groups most frequently encountered by zoologists. It is in quite close agreement with the classification proposed by The Committee on Taxonomy and Taxonomic Problems of the Society of Protozoologists (Honigberg, *et al.*, 1964). A major change is made in the classification of the Sarcodina following the lead of Jahn and Bovee (1965).

Phylum Protozoa. Unicellular animals.

SUPERCLASS I. MASTIGOPHORA. With flagella.

CLASS 1. PHYTOMASTIGOPHOREA. Plantlike flagellates; one to four flagella.

ORDER 1. CHRYSOMONADIDA. One or two yellowish chromatophores; food stored as lipid or leucosin.

ORDER 2. SILICOFLAGELLIDA. Brown chromatophores; siliceous endoskeleton.

ORDER 3. COCCOLITHOPHORIDA. Yellow-brown chromatophores; body covering of calcareous platelets.

ORDER 4. HETEROCHLORIDA. Two unequal flagella; yellow-green chromatophores; food stored as lipid or leucosin.

ORDER 5. CRYPTOMONADIDA. Two flagella originating in depression; food stored as starch or amyloid substances; chromatophores, when present, often brown, green, or red.

ORDER 6. DINOFLAGELLIDA. Many with a thickened cuticle which forms a lorica; two flagella that usually lie in two grooves in the lorica, the longitudinal one in the sulcus, and the transverse one in the girdle; food stored as starch and lipid.

ORDER 7. EBRIIDA. No chromatophores; siliceous endoskeleton.

ORDER 8. EUGLENIDA. Green chromatophores; food stored as paramylum; metaboly.

ORDER 9. CHLOROMONADIDA. Numerous green chromatophores; two flagella, one trailing; food stored as glycogen and lipids.

ORDER 10. VOLVOCIDA. Chromatophore green, often cup-shaped; colonial forms common; food stored as starch.

CLASS 2. ZOOMASTIGOPHOREA. Animal-like flagellates; one to many flagella.

ORDER 1. CHOANOFLAGELLIDA. Collar surrounding base of single anterior flagellum; some colonial.

ORDER 2. BICOSOECIDA. Two flagella, one attaching cell to lorica; some with collar.

ORDER 3. RHIZOMASTIGIDA. One to many flagella and pseudopodia.

ORDER 4. KINETOPLASTIDA. Usually one or two flagella and a nucleic acid containing kinetoplast; most parasitic.

ORDER 5. RETORTAMONADIDA. Two to four flagella; cytostome; all parasitic.

ORDER 6. DIPLOMONADIDA. Eight flagella; bilateral symmetry; two nuclei; most parasitic.

ORDER 7. OXYMONADIDA. Four or more flagella; one or more axostyles; division spindle intranuclear; all parasitic.

ORDER 8. TRICHOMONADIDA. Usually four to six flagella; one or more axostyles; division spindle extra-nuclear; all parasitic.

ORDER 9. HYPERMASTIGIDA. Many flagella; one nucleus; all entozoic in insects.

SUPERCLASS II. OPALINATA. With many uniformly distributed flagella giving a ciliatelike appearance; one type of nucleus; all entozoic in amphibians. One order, Opalinida.

SUPERCLASS III. SARCODINA. With pseudopodia.

CLASS 1. HYDRAULEA. Pseudopodial movement in only one direction at a time; no axial structure in pseudopodium.

ORDER 1. AMOEBIDA. Without test or shell; usually uninucleate, multinucleate condition not the result of aggregation of individuals.

ORDER 2. ARCELLINIDA. Test with single aperture through which pseudopodia are extended.

ORDER 3. MYCETOZOIDA. Without test; complex life cycle including large multinucleate stage followed by spore formation.

CLASS 2. AUTOTRACTEA. Movement of protoplasm may occur in opposite directions on the sides of thin pseudopodia, which frequently contain an axial structure.

ORDER 1. PROTEOMYXIDA. Without test; most parasitic.

ORDER 2. HELIOZOIDA. Axopodia or filopodia; spherical symmetry; no central capsule; mostly fresh-water forms.

ORDER 3. RADIOLARIDA. Skeleton siliceous or of strontium sulfate; central capsule; all marine.

ORDER 4. FORAMINIFERIDA. Test of chitin-like material, usually greatly thickened by the deposition of calcium carbonate; usually many perforations for extension of pseudopodia; no central capsule; nearly all marine.

SUPERCLASS IV. SPOROZOA. No locomotor organelles. All parasitic.

CLASS 1. TELOSPOREA. Formation of spores by adults, ending life of the parent; reproduction both sexual and asexual; spores without polar capsules or polar filaments.

ORDER 1. GREGARINIDA. Coelozoic; reproduction usually by sporogony following association of gamonts in syzygy.

ORDER 2. COCCIDA. Cytozoic; alternation of schizogony and sporogony; sporocyst and cocyst wall surround sporozoites.

ORDER 3. HAEMOSPORIDA. Cytozoic; alternation of schizogony and sporogony; sporozoites naked; two host life cycle.

CLASS 2. CNIDOSPOREA. Spores with polar capsule and polar filament; mostly parasites of fish.

ORDER 1. MYXOSPORIDA. Spores large; usually with two polar capsules.

ORDER 2. MICROSPORIDA. Spores small; usually only one polar capsule.

CLASS 3. ACNIDOSPOREA. Asexual reproduction only; no polar capsules.

ORDER 1. TOXOPLASMIDA. No spores produced; parasites of vertebrates.

ORDER 2. HAPLOSPORIDA. Spores produced; most are parasites of invertebrates or fish.

SUPERCLASS V. CILIATA. With cilia; usually two sizes of nuclei.

CLASS 1. HOLOTRICHEA. Cilia uniformly distributed over entire body.

ORDER 1. GYMNOSTOMATIDA. Cytostome opens on surface of body; no special oral ciliature.

ORDER 2. TRICHOSTOMATIDA. Cytostome opens in a depression (vestibulum).

ORDER 3. CHONOTRICHIDA. Sessile adults lack body cilia; epizoic on crustaceans; vase-shaped; ciliated vestibule is funnel-shaped.

ORDER 4. APOSTOMATIDA. Rosette near cytostome; ciliary meridians spiral around adult.

ORDER 5. ASTOMATIDA. No cytostome; mostly parasites of annelids.

ORDER 6. HYMENOSTOMATIDA. Buccal ciliature consisting of one undulating membrane and three membranelles.

CLASS 2. PERITRICHEA. Typically sessile and stalked; body cilia mostly absent in adult; oral ciliature forms prominent counterclockwise spiral to cytostome. One order, Peritrichida.

CLASS 3. SUCTOREA. Adult sessile, devoid of cilia, and with suctorial tentacles in most species; larval stage produced by budding is free-swimming and uniformly ciliated. One order, Suctorida.

CLASS 4. SPIROTRICHEA. Buccal ciliature forms prominent clockwise spiral to cytostome; body ciliature usually sparse.

ORDER 1. HETEROTRICHIDA. Body cilia uniform when present.

ORDER 2. OLIGOTRICHIDA. Body cilia very sparse; few species.

ORDER 3. TINTINNIDA. Lorica present; prominent oral ciliature; mostly marine.

ORDER 4. ENTODINIOMORPHIDA. No simple cilia on body; parasites of herbivores.

ORDER 5. ODONTOSTOMATIDA. Few body cilia; eight oral membranelles.

ORDER 6. HYPOTRICHIDA. Body ciliature of cirri restricted to ventral surface; typically creeping; body flattened.

References to Literature on the Protozoa

The references listed below are for the most part books and some of the more significant journal articles. In these will be found bibliographies to the literature on Protozoa contained in scientific journals and monographs. Current literature can best be obtained from journals that often include papers on Protozoa and from bibliographies. Among the former are the *Journal of Protozoology, Archiv fur Protistenkunde, Biological Bulletin, Journal of Parasitology*, and *Transactions of the American Microscopical Society*. The bibliographies of most use are the *Zoological Record* and *Biological Abstracts*.

ALLEN, R. D. 1962. Amoeboid movement. *Sci. Am.*, **206**:112–122.

BARNETT, A. 1964. Cytology of conjugation in *Paramecium multimicronucleatum*, syngen 2, stock 11. *J. Protozool.*, **11**:147–153.

BARRETT, J. M. 1958. Some observations on *Actinosphaerium nucleofilum* n. sp., a new fresh water actinophryid. *J. Protozool.*, **5**:205–209.

BECKER, E. R. 1934. *Coccidia and Coccidiosis of Domesticated, Game and Laboratory Animals and of Man*. Collegiate Press, Ames. 147 pp.

BOVEE, E. C. 1960. Studies of feeding behavior of amebas. I. Ingestion of thecate rhizopods and flagellates by verrucosid amebas, particularly *Thecamoeba sphaeronucleolus. J. Protozool.*, **7**:55–60.

——, and T. L. Jahn. 1965. Mechanisms of movement in taxonomy of Sarcodina. II. The organization of subclasses and orders in relationship to the classes Autotractea and Hydraulea. *Am. Midl. Nat.*, **73**:293–298.

CANNING, E. U., E. ELKAN, and P. I. TRIGG. 1964. *Plistophora myotrophica* spec. nov., causing high mortality in the common toad *Bufo bufo* L., with notes on the maintenance of *Bufo* and *Xenopus* in the laboratory. *J. Protozool.*, **11**:157–166.

CALKINS, G. N., and F. N. SUMMERS. 1941. *Protozoa in Biological Research*. Columbia Univ. Press, New York. 1148 pp.

CHALKLEY, A. W., and G. E. DANIEL. 1933. The relation between the form of the living cell and the nuclear phases of division in *Amoeba proteus. Physiol. Zool.*, **6**.

CHALLEY, J. R., and W. C. BURNS. 1959. The invasion of the cecal mucosa by *Eimeria tenella* sporozoites and their transport by macrophages. *J. Protozool.*, **6**:238–241.

CLEVELAND, L. R. 1956. Brief accounts of the sexual cycles of the flagellates of *Cryptocercus. J. Protozool.*, **3**:161–180.

CLEVELAND, L. R. 1957. Correlation between the molting period of *Cryptocercus* and sexuality in its Protozoa. *J. Protozool.*, **4**:168–175.

——. 1958. Photographs of fertilization in *Trichonympha grandis. J. Protozool.*, **5**:115–122.

COLEMAN, G. S. 1963. The growth and metabolism of rumen ciliate protozoa. pp. 298–324 + 1 Pl. In *Symbiotic Associations*. Cambridge Univ. Press. 365 pp.

CORLISS, J. O. 1953. Silver impregnation of ciliated protozoa by the Chatton-Lwoff technic. *Stain Tech.*, **28**:97–100.

———. 1954. The literature on *Tetrahymena*: its history, growth, and recent trends. *J. Protozool.*, **1**:156–169.

———. 1959. An illustrated key to the higher groups of the ciliated protozoa, with definition of terms. *J. Protozool.*, **6**:265–284.

———. 1960. Comments on the systematics and phylogeny of the protozoa. *Syst. Zool.*, **8**:169–190.

———. 1961. *The Ciliated Protozoa*. Pergamon Press, New York. 310 pp.

———. 1965. *Tetrahymena*, a ciliate genus of unusual importance in modern biological research. *Acta Protozoologica*, **3**:1–20.

CUSHMAN, J. A. 1955. *Foraminifera*. Harvard Univ. Press, Cambridge. 605 pp.

DROOP, M. R. 1963. Algae and invertebrates in symbiosis. In *Symbiotic Associations*. Cambridge Univ. Press. 356 pp.

EDMUNDS, L. N. 1964. Replication of DNA and cell division in synchronously dividing cultures of *Euglena gracilis*. *Science*, **145**:266–268.

ELLIOTT, A. M., M. A. ADDISON, and S. E. CAREY. 1962. Distribution of *Tetrahymena pyriformis* in Europe. *J. Protozool.*, **9**:135–141.

ELLIOTT, A. M., and I. J. BAK. 1964. The contractile vacuole and related structures in *Tetrahymena pyriformis*. *J. Protozool.*, **11**:250–261.

ERICSON, D. B., M. EWING, and G. WOLLIN. 1963. Pliocene-Pleistocene boundary in deep-sea sediments. *Science*, **139**:727–737.

FARR, M. M., and D. J. DORAN. 1962. Comparative excystation of four species of poultry coccidia. *J. Protozool.*, **9**:403–407.

FENNELL, R. A., and F. O. MARZKE. 1954. The relation between vitamins, inorganic salts and the histochemical characteristics of *Tetrahymena geleii* W. *J. Morph.*, **94**:587–616.

FINLEY, H. E., C. A. BROWN, and W. A. DANIEL. 1964. Electron microscopy of the ectoplasm and infraciliature of *Spirostomum ambiguum*. *J. Protozool.*, **11**:264–280.

GAVIN, M. A., T. WANKO, and L. JACOBS. 1962. Electron microscope studies of reproducing and interkinetic *Toxoplasma*. *J. Protozool.*, **9**:222–234.

GELBER, B. 1958. Retention in *Paramecium aurelia*. *J. Comp. and Physio. Psych.*, **1958**:110–115.

GIBBONS, I. R., and A. J. ROWE. 1965. Dynein: a protein with adenosine triphosphatase activity from cilia. *Science*, **149**:424–426.

GOLDACRE, R. J., and I. J. LORCH. 1950. Folding and unfolding of protein molecules in relation to protoplasmic streaming, amoeboid movement and osmotic work. *Nature*, **166**:497–500.

HALL, R. P. 1953. *Protozoology*. Prentice-Hall, New York, 682 pp.

———. 1965. *Protozoan Nutrition*. Blaisdell, New York. 90 pp.

HIRSHFIELD, H. I. (Ed.). 1959. The biology of the *Amoeba*. *Ann. N. Y. Acad. Sci.*, **78**:401–704.

HONIGBERG, B. M. 1967. Developments in microscopy in relation to our understanding of Protozoa. *Trans. Am. Micr. Soc.*, **86**:101–112.

HONIGBERG, *et al.* 1964. A revised classification of the Phylum Protozoa. *J. Protozool.*, **11**:7–20.

HUTNER, S. H. 1964. Protozoa as toxicological tools. *J. Protozool.*, **11**:1–6.

——. (Ed.). 1964. *Biochemistry and Physiology of Protozoa.* Vol. III. Academic Press, New York. 616 pp. Hutner, S. H., and Lwoff, A. (Eds.). 1955. *Ibid.* Vol. II. Lwoff, A. (Ed.) 1951. *Ibid.* Vol. I.

HYMAN, L. H. 1940. *The Invertebrates: Protozoa Through Ctenophora.* Vol. I. McGraw-Hill, New York. 726 pp.

JAHN, T. L., and E. C. BOVEE. 1965. Mechanisms of movement in taxonomy of Sarcodina. I. As a basis for a new major dichotomy into two classes, Auto-tractea and Hydraulea. *Am. Midl. Nat.*, **73**:30–40.

——, and F. F. JAHN. 1949. *How to Know The Protozoa.* Brown, Dubuque. 234 pp.

JAHN, T. L., M. D. LANDMAN, and J. R. FONSECA. 1964. The mechanism of loco-motion of flagellates. II. Function of the mastigonemes of *Ochromonas.* *J. Protozool.*, **11**:291–296.

JENNINGS, H. S. 1906. *Behavior of the Lower Organisms.* Columbia Univ. Press, New York. 380 pp.

JEPPS, M. W. 1956. *The Protozoa, Sarcodina.* Oliver and Boyd, Edinburgh. 183 pp.

KAHL, A. 1932–1935. *Urtiere oder Protozoa. I. Wimpertiere oder Ciliata.* Pts. 18, 21, 25, and 30 of *Die Tierwelt Deutschland.* Gustav Fischer, Jena. 886 pp.

KATES, J. R., and L. GOLDSTEIN. 1964. A comparison of the protein composition of three species of amoebae. *J. Protozool.*, **11**:30–35.

KUDO, R. R. 1966. *Protozoology.* 5th Ed. Thomas, Springfield. 1174 pp.

LEVINE, N. D. 1961. *Protozoan Parasites of Domestic Animals and Man.* Burgess, Minneapolis. 412 pp.

——, *et al.* 1962. Survival of *Tritrichomonas foetus* stored at −28 and −95°C after freezing in the presence of glycerol. *J. Protozool.*, **9**:347–350.

LUDVIK, J., *et al.* (Eds.). 1963. *Progress in Protozoology.* Academic Press, New York. 623 + 105 pp.

LUNDIN, F. C., and L. S. WEST. 1962. *The Free-Living Protozoa of the Upper Peninsula of Michigan.* Northern Mich. College Press, Marquette. 192 pp.

MACKINNON, D. L., and R. S. HAWES. 1961. *An Introduction to the Study of Protozoa.* Clarendon Press, Oxford. 506 pp.

MANWELL, R. D. 1961. *Introduction to Protozoology.* St. Martins Press, New York. 642 pp.

MAST, S. O. 1931. Locomotion in *Amoeba proteus. Protoplasma,* **14**:321–330.

——, and R. A. FENNELL. 1938. The relation between temperature, salts, hydro-gen ion concentration and frequency of ingestion of food by *Amoeba. Physiol. Zool.*, **11**:1–18.

NOLAND, L. E., and H. E. FINLEY. 1931. Studies on the taxonomy of the genus *Vorticella. Trans. Am. Micr. Soc.*, **50**:81–123.

PARRISH, F. K., and J. W. PARRISH. 1962. Demonstrating gregarines. *Turtox News,* **40**:236–237.

PHLEGER, F. B. 1960. *Ecology and Distribution of Recent Foraminifera.* Johns Hopkins Press, Baltimore. 297 pp.

PITELKA, D. R. 1963. *Electron-Microscopic Structure of Protozoa.* Macmillan, New York. 269 pp.

——, and C. N. SCHOOLEY. 1955. Comparative morphology of some protistan flagella. *Univ. Calif. Publ. Zool.*, **61**:79–128.

QADRI, S. S. 1962. An experimental study of the life cycle of *Trypanosoma danilewskyi* in the leech, *Hemiclepsis marginata. J. Protozool.*, **9**:254–258.

RATCLIFFE, H. L. 1927. Mitosis and cell division in *Euglena spirogyra* Ehrenberg. *Biol. Bull.*, **53**:109–122.

RINALDI, R. A., and T. L. JAHN. 1963. On the mechanism of ameboid movement. *J. Protozool.*, **10**:344–357.

RUDZINSKA, M. A., and W. TRAGER. 1962. Intracellular phagotrophy in *Babesia rodhaini* as revealed by electron microscopy. *J. Protozool.*, **9**:279–288.

SANDON, H. 1927. *The Composition and Distribution of the Protozoan Fauna of the Soil.* Oliver and Boyd, London. 237 pp.

SCHERBAUM, O., and E. ZEUTHEN. 1954. Induction of synchronous cell division in mass cultures of *Tetrahymena piriformis. Exp. Cell Res.*, **6**:221–227.

SCHMIDT-NIELSEN, B., and C. R. SCHRAUGER. 1963. *Amoeba proteus:* Studying the contractile vacuole by micropuncture. *Science*, **139**:606–607.

SEAMAN, G. R. 1949. The presence of the tricarboxylic acid cycle in the ciliate *Colpidium campylum. Biol. Bull.*, **96**:257–262.

SHORTT, H. E., and P. C. GARNHAM. 1948. The pre-erythrocytic development of *Plasmodium cynomolgi* and *Plasmodium vivax. Trans. Roy. Soc. Trop. Med. and Hyg.*, **41**:785–794.

SMALL, E. B. 1967. The Scuticociliatida, a new order of the class Ciliatea (phylum Protozoa, subphylum Ciliophora). *Trans. Am. Micr. Soc.*, **86**: 345–370. (This new order was established for hymenostome-like ciliates that have a different type of oral development. Included are *Pleuronema* and others. Too late to include in this edition.)

TARTER, V. 1961. *The Biology of Stentor.* Pergamon Press, New York. 413 pp.

TRAGER, W. 1963. Differentiation in Protozoa. *J. Protozool.*, **10**:1–6.

WICHTERMAN, R. 1953. *The Biology of Paramecium.* McGraw-Hill, New York. 527 pp.

WOLKEN, J. 1961. *Euglena.* Rutgers Univ. Press. 173 pp.

YUSA, A. 1957. The morphology and morphogenesis of the buccal organelles in *Paramecium* with particular reference to their systematic significance. *J. Protozool.*, **4**:128–142.

——. 1963. An electron microscope study on regeneration of trichocysts in *Paramecium caudatum. J. Protozool.*, **70**:253–262.

ZEUTHEN, E. 1964. *Synchrony in Cell Division and Growth.* Interscience, New York. 630 pp.

Chapter II
Phylum Porifera

T HE SPONGES seem to be the remnants of a group of animals that separated from the other Metazoa at an early stage in the evolutionary series and have remained in their primitive condition ever since. For this reason the Metazoa are sometimes arranged in two groups, one containing the sponges and designated the Parazoa and the other the Metazoa proper.

Most sponges are marine but a few live in fresh water. The bath sponges that are familiar to all of us consist of the skeleton of certain Porifera that live in the sea.

Sponges are usually attached and stationary sessile animals in the adult stage, distribution being brought about largely by the actively swimming ciliated larvae or by currents of water, which carry the young from place to place before they become attached. The thousands of different species vary greatly in shape, size, structure, and geographical distribution. They were for centuries considered to be plants, and their animal nature was not established until about 1857.

Sponges lack organs but do have some grouping of cells into tissues. Recent interest in sponge regeneration, reorganization, grafting, and development is partially based on similarities to connective tissue of man and the hope that principles of tissue transplantation may be uncovered. Spongin, which forms the fibrous part of the sponge skeleton, is nearly identical to collagen in vertebrate tissues.

Sponges are not easy to classify but are usually arranged in three classes as follows:

CLASS I. CALCAREA (Lat. *calcarius*, lime), with spicules of carbonate of lime.

CLASS II. HEXACTINELLIDA (Gr. *hex*, six: *aktin*, ray), with triaxon spicules of silicon.

121

CLASS III. DEMOSPONGIAE (Gr. *demos*, people; *spongos*, sponge), usually with spicules of silicon, not triaxon, or with spongin, or with both spicules and spongin.

1 / Class I. Calcarea

(1) Leucosolenia

Leucosolenia (Fig. 2–1) is a sponge that will serve to illustrate the structure of the most simple members of the phylum. It is found growing on the rocks near the seashore just below low-tide mark, and consists of a number of horizontal tubes from which branches extend up into the water. These branches have an opening, the *osculum*, at the distal end, and *buds* and *branches* projecting from their sides. The buds and branches are hollow, possessing a single spongocoel, which communicates with the horizontal tubes. The entire mass is a colony of animals, and the tissues connected with a single osculum may be considered an individual sponge.

If a branch is examined under a microscope, it will be found to contain a large number of three-pronged (triradiate) *spicules*, which are embedded in the soft tissues of the body wall (Fig. 2–2); these serve to strengthen the body and hold it upright. The application of acid results in the dissolution of these spicules and the production of an effervescence, thus proving them to be composed of calcium carbonate. The body wall is so flimsy that it is difficult to study even under the best conditions. It is made up of two layers of cells (Fig. 2–3): an outer layer, the *epidermis*, and an inner *choanocyte layer*. These layers, as will be shown later are not comparable to the epidermis and gastro-dermis of the Coelenterata and other Metazoa. Between these two layers is a jelly-like substance similar to the mesoglea of *Hydra* in which are many *amoeba-like wandering* cells (*amoebocytes*).

The choanocyte layer is peculiar, since it consists of a single layer of *collar cells*, the *choanocytes* (Fig. 2–3), which resemble the similar cells of the choanoflagellate Protozoa (Fig. 1–11, B). The flagella of these collar cells beat constantly, creating a current of water.

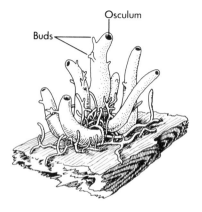

Fig. 2-1. *Leucosolenia:* a small colony. (From Woodruff.)

Area with inner cell layer indicated

Amoebocyte

Choanocytes

Porocyte

Triradiate spicule
Quadriradiate spicule

Fig. 2-2. Portion of body wall of *Leucosolenia*.

If a little coloring matter is placed in the water, it will be drawn into the animal through minute intracellular *incurrent pores*, the *ostia* (Fig. 2–3), in the body wall and will pass out through the openings in a sievelike membrane stretched across the osculum. The osculum is therefore the *exhalant opening*, and not the mouth, as a casual examination might lead one to believe. The course of the current of water in such a sponge is shown by arrows in Figure 2–18, A. The presence of the incurrent pores suggested the name Porifera for members of this phylum.

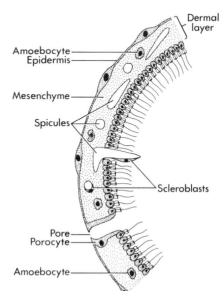

Dermal layer

Amoebocyte
Epidermis

Mesenchyme

Spicules

Scleroblasts

Pore
Porocyte

Amoebocyte

Fig. 2-3. Structure of body wall of an ascon sponge. (From Kerr.)

(2) Scypha

Scypha (*Sycon*) (Fig. 2–4) is a simple sponge inhabiting the salt water along the coast of the New England states just below the low-tide mark. Here it is found permanently attached by one end to rocks and other solid objects. Its distribution in space is effected during the early embryonic stages, at which time external flagella are present, enabling it to swim about. It is closely related to the European genus *Grantia*.

Morphology.   *Scypha* varies in length from one half an inch to almost an inch, and resembles in shape a slender vase that bulges slightly near the center. The distal end of the animal opens to the exterior by a large *excurrent pore*, the *osculum*. This opening is surrounded on all sides by a circlet of long straight needles called *spicules*. Smaller spicules protrude from other parts of the body, giving the animal a ciliated appearance. The body wall is perforated by numerous *incurrent pores*.

A specimen of *Scypha* split longitudinally (Fig. 2–4) shows the body to be a hollow sac, one large central cavity, the *spongocoel* being present. The body wall is honeycombed by a great many canals; some of these, the *radial canals*, open to the spongocoel through minute pores, the *apopyles*, and end blindly near the outer surface; others, the *incurrent canals*, open to the outside through incurrent pores or *ostia*, and end blindly near the inner surface of the body wall; still other canals, the *prosopyles*, even smaller than those already noted, connect the radial with the incurrent canal. Figure 2–4, B shows in cross-section the structure of a simple sponge. Discharging into the spongocoel are the radial canals. The body wall is seen to be crowded with both radial and incurrent canals, which have been cut lengthwise. The relations of the various canals to one another are shown in Figure 2–18; here the arrows indicate the direction of the current of water, which enters the incurrent canal, passes through the prosopyles into the radial canal, and thence into the spongocoel, finally escaping from the body by way of the osculum. The surface area of the epithelium covering the body, and lining the internal cavities, is enormously increased by the canal system.

Scypha is an animal possessing an outer dermal layer of cells, an inner choanocyte layer, and a middle region containing cells of several varieties (Fig. 2–5). The *epidermis* covers the entire outer surface of the body, and lines the incurrent canals. It is composed externally of a single layer of flat cells. Numerous prosopyles occur connecting the incurrent with the radial canals. The prosopyle is an intercellular perforation. Cells, called *scleroblasts*, which produce spicules, are also considered constituents of the dermal layer.

The *choanocyte layer* lines the radial canals. It consists of one layer of collared flagellated cells (Figs. 2–5 and 2–6), the *choancocytes*. The collar of these cells consists of from 20 to 30 protoplasmic fingers fused side by side and capable of contraction. No collar cells are present in the epithelium lining

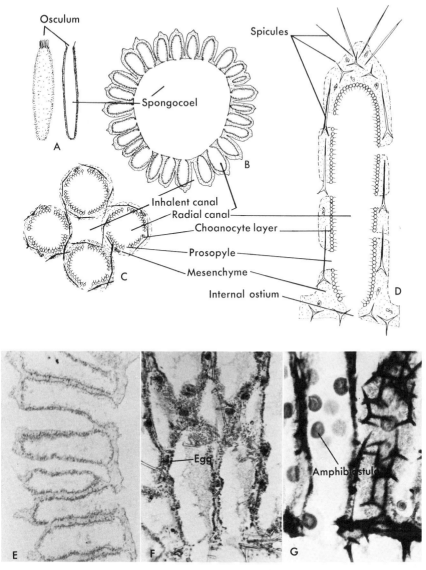

Fig. 2-4. *Scypha.* (A) Entire animal and longitudinal section. (B) Cross-section. (C) Tangential section through canals. (D) Section along a radial canal. (E) Part of wall in cross-section; (F) with eggs; (G) with amphiblastula. (A–D) Diagrammatic, (E–G) photomicrographs.

the spongocoel. The flagella of the collar cells create the current of water continually flowing through the body wall into the spongocoel and out of the osculum.

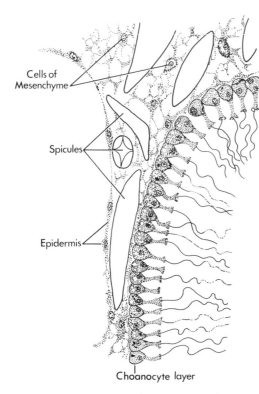

Cells of
Mesenchyme

Spicules

Epidermis

Choanocyte layer

Fig. 2-5. *Grantia:* Part of body wall. (From Dahlgren and Kepner.)

The *middle region* of the body wall, although not so definite nor firm in structure as the outer and inner epithelia, contains cells and much non-cellular material. *Amoebocytes*, which ingest food or act as storage cells, are found here; some serve as the *reproductive cells*, which always arise in the middle layer.

The soft body wall of *Scypha* is supported and protected by a skeleton composed of a great number of *spicules* of carbonate of lime. Four varieties of spicules are always present, (1) long straight monaxon rods guarding the osculum, (2) short straight monaxon rods surrounding the incurrent pores, (3) triradiate spicules always found embedded in the body wall, and (4) T-shaped spicules lining the gastral cavity; four- and five-rayed spicules may also be present. Spicules are built up within cells called *scleroblasts* (Fig. 2–6), which form part of the inner stratum of the dermal layer. A slender organic axial thread is first built up within the cell; around this is deposited the calcareous matter; the whole spicule is then insheathed by an envelope of organic matter like that composing the axial thread. Scleroblasts begin spicule formation as binucleate cells, which form one axis of a spicule. The cell divides to form two cells as the spicule grows, one cell working at each end of the axis. Thus, a pair of cells participate in the formation of each axis, or two cells produce a monaxon spicule and six scleroblasts are needed to

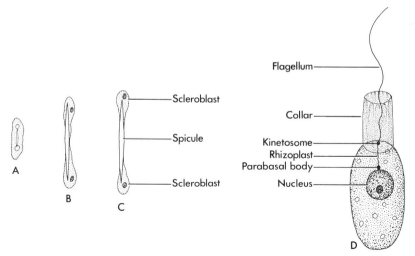

Fig. 2-6. Sponge cells, diagrammatic. (A–C) Scleroblasts secreting a monaxon spicule. (D) Choanocyte showing protoplasmic fingers of the collar.

produce a triradiate spicule. This view of spicule formation has been questioned by some observers.

Nutrition. *Scypha* lives upon the minute organisms and small particles of organic matter that are drawn into the incurrent canals by the current of water produced by the beating of the collar-cell flagella. Food particles are engulfed by the collar cells. *Digestion*, as in the Protozoa, is intracellular, food vacuoles being formed. The distribution of the nutriment is accomplished by the passage of digested food from cell to cell, aided by the amoeboid wandering cells of the middle layer.

Excretory matter is discharged through the general body surface, assisted probably by the amoeboid wandering cells, and possibly by the collar cells also. *Respiration* likewise takes place, in the absence of special organs, through the cells of the body wall.

Sponges do not possess differentiated *nervous organs*, but are able to respond to certain stimuli. The pores and oscula are surrounded by contractile cells, called *myocytes*, which are able to close these openings. Apparently these cells respond to direct stimulation, since no nervous tissue is present. They, therefore, represent what may be considered the very beginning of a neuromuscular mechanism.

Reproduction. Reproduction in *Scypha* takes place by both sexual and asexual methods. In the latter case, a bud arises near the point of attachment, finally becomes free, and takes up a separate existence.

The *sexual reproductive cells* develop in the middle layer of the body wall. Both eggs and sperms occur in a single individual, i.e., *Scypha* is *monoecious* or *hermaphroditic.* In *spermatogenesis* the primordial germ cell, called a spermatogonium, divides, producing a covering cell, the spermatocyst, and a central sperm mother cell, the spermatocyte. The latter forms a number of spermatids by mitosis; these transform into spermatozoa. The *ova* arise by the growth of *oogonia* of the middle layer, which are nourished by neighboring cells. The oogonium divides twice to produce four ova. Spermatozoa are carried to the ova by choanocytes, which become modified into amoeboid cells when the spermatozoans adhere to them.

Embryology (Fig. 2–7). The development of the fertilized egg has been observed in *Scypha.* The egg segments by three vertical divisions into a pyramidal plate of eight cells. A horizontal division now cuts off a small cell from the top of each of the eight, the result being a layer of eight large cells,

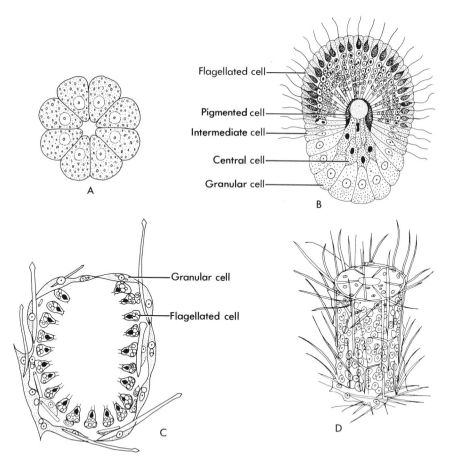

Flagellated cell

Pigmented cell
Intermediate cell

Central cell

Granular cell

A

B

Granular cell

Flagellated cell

C

D

Fig. 2-7. Embryology of sponges. (A) An egg of *Sycandra* that has reached the eight-cell stage. (B) An amphiblastula larva of *Leucosolenia.* (C) Young *Leucosolenia,* four days old. (D) Older stage in *Sycon raphanus.* (A, D, after Schulze; B, C, after Minchin.)

or macromeres, crowned by a layer of eight small cells, or micromeres. The cells now become arranged about a central cavity, producing a *blastula-like sphere*. The small cells multiply rapidly and develop flagella extending into the interior cavity, while the macromeres become granular. A mouthlike opening into the central cavity develops between the micromeres. The embryo is then known as a *stomatoblastula* and is able to engulf maternal amoebocytes for nutrition. Then follows a process of inversion in which the embryo turns itself inside out through the mouth. The inverted embryo, with flagella on the micromeres now directed outward and one hemisphere still composed of eight macromeres, is called an *amphiblastula*. The mass of cells then becomes disk-shaped by the pushing in of the flagellated cells. Two layers are thus formed, between which the middle layer arises. The invaginated side soon becomes attached, and the embryo lengthens into a cylinder at the distal end of which a new opening, the osculum, appears. In the meantime, spicules and the canal system arise in the body wall.

2 / Class III. Demospongiae

(1) Spongilla

Spongilla (Figs. 2–8 and 2–9) is a common, widely distributed, fresh-water sponge. It has a more complex level of canal system development than either

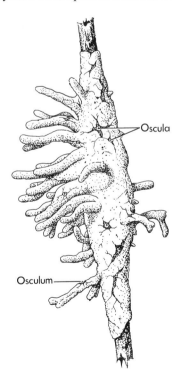

Oscula

Osculum

Fig. 2-8. *Spongilla lacustris*, a fresh-water sponge. (After Weltner.)

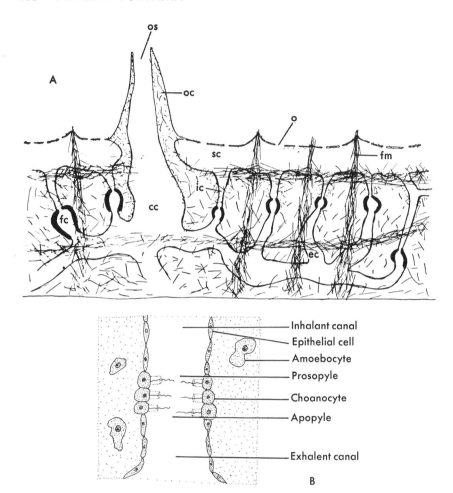

Fig. 2-9. *Spongilla*. (A) Diagrammatic section of peripheral portion of a typical fresh-water sponge. Heavy black lines represent layers of choanocytes lining flagellated chambers. Delicate matrix of spongin not shown. cc, central cavity; ec, excurrent canal; fc, flagellated chamber; fm, fascicle of megascleres; ic, incurrent canal; o, ostium; oc, oscular chimney; os, osculum; sc, subdermal cavity. (B) Enlarged diagram of a flagellated chamber. (A, from Robert W. Pennak. *Fresh-water Invertebrates of the United States.* Copyright 1953 by The Ronald Press Company, New York.)

Leucosolenia or *Scypha*. The choanocytes are restricted to small chambers in the interior. The flagellated chambers propel the water through the canal system of the sponge. The sponges are encrusting in habit and are commonly found on sticks that have been submerged for some time.

Siliceous spicules of *Spongilla* are of the monaxon (one axis, or rodlike) type and of two general sizes. Larger skeletal spicules, called *megascleres*, are held together by spongin fibers and provide support for the colony.

Micropyle of
Heteromeyenia gemmule

Compound gemmules
of Spongilla

Fig. 2-10. Gemmules of fresh-water sponges. (A) *Heteromeyenia*. (B–C) *Spongilla*.

Smaller flesh spicules, called *microscleres*, are embedded in cells of the sponge.

Water enters the colony through numerous dermal pores or *ostia*. From subdermal cavities it enters the flagellated chambers through incurrent canals and leaves through excurrent canals to reach the spongocoel. The spongocoel opens to the exterior by a large opening, the *osculum*. The living portion of *Spongilla* is never more than a few centimeters thick, but a colony may encrust a many times greater area. An individual of the colony may be considered that portion of the sponge associated with one osculum.

Reproduction.   Asexual reproduction can result from regeneration of fragments by vegetative growth or by the development of new sponges from specialized structures termed gemmules. Sexual reproduction in *Spongilla* is probably similar to that process in *Scypha*.

Gemmules (Fig. 2–10) are asexual reproductive bodies resistant to adverse environmental conditions. They are formed by the sponge during the summer and fall and stored in its basal portion. *Amoebocytes* (archaeocytes) loaded with nutrients provide a core material capable of developing into a new sponge. Other amoebocytes secrete a *chitinous covering* and reinforcing *spicules*. A *micropyle*, or opening in the gemmule covering, provides an escape route for the archaeocytes after the winter quiescent period. Gemmules may be released from their location in the sponge by the decay of the parent during the late fall or winter. They provide an important means of dispersal for fresh-water sponges, because they can be carried passively by a wide variety of agents. Because the gemmules are distinctive in structure and spicule types for the different species, they have a great value in species identification. Organization of parts of the sponge, other than gemmules and spicules, shows too great variability to be of as much value in identification.

Embryology. Development of the sponge from the amphiblastula of *Spongilla* differs from that described for *Scypha* in that the flagellated cells from the exterior do not produce the choanocytes. The choanocytes that line the flagellated chambers develop from cells in the interior of the amphiblastula larva.

3 / Other Porifera

Class I. Calcarea

The Calcarea are all marine and live in shallow water. They are comparatively simple in structure. Two orders and about 150 species are known. As their name indicates their chief characteristic is the presence of calcareous spicules.

Order 1. Homocoela. The 50 species in this order are the simplest of all sponges and may be separated into two families, the Leucosoleniidae and the Clathrinidae (Fig. 2–11). The characteristics of the order have been presented by *Leucosolenia* as a type. The body wall is thin; the spongocoel is lined with collar cells and each pore is a perforation in a single cell.

Order 2. Heterocoela (Fig. 2–11). *Scypha* (*Sycon*) has served to introduce this order consisting of about one hundred species. The body wall is thickened:

B   A   C

Fig. 2-11. Types of Calcarea. (A) Homocoela. *Clathrina lacunosa.* (B) Heterocoela. *Grantia labyrinthica;* three stages of growth. (C) Heterocoela. *Leuconia aspera.* (A, C, after Minchin; B, after Dendy.)

the spongocoel is lined with flattened epithelial cells and the collar cells are located in radial canals or chambers. *Scypha ciliata* occurs from Rhode Island to Greenland; *Leuconia* (*Leucandra*) *taylori* lives off the shore of Vancouver Island; and *Amphoriscus thompsoni* in the Gulf of St. Lawrence.

Class II. Hexactinellida

To this class belong the glass sponges. They are mostly deep-sea inhabitants and widely distributed. Their fossil remains are abundant and indicate that they have always been present in large numbers. They are characterized by the possession of siliceous spicules of the triaxon type, that is, with six rays or a multiple of six. The body is often tubular or basket-shaped and the spicules may form a continuous skeleton resembling spun glass. Venus' flower basket, *Euplectella aspergillum* (Fig. 2–12), is especially abundant near the Philippine Islands; its skeleton is often seen in museums. It has a long, curved, cylindrical body held up by a framework of spicules. In nature it is fastened in the mud of the sea bottom by a mass of long siliceous threads at the posterior end. The body wall, as in all Hexactinellida, contains simple thimble-shaped flagellated chambers. The large spongocoel often serves as a residence for a pair of decapod crustaceans, *Spongicola venusta*. *Euplectella suberea* occurs in the West Indies. Another American hexactinellid is

Fig. 2-12. Hexactinellida. *Euplectella:* the "Venus' flower basket" sponge.

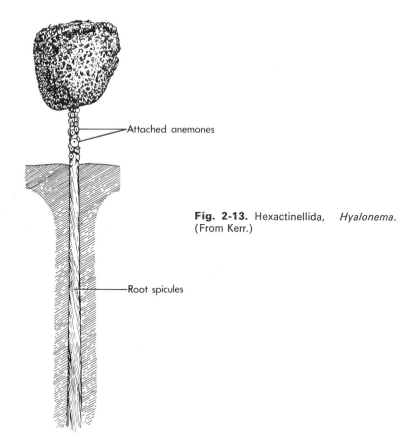

Attached anemones

Root spicules

Fig. 2-13. Hexactinellida, *Hyalonema.* (From Kerr.)

Hyalonema longissimum (Fig. 2–13), which lives off the New England coast at depths of from 60 to 95 fathoms.

Class III. Demospongiae

These are the dominant Porifera of the present time, being widespread in nature and very numerous in species and individuals. Most of the sponges that are generally seen belong to this class. They are often massive and brightly colored, with complicated canal systems connected with small spherical flagellated chambers. The skeleton may consist of siliceous spicules, but these are not triaxon as in the Hexactinellida. Spongin, a substance similar to collagen, may provide all of the skeleton or be combined with siliceous spicules. Some spicules are straight and needle-shaped (monaxon); others have eight rays (tetraxon). They have a parenchymula larval stage.

Order 1. Tetraxonida (Fig. 2–14).   Sponges in the order Tetraxonida live mostly at depths of 50 to 200 fathoms and are usually attached to the bottom by tufts of spicules. They are usually compact and rounded. The outer,

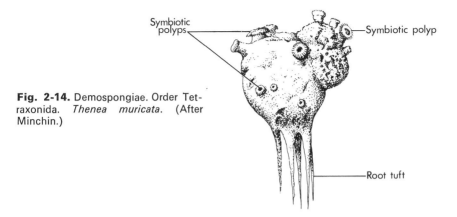

Symbiotic polyps

Symbiotic polyp

Root tuft

Fig. 2-14. Demospongiae. Order Tetraxonida. *Thenea muricata*. (After Minchin.)

dermal layer of the body, the cortex, is thickened and contains skeletal spicules, megascleres, which unite to form the supporting framework. Other spicules, microscleres, lie scattered in the mesoglea. These spicules are modifications of the tetraxon type. Among the members of this order from America are *Thenea echinata*, which occurs on the New England coast north of Cape Cod and is shaped like a mushroom; and *Geodia mülleri*, which is found in the West Indies and is irregularly lobed.

Order 2. Monaxonida (Figs. 2–15 and 2–16). The order Monaxonida contains most of the living species of sponges. They usually inhabit shallow

Oscula

Stalk

Fig. 2-15. Demospongiae. Order Monaxonida. *Chalina oculata*. (After Minchin.)

Fig. 2-16. Demospongiae. Order Monaxonida. (A) *Esperiopsis challengeri.* (B) *Phakellia ventilabrum.* (C) *Tethya lyncurium.* (A, after Ridley, from Minchin; B, C, after Minchin.)

water including one family in fresh water. Their spicules are of the monaxon type. Spongin may be present. In one of the two suborders there is a hard, outer cortex absent from the other suborder. *Suberites compacta* is an American species that ranges from Virginia to Maine with a related sponge on the West Coast. It has a bright yellow, elongated body that may reach a length of 15 cm and is often attached by one edge to the shells of hermit crabs. Another species with a similar range is *Polymastia robusta.* This is a yellowish or grayish species of irregular form with finger-like branches. It reaches a diameter of 30 cm. *Cliona celata*, the sulphur sponge, occurs along our eastern and western coasts. It is bright yellow in color and may form a mass up to 20 cm in diameter. The young clionas are able to bore their way into calcareous rocks or the shells of mollusks forming tunnels in which they live. *Chalina oculata* (Fig. 2–15) is the finger sponge, so named because of its being shaped like a hand with many fingers. The skeleton is of spongin in which siliceous spicules are embedded. It is orange or red in color and is common from Rhode Island to Labrador. *Microciona prolifera* is a bright red species that forms digitate masses up to 51 cm in height on shells and stones and is abundant in Long Island Sound. *Mycale adherens* can be found on the shells of *Pecten* along the West Coast. *Mycale fibrexilis* occurs on the docks at Woods Hole, Mass. It is yellowish-brown in color and irregular in shape and may be covered with hydroids and algae.

Fresh-Water Sponges. These belong to the family Spongillidae in the order Monaxonida. They are usually to be found in clear water encrusting stones, sticks, and plants; but may also occur on the soft mud bottom and in highly colored water and even in waters contaminated by industrial and organic wastes. Fresh-water sponges are usually yellow, brown, or green. The green color is due to the presence of Zoochlorellae. These sponges reproduce by the formation of gemmules and the characteristics of these gemmules are the chief means of identification. More than 20 species occur in this country. Some of the more common are as follows. *Spongilla lacustris* (Fig. 2–8) is the most abundant species. It prefers running water, is a branching form that lives in sunlight, and is usually green. *S. fragilis* is also a common species, but prefers standing water and avoids the light. All fresh-water sponges, except *Spongilla*, have birotulate gemmule spicules. Such spicules have a whorl (of spines, usually) at each end of a shaft (Fig. 2–20). *Meyenia mulleri* is cushion-shaped and rarely branched. It is usually yellow or brown in color and prefers standing water. *Heteromeyenia ryderi* lives in shallow flowing water, is light green, and is massive in type. *Tubella pennsylvanica* lives in shallow water, is gray or green, and is only about 6 mm in diameter. It is averse to light and lives usually under stones and roots. *Carterius tentaspermus* is an irregularly shaped sponge, yellowish-green, that encrusts plants, roots, and stones. It occurs in the eastern United States.

Fig. 2-17. Demospongiae. (A) Keratosa. *Spongia officinalis,* a bath sponge. (B) Myxospongida. *Oscarella lobularis.* (After Schulze, from Minchin.)

Order 3. Keratosa. Everyone is familiar with the skeletons of certain members of this order, because the commercial sponges belong to this group. They occur in tropical and subtropical seas and are characterized by a lack of siliceous spicules but with a skeleton of spongin. About a dozen species of these horny sponges are used by man. These belong to the genera *Spongia*, *Hippospongia*, and *Coscinoderma*. The best sponges come from the Mediterranean and belong to the species *Spongia officinalis mollissima* (Fig. 2–17) and *S. o. adriatica*. The glove sponge, *S. tubulifera*, is an American species of little commercial value.

Order 4. Myxospongida (Fig. 2–17). Comparatively few sponges without any skeleton, and hence encrusting in habit, belong to this order. *Halisarca dujardini*, a slime sponge with elongate, saclike flagellated chambers is an American species living on red algae at a depth of about 5 fathoms off the coast of Rhode Island. *H. sacra* occurs off the coast of California.

4 / Sponges in General

External Features. Sponges may be simple, thin-walled tubular structures like *Leucosolenia* and *Scypha* or massive and more or less irregular in shape. Many sponges are indefinite masses of tissue encrusting the stones, shells, sticks, or plants to which they are attached; others are more regular in shape and attached to the sea bottom by means of masses of spicules. The form exhibited by the members of each species may vary somewhat but is nevertheless constant. Some are branched like trees; others are shaped like a glove, or a cup, or a dome. Sponges vary in size from species no larger than a pinhead to species that attain a diameter of 3 feet and a thickness of 12 inches. Certain sponges appear to be ciliated because of the spicules that protrude from the body. Many sponges are white or gray, but others are colored yellow, orange, red, or green. Green sponges usually owe their color to the green symbiotic algae, Zoochlorellae, contained in them.

Canal Systems. If it were not for the development of elaborate canal systems sponges would have remained in the simple condition of *Leucosolenia* and would never have been able to become massive in size. The canal system serves much the same purposes as the circulatory system does in higher animals; it furnishes a highway for food through the body and for the transportation of excretory matter out of the body. Three morphological types are usually recognized.

The ascon type (Fig. 2–18, A) consists of incurrent pores, a spongocoel lined with collar cells, and an osculum.

The sycon type (Fig. 2–18, B) is more complicated; the water flows through the dermal pores (ostia) into the incurrent canals; then through the chamber pores (prosopyles) into radial canals lined with collar cells; from here it is

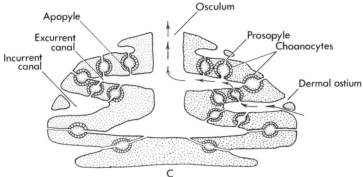

Fig. 2-18. Sponge canal system types. (A) *Ascon* type. (B) *Sycon* type. (C) *Rhagon* type.

propelled by the flagella of the choanocytes into the spongocoel, finally passing out through the osculum.

In the leucon (rhagon) type (Fig. 2–18, C) there are three distinct parts: (1) the water passes through the dermal ostia and by way of incurrent canals reaches (2) a number of small chambers lined with choanocytes, thence it is carried through (3) an excurrent system to the spongocoel and finally out of the osculum.

Skeletal Systems.   All sponges, except those belonging to the small order Myxospongida, are provided with a skeleton. This may consist of carbonate of lime or silicon in the form of spicules or of spongin in the form of fibers more or less closely united. Siliceous spicules are composed of opal, a form of hydrated silica similar to quartz in its chemical reactions. Spicules are of various types and hence of value in arranging sponges into groups. As already noted, the spicules in the class Calcarea are calcareous; those in the class

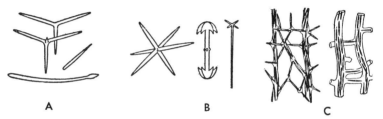

Fig. 2-19. Spicules of sponges. (A) Calcareous spicules (*Leucosolenia*). (B) Siliceous spicules (*Hyalonema*). (C) Siliceous spicules with spongin (*Pachychalina* and *Chalina*). (From Kerr.)

Hexactinellida are of the triaxon type; and those in the class Demospongiae are not triaxon, some being straight and needle-shaped (monaxon) and others eight-rayed (tetraxon). In the Demospongiae, spongin may be present with or without spicules in addition. Spongin is a substance chemically allied to collagen. It is secreted by flask-shaped cells called spongoblasts. Spicules are deposited in cells called scleroblasts and more than one cell may take part in the formation of a single spicule. The carbonate of lime or silicon is, of course, extracted from the surrounding water by the cells. Some of the principal types of spicules are illustrated in Figure 2–19. The arrangement of spongin fibers can be observed easily by placing a minute piece of a bath sponge under the microscope. Massive sponges could never have evolved if it were not for

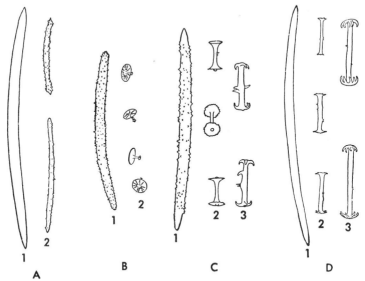

Fig. 2-20. Spicules of fresh-water sponges. (A) *Spongilla fragilis:* 1, skeleton spicule; 2, gemmule spicules. (B) *Tubella pennsylvanica:* 1, skeleton spicule; 2, gemmule spicules. (C) *Heteromeyenia ryderi:* 1, skeleton spicule; 2, short gemmule spicules; 3, long gemmule spicules. (D) *Heteromeyenia repens:* 1, skeleton spicule; 2, short gemmule spicules; 3, long gemmule spicules. (After Old.)

spicules and spongin which form a skeleton that holds the body in shape preventing it from collapsing into a mass of jellylike consistency in which canals and flagellated chambers could not possibly exist.

Histology.   Sponges are many-celled animals in which the somatic cells are differentiated into types for the performance of special functions; that is, division of labor among somatic cells has developed. This is a distinct and important advance over the condition existing even among such complex Protozoa as *Volvox*.

The cells of sponges may be separated into three groups: (1) those of the dermal, or covering, layer; (2) those of the choanocyte layer; and (3) those of the mesenchyme. The principal cell type of the dermal layer is the *pinacocyte*. These are flattened epithelial cells with moderate powers of contraction. Tuzet (1963) has observed them entering the mesenchyme to become nerve cells. However, no physiological evidence of nerve cells exists for sponges. *Porocytes*, which are pierced by an opening which passes through them, conduct water through the three layers in the primitive sponges. Porocytes can constrict sufficiently to close the pore. They are thought to be formed from pinacocytes. *Scleroblasts* secrete the skeletal material. Contractile cells and gland cells also occur in the dermal layer.

The choanocyte layer is composed of choanocytes. The mesenchyme contains much jelly-like material and some cells. The cells are amoebocytes and reproductive cells. The amoebocytes are of several types and it is thought that one or two of them are undifferentiated cells (archaeocytes) capable of becoming the other cell types.

Nutrition.   Sponges obtain their food in the form of minute organic particles, living or lifeless, which enter the incurrent pores suspended in water, and are carried into the flagellated chambers. The current of water flowing through the canal system of the sponge is created by the flagella of the choanocytes which beat continuously. The choanocytes also ingest the food particles either at the side or within the collar; a food vacuole is formed in which digestion takes place and the undigested residue is cast out from inside of the collar. The nutriment is passed from cell to cell and is circulated to a certain extent by the amoeboid wandering cells of the mesenchyme. It is necessary for the sponge to live in water that is circulating more or less, hence we find these animals in clear, not muddy water. Because the current of water passing through the sponge carries with it the excretions from the body, it is important that the water passing out of the osculum be forced away from the body, since it contains no more food particles but is loaded with wastes. Sponges are therefore so organized and so adapted to their environment that they are able to separate efficiently the water forced out of the osculum from that drawn in through the incurrent pores. This is accomplished by different species in different ways. The force and direction of the jet from the osculum is an important feature; also the nature of the currents at the bottom of the sea. It has been experimentally demonstrated that in *Stylotella* the pressure within the flagellated chambers is equivalent to a column of water 3.5 to 4.0 mm in height. In another sponge, *Spinosella*, the osculum discharged about 0.9 c.mm of water per second, or 78 liters per day. An average-sized specimen of *Spinosella* with 20 oscula would thus pass about 45 gallons of water through its canal system per day.

Behavior. Sponges are comparatively inactive animals. The larvae are ciliated and swim about but soon become attached to some solid object and remain fixed for life. At the time of fixation the young sponge may move for a short distance as a result of movements of the cells of attachment and thus reach a position where light and other conditions are more satisfactory. Thus, the young sponge that develops from a gemmule of *Spongilla* may move up the side of an aquarium. Certain adult sponges are capable of slight bending movements.

Activity is more pronounced within the body of sponges. This is due to the presence of contractile cells, the myocytes, which are arranged about the osculum and pores and in the wall of the canals in the form of sphincter-like bands. Stimuli of various sorts applied directly to these sphincters result in the opening and closing of the osculum, pores, and canals and in changes in the flow of water. Thus, the osculum of *Stylotella* closes when the animal is transferred from moving into quiet water but opens when a current of water strikes it directly. Transmission to other oscula does not occur. There appears, however, to be present a sluggish type of transmission through the protoplasm. Until additional studies refute the long claimed absence of nerve cells in sponges it would seem that, in most sponges, this is transmission without differentiated nervous elements such as are present in neural transmission. Studies of the behavior of sponges indicate that no true nervous elements exist. Sponges, therefore, have cells that act as effectors but no receptors or adjustors.

Reproduction and Growth. Reproduction in sponges is either asexual or sexual. By the asexual method there are produced buds and gemmules. Buds may be set free to take up a separate existence, or, as in *Leuco-solenia*, may remain attached to the parent sponge. Often a complex assemblage of individuals is produced that may become very large.

Many marine and fresh-water sponges have a peculiar method of reproduction by the formation of gemmules. A number of cells in the middle layer of the body wall gather into a ball and become surrounded by a layer of cells which secrete a shell reinforced by spicules. In *Spongilla* the gemmules may possess a peripheral layer containing air cells that float them on the surface, and also rodlike spicules. These gemmules (Fig. 2–10) are formed during the summer and autumn. In the spring they develop into new sponges and are hence of value in carrying the race through a period of adverse conditions, such as the winter season. Young sponges that chance to become attached near together tend to coalesce.

In sexual reproduction the eggs and spermatozoa are derived as in *Scypha* from amoeboid wandering cells or modified choanocytes in the middle layer. A flagellated larva is produced from a holoblastic egg. This larva swims about for a period of time, thus effecting the dispersal of the species, then becomes fixed and passes through many changes, finally developing ostia and an osculum which are necessary for the nutritive processes and growth.

A peculiarity in the embryology of certain sponges is this: the flagellated cells of the larva do not become the outer (dermal) epithelium as do the flagellated cells of the larval coelenterate, but produce the inner layer of choanocytes; and the inner cells do not become the inner epithelium, as do the similarly situated cells in the coelenterate, but produce the dermal layer. It, therefore, seems impossible to homologize the ectoderm and endoderm of coelenterates and other Metazoa with the layers in the sponge larva, because the outer layer (ectoderm?) of the latter becomes the inner layer (endoderm?) of the adult sponge. The outer layer is consequently termed "dermal epithelium" instead of "ectoderm," and the inner epithelium instead of "endoderm" is the choanocyte layer. With no digestive tract the choanocyte layer cannot properly be called gastrodermis.

The size and rate of growth of sponges depend on the species and largely on the nature of the environment. Annual sponges, that is, those that live one year or less are naturally smaller than perennials. Sponges may increase in weight as much as 40 per cent in a single day. Cuttings of bath sponges in Florida increased from $2\frac{1}{2}$ cubic inches to $12\frac{1}{2}$ cubic inches in 2 months. Certain commercial sponges, such as the wool sponges of the Caribbean Sea, grow to be $2\frac{1}{2}$ feet in diameter and 25 years of age.

Aggregates of Sponge Cells. Experiments with certain sponges (*Stylotella, Microciona,* etc.) prove that when a specimen is broken up and strained through fine bolting cloth so as to dissociate the cells, the cells will fuse on the bottom of a dish to form plasmodia. These plasmodia in the course of several months acquire canals, flagellated chambers, and a skeleton and develop reproductive bodies. The aggregation of these cells appears to be due to amoebocytes from the middle layer which move about and gather in all the cells they encounter. When cells from two species are intermingled those of each species fuse with one another but not with those of the other species. These studies provide a remarkable case of what is known as regulation, whereby parts of an organism regain all of the characteristics of the species.

Position of Sponges in the Animal Kingdom. As already noted, although sponges are undoubtedly multicellular animals, they are often separated from the Metazoa and placed in an isolated group, the Parazoa, near the foot of

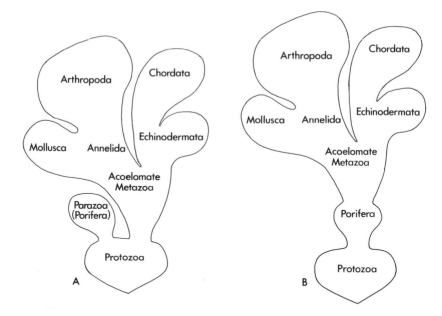

Fig. 2-21. Diagram of suggested phylogenetic positions of the Porifera. (A) Conventional view of sponges as an isolated subkingdom, the Parazoa. (B) Tuzet's view of sponges in the mainstream of metazoan evolution.

the family tree. This is because they are supposed to have branched off from the main evolutionary series at this point and to have given rise to nothing but sponges.

The recent suggestion of Tuzet (1963) that the Porifera gave rise to the other Metazoa (Fig. 2–21, B) via the Coelenterata has some evidence to support it also. The choanocyte, or collared flagellated cells, are not restricted to sponges, as is commonly stated. Similar cells have been reported in some echinoderms. Cells with a single flagellum occur in the coelenterates. Spermatogenesis and oogenesis resemble the same processes in other metazoans. Histological and cytological details show similarities with the metazoans, especially the recently established chemical and physical resemblance between spongin and collagen (an important constituent of vertebrate connective tissue). In either view the development of organ systems and movement characteristic of the remaining phyla could justify retention of the Protozoa, Parazoa, Metazoa concept.

The protozoan origin of the sponges seems clearly indicated when we examine some of the flagellated Protozoa, especially those with collar cells and colonial in habit, like *Proterospongia* (Fig. 2–22). This protozoan not only possesses choanocytes like those of sponges but cells within the colony that resemble those in the middle layer of sponges. It is not difficult to imagine such an organism developing into a sponge.

Fig. 2-22. *Proterospongia haeckeli.* (After Kent.)

The Relation of Sponges to Other Animals and to Man. Because of their habitat sponges are associated principally with aquatic animals. These seldom feed on sponges because of their skeletons of spicules and spongin and because of the distasteful substances they excrete. A number of animals such as hydroids, sea-anemones, polychaete worms, ophiuroids, and crustaceans live, in more or less commensal or symbiotic relations, in the canals or cloaca of sponges.

Sponges are mostly beneficial to man. They may destroy oysters and other bivalves by covering their shells and depriving them of food; but, on the other hand, they supply us with the sponges of commerce, which are the spongin skeletons of certain species living chiefly near the shore of the Mediterranean Sea, and the coast of Australia, the Bahama Islands, Cuba, and Florida. Sponge culture, i.e., the growing of sponges from cuttings, has been developed with some success.

The study of sponge regulation, regeneration, grafting, and development holds promise of revealing basic biological facts of value to medical science especially in the areas of diseases of connective tissue and tissue transplantation.

The History of Our Knowledge of Porifera. Although sponges have been recognized since at least the time of Aristotle (384–322 B.C.) they were not proved to be animals until 1857. Ellis in 1765 appears to have been the first to describe the current of water entering and leaving a sponge. This was worked out more fully by Grant (1825) who observed the incurrent pores and oscula and suggested that the currents were due to ciliary action. After the recognition of the animal nature of sponges, their position in the animal kingdom became an important subject. The embryology of sponges as worked out by Schulze (1878), Bütschli (1884), Solas (1884), Minchin (1897), Maas (1898), and Delage (1898) indicated fundamental differences between them and other Metazoa which has led to their being considered a separate group and called Parazoa.

Classification. Sponges constitute a distinct phylum of animals. They are all multicellular and the somatic cells are arranged in two layers (diploblastic), an outer dermal and an inner choanocyte layer. The cells in these layers are further differentiated for various functions. The body is asymmetrical or radially symmetrical; it is perforated by incurrent pores usually opening into canals or chambers lined with flagellated collar cells (choanocytes), and is, in most species, supported by a skeleton of spicules or spongin or both. The classes and orders are separated for the most part on the basis of the material composing the skeleton and the shape of the spicules.

The conventional classification of the sponges which is given below has rather artificial groupings within the Demospongiae. Study of tissue cultures of sponges coupled with other investigations will eventually make a more accurate phylogenetic classification possible. For example, the Keratosa seem to represent a group that developed from several separate lines by the loss of spicules. Thus, the dramatic lack of spicules may have overshadowed a closer resemblance, in other ways, to forms with spicules. Future revision will probably include increased subdivision of the following groups.

CLASS I. CALCAREA. Marine species, mostly white or gray, living in shallow water; spicules of carbonate of lime, either monaxon or tetraxon; flagellated chambers large.

ORDER 1. HOMOCOELA. Choanocyte layer continuous. Ex. *Leucosolenia* (Fig. 2–1).

ORDER 2. HETEROCOELA. Choanocyte layer discontinuous and restricted to flagellated chambers. Ex. *Scypha* (Fig. 2–4).

CLASS II. HEXACTINELLIDA. Deep-sea sponges; spicules triaxon, of silicon; canal system with thimble-shaped chambers. Ex. *Euplectella*, Venus' flower basket (Fig. 2–12).

CLASS III. DEMOSPONGIAE. Skeleton of siliceous spicules, not triaxon, or with spongin, or with both spicules and spongin; canal system derived from rhagon type (Fig. 2–18): most highly organized of phylum; majority of existing sponges.

ORDER 1. TETRAXONIDA. Typically with tetraxon spicules. Ex. *Thenea* (Fig. 2–14).

ORDER 2. MONAXONIDA. With monaxon, but no tetraxon spicules. All fresh-water sponges belong to this order. Ex. *Spongilla lacustris* (Fig. 2–8).

ORDER 3. KERATOSA. Main skeleton of spongin. Ex. *Spongia officinalis*, the bath sponge (Fig. 2–17).

ORDER 4. MYXOSPONGIDA. Without skeleton; encrusting in habit. Ex. *Oscarella* (Fig. 2–17).

References to Literature on the Porifera

GALTSOFF, P. S. 1925. Regeneration after dissociation. *J. Exp. Zool.*, **42**:183–251.

HYMAN, L. H. 1940. *The Invertebrates: Protozoa Through Ctenophora.* Vol. I. McGraw-Hill, New York. 726 pp.

JEWELL, M. 1959. Porifera. pp. 298–312. In W. T. EDMONDSON. *Fresh-Water Biology.* 2nd Ed. Wiley, New York. 1248 pp.

LEVI, C. 1963. Gastrulation and larval phylogeny in sponges. pp. 375–382. In E. DOUGHERTY. *The Lower Metazoa.* Univ. Calif., Berkeley. 478 pp.

PARIS, J. 1961. Greffes et sérologie chez les Éponges siliceuses. *Vie et Milieu,* supp. no. 11, 74 pp.

PENNAK, R. W. 1953. *Fresh-Water Invertebrates of the United States.* Ronald Press, New York. 769 pp.

PENNY, J. T. 1960. Distribution and bibliography (1892–1957) of the fresh water sponges. *Univ. S. Carolina Publ. Biology. Ser. III,* **3**:1–97.

RASMONT, R. 1962. The physiology of gemmulation in sponges. In D. RUDNICK. *Regeneration.* Ronald Press, New York. 250 pp.

SIMPSON, T. L. 1965. Sponge cells and the taxonomy of sponges. *Am. Zool.,* **5**:216–217.

TUZET, O. 1963. The phylogeny of sponges according to embryological, histological, and serological data, and their affinities with the Protozoa and the Cnidaria. pp. 129–148. In E. DOUGHERTY. *The Lower Metazoa.* Univ. Calif., Berkeley. 478 pp.

Chapter III

Phylum Coelenterata

THE PHYLUM Coelenterata (or Cnidaria) includes the polyps, jellyfishes, sea anemones, and corals. All of these animals have a body wall consisting of two layers of cells, between which is a jellylike substance, the mesoglea. Within the body is a single gastrovascular cavity, or coelenteron. Because of the presence of two cellular layers, coelenterates are said to have a tissue-level organization. They are also acoelomates, i.e., they do not possess a second body cavity, the coelom. All coelenterates are provided with nematocysts.

This phylum contains three classes, as follows:

CLASS I. HYDROZOA. This class includes the fresh-water polyps, the small jellyfishes, the hydroid zoophytes, and a few stony corals.

CLASS II. SCYPHOZOA. Most of the large jellyfishes are placed in this class.

CLASS III. ANTHOZOA. In this class are included the sea anemones, and most of the stony and horny corals.

In the following pages the fresh-water hydroid, *Hydra*, is described in detail because of its simplicity, abundance, and the ease with which it may be collected. *Obelia* represents a marine hydroid and *Gonionemus*, a hydroid jellyfish. The class Scyphozoa is introduced by the common large jellyfish, *Aurelia*, and the Anthozoa by a sea anemone, *Metridium*, and a coral, *Astrangia*.

1 / Class I. Hydrozoa

(1) Hydra—A Fresh-Water Hydrozoan

Hydra (Fig. 3–1) is a simple metazoan abundant in fresh-water ponds and streams. If a quantity of aquatic vegetation is gathered and placed in glass dishes full of water, these little fresh-water polyps may be found clinging to

Fig. 3-1. *Hydra oligactis.* (A) Hanging from a leaf with tentacles well extended. (B) Position assumed when contracted. (C) Male bearing many testes. (After Hyman.)

the plants and the sides and bottom of the dish. They are easily seen with the naked eye, being from 2 to 20 mm in length, and may be likened to a short thick thread frazzled at the unattached, distal end. The great variation in length is due to the fact that both body and tentacles are capable of remarkable expansion and contraction because of the presence of specialized muscle fibrils in many of the cells. A number of species of hydras are recognized by zoologists.

External Characters. The *body* of *Hydra* resembles an elastic tube which varies in length and thickness according as the animal is extended or contracted; in the former case it may reach a length of 2 cm. At the distal end is a circlet of usually from five to nine slender, finger-like projections called *tentacles.* The diameter of the body is frequently increased at certain points by a distention due to the ingestion of large particles of food. Different species of *Hydra* differ in color but the color often depends on the character of the food and hence is not a constant feature. The part of the body which is usually attached to some object is known as the *foot* or *basal disk* and is referred to as the *proximal end.* The foot not only anchors the animal when at rest, but also serves as a locomotor organ. In the common brown species, *Hydra oligactis*, the proximal region is a slender stalk and the distal region constitutes a sort of stomach. A conical elevation, the *hypostome*, occupies the distal end of the body. It is surrounded by the tentacles and has at the top an opening, the *mouth.* This mouth is a circular orifice and the underlying gastrodermis is folded and star-shaped, having clefts running out from the center toward each arm.

The *tentacles* are capable of remarkable expansion, and may stretch out from small blunt projections to very thin threads 7 cm or more in length; in this condition they are so thin as to be barely visible even with a lens. They move independently capturing food and bringing it into the mouth. Their number varies considerably. Six hundred specimens of *Chlorohydra viridissima* possessed from 4 to 12 tentacles each. These occurred in the following proportions: 54 per cent had eight; 24 per cent, seven; 15 per cent, nine; very few animals possessed a greater number than nine, and only occasionally was one found with less than seven. The number of tentacles increases with the

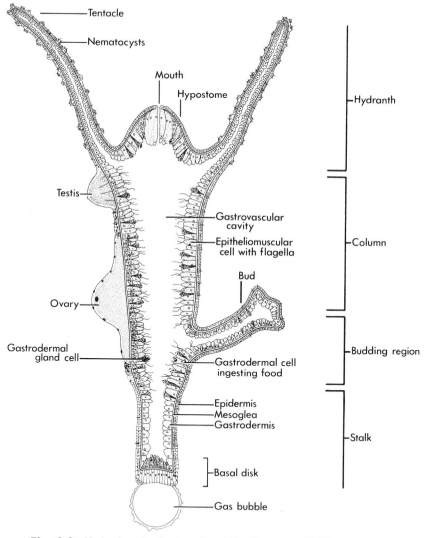

Fig. 3-2. *Hydra*. Longitudinal section. (After Kepner and Miller, modified.)

size and age of the animal, although unfavorable conditions and extreme age result in a decrease.

Frequently specimens of *Hydra* are found which possess *buds* in various stages of development (Figs. 3–1 and 3–2). Several buds are often found on a single animal, and these in turn may bear buds before detachment from the parent. In this way a sort of primitive *Hydra* colony is formed, resembling somewhat the asexual colonies of some of the more complex coelenterates to be described later. In *Hydra oligactis* there is a rather definite budding zone where stalk and body meet.

Reproductive organs may be observed on specimens of *Hydra* in the autumn and winter. Both an *ovary* and *testes* are produced on a single individual in most species; the former is knoblike, occupying a position about one third the length of the animal above the basal disk; the testes, usually two or more in number, are conical elevations projecting from the distal third of the body (Figs. 3–1 and 3–2).

Morphology (Fig. 3–2).   *Hydra* is a diploblastic animal consisting of two cellular layers, an outer thin layer, the *epidermis*, and an inner layer, the *gastrodermis*, twice as thick as the outer. Both layers are composed of *epithelial* cells. A thin layer, formed of a jelly-like substance, the *mesoglea*, separates epidermis from gastrodermis. Not only the body wall, but also the tentacles, possess these three definite regions. Both body and tentacles are hollow, the single central space being known as the *gastrovascular cavity*. At the bases of the tentacles are sphincters that are capable of shutting off the connection between the cavity of the body and the cavities of the tentacles. Because of this, injurious material within the enteron may be prevented from reaching the tentacular cavities.

Epidermis (Fig. 3–3).   The epidermis is primarily *protective* and *sensory*, containing structures characteristic of these functions. Slight differences in structure are observable between the epidermis of the tentacles and that of the body wall, and the latter differs from that of the basal disk. In the epidermis of the body wall are two principal kinds of cells, large epitheliomuscular cells, and small interstitial cells. The *epitheliomuscular* cells (Fig. 3–4) are

Fig. 3-3. *Hydra.* Cross-section of the body wall. (After Kukenthal, modified.)

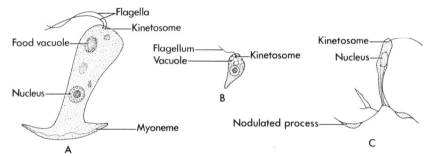

Fig. 3-4. *Hydra oligactis.* Cellular elements enlarged. (A) Epitheliomuscular cell. (B) Secretory cell. (C) Sensory cell. (After Burck.)

shaped like inverted cones. At their inner ends are one or more comparatively long (sometimes 0.38 mm) unstriped *contractile fibers* which form a thin longitudinal muscular layer. These muscle fibers explain the remarkable power of contraction exhibited by *Hydra* when stimulated. Near the middle of each cell, embedded in the alveolar cytoplasm, is a nucleus containing one or two nucleoli and a network of chromatin.

The *interstitial cells* are an important cell type for maintenance of the *Hydra.* They are small cells, abundant near the base of the cells forming the epidermis and gastrodermis, and are capable of developing into the other cell types as well as forming nematocysts. Irradiated hydras, which would otherwise die because the interstitial cells are killed, will recover if they are supplied with a graft containing living interstitial cells. Thus they can be considered embryonic cells of *Hydra.* At certain periods of the year (September and October) some develop into reproductive cells.

Nematocysts or stinging capsules are present on all parts of the body of *Hydra* except the basal disk, being most numerous on the tentacles (Fig. 3–2). Each develops in an interstitial cell known as a *cnidoblast.* These in turn are embedded in little surface tubercles, which give the animal a rough-appearing outline. The tubercles are epidermal cells, each of which usually possesses one or more large nematocysts surrounded by a number of a smaller variety. Four kinds of nematocysts occur in *Hydra.* The largest is known as a *penetrant* (or stenotele) and is 0.013 mm long and 0.007 mm thick; before being discharged it is pear-shaped and occupies almost the entire cell in which it lies (Fig. 3–5). Within it is a *coiled tube* at whose base are three large and a number of small *spines.* A second type is known as a *holotrichous isorhiza* (streptoline glutinant); this type is large and cylindrical and pointed at the end where the thread is discharged. The thread, when discharged, bears a spiral row of minute barbs and tends to coil. *Atrichous isorhizas* (stereoline glutinants) are smaller and oval with a thread that is straight and devoid of barbs when discharged. *Desmonemes* (volvents) are small, pyriform nematocysts containing a thick, smooth thread in a single loop; the thread forms a tight coil when discharged. Projecting from the cnidoblast near the outer end of the

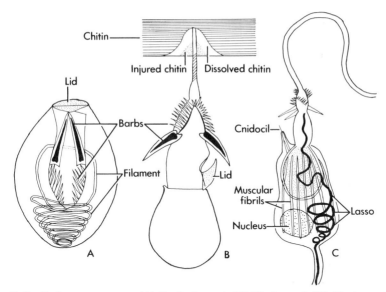

Fig. 3-5. *Hydra:* nematocysts. (A) Undischarged. (B) Discharged. (C) Discharged but retained within cnidoblast. (After Schulze.)

nematocyst is a trigger-like spine, the *cnidocil.* Nematocysts may be exploded by adding a little acetic acid, or better, methyl green, to the water. The tube that is coiled within them is then everted. First, the base of the tube with the spines appears, and then the rest of the tube rapidly turns inside out. Nematocysts are able to penetrate the tissues of other animals, but only at their

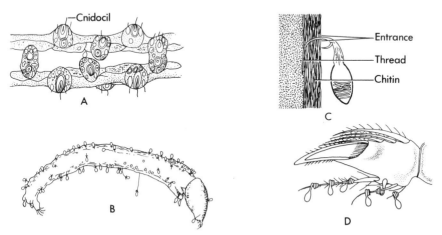

Fig. 3-6. *Hydra:* nematocysts and their action. (A) Portion of a tentacle showing the batteries of nematocysts. (B) Insect larva covered with nematocysts as a result of capture by *Hydra.* (C) A nematocyst piercing the chitinous covering of an insect. (D) nematocysts holding a small animal by coiling about its spines. (A and B from Jennings; C and D from Toppe.)

greatest speed and before eversion is completed. Even the extremely firm chitinous covering of insects may be punctured by these structures (Fig. 3–6, C). Touching the cnidocil was for a long time supposed to cause the explosion of the nematocysts, and for this reason it is known as a "trigger."

However, mechanical shocks alone have little influence upon some nematocysts. Internal pressure produced either by distortion or by osmosis, is effective. For this reason chemicals which increase the osmotic pressure within the cnidoblast cause the eversion of the threadlike tube. In *Physalia* the nematocysts are exploded either by a combination of external and internal pressures. Contraction of a muscle-like covering around the nematocyst is said to produce external pressure.

Discharge of nematocysts seems more readily accomplished by a proper combination of chemical and mechanical stimuli. Lipid-like substances are thought to be among the chemicals involved in natural discharge. Penetrants and desmonemes discharge readily when stimulated by food organisms. Atrichous isorhizas are easily discharged by mechanical shocks and their adhesive threads enable tentacles to adhere to the substrate during locomotion. An animal when "shot" by nematocysts is immediately paralyzed, and sometimes killed, by a poison called hypnotoxin which is injected into it through the tube.

Nematocysts are developed from interstitial cells, each cell producing one nematocyst. A nematocyst, carried by its mother cell or cnidoblast, moves inside an epitheliomuscular cell and to the surface. The outer part is produced to form a cnidocil which pierces the surface. Since the tube of the nematocyst cannot be returned to the capsule, nor another one be developed by the

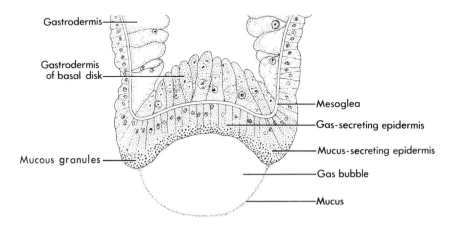

Gastrodermis

Gastrodermis of basal disk

Mucous granules

Mesoglea

Gas-secreting epidermis

Mucus-secreting epidermis

Gas bubble

Mucus

Fig. 3-7. *Hydra.* Longitudinal section of the basal region showing the gastrodermal cells containing food vacuoles and the mucus-secreting epidermal cells containing mucous granules with which the animal attaches itself to the substratum. Formation of a gas bubble is also shown. (Modified from Kepner and Thomas.)

cnidoblast, new capsules must be formed from interstitial cells to replace those already exploded.

The *basal disk* differs somewhat in function from the rest of the body. It is the point by which *Hydra* attaches itself to solid objects, and for this purpose secretes a sticky substance. Epitheliomuscular cells and a few interstitial cells are present, but no nematocysts are to be found here. The columnar epitheliomuscular cells are not only provided with contractile fibers at their bases, but, being secretory, also contain a large number of small refringent granules, as shown in Figure 3–7. Certain ectoderm cells of the basal disk secrete a gas which may be confined within the mucus thus forming a bubble (Figs. 3–2 and 3–7). Such a gas bubble may lift the *Hydra* to the surface where it breaks and spreads out like a raft from which the animal hangs suspended in the water.

The *tentacles* (Fig. 3–2) are provided with an epidermis consisting of large flat cells, thin at the edges and thick in the center. The thicker portions give the surface of the tentacle a lumpy appearance. In the center of each thickening is a nucleus around which are embedded sometimes as many as twelve nematocysts each in its own cnidoblast (Fig. 3–6, A). The cnidocils projecting from the cnidoblasts resemble groups of cilia. Each cnidoblast is drawn out at its base into a contractile fibril which enters the longitudinal muscular sheet at the base of the epidermal cells.

Gastrodermis (Fig. 3–2). The inner layers of cells, the gastrodermis, occupies about two thirds of the body wall. Its functions are *digestive* and *secretory*. The digestive cells are long and club-shaped, with transverse muscular fibrils at their base, forming a circular sheet of contractile substance. Many of them are provided with from one to five flagella, which are non-tapering, lashlike processes that arise from a kinetosome (Fig. 3–4). The epitheliomuscular cells possess one or more flagella; the secreting cells, one or two; and the sensory cells, one. Besides flagella *pseudopodia* may also be thrust out from the free end (Fig. 3–3). The flagella create currents in the gastrovascular fluid, and the pseudopodia capture solid food particles. The gastrodermis of the hypostome contains secreting cells that appear to produce a mucous secretion for lubrication during the ingestion of food. The internal structure of these cells differs before and after the animal is fed. In a starving *Hydra* large vacuoles appear, almost completely filling the cell, the protoplasm being reduced to a thin layer near the cell wall; after a meal, however, the cells are gorged with nutritive spheres, many of which, especially the oil globules, migrate into the epidermis and are stored near the periphery.

The *glandular cells* are smaller than the digestive cells and lack the contractile fibrils at their base (Fig. 3–3). They also differ in appearance according to their metabolic activity: some are filled with large vacuoles containing secretory matter, whereas others, having discharged their secretion, appear crowded with fine granules. Interstitial cells are found lying at the base of the other gastrodermal cells.

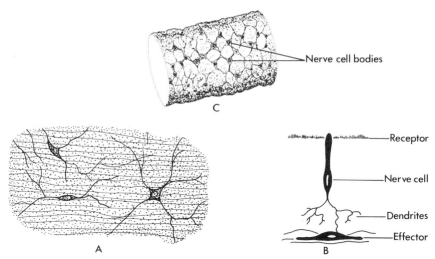

Fig. 3-8. Nerve cells of *Hydra*. (A) Plexus of nerve cells in the ectoderm; the parallel lines represent longitudinal muscle fibers. (B) Receptor-effector system of a hydrozoan. (C) Gross view of nerve net. (A, after Schneider; B, after Parker.)

The tentacles contain no gland cells. The gastrodermis of the basal disk is provided with only a few glandular cells.

Mesoglea (Figs. 3–2 and 3–3). The mesoglea in *Hydra* is so thin as to be difficult to find, even when highly magnified; in some of the other Coelenterates this layer is very thick, constituting by far the largest part of the body.

Nervous System. *Hydra* possesses a nervous system, but complicated staining methods are necessary to make it visible. In the epidermis there is a sort of plexus of nerve cells connected by nerve fibers (Figs. 3–4 and 3–8, A). Sensory cells in the surface layer of cells (Fig. 3–3) serve as external organs of stimulation and are in direct continuity with fibers from the nerve cells. Some of the nerve cells send processes to the muscle fibers of the epithelio-muscular cells, and are therefore motor in function (Fig. 3–8, B). No processes from the nerve cells to the nematocysts have yet been discovered, though they may occur. The gastrodermis of the body also contains nerve cells, but not so many as are present in the epidermis (Fig. 3–3). Nerve impulses may pass in any direction along this nerve net.

Nutrition. *Food.* The food of *Hydra* consists principally of small animals that live in the water. Of these may be mentioned small crustaceans such as *Cyclops*, annelids, and insect larvae. *Hydra* normally rests with its basal disk attached to some object and its body and tentacles extended out into the water. In this position it occupies a considerable amount of hunting territory. Any small aquatic animal swimming in touch with a tentacle is at once shot full of nematocysts (Fig. 3–6, B), which not only seem to paralyze it, but also to hold it firmly. The viscid surface of the tentacle aids in making sure that the victim does not escape.

Ingestion. Ingestion takes place as follows: First, the tentacle, which has captured the prey, bends toward the mouth with its load of food. The other tentacles not only assist in this, but may use their nematocysts in quieting the victim. The mouth often begins to open before the food has reached it. The edges of the mouth gradually enclose the organism and force it into the gastrovascular cavity. The body wall contracts behind the food and forces it down. Frequently organisms many times the size of the *Hydra* are successfully ingested.

Reactions to Food. It is not uncommon to find hydras that will not react to food when it is presented to them. This is due to the fact that these animals will eat only when a certain interval of time has elapsed since their last meal. The physiological condition of *Hydra*, therefore, determines its response to the food stimulus. The collision of an aquatic organism with the tentacle of *Hydra* is not sufficient to cause the food-taking reaction, since it has been found that not only a mechanical stimulus, but also a chemical stimulus must be present. A very hungry *Hydra* will even go through the characteristic movements when it is excited by the chemical stimulus alone. This has been shown by the following experiment. When the tentacles and hypostome of a moderately hungry *Hydra* are brought into contact with a piece of filter paper, which has been soaked for a time in the same culture medium, there is no response. If the filter paper is then soaked in beef juice and offered to the *Hydra*, the usual food reactions are given. Reduced glutathione in low concentrations will also produce feeding reactions.

Beef juice alone calls forth no response in a moderately hungry animal; but does inaugurate the normal reflex, if a very hungry specimen is selected for the experiment. The conclusion reached is that well-fed hydras will not respond to either mechanical or chemical stimuli when acting alone or in combination; that moderately hungry animals will react to a combination of the two, and that hungry animals will exhibit food-taking movements even if a chemical stimulus alone is employed.

Digestion. The nematocysts that have penetrated the food begin the digestive process with proteases they inject. Immediately after the ingestion of the food, the gland cells in the gastrodermis show signs of great activity; their nuclei enlarge and become granular. This is probably the beginning of the process of formation of enzymes, which are discharged into the gastrovascular cavity and begin at once the dissolution of the food. The action of the digestive juices is made more effective by the churning of the food as the animal expands and contracts. The cilia extending out into the central cavity also aid in the dissolution of the food by creating currents. This method of digestion differs from that of *Amoeba* and *Paramecium* in being carried on outside of the cell, i.e., extracellular. Intracellular digestion also takes place in *Hydra*; the pseudopodia thrust out by the gastrodermal cells

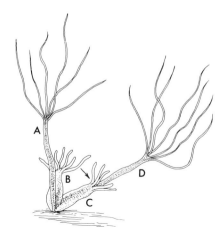

Fig. 3-9. Spontaneous changes of position in an undisturbed *Hydra*, side view. The extended animal *A* contracts *B*, bends to a new position *C*, and then extends *D*. (From Jennings.)

seize and engulf particles of food, which are dissolved within the cells. However, most of the food is digested in the gastrovascular cavity. The digested food is absorbed by the gastrodermal cells; part of it, especially the oil globules, is passed over to the epidermis, where it is stored.

Egestion. All insoluble material is egested from the mouth. This is accomplished by "a very sudden squirt," which throws the debris to some distance.

Symbiosis. One species of hydra, *Chlorohydra viridissima*, is green, because of the presence within the gastrodermal cells of a unicellular alga, *Chlorella vulgaris*. As in *Paramecium bursaria*, the plant uses some of the waste products of metabolism of the hydra, and the hydra uses some of the oxygen resulting from the process of photosynthesis in the plant. In addition about 10 per cent of the carbon dioxide fixed by the alga becomes incorporated

Fig. 3-10. Locomotion in *Hydra:* moving like a measuring worm. (After Wagner.)

in the protoplasm of the hydra. This symbiotic relationship is one of mutualism.

Among the parasites of *Hydra* are *Hydramoeba hydroxena* (Fig. 1–32) and the ciliates *Kerona pediculus* and *Trichodina pediculus* (Fig. 1–80, C).

Behavior. *Chlorohydra viridissima* gives a more prompt and decisive response when stimulated than any species of *Hydra*, and for this reason its behavior has been studied more thoroughly than that of the others. The following paragraphs have been compiled largely from experiments upon green hydras, although enough work has been done with other forms to prove that their reactions are practically the same, only more sluggish.

Normal Position of Hydra (Fig. 3–1).   Hydras may be found attached to the sides or bottom of an aquarium, to parts of water plants, or hanging from the surface film. Usually they are near the top where more oxygen can be obtained from the water than at greater depths. If attached to the bottom, the body is usually held upright; if to the sides, the body is in most cases horizontal, the hypostome generally being lower than the foot; and if to the surface film, the body is allowed to hand directly downward. Suspension from the surface film may be compared with that of a needle placed on the surface of the water. Threads of a gelatinous substance, extending out from the basal disk, help sustain the body, and in some cases a gas bubble attached to the foot keeps the animal afloat. The position of rest in every case gives the *Hydra* the greatest opportunities for capturing food, because in this condition it has control of a large amount of territory.

Spontaneous Movements.   All the movements of Hydra are the result of contraction of one or more sets of muscle fibers, and are produced by two kinds of stimuli, internal, or spontaneous, and external. Spontaneous movements may be observed when the animal is attached and undisturbed. At intervals of several minutes the body, or tentacles, or both, contract suddenly and rapidly, and then slowly expand in a new direction. Hungry specimens are more active than well-fed individuals. The result is to bring the animal into a new part of its surroundings, where more food may be present (Fig. 3–9). These movements finally cease, and the animal's position is changed by locomotion.

The spontaneous contractions are of two types. One is a short series of contractions with the stimulus originating beneath the area of the hypostome. The other spontaneous contractions are periodic ones with the stimuli originating from a number of locations including the basal region. Although the two systems are to some extent independent, interaction does occur (McCullough, 1965).

Locomotion.   Movement from place to place is effected in several ways. In most cases the animal bends over (Fig. 3–10, A) and attaches itself to the substratum by its tentacles (B), probably with the aid of atrichous isorhiza nematocysts. The basal disk is then released and the animal contracts (C). It then expands (D), bends over in some other direction and attaches its foot (E). The tentacles now loosen their hold and an upright position is regained (F). The whole process has been likened to the looping locomotion of a measuring worm. At other times the animal moves from place to place while inverted by using its tentacles as legs. Locomotion may also result from the gliding of the foot along the substratum, and considerable distances are sometimes covered in this way. In *Hydra oligactis* the tentacles may be attached to some object, the basal disk freed, and the body drawn up to the object by the contraction of the tentacles.

Movements are dependent on the contraction of the longitudinal muscle fibers at the base of the epidermal cells and the circular muscle fibers at the base of the gastrodermal cells. Shortening of the longitudinal muscles is accompanied by a simultaneous decrease in length and increase in diameter of the hydra. Fluid, in the gastrovascular cavity and in the cells themselves, serves to transmit the force hydraulically. Analysis of structure and movement in the tentacles indicates that the gastrodermal cells are important in the independent action of the tentacles. They are large and vacuolated and nearly occlude the cavity of the tentacles. Thus, the fluid in the cells when put under pressure by contraction of the circular muscle of the cells can only act locally and cause extension of that part of the tentacle. Because tentacles with a

Fig. 3-11. Extension of *Hydra* tentacles when constant volume is maintained. (A) Tentacle with longitudinal muscles fully contracted. (B) Same tentacle with circular muscles contracted to one-half maximum length. (C) Size that the same segment of tentacle would be if circular muscles contracted to one-quarter maximum length.

portion amputated are able to extend immediately, it appears that fluid pressure in the gastrovascular cavity is not significant in the extension of tentacles. The tentacles maintain a constant volume (Fig. 3–11) and their movements are probably independent of fluid pressure in the gastrovascular cavity of the body.

Reactions to External Stimuli. *Contact.* *Hydra* reacts to various kinds of special stimuli. Reaction to contact accounts for its temporary fixed condition. The attachment while in the resting attitude is a result of this reaction, and not a response to gravity, because hydras have the longitudinal axis of the body directed at every possible angle regardless of the force of gravity. Mechanical shocks, such as the jarring of the watch glass containing a specimen, or the agitation of the surface of the water, cause a rapid contraction of a part or all of the animal. This is followed by a gradual expansion until the original condition is regained.

Mechanical stimuli may be *localized* or *nonlocalized*. That just noted is of the latter type. *Local stimulation* may be accomplished by touching the body or tentacles with the end of a fine glass rod. It has been noted that the stimulation of one tentacle may cause the contraction of all the tentacles, or even the contraction of both tentacles and body. This shows that there must be some sort of transmission of stimuli from one tentacle to another and to the body. The structure of the nervous system would make this possible.

Light. Moderate amounts of light inhibit contractions of hydra. Intense light causes contractions which can be inhibited by reduced glutathione or some foods (Rushforth, *et al.*, 1964). Normal lighting produces no marked response, although the final result is quite decisive. If a dish containing hydras is placed so that the illumination is unequal on different sides, the animals will collect in the brightest region, unless the light is too strong, in which case they will congregate in a place where the light is less intense. *Hydra* therefore has an optimum with regard to light. The movement into or out of a certain area is accomplished by a method of "trial and error." When put in a dark place *Hydra* becomes restless and moves about in no definite direction; but if white light is encountered, its locomotion becomes less rapid and finally ceases altogether. The value to the organism of such a reaction is considerable, because the small animals that serve as food for it are attracted to well-lighted areas. *Colored lights* have the same effect as darkness; blue, however, is preferred by *Hydra* to white.

Temperature. The reactions of *Hydra* to changes in temperature are also indefinite, although in many cases they enable the animal to escape from a heated region. No locomotory change is produced by temperatures below 31°C; at this temperature, however, the basal disk is released and the animal takes up a new position either way from the heated area or further into it. In the former case the *Hydra* escapes, in the latter it may escape if subsequent movements take it away from the injurious heat, otherwise it perishes. *Hydra* does not move from place to place if the temperature is lowered; it contracts less rapidly, and finally ceases all its movements when the freezing point is approached.

Electric Current. An attached *Hydra*, when subjected to a weak constant electric current, bends toward the anode, its body finally becoming oriented with the basal disk toward the cathode and the anterior end toward the anode side. The entire animal then contracts. In an animal attached by the tentacles a similar bending occurs, but the basal disk in this case is directed toward the anode. These reactions are caused by local contractions on the anode side for which the electric current is directly responsible.

Hydra shows no reactions to currents of water. When placed in a current of water, it neither orients itself in a definite way nor moves either up or down stream.

General Remarks. It is evident from the above outline of the reactions of *Hydra* to stimuli that the only movements involved are produced by contraction and expansion of the body when attached, and by undirected changes of position. Being radially symmetrical, the body may be flexed in any direction.

Local stimuli, such as the application of heat or a chemical to a limited area of the body, causes a contraction of the part affected and a bending in that direction. This results in the movement of the tentacular region toward the stimuli, and the contraction of the entire animal follows, thus carrying it out of the influence of the stimulus. The bending produced by a mild stimulus applied to a tentacle is an efficient reflex for putting more of the tentacle and nematocysts around a small food organism to subdue it.

Nonlocalized stimuli, such as the jarring of the vessel containing the animals, produces, immediately, a contraction of the entire body, which, in most cases, is beneficial, since it removes it from an injurious agent. If, however, this simple contraction is not effective, as in the case of a constant application of heat, the *Hydra* usually resorts to some other reaction, e.g., locomotion, which often enables it to escape from the injurious stimulus.

Finally, it should be remembered that the physiological condition of the animal determines to a large extent the kind of reactions produced, not only spontaneously, but also by external stimuli. "It decides whether *Hydra* shall creep upward to the surface and toward the light, or shall sink to the bottom; how it shall react to chemicals and to solid objects; whether it shall remain quiet in a certain position, or shall reverse this position and undertake a laborious tour of exploration" (Jennings).

Reproduction. Reproduction takes place in *Hydra* both *asexually* and *sexually*; in the former case by budding, in the latter, by the production of a fertilized egg. Longitudinal and transverse division have been described in

Hydra, but apparently are not methods of reproduction; they are simply processes that enable an abnormal animal to regain its normal shape.

Budding (Figs. 3–1 and 3–2).   Asexual reproduction by budding is easily observed in the laboratory. Superficially the bud appears first as a slight bulge in the body wall. This pushes out rapidly into a stalk which soon develops a circlet of blunt tentacles about its distal end. The cavities of both stalk and tentacles are at all times directly connected with that of the parent. When full grown, the bud becomes detached and leads a separate existence. The details of the process are briefly as follows. The interstitial cells in a certain region increase in number and volume, producing a slight outbulging of the epidermis. The growing region is located at the point where the edges of the protrusion meet the body wall. Here the cells are well fed and multiply actively. The epidermal and gastrodermal cells of the parent give rise to the corresponding cells of the bud. When the bud is fully grown, the epidermal cells at its proximal end secrete a sticky substance, which is used later for its attachment. The gastrodermal cells in the same region then unite, separating the cavity of the bud from that of the parent. Finally, the bud becomes detached. The food supply determines the rate of growth of the bud, and a bud may be entirely absorbed by a starving animal.

The tentacles of the bud arise first as two outgrowths opposite each other. The third tentacle develops between these on the side toward the oral end of the parent; the fourth, opposite the third and the fifth and sixth on either side of the third.

Sexual Reproduction.   Whether or not there are definite germ cells in the adult *Hydra* is still open to question. So far as is known, both ova and spermatozoa arise from indifferent interstitial cells. Hydras are, with the exception of a few that are hermaphroditic, either male or female. In *H. oligactis* the sex organs are located on the body and not on the stalk. There may be as many as 20 or 30 testes, low and rounded in shape and devoid of nipples. The sexual state can be induced in this species by lowering the temperature, which accounts for the appearance of sex organs in the autumn. During asexual reproduction, sex is inherited, since buds produce the same kind of sex organs as the parent, and all members of a clone are of the same sex.

Spermatogenesis.   The male cells of *Hydra* are formed in little conical elevations called *testes*, which project from the surface of the body (Figs. 3–1, C and 3–2). The testis arises within the epidermis from interstitial cells. A single interstitial cell divides mitotically; then adjacent interstitial cells also divide, multiplication continuing until the epidermis becomes distended. An indefinite number of long multinucleated cysts (Fig. 3–12, A) are formed within the testis, each cyst being the product of a single or several interstitial cells. Each interstitial cell is a primordial germ cell; it gives rise by mitosis to a variable number of spermatogonia, which contain twelve chromosomes, the somatic number. Reduction in the number of chromosomes to six occurs just after the spermatogonia have divided to form the primary spermatocytes. The

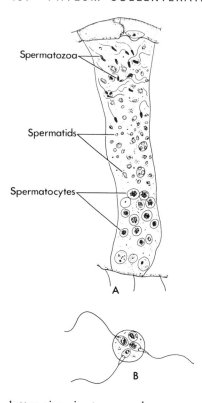

Spermatozoa

Spermatids

Spermatocytes

A

B

Fig. 3-12. Parts of the testis of *Hydra*. (A) A single cyst. (B) Developing spermatozoa. (From Tannreuther.)

latter give rise to secondary spermatocytes which divide at once, producing spermatids. These two spermatocyte divisions take place without the formation of cell walls, i.e., each primary spermatocyte develops into a four-nucleated cell, which represents the four spermatids. Within this cell the spermatids transform into spermatozoa (Fig. 3–12, B). A single cyst may contain representatives of all of these cell generations—spermatogonia, primary spermatocytes, secondary spermatocytes, spermatids, and spermatozoa. The mature spermatozoa break out of the vesicle in which they are formed, and swim about in the distal end of the cyst (Fig. 3–12, A); they finally reach the outside by way of a minute temporary opening in the end of the cyst. The mature spermatozoa swim about in the water searching for an egg; their activity continues from 1 to 3 days.

Oogenesis.   The egg is first distinguished from the interstitial cells of the epidermis by its slightly greater size, its spherical shape, and the comparatively large volume of its nucleus. As the eggs grow in size, the neighboring interstitial cells increase in number by mitosis, and also become larger. The whole structure may at this time be called an ovary (Figs. 3–2, 3–13, and 3–14). The nourishment of the egg is at first similar to that of the other epidermal cells, but later disintegration and resorption of adjacent interstitial cells takes place. Yolk is elaborated from material that enters from the gastro-

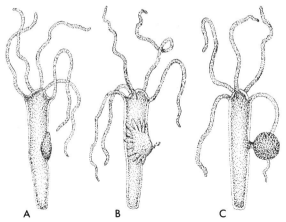

Fig. 3-13. *Chlorohydra viridissima.* Stages in the growth of the egg. (A) Young oogonium. A cross-section through this oogonium is shown in Fig. 3-14. (B) Oocyte with many protoplasmic extensions. (C) Primary oocyte with complete amount of yolk. (After Kepner and Looper.)

dermis. Usually only one egg is developed in a single ovary (Fig. 3–14), but sometimes two may arise and complete their development side by side. In cases, however, when two or more eggs are contained in one ovary, their adjacent walls dissolve and one of the nuclei survives while the others disintegrate. As the ovum grows it becomes lobed, showing distinct proto- plasmic fingers (Fig. 3–13, B); these are drawn in when it has reached its full size. The egg is now nearly spherical (Fig. 3–13, C) and is surrounded by a single layer of epidermal cells. Maturation then takes place. Two polar bodies are formed, the first being larger than the second. During maturation the

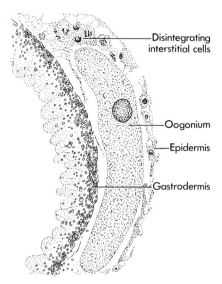

Fig. 3-14. *Chlorohydra viridssima.* Cross- section through the oogonium shown in Fig. 3-13, A (After Kepner and Looper.)

number of chromosomes is reduced from the somatic number, twelve, to six. This occurs at the end of the growth period. Now an opening appears in the epidermis and the egg is forced out, finally becoming free on all sides except where attached to the animal.

Fertilization. Fertilization usually occurs within 2 hours. Several sperm penetrate the egg membrane, but only one enters the egg itself. If not fertilized within 24 hours, the egg becomes sterile. The sperm brings a nucleus containing six chromosomes into the egg. The male and female nuclei unite, forming the fusion nucleus.

Embryology. *Cleavage*, which now begins, is total and regular. A well-defined cleavage cavity is present at the end of the third cleavage, i.e., the eight-celled stage. When the *blastula* is completed, it resembles a hollow sphere with a single layer of epithelial cells composing its wall. These cells may be called the primitive ectoderm. By mitotic division they form endoderm cells, which drop into the cleavage cavity, completely filling it. The *gastrula*, therefore, is a solid sphere of cells differentiated into a single outer layer, the ectoderm, and an irregular central mass, the endoderm. The ectoderm secretes around the gastrula two envelopes. The outer is a thick chitinous shell covered with sharp projections; the inner is a thin gelatinous membrane.

Hatching. The embryo in this condition separates from the parent and falls to the bottom, where it remains unchanged for several weeks. Then interstitial cells make their appearance. A subsequent resting period is followed by the breaking away of the outer chitinous envelope and the elongation of the escaped embryo. Mesoglea is now secreted by the ectoderm and endoderm cells; a circlet of tentacles arises at one end and a mouth appears in their midst. The young *Hydra* thus formed soon grows into the adult condition. The ectoderm of the embryo matures into the epidermis of the adult while the endoderm becomes the gastrodermis. Although the terms ectoderm and endoderm have been used by many to designate the layers of adult coelenterates, they are best reserved for use in the early developmental stages of animals.

Growth. Some doubt may be cast on the role of the interstitial cells in replacing all cell types, because Campbell (1965) has found that most cell types except cnidoblasts undergo division. Autoradiographs of *Hydra* fed labeled thymidine (Fig. 3–15) show uptake of thymidine, and presumably replication of DNA, by nuclei in all regions of *Hydra*. The species investigated was a stalked one and little growth occurred in the stalk. The continual loss of cells from the basal disk and the use of cells in bud formation causes a slow growth of cells from the subhypostomal area toward the stalk.

Depression. Hydras, both in nature and in laboratory cultures, appear to undergo stages of depression during which the tentacles shorten and gradually disappear and the body of the animal becomes shorter due to the disintegra-

Fig. 3-15. Cell proliferation in *Hydra*. Autoradiograph (*left*) through midregion of Hydra shows darkening where tritiated thymidine was incorporated in the tissue. The principal site and time of thymidine incorporation is the nucleus prior to division when new DNA is formed. Nuclei showing isotope incorporation are: gland cell *G*, digestive cell *D*, interstitial cell *I*, and epithelio-muscular cell *E*. Graphs (*right*) show the distribution of labeled nuclei along the length of the hydra. Solid circles represent endoderm (gastrodermis); open circles ectoderm (epidermis). Thymidine index is the percentage of nuclei that are labeled. (From R. D. Campbell. Cell proliferation in *Hydra:* an autoradiographic approach. *Science.* **148**:1231–1232. Copyright 1965 by the American Association for the Advancement of Science.)

tion of the tissues at the distal end. Finally only a ball-like mass of cells representing the basal end remains, and this soon disintegrates. Depression appears to be due to a lowered metabolic state, which may be produced by rich feeding, high temperature, senescence, fouling of the culture water, lack of oxygen, or transfer to clean fresh water. Recovery from depression may occur spontaneously or may be induced by transferring the animals to a culture in which other hydras are flourishing. Often within an hour the body begins to elongate and tentacles begin to appear.

Regeneration. An account of the phenomenon of regeneration is appropriate at this place, since the power of animals to restore lost parts was first discovered in *Hydra* by Trembley in 1740. This investigator found that if hydras were cut into two, three, or four pieces, each part would grow into an entire animal (Fig. 3–16, C). Other experimental results obtained by Trembley are that the hypostome together with the tentacles, if cut off, produce a new individual; that each piece of a *Hydra*, split longitudinally into two or four

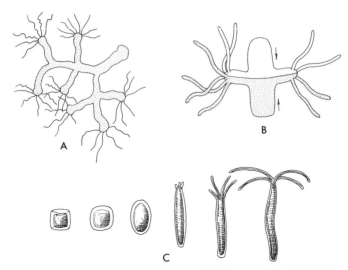

Fig. 3-16. *Hydra*. Regeneration and grafting. (A) A seven-headed *Hydra* resulting from regeneration after the distal ends were split lengthwise. (B) Parts of two hydras grafted together. (C) The regeneration of an entire *Hydra* from a small piece of the stalk. (After several authors.)

parts, becomes a perfect polyp; that when the head end is split in two and the parts separated slightly a two-headed animal results; and that a specimen when turned inside out is able to readjust itself to new conditions forced upon it.

Regeneration may be defined as the replacing of an entire organism by a part of the same. It takes place not only in *Hydra*, but in many other coelenterates, and in some of the representatives of almost every phylum of the animal kingdom. *Hydra* is a species that has been widely used for experimentation. Pieces of *Hydra* that measure $\frac{1}{6}$ mm or more in diameter are capable of becoming entire animals (Fig. 3–16, C). The tissues in some cases restore the lost parts by a multiplication of their cells; in other cases, they are worked over directly into a new but smaller individual.

Experiments have shown that when pieces of hydras too small to regenerate are allowed to come into contact with one another they fuse. The gastrodermis appears to initiate this fusion and controls the process. The gastrodermis of one piece may fuse with the gastrodermis of an adjoining piece rapidly. Epidermis does not fuse with epidermis nor with gastrodermis, and mesoglea appears to have little or no power of fusion. Fusion, as indicated by tissue culture experiments, appears to be the result of the interlacing of amoeboid processes sent out by the gastrodermal cells of the pieces in contact. As a result of this fusion a platelike body is formed which may, within a period of about 12 hours, develop into a sac. This sac becomes attached at a certain point which is the basal disk; it then elongates; tentacles bud out at the distal end and a normal hydra results (Papenfuss).

Grafting. Parts of one *Hydra* may easily be grafted upon another (Fig. 3–16, B). In this way many bizarre effects have been produced. Parts of two hydras of two species have also been successfully united. Lenhoff (1965) has found that normal and mutant hydras grafted together eventually produce by budding a range of hydras having the characteristics from normal to mutant.

Space will not permit a detailed account of the many interesting questions involved in the phenomena of regeneration, but enough has been given to indicate the nature of the process. The benefit to the animal of the ability to regenerate lost parts is obvious. Such an animal, in many cases, will succeed in the struggle for existence under adverse conditions. Regeneration takes place continually in all animals; e.g., new cells are produced in the epidermis of man to take the place of those that are no longer able to perform their proper functions. Both internal and external factors have an influence upon the rate of regeneration and upon the character of the new part.

(2) Obelia—A Colonial Hydrozoan

Obelia (Fig. 3–17) is a colonial coelenterate, that lives in the sea, where it is usually attached to rocks, to wharves, or to *Laminaria*, *Rhodymenia*, and other algae. It may be found in low water and to a depth of 40 fathoms along the coast of northern Europe, from Long Island Sound to Labrador, and the Pacific Coast.

Anatomy and Physiology. An *Obelia* colony consists of a basal stem, the *hydrorhiza*, which is attached to the substratum; this gives off at intervals upright branches, known as *hydrocauli*. At every bend in the zigzag hydrocaulus a side branch arises. The stem of this side branch is ringed and is expanded at the end into a hydra-like structure, the *hydranth*. A single polyp consists of a hydranth and the part of the stalk between the hydranth and the point of origin of the preceding branch. Full-grown colonies usually bear reproductive members (*gonangia*) in the angles where the hydranths arise from the hydrocaulus.

The *Obelia* colony, as just described and as illustrated in Figure 3–17, resembles the structure that would be built up by a budding *Hydra* if the buds were to remain attached to the parent and in turn produce fixed buds.

All of the soft parts of the *Obelia* colony are protected by a chitinous covering called the *periderm*; this is ringed at various places and is expanded into cup-shaped *hydrothecae* to accommodate the hydranths, and into *gonothecae* to enclose the reproductive members. A shelf that extends across the base of the hydrotheca serves to support the hydranth. The soft parts of the hydrocaulus and of the stalks of the hydranths constitute the *coenosarc* and are attached to the periderm by minute projections. The coenosarcal cavities of the hydrocaulus open into those of the branches and thence into the hydranths, producing in this way a common *gastrovascular cavity*.

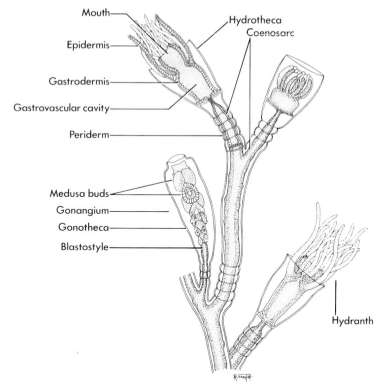

Fig. 3-17. *Obelia*. The colonial polyp, or hydroid, stage. Portion showing both reproductive polyps (gonangia) and nutritive polyps (hydranths).

A longitudinal section of a hydranth and its stalk (Fig. 3–17) shows the
coenosarc to consist of two layers of cells—an outer layer, the *epidermis*, and
and inner layer, the *gastrodermis*. These layers are continued into the hydranth.
The *mouth* is situated in the center of the large knoblike *hypostome*, and the
tentacles, about 30 in number, are arranged around the base of the hypostome in a single circle. Each tentacle is solid, consisting of an outer layer of

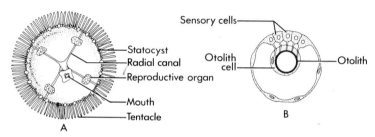

Fig. 3-18. *Obelia*. (A) Medusa. (B) Statocyst. (A, after Parker and Haswell; B, after
Kerr.)

epidermal cells and a single axial row of gastrodermal cells; at the extremity are a large number of one type of nematocyst. The hydranth captures, ingests, and digests food as in *Hydra*.

The reproductive polyps arise, as do the hydranths, as buds from the hydrocaulus, and represent modified hydranths. The central axis of each is called a *blastostyle*, and together with the gonothecal covering is known as the *gonangium*. The blastostyle gives rise to *medusa-buds*, which soon become detached and pass out of the gonotheca through the opening in the distal end.

Some of the *medusae* of *Obelia* (Fig. 3–18, A) produce eggs, and others produce spermatozoa. The fertilized eggs develop into colonies like that which gave rise to the medusae. The medusae provide for the dispersal of the species, because they swim about in the water and establish colonies in new habitats. The medusa of *Obelia* is shaped like an umbrella with a fringe of tentacles and a number of organs of equilibrium on the edge (Fig. 3–18, B). Hanging down from the center is the *manubrium* with the mouth at the end. The gastrovascular cavity extends out from the cavity of the manubrium into four *radial canals* on which are situated the reproductive organs.

The *germ cells* of the medusae of *Obelia* arise in the epidermis of the manubrium, and then migrate along the radial canals to the reproductive organs. When mature, they break out into the water. The eggs are *fertilized*

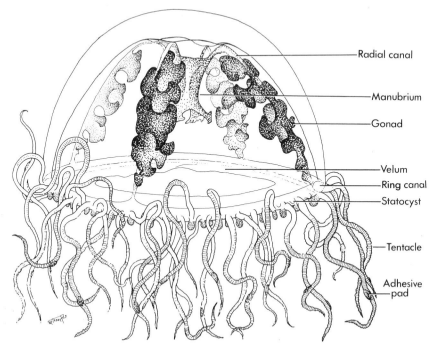

Fig. 3-19. *Gonionemus:* a hydrozoan jellyfish.

by spermatozoa which have escaped from other medusae. *Cleavage* is similar to that of *Hydra*, and a hollow *blastula* and solid *gastrula-like* structure are formed. The gastrula-like structure soon becomes ciliated and elongates into a free swimming larva called a *planula*. This soon acquires a central cavity, becomes fixed to some object, and proceeds to found a new colony. The physiological processes of *Obelia* are similar to those described in *Hydra*.

(3) Gonionemus—A Hydrozoan Medusa

The structure of a hydrozoan jellyfish or medusa may be illustrated by *Gonionemus* (Fig. 3–19). This jellyfish is common along the eastern and western coasts of the United States. It measures about half an inch in diameter, without including the fringe of tentacles around the margin. In general form it is similar to the medusa of *Obelia* (Fig. 3–18, A). The convex or aboral surface is called the *exumbrella*; the concave, or oral surface, the *subumbrella*. The subumbrella is partly closed by a membraneous ledge called the *velum*. Water is taken into the subumbrellar cavity and is then forced out through the central opening in the velum by the contraction of the body; this propels the animal in the opposite direction, thus enabling it to swim about.

The *tentacles*, which vary in number from 16 to more than 80, are capable of considerable contraction. Near their tips are *adhesive pads* at a point where the tentacle bends at a sharp angle. Hanging down into the subumbrellar cavity is the *manubrium* with the *mouth* at the end surrounded by four frilled *oral lobes*. The mouth opens into a *gastrovascular cavity*, which consists of a central "*stomach*" and four *radial canals*. The radial canals enter a *circumferential canal*, which lies near the margin of the umbrella.

The cellular layers in *Gonionemus* are similar to those in *Hydra*, but the *mesoglea* is extremely thick and gives the animal a jellylike consistency. Scattered about beneath the epidermis are many *nerve cells*, and about the velum is a *nerve ring*. *Sensory cells* with a tactile function are abundant on the tentacles. The margin of the umbrella is supplied with two kinds of sense organs: (1) at the base of the tentacles are round bodies, which contain pigmented endoderm cells and communicate with the circumferential canal; (2) between the bases of the tentacles are small outgrowths, which are organs of

Fig. 3-20. *Gonionemus:* hydra-like stage in development. One of the tentacles is carrying a worm (W) to the mouth. The tentacles are in a contracted state. (After Perkins.)

equilibrium, the *statocysts*. *Muscle fibers*, both exumbrella and subumbrella, are present, giving the animal the power of *locomotion*.

Suspended beneath the radial canals are the sinuously folded *reproductive organs* or *gonads*. *Gonionemus* is dioecious, one individual producing either eggs or spermatozoa. These reproductive cells break out directly into the water, where *fertilization* takes place. A ciliated *planula* develops from the egg as in *Obelia*. This soon becomes fixed to some object, and a mouth appears at the unattached end. Then four tentacles grow out around the mouth and the hydra-like larva is able to feed (Fig. 3–20). Other similar hydra-like polyps bud from its walls. The medusae are thought to arise from these polyps as lateral buds.

The physiological processes of *Gonionemus* are very similar to those of *Hydra*. Food is captured while the animal is swimming, with the aid of nematocysts, and conveyed to the mouth by the tentacles, or the *Gonionemus* lies with its aboral surface up, and any food that drops on its tentacles or manubrium are similarly engulfed. Only one type of nematocyst occurs in *Gonionemus*.

(4) Other Hydrozoa

Most members of this class are colonial, and typical species exist as polyps, which give rise by budding to free or sessile medusae. The medusae (with a few exceptions, e.g., *Obelia*) possess a velum and a nerve ring. There are no mesenteries in the polyp; the tentacles are usually solid; and the reproductive cells are ectodermal and discharged directly to the exterior. Four orders and a number of suborders are included here.

Order 1. Hydroida.   Hydrozoa with an attached hydroid stage.
Suborder 1. Anthomedusae (**Gymnoblastea**).   Perisarc usually covering coenosarc but not the polyps and reproductive individuals; medusae with gonads on the manubrium and with ocelli.

Hydra lives in fresh water; is solitary; has from 4 to 12 hollow tentacles; perisarc absent; no medusa. Most of the commonly occurring hydras of North America are dioecious, although a few species are hermaphroditic. *Hydra americana* is easily distinguished by the tentacles, of the extended individual, which are shorter than the column. *H. oligactis* and *H. pseudoligactis* are large hydras with a distinct stalk at the basal end. The male of the latter species has nipples on the testes and the threads within the holotrichous isorhizas are coiled transversely. *H. oligactis* lacks nipples on the testes, and the threads are coiled lengthwise in the isorhizas. *H. carnea* is small, reddish-brown, and the theca of the embryo has short spines. *H. littoralis*, found along shores and in moving water, has long spines on the theca of the embryo.

Chlorohydra viridissima, the green hydra, is small and hermaphroditic. Albino strains have been produced in the laboratory. It seems likely that the green hydra must acquire its symbiotic algae after hatching, because the

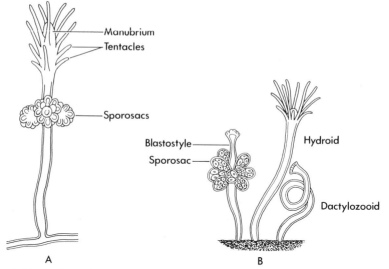

Fig. 3-21. Anthomedusae. (A) *Clava:* a hydroid bearing sporosacs. (B) *Hydractinia:* four types of individuals. (After Allman, from Fowler.)

reproductive structures develop in the epidermis, which lacks the algae found in the gastrodermis. Many of those hatched from eggs are albino.

Clava (Fig. 3–21, A) forms a nonbranching colony; the polyps rise from a filiform hydrorhiza and the tentacles are scattered irregularly over the hydranth; sporosacs are present at the base of the tentacles. *C. leptostyla* has reddish hydranths, about 20 tentacles, and pink (male) or purple (female) sporosacs; on *Fucus*, piles, etc.; Long Island northward.

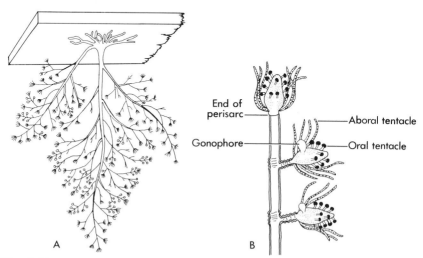

Fig. 3-22. Anthomedusae. (A) *Bougainvillia:* colony, natural size, hanging from floating object. (B) *Pennaria:* tip of branch. (A, after Allman; B, after Borradaile.)

Bougainvillia (Fig. 3–22, A) forms an arborescent colony; the hydranths possess a single whorl of filiform tentacles; the free-swimming medusa has four clusters of tentacles. *B. carolinensis* is about 10 cm high with prominent hypostome and 12 tentacles; the medusa is about 4 mm in diameter; on *Fucus*, piles, etc.; Cape Cod southward.

Eudendrium forms a branching colony; the polyps rise from a reticulated hydrorhiza; the hypostome is trumpet-shaped and has a single whorl of filiform tentacles; no medusae but sporosacs present. *E. ramosum* forms large colonies about 12 cm high; about 20 tentacles; sporosacs red (male) or orange (female); on rocks, piles, etc.; North Carolina northward.

Hydractinia (Fig. 3–21, B) forms an encrusting colony; the polyps are nutritive, reproductive, or defensive in function; no medusae. *H. echinata* forms a colony about 10 mm high; no tentacles are present on the reproductive polyps; on *Fucus*, rocks, piles, hermit crab shells, etc.; Atlantic Coast; similar to *H. milleri* of the Pacific Coast.

Podocoryne resembles *Hydractinia* but has a medusa with 8 or more long tentacles. *P. fulgurus* has a medusa about 1 mm high and 4 oral and 8 marginal tentacles; may be phosphorescent; Massachusetts to North Carolina.

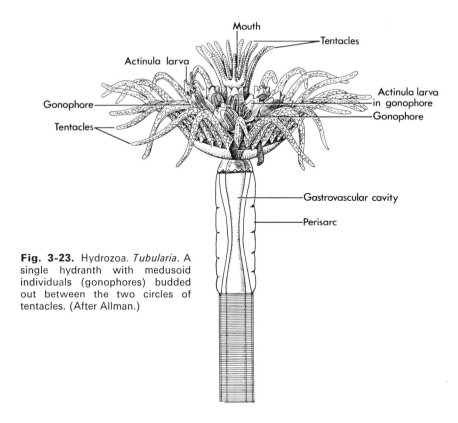

Fig. 3-23. Hydrozoa. *Tubularia*. A single hydranth with medusoid individuals (gonophores) budded out between the two circles of tentacles. (After Allman.)

Pennaria (Fig. 3–22, B) forms a regularly branching colony; the hydranth possesses 10 to 12 filiform basal tentacles and knobbed tentacles on the hypostome; medusa either sessile or free. *P. tiarella* is about 12 cm high; bright pink in color; medusae buds on side of hydranth, sessile or free; on rocks, piles, etc.; Maine southward.

Tubularia (Fig. 3–23) is solitary or forms large, pink colonies; the hydranth has one basal and one distal whorl or filiform tentacles; medusae attached to polyp; free-swimming, hydroid-like bodies are formed by medusoids. *T. crocea* forms dense tuft-like colonies about 9 cm high; with 20 to 24 basal tentacles; on piles, etc.; Massachusetts southward; California.

Suborder 2. Leptomedusae (*Calyptoblastea*). Perisarc covering coenosarc and becoming hydrothecae over nutritive polyps and gonothecae over reproductive polyps; medusae with gonads on the radial canals; usually statocysts.

Obelia has already been described in detail.

Sertularia has opposing pairs of hydrothecae along the stem; not joined to the stem by a stalk. *S. pumila* forms a branched colony about 3 cm high; gonangia oval; on *Fucus*, etc.; New Jersey northward. *S. furcata* is common on eelgrass, Pacific Coast.

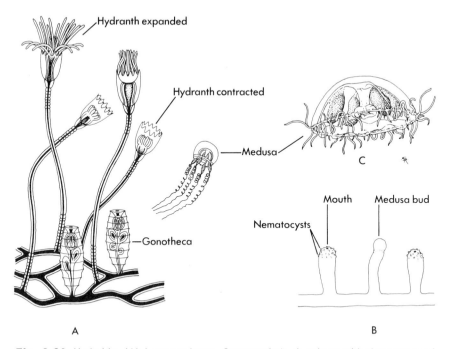

Fig. 3-24. Hydroida. (A) Leptomedusae. *Campanularia*. A colony with three types of individuals. (B) Limnomedusae. *Craspedacusta sowerbyi*. Polyp stage of the fresh-water jellyfish. (C) *C. sowerbyi*, medusa stage. (A, after Allman.)

Campanularia (Fig. 3–24) forms a simple or branched colony; hydrothecae bell-shaped and without operculum. *C. flexuosa* forms an irregularly branched colony about 25 mm high; stem annulated near base of branches; stalks of hydrothecae annulated; on piles, etc.; Long Island northward.

Suborder 3. Limnomedusae. Includes the fresh-water medusae and forms such as *Gonionemus*, already described in detail.

Craspedacusta sowerbyi (Fig. 3–24) lives in fresh water; has a small, colonial hydroid stage which lacks tentacles; medusae bud from the colony and develop up to 300 tentacles in four size groups; lithocysts up to 200 or more; manubrium long. The medusa has considerable resemblance to the medusa of *Gonionemus*. *Craspedacusta* occurs widely but sporadically in lakes and ponds in the United States. Populations of only one sex seem to occur more frequently than those with both sexes. Before the relationship of the hydroid and medusoid stage was known, the hydroid stage of *Craspedacusta* was named *Microhydra ryderi*.

Order 2. Trachylina. Hydrozoa without alternation of generations; medusae usually develop directly from eggs; tentaculocysts present; gonads on radial canals or on floor of gastric cavity.

Suborder 1. Trachymedusae. Marginal tentacles on edge of umbrella; gonads on radial canals; sense tentacles in pits or vesicles.

Liriope (Fig. 3–25, A) is hemispherical and has a long manubrium and six or eight closed lithocysts. *L. exigua* is about 2 cm in diameter; Gulf Stream, New England.

Aglantha has eight radial canals, eight gonads on the radial canals and free lithocysts. *A. digitale* is about 3 cm high and 1.5 cm in diameter; many tentacles; gonads long; North Atlantic.

Suborder 2. Narcomedusae. Marginal tentacles aboral from edge of umbrella; gonads on oral wall of stomach; sense tentacles not enclosed. No manubrium.

Cunina is rather flat and transparent; the larvae live as parasites within the umbrella of the mother or other medusae. *C. lativentris* is about 1.5 cm in diameter; 10 to 12 marginal lobes, tentacles and gastric pouches; four lithocysts on each lobe; Atlantic and Mediterranean.

Fig. 3-25. (A) Trachymedusae. *Liriope scutigera.* (B) Narcomedusae. *Cunoctantha octonaria.* (A, after Fewkes; B, after Brooks.)

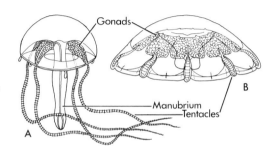

Cunoctantha (Fig. 3–25, B) has eight marginal lobes, tentacles and gastric pouches; larvae parasitic as in *Cunina*; larvae produce larvae by budding, *C. octonaria* is about 7 mm in diameter; cosmopolitan.

Suborder 3. Pteromedusae.   Contains the single genus, *Tetraplatia*, which is elongated along an oral-aboral axis. It possesses four equatorial swimming flaps, each with two statocysts. The nematocysts are all atrichous isorhizas, a condition found in one ctenophore. Other resemblances of trachyline medusae to the Ctenophora can be found in the genus *Hydroctena*.

Order 3. Hydrocorallina.   Hydrozoa with branched hydrorhiza; calcareous exoskeleton; polyps of two types, nutritive (gastrozooids) and for capturing prey (dactylozooids), arising from skeletal pits; medusoids from buds of the coenosarc, mostly confined to skeletal pits (ampullae).

Suborder 1. Milleporina.   Contains the single genus, *Millepora*, with separate pores for gastrozooids and dactylozooids. A common member of the coral reef fauna, *Millepora* (Fig. 3–26) forms a massive base from which irregular branches arise; polyps very contractile; gastrozooids with four or five knobbed tentacles; dactylozooids bear tentacles; each gastrozooid surrounded by five or six dactylozooids; medusa simple, with four or five rudimentary tentacles. *M. alcicornis* lives on the Florida coast; it is sometimes called the stinging coral because of its powerful nematocysts.

Suborder 2. Stylasterina.   These close relatives of the Milleporina have branching or encrusting calcareous exoskeletons. Tabulae are lacking in the polyp tubes, instead, a calcareous style extends up from the bottom of the tube into the base of the polyp. The polyp tubes contain grooves around the periphery, which are occupied by the dactylozooids surrounding the gastrozooid.

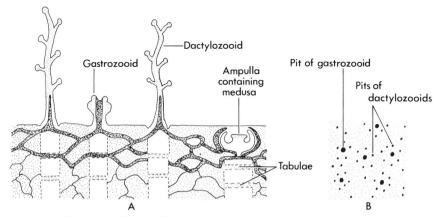

Fig. 3-26. Hydrocorallina. *Millepora.* (A) Diagrammatic section. Living canals shown in black; degenerating canals, by lines; skeleton, by stippling. (B) Surface view of skeleton. (A, from Borradaile and Potts, after Hickson.)

Order 4. Siphonophora. Pelagic, colonial Hydrozoa highly polymorphic; medusoid and hydroid members of the colony bud off from a coenosarc that arises from a planula larva. A *pneumatophore*, a sac filled with gas secreted by part of the epithelium, serves as a float for the colony, which may contain the following types of individuals.

1. *Hydrophyllium*: leaf-shaped; shields other members of the colony.

2. *Nectophore* (or *nectocalyx*): medusoid member modified for swimming; provides propulsion for the colony.

3. *Gastrozooid*: a hydroid member of the colony; mouth for ingestion of food; usually a single basally attached tentacle.

4. *Dactylozooid*: a hydroid member that lacks a mouth; long and tentacular; armed with nematocysts for defense and capture of prey.

5. *Gonozooid*: a medusoid member that produces the eggs or sperm.

Nanomia bijuga is a small siphonophore, which is so abundant at depths of about 1,000 feet over much of the ocean that depth-recording echo-sounders can detect their depth. Gas secreted within the pneumatophore of *Nanomia* is principally carbon monoxide. The bubble produced is less than 2 mm in diameter but effective in producing the sonic reverberations of the deep scattering layer of the ocean.

Fig. 3-27. Siphonophora. *Physalia*, the Portuguese man-of-war capturing a fish. (After Newman.)

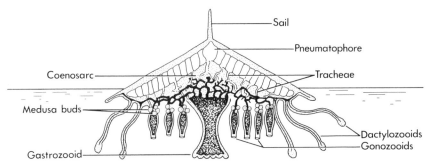

Fig. 3-28. Siphonophora. *Velella*. Vertical section. The cavity of the pneumatophore is in white; the network of the gastrodermal tubes are shown very dark. (After Haeckel, modified.)

Physalia (Fig. 3–27) has a bladder-like pneumatophore with a dorsal crest up to 12 cm in length that may contract forcing out the gas through a dorsal pore and thus bringing about submergence; a fresh supply of gas may be secreted bringing the colony to the surface again. There are no nectophores, movement from place to place being due to currents in the water or winds against the pneumatophore. *P. pelagica*, the Portuguese man-of-war, has stinging dactylozooids up to 45 feet long; it occurs in the Gulf Stream from Florida northward; specimens are often cast up on the shores. The dactylozooids are able to catch large fish, which, by contraction, they draw up to the gastrozooids; these enclose the prey in a digestive sac by spreading their lips over it. The dactylozooids are able to contract to one seventieth of their maximum length. They exhibit rhythmic contraction waves, neuromuscular in nature, that travel at an average rate of 121 mm per second.

Velella (Fig. 3–28) forms a colony that resembles a single medusa in appearance. The pneumatophore is a chambered disk from the center of the ventral surface of which hangs a single large gastrozooid surrounded by gonozooids, with a circlet of dactylozooids around the outer edge. Free medusae arise from the gonozooids. *V. mutica* has a pneumatophore about 4 cm long with an elevated ridge on the dorsal surface that serves as a sail; it occurs on the Atlantic Coast, especially southward. *V. lata* is often stranded in large numbers on California beaches.

Members of this order are especially dangerous to man when contact is made with their nematocysts.

2 / Class II. Scyphozoa

(1) Aurelia—A Scyphozoan Medusa

Aurelia (Fig. 3–29) is one of the commonest of the scyphozoan jellyfishes of both coasts. The species *A. flavidula* ranges from the coast of Maine to Florida. Members of the genus may be recognized by the eight shallow lobes of the umbrella margin, and the fringe of many small tentacles.

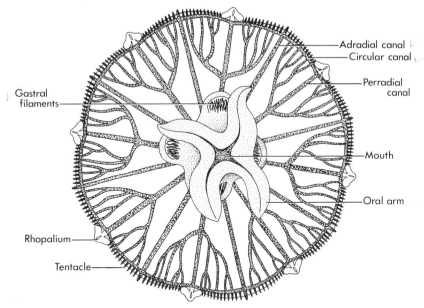

Fig. 3-29. Scyphozoa. *Aurelia aurita*. Ventral view. (After Shipley and MacBride, modified.)

In structure *Aurelia* differs from *Gonionemus* and other hydrozoan medusae in the absence of a velum, the characteristics of the canal system, the position of the gonads, and the arrangement and morphology of the sense organs.

The *oral lobes* or *lips* of *Aurelia*, which hang down from the square mouth, are long and narrow, with folded margins. The *mouth* opens into a short

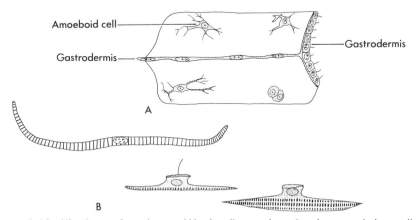

Fig. 3-30. Histology of medusae. (A) *Aurelia;* section showing wandering cells, gastrodermal cells and mesoglea. (B) *Lizzia;* above, muscular cell from subumbrella; below, two epithelio-muscular cells from base of tentacle. (After Hertwig, from Lankester.)

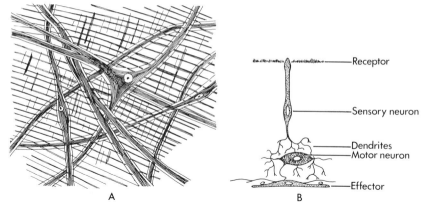

Fig. 3-31. *Aurelia aurita;* nerve cells. (A) Scattered nerve-ganglion cells from sub-umbrella. (B) Diagram of receptor-effector system. (A, after Schafer; B, after Parker.)

gullet, which leads to the somewhat rectangular "*stomach.*" A *gastric pouch* extends laterally from each side of the stomach. Within each gastric pouch is a *gonad* and a row of small *gastric filaments* bearing *nematocysts.* Numerous *radial canals,* some of which branch several times, lead from the stomach to a *circumferential canal* at the margin.

The circulation of fluid within the canals is due to the beating of cilia attached to the gastrodermal cells (Fig. 3–30, A); is definite in direction; and occupies a period of about 20 minutes. Water flows through the mouth into the gastric cavity; thence into the gastric pouches; through the adradial canals to the circular canal; into the interradial and perradial canals and out of exhalent grooves on the oral arms. Food particles carried by the circulating fluid are engulfed by gastrodermal cells.

The epidermal cells are more highly specialized for contraction than those of *Hydra* or *Gonionemus*; their bases are elongated into a cross-striated fiber capable of rapid rhythmic contraction (Fig. 3–30, B). An epidermal nerve net more complex than that of *Hydra* is also present (Fig. 3–31, A). A simple receptor-effector system exists in certain medusae similar to that illustrated in Figure 3–31, B. It consists of a receptor at the body surface ending in a nerve net which is associated with a nerve cell and thence with a muscle cell (effector).

There is a double nerve net in *Aurelia.* A main subumbrellar nerve net stimulates the muscles to cause pulsations of the medusa for locomotion. This net communicates at the rhopalial ganglia with a more diffuse net of the oral and aboral epidermal layer. The latter net controls feeding and other localized activities.

The eight *sense organs* of *Aurelia* lie between the marginal lappets (Figs. 3–29 and 3–32) and are known as *rhopalia.* They contain organs of *equilibrium.* As shown in Figure 3–32, each rhopalium is a hollow projection

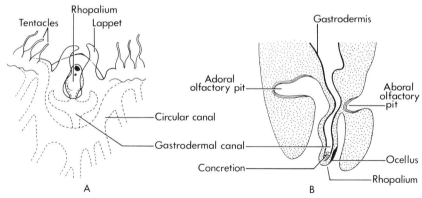

Fig. 3-32. *Aurelia aurita;* rhopalium. (A) Oral aspect. (B) Longitudinal section. (A, after Fowler; B, after Eimer, from Fowler.)

connected with the gastrodermal canal. It contains a number of calcareous concretions formed by the gastrodermis, and bears an epidermal pigment spot, the ocellus (Fig. 3–33), which is sensitive to light. The rhopalium is protected by an aboral hood and by lateral lappets. *Olfactory pits* are situated near by.

The gonads are frill-like organs lying in the floor of the gastric pouches. They have a pinkish hue in the living animal. The eggs or spermatozoa pass through the stomach and out of the mouth. An *alternation of generations* occurs in *Aurelia*, but the hydroid stage is subordinate. The eggs develop into free-swimming planulae which become attached to some object and produce hydra-like structures, each of which is called a *scyphistoma* (Fig. 3–34). This

Fig. 3-33. *Aurelia aurita;* section of double eye. (After Schewiakoff, from Dahlgren and Kepner.)

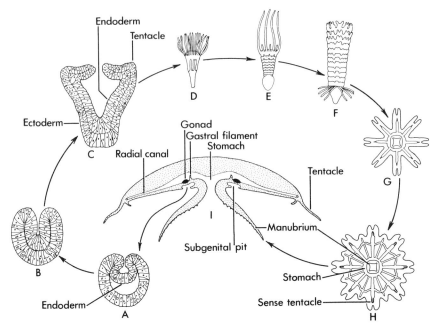

Fig. 3-34. *Aurelia:* life history. *A, B, C,* longitudinal sections through gastrula stages; *D,* scyphistoma; *E, F,* strobila; *G, H,* ephyra; *I,* vertical section through adult. (*A, B,* and *C* are more highly magnified than the other figures.) (From Kerr.)

buds like *Hydra* during most of the year, but finally a peculiar process called *strobilization* takes place. The scyphistoma divides into disks which cause it to resemble a pile of saucers. Each disk develops tentacles, and, separating from those below it, swims away as a minute medusa called an *ephyra*. The ephyra gradually develops into an adult jellyfish.

(2) Other Scyphozoa

Most of the larger jellyfishes belong to the Scyphozoa. They can be distinguished easily from the hydrozoan medusae by the presence of notches, usually eight in number, in the margin of the umbrella. They are called acraspedote (without velum or craspedon) medusae in contrast to the craspedote (with velum or craspedon) medusae of the Hydrozoa. The Scyphozoa usually range from an inch to 3 or 4 feet in diameter, but some have been reported over 7 feet in diameter with tentacles over 90 feet long. They are all marine and are usually found floating near the surface of the sea, though some of them are attached to rocks and weeds. There is an alternation of generations in their life history, but the asexual stage (the scyphistoma, Fig. 3–34, D) is subordinate. The class contains five orders.

Order 1. Stauromedusae (Fig. 3–35, A). Scyphozoa without rhopalia; tentacles perradial and interradial; umbrella goblet-shaped, temporarily

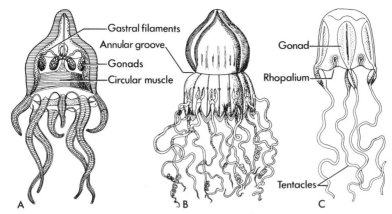

Fig. 3-35. Scyphozoa. (A) Order Stauromedusae: *Tercera princeps.* (B) Order Coronatae: *Periphylla hyacinthina.* (C) Order Cubomedusae: *Charybdea marsupialis.* (From Sedgwick, after Haeckel.)

attached by a narrow stalk at aboral pole; a stomodaeum is present, suspended by four mesenteries; no alternation of generations.

Lucernaria has no rhopalioids (adhesive pads) between the eight lobes; stalk cylindrical. *L. quadricornis* is about 7 cm high and 5 cm in diameter; red, gray, or green; 100 or more tentacles on each lobe; Massachusetts northward, Europe.

Haliclystus has a margin with eight lobes bearing many knobbed tentacles and eight rhopalioids between the lobes; stalk quadrate. *H. auricular* is about 3 cm high and 3 cm in diameter; 100 or more tentacles on each lobe; Massachusetts northward, Alaska, Europe.

Order 2. Coronatae. Scyphozoa with four interradial rhopalia; tentacles perradial and adradial; umbrella conical, with transverse constriction; a stomodaeum is present suspended by four mesenteries; no alternation of generations.

Periphylla has 16 marginal lobes, 12 tentacles, and horseshoe-shaped gonads. *P. hyacinthina* (Fig. 3–35, B) is about 8 cm high and 4 cm in diameter; reddish in color; cosmopolitan.

Order 3. Cubomedusae. Scyphozoa with four perradial rhopalia; tentacles interradial; umbrella four-sided, cup-shaped; no alternation of generations.

Charybdea (Fig. 3–35, C) has a bell from 2 to 23 cm high and 4 interradial tentacles. *C. xaymacana* is transparent; lives in shallow water; is an active swimmer and a voracious feeder, ingesting comparatively large fish.

Order 4. Semaeostomeae. Scyphozoa with four or more perradial and four or more interradial rhopalia; umbrella disk-shaped; alternation of generations. This order contains most of the Scyphozoa.

Aurelia has already been described in detail.

Dactylometra has a quadrate mouth with four long, oral lobes, 40 hollow marginal tentacles, 48 marginal lobes, and eight rhopalia. *D. quinquecirrha*, the common sea nettle, reaches a diameter of 25 cm; Long Island southward.

Cyanea is a large disk-shaped medusa with no marginal tentacles but eight groups of very long tentacles on the subumbrella; long, large oral lobes. *C. capillata* is our largest jellyfish ranging from 10 cm to 2 meters in diameter and possessing tentacles over 40 feet long; North Carolina northward.

Order 5. Rhizostomeae. Scyphozoa with no tentacles; typically eight rhopalia; mouth obliterated by fusion of the oral arms, secondary mouths remain at the ends of the oral arms where the grooves have not completely fused. *Cassiopeia* has eight mouth arms bearing numerous small appendages; Florida and the West Indies.

3 / Class III. Anthozoa

(1) Metridium—A Sea Anemone

Metridium marginatum (Fig. 3–36) is a sea anemone, which fastens itself to the piles of wharves and to solid objects in tidepools along the North Atlantic Coast and the Pacific Coast. It is a cylindrical animal with an *oral disk* consisting of hollow *tentacles* arranged in a number of circlets about the slit-like

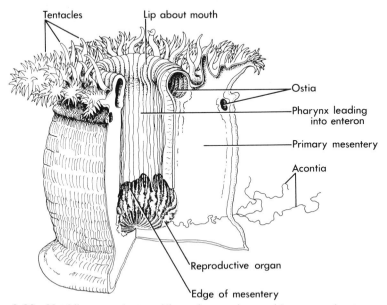

Fig. 3-36. *Metridium marginatum.* View of a specimen with one quadrant removed. (From Woodruff.)

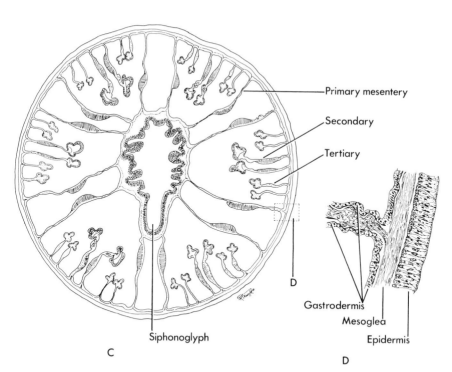

Fig. 3-37. Mesenteries (septa) of sea anemones as seen in transverse sections. (A) Section through the stomodeum of *Peachia*. (B) Section through a typical actinian. (C) Transverse section of *Metridium*. (D) Junction of mesentery and body wall of *Metridium*. (A, from Kerr; B, from Borradaile and Potts; C, D, original.)

mouth. The tentacles as well as the body, or *column*, can be expanded and contracted, and the animal's position may be changed by a sort of creeping movement of its *basal disk.* The *skin* is soft but tough and contains no skeletal structures. The tentacles capture small organisms by means of *nematocysts,* and carry the food thus obtained into the mouth. The beating of the *cilia* which cover the tentacles and part of the mouth and *gullet* is necessary to force the food into the *gastrovascular cavity.* At either side of the pharynx, or *stomodaeum,* is a ciliated groove called the *siphonoglyph.* Usually only one or two siphonogylphs are present, but sometimes three occur in a single specimen. A continual stream of water is carried into the body cavity through these siphonoglyphs, thus maintaining a constant supply of oxygenated water.

If a sea anemone is dissected, the central or *gastrovascular cavity* will be found to consist of six radial chambers; these lie between the pharynx or stomodaeum and the body wall, and open into a common basal cavity. The six pairs of thin, double partitions between these chambers are called *primary septa* or *mesenteries* (Fig. 3–37). Water passes from one chamber to another through pores (*ostia*) in these mesenteries. Smaller mesenteries project out from the body wall into the chambers, but do not reach the stomodaeum; these are *secondary septa. Tertiary septa* and *quaternary septa* lie between the primaries and secondaries. There is considerable variation in the number, position, and size of the septa.

Each mesentery possesses a longitudinal retractor *muscle band.* The bands of the pairs of mesenteries face each other except those of the primaries opposite the siphonoglyphs. These primaries, which are called *directives,* have the muscle bands on their outer surfaces. The edges of the mesenteries below the stomodaeum are provided with *septal filaments* having a secretory function. Near the base these filaments bear long, delicate threads called *acontia.* The acontia are armed with *gland cells* and *nematocysts,* and can be protruded from the mouth or through minute pores (cinclides) in the body wall. They probably serve as organs of digestion, offense, and defense.

Near the edge of the mesenteries lying parallel to the mesenteric filaments are the *gonads.* The animals are dioecious, and the eggs or spermatozoa are shed into the gastrovascular cavity and pass out through the mouth. The fertilized egg develops as in other sea anemones, forming first a free-swim-

Fig. 3-38. *Metridium.* A stage in binary fission. (After Agassiz and Parker.)

Fig. 3-39. *Astrangia*. A specimen with tentacles extended from the theca. (From Johnson and Snook.)

Corallite

Sclerosepta

ming planula and then, after attaching itself to some object, assuming the shape and structure of the adult.

Asexual reproduction is of common occurrence, new anemones being formed by *budding* or *fragmentation* at the edge of the basal disk. *Longitudinal fission* has also been reported (Fig. 3–38). Fragmentation, or *pedal laceration*, which results when the animal creeps away on the basal disk while a portion remains attached, is a successful method of reproduction because of the great regenerative powers of the basal disk. The presence or absence of directives in the regenerating fragments has considerable influence on the organization that develops, e.g., those without directives may lack a siphonoglyph. Thus, anemones produced by this method of reproduction show great variation.

(2) Astrangia—A Coral Polyp

Astrangia danae (Fig. 3–39) is a coral polyp inhabiting the waters of our North Atlantic Coast. A number of individuals live together in colonies attached to rocks near the shore. Each polyp looks like a small sea anemone, being cylindrical in shape and possessing a crown of tentacles. The most noticeable difference is the presence of a basal cup of calcium carbonate termed the *corallite* (Fig. 3–40). This structure of calcium carbonate is what

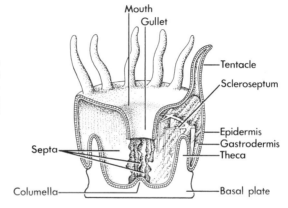

Mouth

Gullet

Fig. 3-40. Semidiagrammatic view of one-half of a simple coral polyp showing relationship of soft parts to theca (corallite). (From Shipley and MacBride.)

Tentacle

Scleroseptum

Epidermis

Gastrodermis

Theca

Septa

Columella

Basal plate

we commonly call coral. It is produced by the epidermis of the coral polyp and increases gradually during the life of the animal.

The corallite is divided into chambers by a number of radial *sclerosepta*, which are built up between the pairs of mesenteries of the polyp. The center of the cup is occupied by a *columella* formed in part by the fusion of the inner ends of septa, and in part by projections from the base of the polyp. Although *Astrangia* builds a cup less than half an inch in height, it produces enormous masses of coral in the course of centuries.

The food of *Astrangia* consists of small organisms, such as algae, Protozoa, hydroids, worms, crustaceans, and mollusks. These organisms are ingested as a result of the muscular action of the tentacles and central part of the oral disk. The mucus secreted by the oral disk and cilia of the stomodaeum also play a part in ingestion. A protease of digestive value is secreted into the gastrovascular cavity, but most digestion is intracellular. Food particles are engulfed by the mesenterial filaments in which food vacuoles are formed. The reaction of these vacuoles is at first acid but changes to alkaline. Digestion probably occurs during the period of alkalinity. Some specimens contain Zooxanthellae, which utilize some of the waste products of the polyp and release some oxygen that the polyp can use. Some may also be digested by the polyp. The colorful flesh of most corals of shallow water is due to the presence of these flagellates.

(3) Other Anthozoa

The Anthozoa or Actinozoa are solitary or colonial coelenterates with a polyp stage but no medusae. The polyps have a coelenteron divided into chambers by radially arranged membranes known as mesenteries. A stomodaeum is present. Most of the Anthozoa secrete a calcareous skeleton, which we know as coral. Two subclasses with several orders in each are presented in the following discussion.

Subclass I. Zoantharia

Anthozoa with usually many simple hollow tentacles, arranged generally in multiples of five or six; two siphonoglyphs as a rule; mesenteries vary in number; skeleton absent or present; simple or colonial; dimorphism rare.

Order 1. Actiniaria. Zoantharia usually solitary; many complete mesenteries; no skeleton. These are the sea anemones many of which are beautifully colored; in the large *Stoichactis* of the Great Barrier Reef of Australia, gray, white, lilac, green, and yellow may be found on the same individual.

Metridium has already been described in detail.

Edwardsia is a slender, solitary type of sea anemone with 16 tentacles in two circlets of eight each. *E. leidyi* is about 3 cm long and 1.5 mm in diameter; it is parasitic on a ctenophore, *Mnemiopsis leidyi*.

Fig. 3-41. Corals on the Great Barrier Reef of Australia. (A) A shallow pool showing several types of coral colonies. (B) The underside of a fragment of coral rock covered with many invertebrates. (Photos by author.)

Halcampa has a long, slender body consisting of three parts, a foot region, a central region usually covered with sand, and an oral retractile region; habitat, sand or mud. *H. farinacea* is about 2 cm long and 3 mm in diameter; 12 tentacles in two circlets: Massachusetts northward.

Sagartia possesses a sphincter, acontia, and cinclides; three or four circlets of retractile tentacles; surface smooth; oral disk not lobed. *S. luciae* is about 8 mm long and 6 mm in diameter; four rows of tentacles, 84 in all; olive green with orange longitudinal stripes; Long Island northward.

Order 2. Madreporaria or Scleractinia (Figs. 3–41 and 3–42). Zoantharia usually colonial; many complete mesenteries; calcareous skeleton formed by ectoderm cells. Most of the stony corals belong to this order. Many of the coral polyps are tinted with pink, lilac, yellow, green, violet, red, etc., and give the coral reefs the wonderful color effects for which they are famous.

Astrangia has already been described.

Porites forms a more or less branching porous colony with zooids close together; cup with 12 short septa. *P. porites* occurs in Florida and the West Indies.

Fig. 3-42. Coral skeletons showing variations produced by different sizes and arrangements of polyps.

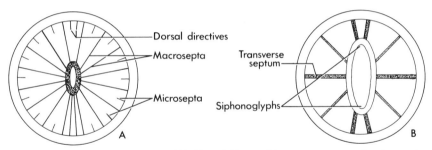

Fig. 3-43. Septal arrangement. (A) Zoanthidea, with macrosepta and microsepta. The gonads develop on the macrosepta. (B) Antipatharia, gonads develop on the transverse septa.

Oculina forms a dendritic compact colony with zooids spirally arranged and widely separated. *O. diffusa* is much branched; cup 3 mm. in diameter; North Carolina to Florida.

Meandrina has confluent zooids with septa in rows. *M. sinuosa* forms massive, encrusting colonies up to 25 cm or more in diameter and is known as brain coral; the sinuous ridges on the surface are septa and grooves; Florida and West Indies.

Fungia has no siphonoglyph; solitary; large; concave below and convex above. *F. elegans* is about 6 cm in diameter; Gulf of California.

Acropora is an important genus of reef-building corals. Most species of *Acropora*, such as the stag-horn coral, are branched colonies.

Order 3. Zoanthidea. Zoantharia without skeletons; macrosepta alternate with microsepta (Fig. 3–43, A) except in the region of the directives; gonads occur on the macrosepta. Solitary and colonial forms occur. Usually small polyps.

Order 4. Antipathidea (Fig. 3–43, B). Colonial Zoantharia with a horny, usually branching axial skeleton, but no calcareous spicules; in all the large seas, usually at a depth of from 50 to 500 fathoms; black corals.

Antipathes forms branching colonies of long slender stalks; polyps with six tentacles. *A. larix* has an axis with many long spines; up to 3 feet long; six longitudinal rows of parallel branches from 3 to 10 cm long along main stalk; West Indies, Mediterranean.

Cirripathes is unbranched. *C. spiralis* has a flexible spiral stalk over 3 feet long; West Indies, Mediterranean, Indian Ocean.

Order 5. Ceriantharia. Large, solitary Zoantharia that live embedded in the sand. *Cerianthus* (Fig. 3–44) is the best known representative. It possesses many tentacles in two rows and one siphonoglyph. The epidermis secretes a long tube of mucus in which the animal lives. Several species are found in California. *C. americanus* occurs from Cape Cod to Florida. It reaches a length of 60 cm and is about 25 mm in diameter. As many as 130 tentacles

Fig. 3-44. Actiniaria. *Cerianthus,* a solitary sea anemone with many tentacles. (After Andres, from Hickson.)

may be present. Members of this order may have a variety of foreign objects embedded in their secreted tubes.

Subclass 2. Alcyonaria

Anthozoa with eight hollow, pinnate tentacles, and eight complete septa; usually with one siphonoglyph, ventral in position; retractor muscles of the septa all on the side toward the siphonoglyph; nematocysts are atrichous isorhizas; all are colonial and embedded in a *coenenchyme* of mesoglea; polyps are connected in the coenenchyme by a network of gastrodermal tubes, the *solenia,* and at the surface by the epidermis (Fig. 3–45); new polyps arise from solenial buds; many have a horny or calcareous skeleton secreted by the coenenchyme.

Order 1. Alcyonacea. Massive or creeping colonies. May be separated into four suborders.

Suborder 1. Alcyonaceae. The soft corals. Alcyonarians with the polyps embedded in a fleshy coenenchyme. *Alcyonium* (Fig. 3–45) forms a colony of thick, soft, leathery lobes; polyps long but all except distal end buried in the mesoglea. *A. carneum* is from 4 to 10 cm high; yellow or red; Long Island northward.

Suborder 2. Coenothecaleae. The blue coral, *Heliopora,* of the Indo-Pacific is the only genus. Polyps brown, skeleton blue from iron salts.

Suborder 3. Stoloniferae. Typically with the polyps arising singly from a creeping base. However, in *Tubipora musica* (Fig. 3–46), the organ pipe coral, the polyps are joined together by horizontal bars. The polyps are bright

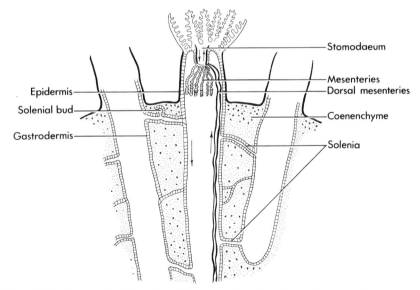

Fig. 3-45. Alcyonaria. *Alcyonium.* Diagram of section through colony showing extended polyps with pinnate tentacles and coenenchyme. The direction of water circulation is shown by arrows. The mesoglea is indicated by dots and the spicules it contains by small crosses. (From Borradaile and Potts.)

green and when disturbed will retract into their tubes and thus reveal the dull red skeleton. Found on coral reefs in Old and New World.

Suborder 4. Telestaceae. With lateral polyps arising from elongated polyps which are connected by the creeping base.

Order 2. Gorgonacea (Fig. 3–47, C). Colonial Alcyonaria; skeletal axis branched and not perforated by gastrovascular cavities of the zooids; the horny corals such as the sea whips.

A

B

Fig. 3-46. Alcyonacea. *Tubipora musica,* skeleton of the organ-pipe coral. (A) Surface view. Note lack of sclerosepta. (B) Perspective view.

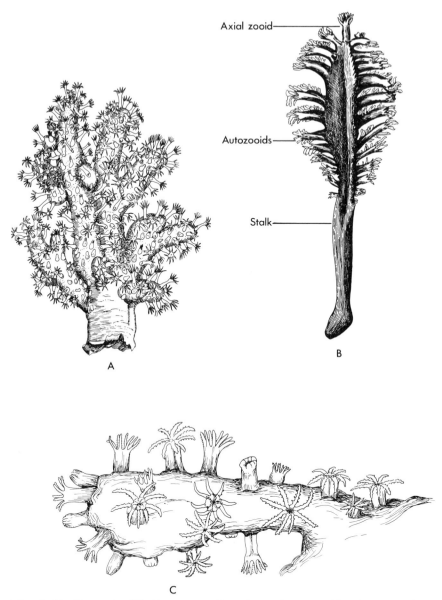

Fig. 3-47. Alcyonaria. (A) Alcyonacea. *Alcyonium palmatum*, with polyps extended. (B) Pennatulacea. *Pennatula*, a sea feather or sea pen. (C) Gorgonacea. *Euplexaura marki*, with polyps extended. (A, from Kerr; B, after Jungerson; C, from Johnson and Snook.)

Corallium forms the precious red coral of commerce; polyps retractile, white; axis hard, red. *C. nobile* (*rubrum*) is up to 30 cm high; Mediterranean.

Gorgonia produces a fan-shaped colony in which the branches unite to form a network in one plane. *G. flabellum* is the sea fan; up to 50 cm high and wide; yellow or red; West Indies, South Atlantic.

Order 3. Pennatulacea. Alcyonaria forming bilaterally symmetrical colonies; zooids usually borne on branches of an axial stem, which is supported by a calcareous or horny skeleton; zooids dimorphic; sea pens and sea feathers. *Pennatula* (Fig. 3–47, B) is called a sea feather; stalk embedded in sand or mud; distal end of stalk (rachis) with paired lateral branches (pinnulae). *P. aculeata* has from 20 to 50 long pinnulae on each side; about 10 cm long; red; South Carolina northward.

Renilla forms a circular or reniform (kidney-shaped) rachis; polyps all dorsal. *R. reniformis* has white polyps; dorsal surface of rachis pink or violet; about 7 cm long; North and South Carolina, West Indies.

4 / Coelenterata in General

Morphology. The foregoing account has shown that coelenterates all possess a body wall composed of three layers, the outer epidermis and inner gastrodermis separated by mesoglea. In the *Hydra* the mesoglea is an essentially noncellular layer. Most have thicker mesoglea containing cells but no organs and thus show a tissue-level organization. Mesoglea is especially extensive in the jellyfish composing most of the jelly-like material of the organism. In the Anthozoa the mesoglea is most highly developed as a tissue and contains a variety of cells and fibers. The body wall encloses a single cavity, the *coelenteron* or *gastrovascular cavity*, in which both digestion and circulation take place. In some of the coelenterates, like *Hydra* (Fig. 3–2), this cavity is simple, but in others, like *Aurelia* (Fig. 3–29), it is modified so as to include numerous pouches and branching canals.

All coelenterates possess stinging cells called *nematocysts*; these are organelles of offense, defense, locomotion and, probably, digestion. *Muscle fibrils* (Fig. 3–30) are present in a more or less concentrated condition. *Nerve fibers* and *sensory organs* are characteristic structures; they may be few in number and scattered as in *Hydra* (Fig. 3–8), or numerous and concentrated as in *Aurelia* (Fig. 3–31). Nerve fibers form a network, which is nonpolarized, i.e., the impulses may be conducted in any direction over the network. Some are reported to have synaptic junctions between neurons as well as nonsynaptic ones, which are more characteristic of coelenterates. Two networks of nerve fibers may occur in coelenterates, one in the epidermis and one in the mesoglea, with some interconnections. Some coelenterate epithelial tissues lack nerve fibers but are able to conduct impulses.

Hydroid and Medusa Compared. The two principal types of coelenterates are the *polyp* or *hydroid*, and the *jellyfish* or *medusa*. These are fundamentally similar in structure (Fig. 3–48), but are variously modified (Fig. 3–49). Both

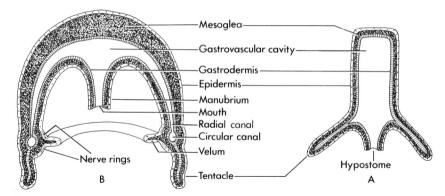

Fig. 3-48. Diagrams showing the similarities of a polyp (A) and a medusa (B). (From Parker and Haswell.)

polyps and medusae are *radially symmetrical.* Although the medusae upon superficial examination appear to be very different from the polyps or hydroids, they are constructed on the same general plan as the latter. Figure 3–48 illustrates in a diagrammatic fashion the resemblance between the hydrozoan polyp (A) and medusa (B) by means of longitudinal sections. If the medusa were grasped at the center of the aboral surface and elongated, a hydra-like form would result. Both have similar parts, the most noticeable difference being the enormous quantity of mesoglea present in the medusa.

Metagenesis. Metagenesis is the alternation of a generation which reproduces only asexually by division or budding with a generation which reproduces only sexually by means of eggs and spermatozoa. This phenomenon occurs in other groups of the animal kingdom, but finds its best examples among the Hydrozoa. *Obelia* is an excellent illustration of a metagenetic animal. The asexual generation, the colony of polyps (Fig. 3–17), forms buds of two kinds, the hydranths and the gonangia. The medusae (Fig. 3–18, A), or sexual generation, reproduce the colony by means of eggs and spermatozoa.

The polyp and medusa stages are not equally important in all Hydrozoa; for example, *Hydra* has no medusa stage and *Geryonia* no polyp or hydroid stage. Various conditions may be illustrated by different Hydrozoa. In the following list, O represents the fertilized ovum, H, a polyp, M, a medusa, m, an inconspicuous or degenerate medusa, and h, an inconspicuous or degenerate polyp.

1. O—H—O—H—O (*Hydra*).
2. H—m—O—H—m—O (*Sertularia*).
3. O—H—M—O—H—M—O (*Obelia*).
4. O—h—M—O—h—M—O (*Liriope*).
5. O—M—O—M—O (*Geryonia*).

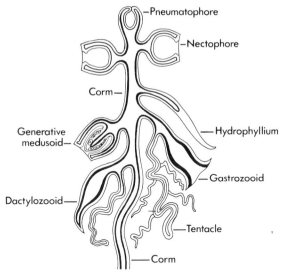

Fig. 3-49. Siphonophora. Diagram showing possible modifications of medusoids and hydroids. The thick black line represents gastrodermis, the thinner line epidermis. (After Allman.)

The past tendency to emphasize the importance of the concept of metagenesis is dwindling in significance. Some zoologists think that the generations represent developmental (larval?) stages in the life cycle leading to the sexually mature adult (the medusae when present). Thus, the complete cycle from egg to egg is one generation. Probably the most significant fact of metagenesis, or different stages in the life cycle of invertebrates, is the ecological advantages it confers on the species.

In those with a sessile stage, the alternation with a planktonic stage provides a means of dispersal as well as a location where a different food source may be involved. When each has a large reproductive capacity, one sexual, the other asexual, the species is less likely to be eliminated due to predation, disease, or competition if a stage occupying another habitat can restock the original habitat.

Polymorphism.   The division of labor among the cells of a Metazoan has already been noted. When division of labor occurs among the members of a colony, the form of the individual is suited to the function it performs. A colony containing two kinds of members is said to be *dimorphic*; one containing more than two kinds, *polymorphic*. Some of the most remarkable cases of polymorphism occur among the Hydrozoa (Fig. 3–49). The "Portuguese man-of-war" (Fig. 3–27), e.g., consists of a float with a sail-like crest from which a number of polyps hang down into the water. Some of these polyps are nutritive, others are tactile; some contain batteries of nematocysts, others are male reproductive zooids, and still others give rise to egg-producing medusae. The following outline indicates some of the modifications that may occur among the members of colonial Hydrozoa.

A. Polymorphic modifications of hydrozoan medusae.
   1. Sexual Medusoid.
      a. Structure. Like typical medusa of Anthomedusae or modified because of arrested development. (The hydrophyllium (bract), pneumatophore, and aurophore are considered by some to be modifications of a part of a medusa.)
      b. Function. Production of ova or spermatozoa. (Hydrophyllia are protective, pneumatophores are hydrostatic structures, and aurophores of unknown function.
   2. Nectophore.
      a. Structure. Without tentacles, manubrium, or mouth.
      b. Function. Locomotion.
B. Polymorphic modifications of hydrozoan hydroids.
   1. Gastrozooid.
      a. Structure. With large mouth, nematocysts, and tentacle bearing nematocysts.
      b. Function. Ingestion of food.
   2. Dactylozooid.
      a. Structure. Without mouth; with many nematocysts and tentacles.
      b. Function. Offense and defense.
   3. Blastostyle.
      a. Structure. Without mouth or tentacles.
      b. Function. Produces sexual medusoids by budding.

Physiology. The *food* of coelenterates consists principally of small, free-swimming animals, which are usually captured by means of nematocysts and carried into the mouth by tentacles and cilia. *Digestion* is mainly *extracellular*, enzymes being discharged into the gastrovascular cavities for this purpose. Starch digestion has not been observed in coelenterates. Nematocysts are thought to be an important source of proteases in the early stages of digestion. The digested food is transported to various parts of the body by currents in the gastrovascular cavity and is then taken up by the gastrodermal cells; some is passed over to the epidermal cells. Both *respiration* and *excretion* are performed by the general surface of the epidermis and gastrodermis. *Motion* is made possible by muscle fibrils, and many species have also the power of *locomotion*. Planktonic forms may swim by pulsations that expel currents of water, bottom dwelling forms may use various methods of creeping. There is no true skeleton, although fluid in the gastrovascular cavity or in the cells may serve as a hydraulic skeleton (Fig. 3–11), and the stony masses built up by coral polyps support the soft tissues to a certain extent. The nervous tissue and sensory organs provide for the perception of various kinds of stimuli and the conduction of impulses from one part of the body to another. Coelenterates are generally sensitive to light intensities, to changes in the temperature, to mechanical stimuli, to chemical stimuli, and to gravity. *Reproduction* is both asexual, by budding and fission, and sexual, by means of eggs and spermatozoa.

Asexual reproduction is characteristic of some coelenterates and rare or absent in others. The most common method is by *budding.* The wall of the hydroid sends out a hollow protrusion which may become either a new hydroid or a medusa. Certain medusae also produce medusae by budding. *Fission* is rare in hydroids and very rare in medusae.

Sexual Reproduction.   Both male and female germ cells are rarely developed by a single individual as in certain hydras. Usually a colony produces either ova or spermatozoa, or these originate in different individuals of a single colony. Sometimes one blastostyle may give rise to both kinds of germ cells.

Embryology.   *Tubularia* may be selected to illustrate the embryology of a hydrozoan (Fig. 3–50). Segmentation of the egg results in a hollow *blastula* of cells of different sizes. Cells are divided off from the wall into the cavity of the blastula until this cavity is completely filled. Spaces now appear among

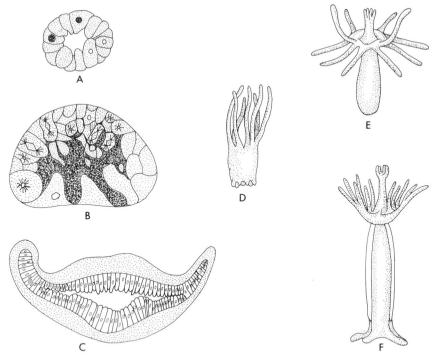

Fig. 3-50. *Tubularia.* Stages in the embryology of a hydrozoan. (A) Blastula. (B) Endoderm cells budding off from wall of blastula. (C) Formation of aboral tentacles. (D) Aboral tentacles well developed; oral tentacles appearing. (E) Larva in creeping stage. (F) Larva at time of attachment to substratum. (A, B, C, after Brauer; D, E, F, after Allman.)

the inner mass of cells due to their absorption, and eventually a single central cavity results which will become the *coelenteron* or gastric cavity. The outer layer of cells of this *gastrula* is the *ectoderm* and the inner layer, the *endoderm*. The embryo now becomes disk-shaped and from the edge *aboral tentacles* grow out. Then the embryo elongates into a cylindrical form; a *mouth* opening appears in the center of the end opposite the aboral tentacles; and *oral tentacles* are pushed out around the mouth. This *actinula larva* (Figs. 3–23 and 3–50, E) escapes from the gonophore and sinks to the bottom where it becomes attached by the aboral end. It increases in length; *buds* appear at the sides; and creeping *stolons* grow out from the base. The latter give rise to upright shoots each of which produces daughters by lateral budding.

The embryology of a scyphozoan such as *Aurelia* (Fig. 3–34), differs considerably from that of *Tubularia*. The egg of *Aurelia* undergoes *cleavage* that results in the formation of a hollow, spherical *blastula*. This becomes invaginated into a *gastrula* with two layers of cells, an outer *ectoderm* and an inner *endoderm*, and with a central cavity, the *coelenteron*, which communicates with the outside through a *blastopore*. The ectoderm becomes ciliated and the gastrula changes from spherical to oval in shape. After a free-swimming existence of 4 or 5 days the *planula* larva attaches at the aboral end and assumes a cup shape. A cone now arises with the blastopore in the center and four *primary tentacles* grow out around the blastopore which may now be called the *mouth*. These tentacles are solid, with a central core of endoderm covered by a layer of ectoderm. The larva changes gradually into the *scyphistoma* stage. Four *secondary tentacles* now grow out alternating with the primary tentacles; next eight more tentacles develop and soon another set of eight all of which form a single circlet of 24 tentacles around the mouth. Meanwhile *nematocysts* are formed in the epidermis and groups of them appear like warts on the tentacles.

Phylogeny. Speculation regarding the origin of the Coelenterata and their differentiation into classes is a fascinating pastime. Three views having some adherants are the (1) protozoan origin of coelenterates by way of the ciliates or flagellates and a planula-like intermediate form, (2) origin from the sponges (Fig. 2–21, B), and (3) origin from the flatworms. Elaborate arguments for the latter view have been presented by Hadzi (1963) and rejected by Hand (1963). Variations of the first view are most popular and Hyman (1940) describes an actinula-like ancestral type for the coelenterates that is as plausible as any. Interrelationships of the coelenterate classes is also speculative. The Hydrozoa with well-developed medusae and hydroid stages seem nearest the ancestral type with the Trachylina showing closest affinities to the Scyphozoa and Anthozoa.

Only a few deny that the Coelenterata gave rise to the Ctenophora. They also seem to be near the ancestral type of the Platyhelminthes. The danger of such assumptions is pointed out by Ax (1963),

In numerous phylogenetic speculations is to be found the erroneous suggestion that one recent great systematic group is derived directly from another. But the undeniable fact is that contemporaneous orders, classes, and phyla have a long evolutionary history extending far back in geological time. Thus it is quite impossible to derive the Turbellaria directly from such recent groups as the Ciliata, Cnidaria, Ctenophora, or Annelida.

As with many invertebrates, the fossil record of the coelenterates, other than corals, is rather meager and inadequate to prove their phylogeny. Even the question of whether their primitive symmetry was radial, as in most adult coelenterates, or bilateral, as in the planula larva (and perhaps many corals) is not solved.

The History of Our Knowledge of the Coelenterata. The coelenterates were originally called Zoophyta or plant-animals. They were included by Cuvier, together with the ctenophores and echinoderms, in a division known as Radiata, principally because of their radial symmetry. The study of echinoderm embryology proved these animals to be fundamentally bilaterally symmetrical, and a comparison of the anatomy of adult coelenterates and echinoderms revealed the absence of a coelom in the former, as well as many other profound differences. Leuckart in 1847 coined the term Coelenterata for the group and elevated them to a distinct phylum. The term *polypus* we owe to Trembley who introduced the name in 1744 because *Hydra* resembles somewhat in appearance the octopus which was known to the ancients as the polyp. Linnaeus and his predecessors called the jellyfish *medusae* since their tentacles reminded them of the curls of *Medusa*. At first the coelenterates and ctenophores were both included in the phylum Coelenterata but the ctenophores are so distinct they are now usually considered as a separate phylum.

Relations of Coelenterates to Man. Coelenterates as a whole are of very little economic importance. They are probably very seldom used as food by man but are eagerly devoured by fishes. Some corals are used as ornaments and for the manufacture of jewelry. Coral polyps build *fringing reefs, barrier reefs,* and *atolls* (Fig. 3–41). These occur where conditions are favorable, principally in tropical seas, the best known being Bikini Atoll, Eniwetok Atoll, and the Fiji Islands of the Pacific Ocean, the Great Barrier Reef of Australia, and in the Bahama Island region.

A *fringing* or *shore reef* is a ridge of coral built up from the sea bottom so near the land that no navigable channel exists between it and the shore. Frequently breaks occur in the reef, and irregular channels and pools are created which are often inhabited by many different kinds of animals, some of them brilliantly colored.

A *barrier reef* is separated from the shore by a wide, deep channel. The Great Barrier Reef of Australia is over 1100 miles long and encloses a channel from 10–25 fathoms deep and in some places 30 miles wide. Often a barrier reef entirely surrounds an island.

An *atoll* is a more or less circular reef enclosing a lagoon. Several theories have been advanced to account for the production of atolls. Charles Darwin, who made extensive studies of coral reefs and islands, is responsible for the subsidence theory. According to Darwin, the reef was originally built up around an oceanic island which slowly sank beneath the ocean, leaving the coral reef enclosing a lagoon. This view has been substantiated by borings made on atolls in recent years because coral sediments extend down to great depths, and coral reef development occurs very slowly, if at all, below 200 feet. Reef development also requires warm water, at least 20°C, and a salt content near that of the open ocean. Thus living reefs are restricted to the tropics by temperature. Their need for a high salt content prevents their development near the mouths of large rivers, such as the Amazon, and in the lagoon area of atolls. If once established in shallow water their growth may keep pace with rising sea levels of postglacial ages, or subsiding ocean bottoms or sea mounts.

The study of coral reefs has significance to the petroleum geologist. Ancient reefs incorporated in continental land masses are now important reservoirs of petroleum. The ancient reefs presumably formed under similar ecological conditions to those today. Thus knowledge of modern ones will aide in predictions of location and extent of ancient ones.

Coral reefs have the most varied and abundant collection of animal life of any natural habitat. They are a scuba divers paradise, but not without dangers.

Coelenterates are convenient organisms for some lines of research in basic biology. Some which may have application in human medicine deal with development, regeneration, and connective tissue.

References to Literature on the Coelenterata

Ax, P. 1963. Relationships and phylogeny of the Turbellaria. pp. 191–224. In E. Dougherty. *The Lower Metazoa.* Univ. Calif., Berkeley. 478 pp.

Brien, P. 1960. The fresh-water hydra. *Am. Scientist*, **48**:461–475.

Burnett, A. L. 1962. The maintenance of form in *Hydra*. In D. Rudnick. *Regeneration.* Ronald Press, New York. 250 pp.

Campbell, R. D. 1965. Cell proliferation in *Hydra*: an autoradiographic approach. *Science*, **148**:1231–1232.

Crowell, S. (Ed.). 1965. Behavioral Physiology of Coelenterates. *Am. Zoologist*, **5**(3):335–589.

Dakin, W. J. 1950. *Great Barrier Reef.* Aust. Nat. Travel Assn., Melbourne. 135 pp.

Fraser, L. A. 1962. The histology of the musculature of *Gonionemus. Trans. Am. Microsc. Soc.*, **81**:257–262.

Forrest, H. 1963. Taxonomic studies on the hydras of North America. VIII. Description of two new species, with new records and a key to the North American hydras. *Trans. Am. Microsc. Soc.*, **82**:6–17.

HADZI, J. 1963. *The Evolution of the Metazoa.* Macmillan, New York. 499 pp.

HAND, C. 1963. The early worm: a planula. pp. 33–39. In E. DOUGHERTY. *The Lower Metazoa.* Univ. Calif., Berkeley. 478pp.

HYMAN, L. H. 1940. *The Invertebrates: Protozoa through Ctenophora.* (Vol. I) McGraw-Hill, New York. 726 pp.

LANE, C. E. 1960. The Portuguese Man-of-War. *Sci. Am.* **202**:158–168.

LENHOFF, H. M. 1965. Cellular segregation and heterocytic dominance in hydra. *Science,* **148**:1105–1107.

——, and W. F. LOOMIS (Eds.). 1961. *The Biology of Hydra and of Some Other Coelenterates.* Univ. Miami, Coral Gables. 467 pp.

LENTZ, T. L. 1965. Hydra: induction of supernumerary heads by isolated neuro-secretory granules. *Science,* **150**:633–635.

LYTLE, C. F. 1962. *Craspedacusta* in the Southeastern United States. *Tulane Stud. in Zool.,* **9**:309–314.

MCCULLOUGH, C. B. 1965. Pacemaker interaction in *Hydra. Am. Zoologist,* **5**:499–504.

PARK, H. D., N. E. SHARPLESS, and A. B. ORTMEYER. 1965. Growth and differentiation in *Hydra.* I. The effect of temperature on sexual differentiation in *Hydra littoralis. J. Exp. Zool.,* **160**:247–254.

PICKWELL, G. V., E. G. BARHAM, and J. W. WILTON. 1964. Carbon monoxide production by a bathypelagic siphonophore. *Science,* **144**:860–862.

ROSS, D. M. 1965. Preferential settling of the sea anenome *Stomphia coccinea* on the mussel *Modiolus modiolus. Science,* **148**:527–528.

RUSHFORTH, N. B., I. T. KROHN, and L. K. BROWN. 1964. Behavior in *Hydra*: inhibition of the contraction responses of *Hydra pirardi. Science,* **145**:602–604.

Chapter IV
Phylum Ctenophora

T HE PHYLUM Ctenophora (Gr. *ktenos*, of a comb; *phoreo*, I bear) includes a small group of free-swimming marine animals that are even more nearly transparent than the coelenterate jellyfishes. They have been placed by many authors under the phylum Coelenterata, but the present tendency is to separate them from that group and rank them as a distinct phylum. They are widely distributed, being especially abundant in warm seas.

Morphology. Ctenophores are commonly called *sea walnuts* because of their shape (Fig. 4–1), or *comb jellies* on account of their jelly-like consistency and the comb-like locomotor organs arranged in eight rows on the sides of the body. A few species have a slender ribbon-like shape and may, like Venus' girdle (Fig. 4–4), reach a length of from 6 inches to 4 feet.

The general *structure* of a ctenophore is shown in Figure 4–1. It is said to possess *biradial symmetry*, since the parts, though in general radially disposed, lie half on one side and half on the other side of a median longitudinal plane. An end view, as in Figure 4–1, B, illustrates this fact. The *mouth* is situated at one end (*oral*) and a *sense organ* at the opposite or *aboral* end. Extending from near the oral surface to near the aboral end are eight meridional *comb rows* (ciliated bands); these are the *locomotor organs*. Each band has the cilia arranged upon it in transverse rows and fused at the base; each row thus resembles a comb. These are raised and lowered alternately, starting at the aboral end, and cause an appearance like a series of waves traveling from this point toward the mouth. The animal is propelled through the water with the oral end forward. Light is refracted from these moving rows of cilia, and brilliant, changing colors are thus produced. Some species are phosphorescent.

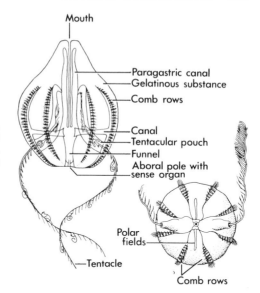

Fig. 4-1. Ctenophora. Tentaculata. Left, *Hormiphora plumosa*, side view. Right, *Pleurobrachia pileus*, aboral view. (Left, after Chun; right, from Lankester's *Treatise*.)

Most ctenophores possess two solid, contractile *tentacles* (Fig. 4–1) which emerge from blind pouches, one on either side. With one exception, the tentacles are not provided with nematocysts as are those of the Coelenterata, but are supplied with adhesive cells called *colloblasts* (Fig. 4–2). The colloblasts produce a secretion of use in capturing small animals, which serve as food. The spiral filament in each colloblast is contractile, and acts as a spring, often preventing the struggling prey from tearing the cell away.

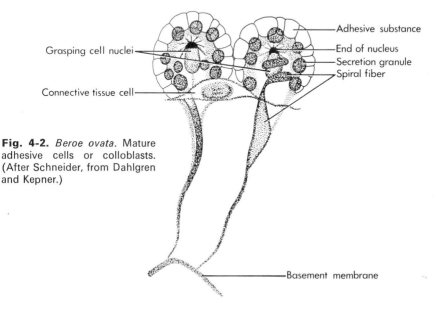

Fig. 4-2. *Beroe ovata*. Mature adhesive cells or colloblasts. (After Schneider, from Dahlgren and Kepner.)

The *mouth* (Fig. 4–1) opens into a flattened *stomodaeum*, where most of the food is digested; this leads to the *stomach*, which is flattened at right angles to the stomodaeum. Six canals arise from the stomach. Two of these, called *anal canals*, open to the exterior near an aboral sense organ; undigested food passes through them, or is ejected through the mouth. The two *paragastric canals* lie parallel to the stomodaeum, ending blindly near the mouth. The two *tentacular canals* pass out toward the pouches of the tentacles, then each gives rise to four branches; these lead into *meridional canals* lying just beneath the comb rows.

Physiology. The *food* of *Mnemiopsis* consists of plankton organisms. A particle of food that is caught in the current produced by the cilia in the auricular grooves is whirled about until it touches one of the small tentacles along the tentacular ridge. The tentacle, often with the aid of several other tentacles, entangles it and then contracts and it is drawn over the labial ridge into the labial trough toward the mouth. Thence the food passes through the mouth into the stomodaeum. Undigested matter is cast out of the mouth or may enter the food canals and pass out through the anus.

The aboral sense organ (Fig. 4–3) is a *statocyst* or organ of equilibrium. It consists of a vesicle of fused cilia enclosing a ball of calcareous granules, the statolith, which is supported by four tufts of fused cilia (balancer cilia). The balancer cilia respond to changed pressure from the statolith by modifying the beat of the comb rows they head. The impulse from the balancer cilia seems to be transmitted by a cell to cell conduction in the epidermis, although inhibitory stimuli are transmitted by an underlying nerve network. *Pleurobrachia* normally swims upward in response to gravity but a disturbance causes it to swim downward in response to gravity. Besides such generalized responses, localized responses seem to be under the control of subunits of the

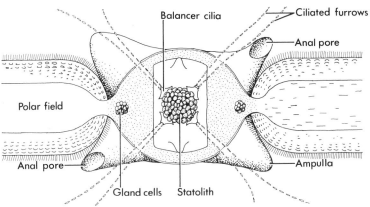

Fig. 4-3. *Hormiphora plumosa.* Aboral sense organ viewed from above. (From Lankester's *Treatise.*)

nerve net. At least some of the nerve junctions have been proven to be synaptic.

Ctenophores are *hermaphroditic*. The *ova* are formed on one side and the *spermatozoa* on the other side of each meridional canal just beneath the comb rows (Fig. 4–1). The fertilized eggs may escape through the epidermis over-lying the meridional canals. The fertilized eggs develop into a larval stage, the *cydippid larva*, similar in general structure to adults such as *Pleurobrachia*, or others in the order Cydippida. This peculiar larval type helps to establish the ctenophore nature of aberrant forms such as *Cestus* and *Coeloplana*.

The cellular layers of ctenophores constitute a very small part of the body, most of it being composed of the transparent jelly-like *mesoglea*. The thin ciliated *epidermis* covers the exterior and lines the stomodaeum; and the *gastrodermis*, also ciliated, lines the stomach and the canals to which it gives rise. The muscle fibers that lie just beneath the epidermis and gastrodermis are derived from the *mesenchymal* cells of the embryo. They have more complex organization than coelenterates. Cleavage of the egg is symmetrical and determinate. It is determinate in that each embryonic cell will develop into a particular part even if its position is modified.

Phylogeny. The Cydippida seem to be nearest the ancestral type of the Ctenophora on the basis of their resemblance to all ctenophore larvae. Little, if any, evidence is present to link them with the polyclad flatworms as some (e.g., Hadzi, 1963) have proposed. The presence of nematocysts in one species, tetramerous symmetry, and a usual planktonic existence support the preferred view that they share a common ancestry with hydrozoan medusae of the Trachylina. The Ctenophora have not given rise to any other inverte-brate groups and thus represent an evolutionary dead end.

Classification. Ctenophores are triploblastic animals that exhibit radial combined with bilateral symmetry and possess eight radially arranged comb rows.

The Ctenophora differ from the coelenterates in several important respects besides the presence of a distinct mesoderm. With one exception, ctenophores do not possess nematocysts, and the adhesive cells that take their place are not homologous to nematocysts. Their ciliated bands, aboral sense organs, and pronounced biradial symmetry are peculiarities that warrant placing ctenophores in a phylum by themselves. They are evolved from coelenterate-like ancestors, but can no longer be combined with that phylum. Five orders are listed here.

Order 1. Cydippida. Body spherical, ovoidal, or cylindrical; two long tentacles that may be retracted into aboral tentacular sacs.

Pleurobrachia (Fig. 4–1, B) is ovoidal and slightly compressed laterally; the ciliated bands are eight in number and of equal length. *P. pileus* is about

Fig. 4-4. Cestida. *Cestus pectenalis*, Venus' girdle. (After Bigelow.)

2 cm long and possesses tentacles about 15 cm long; Long Island northward, Pacific Coast, Europe.

Order 2. Lobata. Body ovate; two large oral lobes; tentacles and tentacular sacs in larva but not in adult.

Mnemiopsis has a pair of long projections (auricles) at the base of each oral lobe upon which the ciliated bands extend. *M. leidyi* is about 10 cm long; transparent and phosphorescent; Long Island to South Carolina.

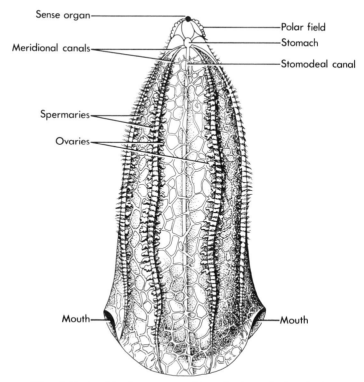

Fig. 4-5. Beroida. *Beroe ovata*. (From Lankester's *Treatise*.)

Order 3. Cestida. Body shaped like a ribbon; two tentacular sacs and two more or less rudimentary tentacles; many lateral tentacles.

Cestus is a genus containing several species. *C. veneris*, known as Venus' girdle (Fig. 4–4), may be 2 inches wide and nearly 3 feet long; transparent but showing green, blue, and violet colors; tropical seas.

Order 4. Beroidea. Tentacles and oral lobes absent. Body conical or ovate and laterally compressed; mouth very large and stomach voluminous; voracious.

Beroe ovata (Fig. 4–5) is about 10 cm long; cosmopolitan.

Order 5. Platyctenea. Creeping ctenophores with two sheathed tentacles. Comb rows in larvae only. Adult flattened. *Coeloplana*; along many coastal regions.

References to Literature on the Ctenophora

HADZI, J. 1963. *The Evolution of the Metazoa.* Macmillan, New York. 499 pp.

HYMAN, L. H. 1940. *The Invertebrates.* Vol. I. *Protozoa through Ctenophora.* McGraw-Hill, New York. 726 pp.

HORRIDGE, G. A. 1965. Relations between nerves and cilia in ctenophores. *Am. Zoologist*, **5**:357–375.

KOMAI, T. 1963. A note on the phylogeny of the Ctenophora. pp. 181–188. In E. DOUGHERTY. *The Lower Metazoa.* Univ. Calif., Berkeley. 478 pp.

MAYER, A. G. 1912. *Ctenophores of the Atlantic Coast of North America.* Publ. **162.** Carnegie Inst. Wash.

Chapter V
Phylum Platyhelminthes

THE PHYLUM Platyhelminthes contains a group of animals which at first were included with other wormlike animals in a phylum called Vermes. They are known as flatworms because they are much flattened dorso-ventrally. Among them are both free-living and parasitic species; the former live principally in fresh or salt water; the latter are mostly endoparasitic. The parasitic flatworms are known as trematodes or flukes and cestodes or tapeworms. They are widely distributed among human beings and lower animals and are often pathogenic and sometimes bring about the death of the host. Free-living flatworms may be obtained from ponds and streams or in bodies of salt water. Each species has its own particular habitat which should be determined before collecting is attempted.

Three classes of Platyhelminthes are recognized: (1) Turbellaria, (2) Trematoda, and (3) Cestoda. Most Turbellaria are free-living and inhabit either fresh or salt water; a few live in moist soil and a few are parasitic. The trematodes and cestodes are all parasitic. Characteristics of the three classes follow.

PHYLUM PLATYHELMINTHES. Unsegmented, triploblastic, bilaterally symmetrical animals; body flattened dorsoventrally; without circulatory system, anus, or coelom; usually hermaphroditic.

CLASS I. TURBELLARIA. Mostly free-living; enteron present; body usually covered with cilia; rhabdites usually present; suckers usually absent; life cycles simple.

CLASS II. TREMATODA. Parasitic; enteron present; no cilia in adult, but cuticle present; suckers on ventral surface; typically with complex life cycles.

CLASS III. CESTODA. Endoparasites; enteron absent; no cilia in adult, but cuticle present; proglottids usually formed; typically with more than one host in life cycle.

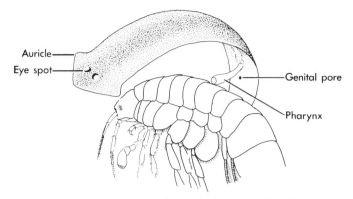

Fig. 5-1. *Dugesia*, with pharynx extended to feed on a small fresh-water crustacean.

1 / Class I. Turbellaria

(1) Dugesia: A Fresh-Water Flatworm

External Features (Fig. 5–1). *Dugesia tigrina* (*Planaria maculata*) is a common planarian of the class Turbellaria and serves to illustrate the typical organization of a platyhelminth better than any of the Trematoda or Cestoda, because the latter are considerably modified for a parasitic existence. It is a flatworm found only in fresh water, usually clinging to the underside of logs or stones. Like most of the members of the phylum Platyhelminthes, its body is extremely flattened dorso-ventrally and exhibits bilateral symmetry. *Dugesia* is broad and blunt at the anterior end and pointed at the posterior end. The length of an adult specimen may exceed half an inch. The dorsal surface contains many black pigment cells, or *melanophores*, which make it difficult to determine the location of the internal structures in the living animal. The pigment cells may be bleached prior to staining preserved specimens for study of internal structures. After observation at very low magnification of the living animal in a small amount of water, the soft, contractile body is usually placed on a slide, and then pressed out slightly with a cover glass.

Cephalization, or the concentration of nervous structures in a head region, occurs in Turbellaria such as *Dugesia*. The lateral projections of the triangular head are tactile lobes or *auricles*. Sensory pits may be present on the dorsal posterior region of the auricles. A pair of eye spots are present on the dorsal surface near the anterior end. The *mouth* is in a peculiar position near the middle of the ventral surface. From it the muscular *pharynx* may extend. Posterior to the mouth is a smaller opening, the *genital pore*. The ventral surface of the body is covered with *cilia*, which propel the animal through the water. This is not the only method of locomotion, because muscular contraction is also effective.

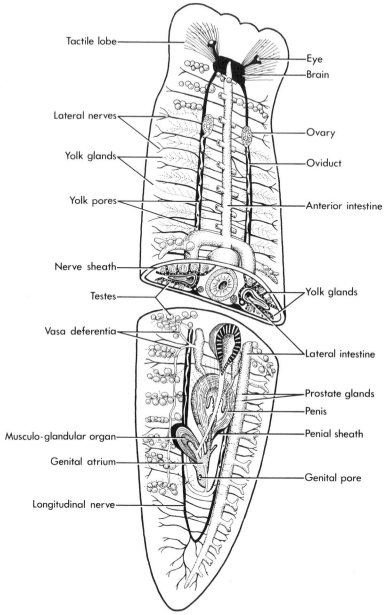

Fig. 5-2. *Procotyla fluviatilis.* Diagram showing the structure of a fresh-water turbellarian. (From Gamble.)

Morphology.   A study of the structure of the adult and of the early embryonic stages shows *Dugesia* to be a triploblastic animal (i.e., possessing the three germ layers, ectoderm, mesoderm, and endoderm, from which several systems of organs have been derived). The mesoderm lying between the body wall and the intestine forms large cells, the parenchyma or mesenchyme, with long irregular processes among which are large intercellular spaces. There are well-developed muscular, nervous, digestive, excretory, and reproductive systems (Fig. 5–2); these are constructed in such a way as to function without the coordination of a circulatory system, respiratory system, coelom, and anus.

A feature of special interest in the turbellarian epidermis is the presence of *rhabdites*. Rhabdites are of unknown function but may be of use in the formation of surface secretions. They occur only in the Turbellaria and are a characteristic of the class. They are intracellular rods that are more numerous in the dorsal epidermis of *Dugesia*. Evidence is lacking for the suggestion that they are structures with a phylogenetic relationship to nematocysts.

Digestive System. The digestive system (Fig. 5–2) consists of a *mouth*, a *pharynx* lying in a muscular sheath, and an *intestine* of three main trunks with a large number of small lateral extensions. The muscular pharynx can be extended as a proboscis (Fig. 5–1); this facilitates the capture of food. Digestion is both *extracellular* and *intracellular*; i.e., part of the food is digested in the intestinal trunks by secretions from cells in their walls, whereas other food particles are engulfed by pseudopodia thrust out by cells lining the intestine, and are digested inside of the cells in vacuoles. The digested food is absorbed by the walls of the intestinal trunks, and, because branches from these penetrate all parts of the body, no circulatory system is necessary to carry

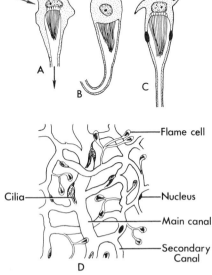

Fig. 5-3. Flame cells and excretory ducts of Platyhelminthes. (A) From a planarian. (B) From the miracidium stage of the liver fluke, *Fasciola*. (C) From the tapeworm, *Taenia*. (D) Excretory canals ending in flame cells. (A, B, C, after Kerr; D, after Benham.)

nutriment from one place to another. As in *Hydra*, no *anus* is present, the *feces* being ejected through the mouth.

The food of *Dugesia* consists largely of small living crustaceans, worms, and dead animals. These are captured by the proboscis and ingested after being covered with slime secreted by the slime glands; or the pharynx is attached to the prey, digestive fluid is poured out, and the dissolved particles are pumped into the intestine.

Excretory System. The excretory system comprises a pair of longitudinal, much-coiled tubes, one on each side of the body; these are connected near the anterior end by a transverse tube and open to the exterior by two small pores on the dorsal surface. The longitudinal and transverse trunks give off numerous finer tubes, which ramify through all parts of the body, usually ending in a *flame cell* (Fig. 5–3). The flame cell is large and hollow, with a bunch of flickering cilia extending into the central cavity. Because it communicates only with the excretory tubules it is considered excretory in function, though it may also carry on respiratory activities and regulate water content.

Muscular System. The power of changing the shape of its body, which may be observed when *Dugesia* moves from place to place, lies principally in three sets of muscles, a circular layer just beneath the epidermis (Fig. 5–4), external and internal layers of longitudinal muscle fibers, and a set of oblique fibers lying in the mesenchyme.

Nervous System and Sense Organs. *Dugesia* possesses a well-developed nervous system, consisting of a bilobed mass of tissue just beneath the eye spots, called the *brain* (Fig. 5–2) and two lateral *longitudinal nerve cords* connected by transverse nerves. From the brain, nerves pass to various parts of the anterior end of the body, imparting to this region a highly sensitive nature.

Fig. 5-4. *Procotyla fluviatilis.* Section through the skin. (After Hallez, from Petrunkevitch.)

Fig. 5-5. Turbellaria. *Planaria*. Histology of the eye. (After Hesse-Doflein, modified.)

Each eye (Fig. 5–5) consists of a highly pigmented retina of a single cup-shaped cell, inside of which are from 2 to 30 nerve cells, the fibrillae of which are in contact with the retina and the opposite ends united into an optic nerve that passes to the brain. There is no lens but the epidermis over the eye is not pigmented. The ciliated pits on either side of the head contain special sensory cells with long cilia and are connected with the underlying nervous network. In some Turbellaria tentacles occur near the anterior end with very long cilia; these are probably organs of chemical sense that aid in finding food. Cells, probably of chemical sense, are scattered over the surface of certain rhabdocoeles. An otocyst located above the brain is present in some Turbellaria.

Reproductive System.   Reproduction is by *fission* or by the sexual method. Each individual possesses both male and female organs, i.e., it is *hermaphroditic*. The *male organs* (Fig. 5–2) consist of numerous spherical *testes* connected by small tubes called *vasa deferentia*; the *vas deferens* from each side of the body joins the *cirrus* or *penis*, a muscular organ that enters the *genital cloaca*. A *seminal vesicle* lies at the base of the penis, also a number of unicellular *prostate glands*. Spermatozoa originate in the testes, and pass, by way of the *vasa deferentia*, into the seminal vesicle, where they remain until needed for fertilization. The *female reproductive organs* comprise two *ovaries*, two long *oviducts* with many yolk glands entering them, a *vagina*, which opens into the genital cloaca, and the *uterus*, which is also connected with this cavity. The *eggs* originate in the ovary, pass down the oviduct, collecting yolk from the yolk glands on the way, and finally reach the uterus. Here fertilization occurs, and *cocoons* are formed, each containing from four to more than twenty eggs, surrounded by several hundred yolk cells. During copulation spermatozoa from one animal are transferred by the penis to the other member of the pair. The genital organs are so constructed that self-fertilization is prevented and cross-fertilization assured.

Regeneration and Starvation.   Planarians show remarkable powers of regeneration. If an individual is cut in two (Fig. 5–6), the anterior end will

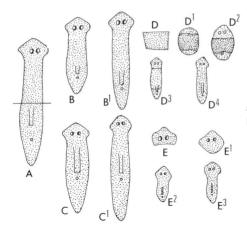

Fig. 5-6. Tricladida. Diagrams illustrating the regeneration of entire planarians from small pieces. (From Morgan.)

regenerate a new tail (*B*, *B'*), while the posterior part develops a new head (*C*, *C'*). A crosspiece (*D*) will regenerate both a head at the anterior end, and a new tail at the posterior end ($D'-D^4$). The head alone of a planarian will grow into an entire animal ($E-E^3$). Pieces cut from various parts of the body will also regenerate completely. No difficulty is experienced in grafting pieces from one animal upon another, and many curious monsters have been produced in this way. New tissue appears to be formed by the differentiation of formative cells, most of which migrate through the parenchyma to the region of differentiation.

If *Dugesia* is starved it absorbs its internal organs as food, in regular order; first the mature eggs are absorbed, then the yolk glands, the rest of the reproductive organs, parenchyma, intestine, and muscles. The size of the body decreases during this process; for example, in certain experiments the animals decreased from 13 mm long and 2 mm broad to 3.5 mm long and 0.5 mm broad in nine months. When starved specimens are given food, they regenerate the lost organs and become normal in size. The structural changes involved in regeneration of planarians involves replacement of missing tissue by new growth and reorganization of old tissue.

Axial Gradients. *Dugesia* fragments exhibit a *polarity* when regenerating, i.e., a tail normally regenerates in the direction of the old tail and the head in the direction that the old head was in when the fragment was in the donor organism. The theory of axial gradients seems to partially explain the control of such proper regenerative responses. The primary axis or axis of polarity is an imaginary line extending from the anterior to the posterior end of the body. In *Planaria* the head has a relatively high rate of metabolism and dominates the rest of the body. Experiments have shown that a gradient of metabolic activity proceeds from the anterior to the posterior end. For example, if planarians are cut into four pieces the anterior piece will be found to use up more oxygen and give off more carbon dioxide than any of the others; the second piece comes next in its rate of metabolism; the third piece next; and the tail piece gives the lowest rate of all. Thus is demonstrated an axial gradient in the metabolism of the animal from the anterior to the posterior end. This is particularly well brought out in older planarians especially at the time of transverse division.

When a planarian is young, it is relatively short and its whole body, especially the head, has a relatively high rate of metabolism. As it grows older it becomes longer and its whole metabolic rate slows down. When young, the high metabolic rate of the head was able to exercise a dominance, through the transmission of stimuli down the gradient, over the entire length of the animal. With a slowing down of the metabolic rate of the apical end and an increase in the length of the path over which the impulse travels, there comes a time when the apical end can no longer maintain a physiological dominance over the entire axis. At the point where dominance fades out, an independent part of the body arises through what is known as physiological isolation. The isolated piece, the second zooid, has its own gradient, the metabolic rate of the anterior end being the highest. This region now becomes a new apical end or, morphologically speaking, the head of a new zooid. No structural indications of a new individual are visible, however, at this time. The only tests of the presence of a second or third individual are physiological tests. The isolated posterior zooid now forms a new head, with eyes, brain, and other parts. The new head then reorganizes the rest of the piece into a complete new individual.

The physiological dominance that prevents development of a second head seems to be due to a diffusible substance formed in the brain which inhibits development of other heads. When action of the inhibitor can be prevented a bipolar, or two-headed individual may result. Such animals can be produced by chemical treatment and have even been observed in very long individuals in a stock culture (Jenkins, 1963).

Memory Transfer.   One of the most interesting aspects of behavior in *Dugesia* is the reported ability of RNA from a trained planarian to elicit responses comparable to trained ones from untrained ones given the RNA. Most of the studies relating to this phenomenon have been done by psychologists. The early studies showed that planarians could be conditioned to respond to stimuli to which they do not ordinarily respond, or the type of response could be modified. The conditioning was done by using electrical shock as an unconditioned stimulus, which causes contraction of the planarian. With the electrical shock was given a light shock which, by itself, was insufficient to cause a contraction. After many exposures to coincident stimuli the planarians would develop a high rate of contractions to the light alone. The learning, or memory, was not in the brain alone, because anterior and posterior halves regenerated from conditioned planarians both had high levels of retention of the conditioning. The fact that planarians fed upon trained planarians showed a higher rate of response to the light shocks alone than untrained planarians indicated a chemical factor was involved. Ribonuclease destroyed the effectiveness of minces of the trained food source. RNA from trained animals was effective in transferring the memory, or, more accurately stated, inducing a higher rate of response in experimental organisms than the rate found in control organisms. Although all studies have not supported this concept, the majority of recent studies indicate the effects of conditioning can be transferred by RNA in *Dugesia*.

(2) Other Turbellaria

Eight orders of Turbellaria are recognized here. The old order Rhabdocoelida has been split into five orders, in all of which the intestine is a single straight tube, which may have short diverticula in one order. The Acoela have no intestine; the Tricladida have an intestine with three main branches; and the Polycladida have a central cavity with many branches serving as the intestine. The condition of the pharynx and the protonephridia (flame cells) are useful in separating most of the other orders. A simple pharynx occurs in the Catenulida and Macrostomida; a bulbose, muscular pharynx in most Neorhabdocoela, Temnocephalida, and Alloeocoela.

The principal features of the Turbellaria have been illustrated in *Dugesia*. The body is usually soft and less than an inch in length, more or less completely covered with cilia and with mucus-like secretions of glands from the

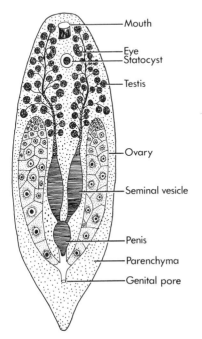

Mouth

Eye
Statocyst

Testis

Ovary

Seminal vesicle

Penis

Parenchyma

Genital pore

Fig. 5-7. Acoela: plan of structure. (From von Graff.)

epidermis and parenchyma. Rod-shaped bodies, called rhabdites, of unknown function are formed in special cells, among or beneath the epidermal cells, and distributed to the epidermal cells (Fig. 5-4). The parenchyma completely fills the space between the body wall and intestine, hence no coelom is present. The muscular pharynx of many is a conspicuous feature of the digestive system. The excretory system is of the protonephridial type with flame cells or flame bulbs at the inner terminations. From two to numerous longitudinal nerve trunks arise from an anterior brain. Numerous interconnections occur between the trunks. Most species are hermaphroditic but seem to require cross-fertilization. The eggs are laid by many species in capsules attached to solid objects in the water, such as stones or vegetation. Fresh-water, marine, and a few terrestrial species occur. Most of them feed on other small animals but a few are parasitic.

Order 1. Acoela (Fig. 5-7).   These have no muscular pharynx and are without an intestine, the latter being represented by a group of endoderm cells. The Acoela are small and marine in habitat, and may be found among rocks and seaweed. One species, *Convoluta henseni*, is a free-swimming plankton organism; another, *C. roscoffiensis*, has symbiotic algae living in its parenchyma. The Acoela lack excretory structures. A temporary digestive space is formed among the parenchymal cells when food is ingested.

Order 2. Catenulida.   Pharynx simple; intestine saclike; one protonephridium, median in position. *Stenostomum* is a cosmopolitan, common genus. It reproduces by transverse divisions, which are completed slowly so

Fig. 5-8. Macrostomida. *Microstomum lineare*, undergoing division. The individual has first divided into two, near its middle, and each of these sections has again divided. Each of the four zooids has again divided into two, and so on, until sixteen individuals are here marked out. (From von Graff.)

that chains of individuals (zooids) (Fig. 5–8) result. Ciliated pits are found on *Stenostomum*. The very similar *Catenula* has a statocyst. Sexual reproduction occurs rarely. These are found only in fresh water.

Order 3. Macrostomida.   Pharynx simple; intestine saclike; two proto-nephridia. Reproduction is as in the Catenulida in *Microstomum lineare* (Fig. 5–8), a species that sometimes possesses nematocysts (Fig. 5–22) derived from ingested hydras. No asexual reproduction occurs in *Macrostomum*, a common genus. Both fresh-water and marine species exist in this order.

Order 4. Neorhabdocoela.   Pharynx bulbose; intestine saclike; two proto-nephridia; sexual reproduction only; both fresh-water and marine species. *Dalyellia viridis* is large (5 mm), green with zoochlorellae, and common in fresh water in the United States in the springtime. Many different colors, or no pigmentation, occurs in different species of this order.

Order 5. Temnocephalida.   Ectocommensal, fresh-water turbellarians with internal structures indicating a close relationship to the Neorhabdocoela. Peculiar external features include tentacles and an adhesive disk once thought to indicate a relationship to the Trematoda. External cilia usually lacking. Principally tropical and Southern Hemisphere in distribution. Usually on crustaceans. *Temnocephala caeca* (Fig. 5–9) occurs on the large, subterreanean isopod *Phreatoicopsis terricola* in Australia.

Order 6. Alloeocoela.   Simple, bulbose, or plicate pharynx; intestine with short diverticula; small size; mostly marine. *Plagiostomum* is a common littoral marine genus with some fresh-water members.

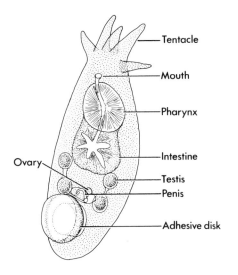

Tentacle

Mouth

Pharynx

Ovary

Intestine

Testis

Penis

Adhesive disk

Fig. 5-9. Temnocephalida. *Temnocephala caeca*, an ectocommensal on a subterranean isopod. (Original.)

Order 7. Tricladida. Plicate pharynx; intestine with three main branches, each with many diverticula; mouth near the center of the ventral surface; ventral surface ciliated. Three suborders are recognized.

Suborder 1. Paludicola. Fresh-water or brackish-water species, including *Dugesia tigrina* and *D. dorotocephala* the common large, black, two-eyed planarians with prominent auricles. The latter species is larger and has pointed auricles. *Procotyla fluviatilis* is a translucent species and its organs are easier to observe than those of *Dugesia*; it has an adhesive disk on the anterior end. *Polycelis coronata* has many eyes arranged somewhat like a coronet, and *Phagocata gracilis* possesses many pharyngeal tubes lying in a common chamber and opening separately into the intestinal tract.

Suborder 2. Maricola. Marine species, a few parasitic, with the mouth located in the posterior part of the body. This group includes *Procerodes wheatlandi*, and *Bdelloura candida*, which attaches itself to the living crab,

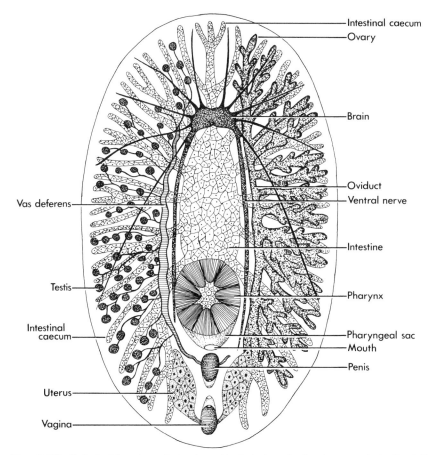

Fig. 5-10. Polycladida: plan of structure. Ventral view, testis shown only to the left, ovaries only to the right. (From von Graff.)

Limulus. Bdelloura is of particular value for study because of the absence of pigment and, hence, its internal organs are clearly visible.

Suborder 3. Terricola. These so-called planarians live in very moist places and resemble small slugs. *Bipalium kewense* is a cosmopolitan species that is an inhabitant of the tropics but may appear in greenhouses in temperate regions on tropical plants; it may reach a length of one foot.

Order 8. Polycladida (Fig. 5–10). The order Polycladida contains marine species only; they have a central digestive cavity, from which branches extend to various parts of the body, and a posteriorly located mouth. Many polyclads are very broad and thin and may reach a length of 6 inches or more. *Planocera inquilina* lives in the mouth cavity of the gastropod *Fulgur*; *Stylochus ellipticus* is a common large species on the New England coast and possesses many frontal and marginal eye spots; *Leptoplana variabilis* has two groups of cerebral ocelli of about 30 each, and two groups of dorsal ocelli of about 15 each.

2 / Class II. Trematoda

(1) Opisthorchis sinensis (Clonorchis sinensis)

Opisthorchis sinensis is a liver fluke of man, and it also occurs in cats and dogs, which serve as reservoir hosts. Although common in the Orient, it does not occur in the Western Hemisphere. It is selected as the type example for the trematodes because it is less specialized structurally than *Fasciola hepatica*, the sheep liver fluke. *O. sinensis* lives as an adult in the bile ducts of man and in severe infections can cause death.

Morphology. Figure 5–11 shows the shape and most of the anatomical features of a mature worm. The *mouth* is situated at the anterior end and lies in the middle of a muscular disk, the anterior sucker or *oral sucker*. The *ventral sucker* (*acetabulum*) is a short distance back of the mouth; it serves as an organ of attachment. The *genital pore* opens just anterior to the ventral sucker. The *excretory pore* lies at the posterior end of the body, and another pore, the opening of Laurer's canal, is situated in the middorsal line about one-third the length of the body from the posterior end.

The digestive system is simple. The mouth opens into a short muscular *pharynx*, which leads into another short tube, the *esophagus*. The *intestine* (Fig. 5–11) consists of two branches, one extending from near the anterior to the posterior end on each side of the body. No circulatory system is present but food materials, consisting of blood cells and materials from the lining of the bile ducts, are digested in the intestine, which is close to all regions of the body.

The excretory system does not require the transportative functions of a circulatory system either, because *flame bulbs* are widely distributed in the parenchyma of the body. From the flame bulbs run small excretory vessels

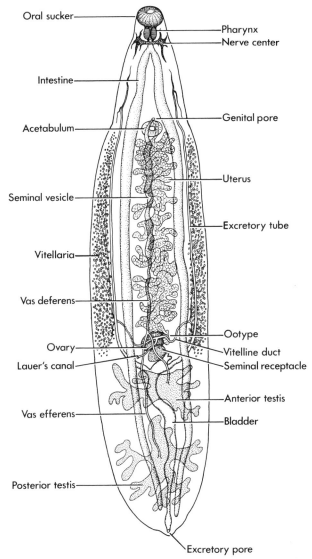

Fig. 5-11. *Opisthorchis sinensis*, a liver fluke that lives in man. (After Faust.)

that unite eventually to form two main excretory vessels that empty into the *bladder*, located in the midline of the posterior third of the fluke. The bladder opens through the excretory pore at the posterior end of the body.

The nervous system consists principally of a bilobed brain dorsal to the esophagus, three pair of longitudinal nerves, and a number of transverse nerves.

The muscular system resembles that of *Dugesia*. The suckers have many radial muscles as well as circular and longitudinal muscles on both surfaces.

The outer circular muscles and inner longitudinal and diagonal muscles of the body wall are covered by a noncellular *cuticle,* which is thought to be secreted by cells sunken into the parenchyma with processes extending through the muscle layers to the cuticle. The *parenchyma* is a loose tissue lying between the body wall and the alimentary canal; within it are embedded the various internal organs described above, as well as the reproductive system.

Both male and female *reproductive organs* are present in every adult (Fig. 5–11); they are extremely well developed, and, as in *Dugesia,* quite complex. The *male* organs are as follows: (1) a pair of branched *testes* (one anterior to the other) in which the spermatozoa arise; (2) two ducts, the *vasa efferentia,* which unite to form (3) a *vas deferens* that anteriorly enlarges into (4) a thicker, elongate *seminal vesicle,* where spermatozoa are stored until discharged through (5) a narrow *ejaculatory duct,* (6) *genital atrium,* and (7) the *genital pore.* Copulatory organs such as a *penis* or *cirrus* are common in trematodes but lacking in *Opisthorchis.*

The *female organs* are (1) a single *ovary* in which the eggs are produced; (2) a short *oviduct* which receives a duct from (3) *Laurer's canal* and the (4) *seminal receptacle* before entering (5) the *shell gland* or *ootype,* at which place (6) the *vitelline* or *yolk duct* brings in and surrounds the eggs with yolk globules derived from (7) the *vitelline* or *yolk glands,* the shell forms and the eggs pass on into (8) a sinuous, looping *uterus,* which leads to the (9) *genital atrium* and (10) *genital pore.*

Although self-fertilization may occur, we infer from the arrangement of the reproductive system that spermatozoa are introduced through the dorsal pore of *Laurer's canal* and stored in the *seminal receptacle* until leaving to join the *ova* from the *ovary* to produce the fertilized *egg.*

Life Cycle.   *Opisthorchis sinensis* has a complex life cycle with the production of the following stages: the *adult fluke* described above, the *egg,* the ciliated *miracidium,* the *sporocyst,* the *redia,* the *cercaria,* and the *metacercaria,* which becomes the adult in the definitive host. The life cycles of flukes typically involve snails as an *intermediate host* for the sporocyst and redia stages with a vertebrate as the *definitive host* where the sexually mature adults occur. Many variations occur in life cycles of different species, especially in the absence or modification of the cercarial stage. The life cycle of *Fasciola hepatica* (Fig. 5–12), the sheep liver fluke, was the first trematode life cycle to be determined.

The Egg.   The egg of *O. sinensis* (Fig. 5–13, C) is provided with a zygote embedded in a mass of yolk cells. The capsule covering is formed by the fusion of material carried by the yolk cells. The shell is operculated, i.e., a lid, or *operculum,* covers one end. A ciliated miracidium develops within the egg. The eggs are passed with the feces of the host.

The Miracidia.   Miracidia escape from the eggs in the intestine or rectum of a suitable fresh-water snail host after they are ingested by the snail. The

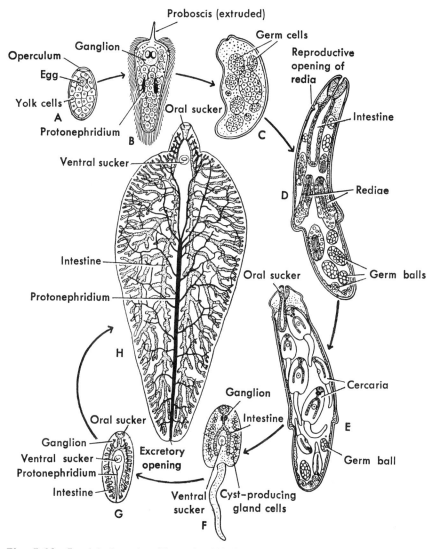

Fig. 5-12. *Fasciola hepatica;* life-cycle. (A) "Egg." (B) Miracidium. (C) Sporocyst. (D, E) Rediae. (F) Cercaria. (G) Tail-less encysted stage (metacercaria). (H) Adult (neither reproductive organs nor nervous system are shown). (From Kerr.)

miracidia penetrate the intestinal wall and develop into sporocysts in the surrounding blood spaces.

Sporocysts. As the miracidium enlarges to become the sporocyst, the germ cells at the posterior grow and produce germ balls, which differentiate into the next larval type, the rediae. The sporocysts from which they rupture are thin-walled, saclike structures.

Rediae.   The rediae migrate to the hepatopancreas, or liver, of the snail where they grow and produce cercariae by an asexual process similar to the formation of rediae within the sporocysts. A number of germ balls differentiate simultaneously into cercariae. Rediae can be distinguished from sporocysts by the presence of a pharynx and short saclike intestine.

Cercariae.   A cercaria (Fig. 5–14) has an oral sucker and ventral sucker as well as rudiments of other systems. The long, flattened tail used for locomotion after the cercaria emerges from the first intermediate host enables it to swim about in search of a suitable fish, usually a cyprinid, where it bores into the flesh to encyst as a metacercaria.

Metacercariae.   Encysted metacercariae undergo loss of cercarial features such as eyespots and tail and further development of adult features such as development of the two intestinal branches and elongation of the excretory bladder. Ingestion of the second intermediate host by the definitive host (man or a fish-eating carnivore such as the dog or cat) is followed by release of the juvenile fluke from the metacercarial cyst. The young fluke migrates through the digestive tract and up the bile duct to one of the bile ducts of the liver where it matures within a month.

The *adult* has already been described. A large number of adults could potentially be produced from each egg. The great number of eggs produced by a single fluke is necessary, because the majority of the eggs may not be ingested by the particular kind of snail required, and only a few of the resulting cercariae may find the proper fish host with even fewer reaching the definitive host. The generations within the snail increase the number of larvae that may develop from a single egg. This complicated *life history* may be looked upon as (1) providing a reproductive mechanism with both sexual and asexual features; (2) enabling the fluke to gain access to new hosts; and (3) reducing competition between different stages in the life cycle. The sexual reproductive method provides great numbers of eggs. It also provides a mechanism for variability or stability depending upon selective pressures over long periods of time. The asexual method provides a method of producing many genetically identical progeny, thus rapidly capitalizing on valuable changes which may occur. Because heavy infections with *O. sinensis* can be fatal, it would be of little value to the species to produce heavy reinfections of the same host by direct development of eggs within the host. An intermediate host provides a means of access to other definitive hosts of the same species, that may be especially valuable when strong territoriality is exhibited by the definitive host. Because developmental stages may have nutritional requirements that differ from the adult, they may find it more readily in a different host. More importantly it reduces the stress on the definitive host as compared to one that might harbor all stages in various organs. The evolutionary advantage of a compatible relationship with the host is unknown because there are no statistics on the number of parasites that become extinct because they cause the extinction of their host.

(2) Other Trematoda

The trematodes resemble Turbellaria in many respects but differ from them in others, largely because of specialization for a parasitic existence. Organs of attachment and of reproduction are highly developed but organs of locomotion, sense, and digestion are reduced or lost entirely. Most trematodes are small, ranging from 1 mm to 2 or 3 cm in length. Suckers are present on the ventral surface varying in size and location according to the species. The ectoderm cells of trematodes are sunk into the parenchyma and outwardly are fused as a syncytial cuticula (Fig. 5–24) often armed with spines. Beneath the cuticula is a dermo-muscular sac consisting of an outer layer of circular muscles, a thinner middle layer of diagonal muscles, and an inner layer of longitudinal muscles. There are also dorso-ventral muscles and muscles connected with the suckers. No coelom is present, the body between the intestine and dermo-muscular sac being filled with parenchyma.

The digestive system consists of a mouth located in the oral sucker, a muscular pharynx, and a thin esophagus into which salivary glands pour their secretions; then comes an intestine of two branches more or less elongated and ending blindly. The food of trematodes consists of the intestinal contents of the host, mucus, and other secretions, epithelial cells, etc., according to the species. Undigested particles are egested through the mouth. Excretory matter is collected by the flame cells (Fig. 5–3) from the surrounding parenchyma, passes through capillaries into collecting tubes, and is carried to a bladder, usually near the posterior end, and then expelled through an excretory pore. There are no circulatory nor respiratory systems. The nervous system resembles that of the Turbellaria. There are two cerebral ganglia above the pharynx, connected by a commissure; from these ganglia three pairs of nerve cords arise and pass backward, being located near the dorsal, ventral, and lateral surfaces, respectively. Adult trematodes have no sense organs.

The reproductive organs of trematodes are complex and life cycles usually involve several different hosts, which results in enormously increased powers of reproduction. The production of large numbers of offspring is necessary in parasitic animals because the chances that any one individual will reach a new host are rather slight. Most trematodes are hermaphroditic. The description and illustration of the reproductive organs of the liver fluke indicate their character. The eggs (Fig. 5–13) of one worm may be fertilized by spermatozoa from the same worm, or cross-fertilization may occur. The larvae that hatch from the eggs of ectoparasitic trematodes are ciliated and swim about until they attach themselves to a new host. Endoparasitic trematodes usually pass through a complicated life cycle as in the liver fluke (Fig. 5–12).

Variations from the type of life cycle illustrated by *Opisthorchis* include: a miracidium hatched in the water which actively penetrates a snail after locating it as in *Fasciola hepatica*; daughter sporocysts may be produced by

Fig. 5-13. Trematoda. Eggs of certain species that live in man. (A) *Fasciolopsis buski*, an intestinal fluke; China. (B) *Paragonimus westermani*, a lung fluke; Far East, America. (C) *Opisthorchis sinensis*, a liver fluke; Far East. (D) *Metagonimus yokogawai*, an intestinal fluke; China, Japan. (E) *Schistosoma japonicum*, a blood fluke; China, Japan, Philippines. (F) *Schistosoma mansoni*, a blood fluke; Africa, America. (G) *Schistosoma haematobium*, a blood fluke; Africa, Near East. (After Cort.)

the sporocysts, or the sporocyst stage may be omitted with miracidia developing directly into rediae; daughter rediae may be produced by the redia until a generation of rediae is produced in which the cercariae develop (perhaps the host tissue invaded influences whether germ balls will develop into redia or cercariae as one snail was known to release cercariae over a seven-year period when reinfection was prevented); cercariae (Fig. 5–14) show variation in structure and development, some penetrate the definitive host and develop into mature flukes as do the schistosomes, others become metacercariae encysted on vegetation as does *Fasciola hepatica* or in a second intermediate host, or a tail-less juvenile may occur in a molluscan intermediate host; except in the schistosomes, or blood flukes, which actively penetrate their definitive host, digenetic trematodes reach their definitive hosts when they are ingested by them. The adults of various species localize in particular organs such as the intestine, bile ducts, bladder, lung, mouth, or blood vessels. A sample of the types of adult trematodes is given in Figure 5–15.

Fig. 5-14. Trematoda. Cercarial types. (A) Pleurolophocercous type of *Opisthorchis*. (B) Furcocercous type of *Schistosoma*. (C) Cercaria of *Fasciola hepatica*. (Modified after several authors.)

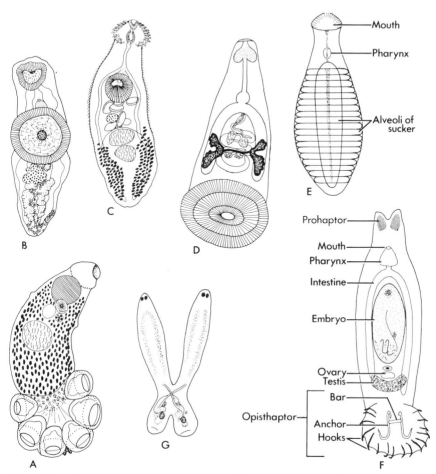

Fig. 5-15. Types of adult trematodes. (A) *Polystoma megacotyle*, from the mouth cavity of the turtle. (B) *Gorgodera minima*, from the bladder of the frog. (C) *Stephanoprora gilberti*, from the intestine of aquatic birds. (D) *Megalodiscus temperatus*, from the rectum of the frog. (E) *Aspidogaster*. (F) *Gyrodactylus*, epizoic on fish; viviparous. (G) *Diplozoon*, from gills of fish, two individuals fused in permanent copulation. (After several authors.)

An example of one of the more complex life cycles is that of *Alaria mustelae*, which involves four different species of hosts. The sporocysts in (1) the snail, *Planorbula armigera*, produce cercariae which penetrate into (2) tadpoles or frogs in which they become mesocercariae; these when eaten by (3) a mammal, such as a mink, raccoon, or mouse, become metacercariae in the muscles or lungs; the metacercariae grow to the adult state when eaten by (4) another mammal, such as a mink, weasel, cat, dog, or ferret, in the intestines of which they deposit their eggs. From the latter, miracidia hatch which are capable of infecting the snail.

Many larval trematodes, the cercariae, have been described, the adult stages of which are unknown. These cercariae possess certain adult characteristics such as suckers, digestive and excretory systems and temporary larval characteristics, such as tails, stylets, and cystogenous and cephalic glands. Cercariae may be obtained by placing fresh-water snails in a glass of water and watching for them with a hand lens as they emerge from these hosts. They have been given names and classified in various ways but their true relations can only be determined when the adults in which they develop become known.

Classification of Trematodes. Three orders of Trematoda are accepted: the Aspidobothrea, the Monogenea, and the Digenea.

Order 1. Aspidobothrea. Aspidobothrea lack an oral sucker but have a very large, compartmented ventral sucker; usually with only one host, a mollusk or a cold-blooded vertebrate. A common species is *Aspidogaster conchicola* (Fig. 5–15, E) found in the pericardial cavity of fresh-water clams.

Order 2. Monogenea. The Monogenea are principally ectoparasites of fish, turtles, and amphibians. Each species is usually restricted to a single species of host. They attach themselves to the gills of fish, but some species live in the mouth, cloaca, bladder, or on the fins. The oral sucker may be reduced or divided into a double structure. The ventral sucker is commonly at the posterior of the body where it may consist of multiple suckers or be supplied with a number of hooks. The variable anterior adhesive structure is termed a *prohaptor*, whereas the posterior structure is termed an *opisthaptor*. Two suborders are included in the Monogenea.

Suborder 1. Monopisthocotylea. The members of this suborder have double excretory pores that are anterior and dorsal. The opisthaptor is single; the vagina is unpaired; the uterus contains a single egg; and there is no genito-intestinal canal. Common genera with species occurring on the gills of many fresh-water fish include *Ancyrocephalus*, *Dactylogyrus*, and *Gyrodactylus* (Fig. 5–15, F), which differ in the number of hooks, anchors, and bars on the opisthaptor.

Suborder 2. Polyopisthocotylea. Polyopisthocotylea have an opisthaptor with multiple adhesive structures, a double vagina, and a genito-intestinal canal. A genus that contains a number of species from North America is *Polystoma* (Fig. 5–15, A). It has six suckers in a circle or in two rows at the posterior end. Species have been described from the mouth cavity and urinary bladder of turtles and frogs. *Polystoma integerrimum* is influenced by the hormonal cycle of its frog host to deposit eggs at the time the frog breeds. Thus, the parasite's eggs hatch in a suitable location for infecting young tadpoles. *Diplozoon* (Fig. 5–15, G) is a curious gill parasite of minnows that during the larval stage fuses with another specimen permanently so that the sperm duct of one enters the yolk duct of the other and they remain in permanent copulation.

Order 3. Digenea.   The order Digenea contains endoparasitic trematodes including all of the species parasitic in man. Their life cycle involves two or more species of hosts. Terms descriptive of the general arrangement of the suckers include *amphistome* when the suckers are at the extreme anterior and posterior ends, *monostome* when only an oral sucker is present, *holostome* when the ventral sucker (acetabulum) is in a median position with an adhesive organ behind it, and *distome* when the ventral sucker is closer to the oral sucker. More than 40 families exist. Nine of the more important, or commonly encountered, families are mentioned below.

BUCEPHALIDAE (GASTEROSTOMATIDAE).   In the Bucephalidae the anterior sucker is not the oral sucker, the mouth is in the center of the ventral sucker centered on the ventral surface; intestine saclike; genital pore at the posterior end. These forms live in the intestine of both fresh-water and marine fish as adults and in bivalve mollusks as larvae. *Bucephalus gracilescens* lives in marine fish and as a larva in the internal organs of the oyster.

PARAMPHISTOMATIDAE.   The family Paramphistomatidae contains amphistome flukes that are parasites in the digestive tract of hosts from all classes of air-breathing vertebrates; examples are *Megalodiscus temperatus* (Fig. 5–15, D) in the rectum of frogs and *Gastrodiscoides hominis* in man.

GORGODERIDAE.   Members of the Gorgoderidae are distome flukes that are parasites in the urinary bladder of amphibians. *Gorgodera minima* (Fig. 5–15, B) is common in the bladder of the frog; species of *Phyllodistomum* have the rear of the body expanded, disklike, posterior to the acetabulum. Sphaeriid clams serve as the molluscan host.

PLAGIORCHIDAE.   The large family Plagiorchidae contains parasites of fish, amphibians, reptiles, birds, and mammals, including two occasionally found in man. The site of infection is usually the digestive tract, but some occur in respiratory, excretory, or reproductive organs. They are distomes with a forked urinary bladder and a spiny cuticle. Flukes of the genus *Haematoloechus* may be found in the lungs of most adult leopard frogs supplied by biological supply houses or caught in their natural habitat.*

---

* *Parasites of the frog.*   Laboratory study of parasites from a freshly pithed frog provides an opportunity to observe a large variety of parasites in the living state, the method of movement of flukes and tapeworms is usually not otherwise observed. Parasites of other phyla that are frequently encountered include *Trypanosoma* in the blood, especially from the liver; *Trichomonas* and *Opalina* in the intestine; and nematodes in organs or beneath the peritoneum. The eggs of *Haematoloechus* may be found in the digestive tract contents, as well as eggs of other flukes less frequently. The egg of *Halipegus* may be recognized by a long tapered threadlike process extending from one end and several times the length of the egg capsule, the adult fluke may be found in the mouth cavity. *Gorgodera* (Fig. 5–15, B) may be in the bladder, or *Megalodiscus* (Fig. 5–15, D) in the rectum. A lung everted over the end of a pencil or similar object may show the lung flukes as darker spots. Dissected organs or flukes may be placed in 0.7 per cent sodium chloride, which is a favorable solution for observation of the parasites. When submerged they may be revealed by their movements.

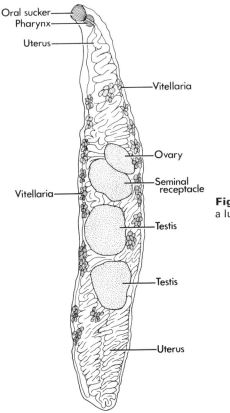

Fig. 5-16. *Haematoloechus medioplexus,*
a lung fluke from the frog. (After Cort.)

Haematoloechus medioplexus (Fig. 5–16) has a life history that has been experimentally determined in the laboratory using *Rana pipiens* for the definitive host. It lives as an adult parasite in the lungs of the leopard frog and has larval stages in a snail, *Planorbula armigera,* and certain dragonflies of the genus *Sympetrum.* The parasites produce in great numbers eggs which pass from the lungs through the glottis into the mouth cavity. They are swallowed, pass through the digestive tract, and are voided with the feces. The eggs, containing mature miracidia, are deposited in this way in the shallow water along the margins of ponds and lakes where snails are usually abundant. The miracidia remain alive within the eggs for weeks without hatching, and it is necessary for the snails to eat the eggs in order to become infected. The miracidia are small (25 microns in length) covered with a dense coating of long cilia, and move relatively slowly. The elongated, sausage-shaped daughter sporocysts are located in the digestive gland of the snail where they give rise to comparatively few cercariae which make their escape from the snail. Cercariae swimming in the vicinity of a dragonfly nymph are caught by the respiratory currents produced by the gills in the rectum and are swept into the chamber of the branchial basket through the anal opening. They pene-

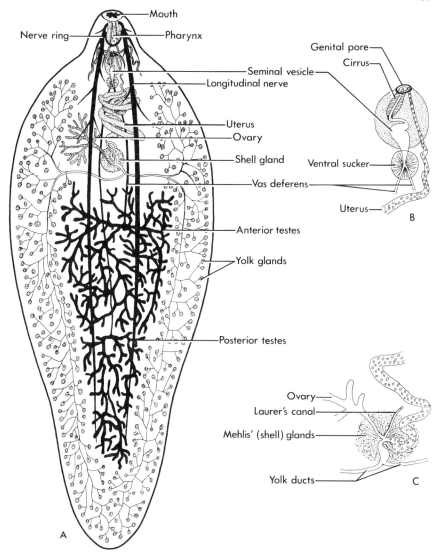

Fig. 5-17. *Fasciola hepatica.* (A) Diagram of the reproductive and nervous systems. (B) Male structures in the region of the genital pore. (C) Female ducts. (Modified after Leuckart and others.)

trate through the chitin into the tissues of the lamellae, and the metacercariae encyst shortly within thin, structureless, transparent, pliable cysts where they ordinarily attain maximum size in from 14 to 20 days. The encysted metacercariae remain in the lamellae until the nymph transforms into an adult dragonfly. Hundreds may be found in a single insect. They live here in a more or less inactive condition until the host dies in the fall of the year or until such a parasitized dragonfly is eaten by a leopard frog or a common toad. In the stomach of either animal the insect is sufficiently digested to free the meta-cercariae. These are stimulated to activity by the digestive fluid and creep up the esophagus in measuring-worm fashion. From the esophagus they pass through the glottis into the lungs, where they reach maturity, under optimum conditions, in 28 or 30 days from the time they enter the frog. The flukes grow considerably after attaining maturity.

OPISTHORCHIDAE. The Opisthorchidae are distome flukes such as *Opisthorchis sinensis* (Fig. 5–11) from man; adults in the bile ducts of fish-eating mammals, birds, and reptiles; molluscan host commonly *Bythinia*; second intermediate host usually a minnow.

TROGLOTREMATIDAE. Family Troglotrematidae includes the distome lung fluke of mammals, *Paragonimus*, and a monostome, *Collyriclum faba* in the English sparrow. Most members of the family have a scaly cuticle and live in cysts in various organs of the host, two or more per cyst.

FASCIOLIDAE. The family Fasciolidae, large flattened flukes with highly branched intestines, includes *Fasciola hepatica* (Figs. 5–12 and 5–17), the sheep liver fluke, and *Fasciolopsis buski*, an intestinal fluke of man.

STRIGEIDAE. The Strigeidae are the holostome flukes. Adults are para-sitic in the intestine of fish-eating birds; body frequently with anterior and posterior divisions; adhesive organ behind the acetabulum; a second inter-mediate host is required for development of the metacercariae. *Lymnaea stagnalis*, a common pond snail, can serve as either first or second inter-mediate host for the strigeid of ducks, *Cotylurus*, but presence of sporocysts confers immunity from penetration by cercariae, although cercariae will penetrate uninfected snails to become metacercariae.

SCHISTOSOMATIDAE. Schistosomes are flukes with sexual dimorphism, sexes being separate; blood flukes of birds and mammals; entrance to defini-tive host gained by the furcocercous cercaria (Fig. 5–14, B) boring into the

Fig. 5-18. *Schistosoma haematobium,* a human blood fluke. The larger male is carrying the more slender female in the gynaecophoric canal. (From Augustine, after Manson-Bahr.)

host. Three species of *Schistosoma* (Fig. 5–18) produce the most serious trematode infections of man. Pulmonate snails serve as the intermediate host and the resulting cercariae penetrate the skin of the definitive host when it enters the water. Cercaria of bird schistosomes will attempt to penetrate the skin of man but can enter only far enough to produce the allergic response known as "swimmer's itch."

Reservoir Hosts. The requirement of a particular species of host by a particular parasite, or host-parasite specificity, is not of much significance in the trematodes. Of particular interest from a public health standpoint is that many trematode parasites of man can complete their life cycle in a mammal other than man and those thus serve as reservoir hosts. Examples of this can be seen in the table on Some Common Trematodes of Man.

Some Common Trematodes of Man

	Scientific Name	Developmental Stages	Geographical Distribution	Hosts
Intestinal Flukes	*Fasciolopsis buski*	in water-grown vegetables	China, Indo-China, Formosa, Sumatra, India	man, pigs
	Heterophyes heterophyes	in fresh-water fish	Egypt, China, Japan	man, cat, dog, and fox
	Metagonimus yokogawai	in trout	Spain, China, Russia, Japan	man, cat, and dog
Liver Flukes	*Opisthorchis sinensis* (Fig. 5-11)	in fresh-water fish	China, Japan, Korea, Indo-China	man, cat, dog, and fish-eating mammals
	Fasciola hepatica (Fig. 5-12)	on vegetation	America, Asia, Europe, Africa	sheep, cattle, pigs, man
	Opisthorchis filineus	in fresh-water fish	Baltic countries, Annam, Philippines	man, cat, dog
Lung Flukes	*Paragonimus westermani*	in fresh-water crabs or crayfish	Japan, Korea, Formosa, Philippines, America	man, tiger, dog, cat, pig, mink
Blood Flukes	*Schistosoma haematobium* (Fig. 5-18)	in fresh-water	Africa, Asia	man, monkey; experimentally in rat, mouse, monkey
	Schistosoma mansoni	in fresh-water	Africa, West Indies, South America	man, experimentally in other mammals
	Schistosoma japonicum	in fresh-water	Eastern Asia	man, cat, dog, pig, etc.

3 / Class III. Cestoda

(1) Taenia—A Tapeworm

The tapeworm, *Taenia solium*, is a common parasite, which lives as an adult in the alimentary canal of man. A nearly related species, *Taeniarhynchus* (*Taenia*) *saginata*, is also a parasite of man. Each adult tapeworm (Fig. 5–19) is a long flatworm consisting of a knoblike head or holdfast organ, the *scolex*, and a great number of similar parts, the *proglottids*, arranged in a linear series. The animal clings to the wall of the alimentary canal by means of *hooks*

Fig. 5-19. Cestoda, tapeworms living in man. (A) *Taeniarhynchus saginata*, adult; the beef tapeworm. (B) *T. saginata;* egg surrounded by its membrane; note hooks within the egg. (C) Cysticercus or bladderworm with head evaginated and capable of attachment to the intestinal wall. (D) *T. saginata*, ripe proglottid. (E) *Taenia solium*, scolex showing hooks and suckers. (F) Cysticercus in median section showing scolex at bottom of invagination. (After various authors.)

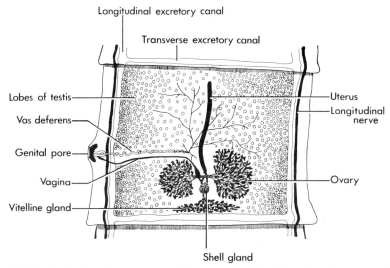

Fig. 5-20. *Taeniarhynchus saginata.* Mature proglottid of the "beef tapeworm" of man. (After Leuckart.)

(lacking in *Taeniarhynchus*) and *suckers* on the scolex. Behind the scolex is a short *neck* followed by a string of proglottids which gradually increase in size from the anterior to the posterior end. The worm may reach a length of 10 feet and contain 800 or 900 proglottids. Since the proglottids are budded off from the neck, those at the posterior end are the oldest. The production of proglottids may be compared to the formation of ephyrae by the scyphistoma of *Aurelia* (Fig. 3–34, E and F), and is called *strobilization*.

The anatomy of the tapeworm is adapted to its parasitic habits (Fig. 5–20). There is *no alimentary canal*, the digested food of the host being absorbed through the body wall. The *nervous system* is similar to that of *Planaria* and the liver fluke, but not so well developed. Longitudinal *excretory tubes*, with branches ending in *flame cells*, open at the posterior end and carry waste matter out of the body.

A *mature proglottid* is almost completely filled with *reproductive organs*; these are shown in Figure 5–20. *Spermatozoa* originate in the spherical *testes*, which are scattered about through the proglottid; they are collected by fine tubes and carried to the *genital pore* by way of the *vas deferens*. *Eggs* arise in the bilobed *ovary* and pass into a tube, the *oviduct*. Yolk from the *yolk gland* enters the oviduct and surrounds the eggs. A shell is then formed in the *shell gland* and the eggs pass into the *uterus*. The eggs have in the meantime been *fertilized* by spermatozoa, which may come from the same proglottid, and move down the vagina. As the proglottids grow older, the uterus becomes distended with eggs and sends off branches, and the rest of the reproductive organs are absorbed. The ripe proglottids break off and pass out of the host with the feces.

The eggs of *Taenia* develop into six-hooked embryos (Fig. 5–19, B) while still within the proglottid. If they are then eaten by a pig, they escape from their envelopes (Fig. 5–19, D) and bore their way through the walls of the alimentary canal into the voluntary muscles, where they form *cysts* (Fig. 5–19, F). A head is developed from the cyst wall and then becomes everted. The larva is known as a *bladder-worm* or *cysticercus* (Fig. 5–19, C) at this stage. If insufficiently cooked pork containing cysticerci is eaten by man, the bladder is thrown off, the head becomes fastened to the wall of the intestine, and a series of proglottids is developed.

(2) Other Cestoda

The Cestoda or tapeworms are highly modified for a parasitic existence. They are all endoparasitic and almost all of them live as adults in the digestive tract of vertebrates and as larvae in the tissues of vertebrates and invertebrates. No digestive system is present even in the simple trematode-like cestodes, and nutriment is absorbed through the surface of the body. Most cestodes are shaped like a band or ribbon (Fig. 5–19) and consist of many segments called proglottids (Fig. 5–20); these, however, are not true segments like those of higher invertebrates, such as the annelids. The adults are often several yards in length and consist of a small head or scolex, a short neck, and a long chain of proglottids or strobila. The scolex usually bears suckers, or acetabula, and is sometimes armed with hooklets. The neck is the growing region, from the posterior end of which proglottids are budded off. The proglottids increase in size as they are pushed back and various systems of organs develop in them.

Each proglottid usually possesses a genital pore on one of the lateral borders or on the surface, but some species have a separate uterine pore. The body is covered with a cuticula as in the trematodes and the internal organs lie in a mass of parenchyma cells in which are also embedded calcareous corpuscles. Circular, longitudinal, transverse, and dorso-ventral muscle fibers are present as in the trematodes and also nerve bundles in the scolex from which arise longitudinal nerve fibers. The excretory system likewise resembles that of the trematodes.

Tapeworms are hermaphroditic. The reproductive organs vary in different groups; those of *Taenia*, already described, indicate their character. Each proglottid contains a complete set of both male and female organs. Apparently the eggs formed in a proglottid are fertilized by spermatozoa from the same proglottid, although copulation is known to occur between proglottids of the same worm and of different worms. In some species the eggs are continually being discharged through a uterine pore, but in most species they are stored up in the proglottids which become "gravid," separate from the chain and pass out in the feces of the host. The eggs in these proglottids contain embryos that, when fully developed, are called onchospheres; these are able to continue their development only when ingested by a proper host. The onchospheres escape from the egg and burrow through the intestinal wall into the body cavity or vascular spaces or into certain tissues. The onchospheres of the lower cestodes become spindle-shaped, hooked procercoids, which develop in a second intermediate host into wormlike, hookless plerocercoids. The larvae of certain higher cestodes are called cysticercoids; they have a rudimentary bladder and may possess a tail. The true bladder-worms are (1) the small cysticercus, which gives rise to one scolex, (2) the large coenurus from which many scolices arise, and (3) the echinococcus or hydatid, which

Fig. 5-21. Cestodes that live in man. (A) *Dibothriocephalus latus*, the fish tapeworm of man. (B) *D. latus*, ciliated embryo (coracidium) escaping from egg. (C) *Echinococcus granulosus*, adult stage that lives in the dog. (D) *E. granulosus*, formation of scolices from the germinative membrane of a hydatid cyst. (E) *Hymenolepis nana*. (F) *H. nana*, egg. (Mostly after Leuckart.)

gives rise to daughter and granddaughter cysts in which many scolices are developed from brood pouches (Fig. 5–21, C and D). The bladder-worms are the stage infective to the definitive host and each scolex may give rise to a tapeworm. Tapeworms, when alive, successfully resist the digestive juices of the host, but soon disintegrate when dead. They may live for many years; several cases are on record of tapeworms that lived for twenty years or more.

Classification of the Cestoda. The cestodes are usually divided into two subclasses. One subclass, the Cestodaria lacks division into proglottids and has larva with ten instead of the usual six hooks, but is a cestode in that it lacks epidermis and digestive system, has only anterior organs of attachment, and are all endoparasites. Cestodarians are rarely encountered and most are parasites of primitive marine fish.

The other subclass, the Eucestoda, contains most of the cestodes. Most have chains of proglottids in the adults. Of the eleven orders of Eucestoda, only two contain parasites of mammals and man, the Pseudophyllidea and Cyclophyllidea. Holdfast organs on the scolex may include *hooks*, *suckers*, folds termed *bothria*, or extended and folded *bothridia*.

Order 1. Proteocephalidea. Small tapeworms; scolex with four suckers; vitellaria as lateral bands; parasites of fishes, amphibians and reptiles.

Order 2. Tetraphyllidea. Medium-sized tapeworms; scolex with four bothridia; vitellaria in lateral bands; parasites of elasmobranch fishes. *Calliobothrium verticillatum* occurs in the spiral valve of the smooth dogfish.

Order 3. Disculiceptidea. Only one species known from an elasmobranch fish. Scolex with only a single flattened anterior expansion. Life cycle unknown.

Order 4. Lecanicephalidea. Scolex with a variable anterior portion and a posterior portion bearing four suckers; parasites of elasmobranch fishes.

Order 5. Pseudophyllidea. Small to large tapeworms; scolex with two bothria; vitellaria as scattered follicles; uterine pore opens on surface; parasites of fishes, birds, and mammals. The most important human species is the broad or fish tapeworm, *Dibothriocephalus latus* (Fig. 5–21, A and B), which has two intermediate hosts, fresh-water copepods and fish. It may reach a length of 20 feet, live more than 20 years, and may cause various symptoms such as anemia in man.

Order 6. Trypanorhynchidea. The scolex in this group is very long and consists of a head with two or four bothria and four retractile, spinose proboscides, and a long stalk. The genital pores are marginal. The larvae encyst in teleost fish and the adults parasitize elasmobranchs.

Order 7. Cyclophyllidea. Tapeworms with a scolex having four suckers; may have a hooked rostellum; no uterine pore; vitellaria posterior to ovary; genital pore opens laterally; the proglottids break from the strobila when gravid; the eggs are not operculated, and the onchospheres are not ciliated. These are taenioid cestodes. Many of the more important cestode parasites of human and other mammalian species belong to the family Taeniidae from which our type was selected. Among these are *Taenia solium*, the pork tapeworm of man, *Taeniarhynchus saginata*, the beef tapeworm of man, *Taenia pisiformis* of cats and dogs, *Echinococcus granulosus* (Fig. 5–21, C) of dogs and other carnivores which produces larval stages known as hydatids in man and other mammals. Common species that belong to other families are *Raillietina tetragona* in domestic fowls, *Moniezia expansa* in sheep, *Hymenolepis nana* (Fig. 5–21, E) or the dwarf tapeworm of man, *H. diminuta* of rats and mice, and *Dipylidium caninum* of cats and dogs.

Order 8. Aporidea. Scolex variable, usually large with four suckers; no external evidence of proglottid formation; small parasites of swans and ducks.

Order 9. Nippotaeniidea. Scolex with one anterior sucker; few proglottids; parasites of fish in Japan and Russia.

Order 10. Caryophyllidea. No proglottids formed; parasites of fishes and oligochaetes; thought to represent tapeworms that have developed sexual maturity in a larval procercoid stage; few species.

Order 11. Spathebothridea. Scolex variable; no external proglottid formation; parasites of sturgeons and marine fish.

A few important tapeworms of man are listed in the table on Some Common Cestodes of Man.

Some Common Cestodes of Man

Scientific Name	Developmental Stages	Geographical Distribution	Hosts
Dibothriocephalus latus	in copepods and fresh-water fish	world-wide, especially Europe, Africa, North America, Japan	man, dog, cat, fox (intestine)
Echinococcus granulosus	in liver, brain, lungs, etc., of man, pig, sheep, etc.	world-wide, especially Iceland, Australia, Argentine	dog and other carnivores (intestine)
Hymenolepis nana	man, rat, mouse	world-wide	man, rat, mouse
Taeniarhynchus saginata	in muscles of cattle	world-wide	man
Taenia solium	in muscles of pig	world-wide	man

4 / Platyhelminthes in General

The flatworms differ greatly among themselves due largely to the fact that the Turbellaria are mostly free-living, whereas the Trematoda and Cestoda are all parasitic in habit. The turbellarians, therefore, exhibit the typical organization of the group, the other two groups being modified considerably for a parasitic existence.

External Features.   The Platyhelminthes are flat and unsegmented, with definite anterior and posterior ends and bilateral symmetry. The epidermis is ciliated in the Turbellaria, but in the Trematoda and Cestoda the surface is covered by a thick cuticle (Figs. 5–24 and 5–25) secreted by cells in the parenchyma. Minute projections and pores are visible on the cuticle with the electron microscope. In some species sense organs are present.

Body Wall.   Beneath the epidermis or cuticle are two layers of muscle, an outer layer of circular muscles and an inner layer of longitudinal muscles. In the Cestoda there are usually additional well-developed zones of longitudinal, dorso-ventral, and transverse muscles embedded in the inner regions of the parenchyma. Filling the area between the body wall and the organs is a mass of parenchymatous tissue (Fig. 5–4), which is very primitive in nature; it is of value in the reparation of lost parts and probably serves for the transportation of nutritive material. There is no coelom.

The nematocysts of *Hydra* are sometimes appropriated by a flatworm, *Microstomum caudatum* (Fig. 5–22). The worm eats and digests the *Hydra*,

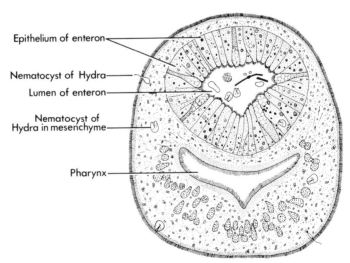

Epithelium of enteron

Nematocyst of Hydra

Lumen of enteron

Nematocyst of Hydra in mesenchyme

Pharynx

Fig. 5-22. Turbellaria. *Microstomum caudatum.* Cross-section through body near anterior end showing especially the location of nematocysts appropriated from hydras ingested as food. (After Kepner.)

leaving the nematocysts free in the enteron. The endoderm cells of the worm engulf these nematocysts and pass them on to wandering mesenchyme cells which then become cnidophages. The nematocysts are uniformly distributed over the surface of the *Microstomum* within 12 hours after the ingestion of a *Hydra*. The worm appears to devour the *Hydra* not because of its food value but in order to secure the nematocysts which it employs, as does *Hydra*, as weapons of defense and offense. This is indicated by the fact that a worm already supplied with nematocysts does not attack *Hydra* readily although one with few nematocysts does; that a worm with many nematocysts may retain the body of an ingested *Hydra* but egest the nematocysts, whereas a worm with few nematocysts may egest the body and retain the nematocysts; and that *Microstomum* has actually been seen to sting and paralyze other animals with the nematocysts obtained from *Hydra*.

Digestive System.   In the Turbellaria and Trematoda there is a saclike intestine with a single opening, which serves both as mouth and anus. In the simplest forms the intestine is unbranched but in others, branches occur that may penetrate to all parts of the body thus rendering a circulatory system unnecessary. The Cestoda have lost the intestine and absorb nutriment through the general surface of the body.

Excretory System.   A protonephridial excretory system occurs in almost all of the flatworms and in some is very complicated. The most characteristic feature of this system is the flame cell.

Nervous System.   This consists of a network with a concentration of nervous tissue at the anterior end, forming the cerebral ganglia, and several longitudinal nerve cords. Sense organs occur in free-living Turbellaria and may be present in the free stages of Trematoda and Cestoda. They exist as eyes, otocysts, taste cells, tentacles, and ciliated ectodermal pits.

Reproductive System.   The flatworms are characterized by a complex reproductive system. The structure and differences have already been described for representatives of the classes. The trematodes and cestodes lay eggs more or less continuously but the turbellarians recognize the seasons in their reproductive activity. As noted above, the latter commonly multiply by asexual reproduction also.

In some Turbellaria, for example, *Procotyla fluviatilis*, egg-laying proceeds during the entire year; in others, for example *Crenobia alpina*, eggs are produced only during the winter months. Two different kinds of eggs are produced by *Mesostomum*; (1) "winter eggs," which have a thick shell, a large amount of yolk, escape only when the mother dies, and remain dormant for a long period, and (2) "summer eggs," which have a thin shell, a small amount of yolk, escape from the living parent, and develop quickly.

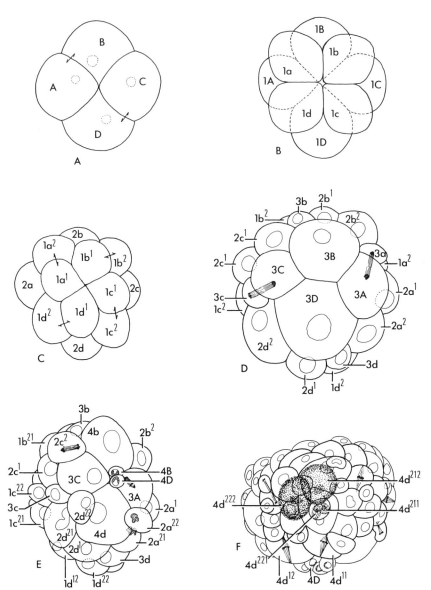

Fig. 5-23. Cell lineage of a flatworm, *Holoplana inquilina*. (A) Four-cell stage. (B) Eight-cell stage with 4 macromeres (1*A*, 1*B*, 1*C*, 1*D*) and 4 micromeres (1*a*, 1*b*, 1*c*, 1*d*). (C) Sixteen-cell stage viewed from animal pole, showing three quartets of micromeres. (D) Thirty-two-cell stage viewed from vegetative pole, showing dexiotropic formation of 3*a* and 3*c*. (E) Thirty-six-cell stage viewed from near animal pole, showing especially cell 4*d*. (F) Stage with more than 100 cells, showing endoderm cells ($4d^{11}$, $4d^{12}$, $4d^{211}$, $4d^{221}$) and mesoderm cells ($4^{212}d$, $4d^{222}$). The number and letter tell which division and from which macromere the cell is derived; the exponents indicate subsequent cell lineage, so that ^{1} is the daughter cell nearer to and ^{2} is farther from the animal pole. (After Surface.)

Embryology.   The development of the egg of the polyclad, *Holoplana inquilina*, has been worked out in detail (Surface, 1907) and an account of the embryology of this species is appropriate at this point. This flatworm lives in the mantle cavity of certain gastropods. The eggs are spherical and about one tenth of a millimeter in diameter. They are laid in spiral gelatinous capsules containing from 100 to 2,000 eggs each. The early cleavage stages occur at intervals of about one hour. On the sixth day the larvae break through the egg membranes and emerge as free-swimming organisms known as Müller's larvae. These swim about for a time and fall to the bottom where they change into the polyclad form.

Cell Lineage (Fig. 5–23).   It is possible to follow the cleavage cells and their descendants from stage to stage until the larval condition is reached and in this way to ascertain the fate of each cell. Observations of this kind have been recorded for various types of animals and constitute what is called *cell lineage*. The egg of *Holoplana* undergoes *total cleavage* into two and these into four cells (A). One of these four, designated by the letter *D*, is larger than the other three, which makes it possible to distinguish the different cells as cleavage advances. When the four cells, labeled *A*, *B*, *C*, *D*, divide to form eight (B), the four near the animal pole are smaller than the other four; they are known as *micromeres* and labeled $1a$, $1b$, $1c$, and $1d$. At this stage, therefore, a quartet of micromeres are present and a quartet of larger, sister cells, called *macromeres* to which the labels $1A$, $1B$, $1C$, and $1D$, are applied. All the cells that are descended from any cell of the four-cell stage comprise a *quadrant*. The cleavage spindles during the division from the four-cell to the eight-cell stage are oblique and the micromeres come to lie in the furrows between the macromeres, that is, alternate with them (B). This is known as *spiral cleavage*. In most cases when the egg is viewed from the animal pole, the micromeres lie in the furrow clockwise of the corresponding macromere; that is, cleavage is *dexiotropic* (B). Sometimes the micromeres lie in the furrow counter-clockwise of the corresponding macromere, in which case cleavage is said to be *laeotropic*.

The eight-cell stage develops into the 16-cell stage by the laeotropic division of the quartet of micromeres ($1a$, $1b$, $1c$, $1d$, to form $1a^1$, $1a^2$, $1b^1$, $1b^2$, $1c^1$, $1c^2$, $1d^1$, $1d^2$) and the production of a second quartet of micromeres ($2a$, $2b$, $2c$, $2d$) by the macromeres (C). The three quartets of micromeres present at this stage are destined to form the entire ectoderm of the animal, and the macromeres the endoderm and mesoderm. The 32-cell stage (D) is attained by the production of a third quartet of micromeres ($3a$, $3b$, $3c$, $3d$) by a dexiotropic division of the macromeres, and the division of each of the three quartets of micromeres. After the 32-cell stage division is not synchronous, and the various groups of cells must be considered separated.

Cell $4d$, which results from the division of macromere *D* at about the 40-cell stage, is of particular interest (E) since it gives rise to all of the endoderm ($4d^{11}$, $4d^{12}$, $4d^{211}$, $4d^{221}$) and part of the mesoderm ($4d^{212}$, $4d^{222}$). At about the 100-cell stage, $2a^{112}$, $2b^{112}$, $2c^{112}$, and $2d^{112}$ are set aside as *mesoderm cells*. In many protostomes the $4d$ cell gives rise to only the mesoderm. Primitive ganglion cells are recognizable at about this time ($1a^{112212}$, $1b^{112212}$, $1c^{112212}$, $1d^{112212}$).

Regeneration and Behavior.   The regenerative ability of the turbellarians has contributed much interesting information on development. Of great recent interest is the transmission of some types of learned behavior by RNA in regenerating planarians, which is still questioned by many zoologists.

Phylogeny and Interrelations.   The flatworms, especially the Turbellaria, resemble the coelenterates in certain respects, which indicate that they were derived from coelenterate-like ancestors. There is a single opening for the ingestion of food and egestion of waste material; a nerve net reminiscent of the coelenterates; and sense organs, such as otocysts, characteristic of coelenterates. The relation of flatworms to ctenophores is even more striking; polyclads being much like ctenophores that have adopted the creeping habit. In both groups the large macromeres produce ectoderm-forming micromeres; the nervous center is at the upper pole; an ectodermal stomodaeum is at the lower pole; and the primary locomotor organs are eight ciliated bands forming combs of cilia in the adult ctenophore and in Müller's larva. The latter is what we may imagine the ctenophore-like ancestor of the polyclads to resemble. The strong preference for vertebrate definitive hosts by the

Fig. 5-24. Electron micrograph of adult *Acanthoparyphium spinulosum* integument. Integument contains dark globules mingled with many mitochondria; cytoplasmic connection can be seen with some globular material extending down to the integumentary cell having the nucleus (N) visible near the bottom. × 3,500. (From R. F. Bils and W. E. Martin. 1966. Fine structure and development of the trematode integument. *Trans. Am. Microsc. Soc.*, **85** (1): 78–88. Courtesy of Dr. Walter E. Martin and Dr. R. F. Bils.)

parasitic flatworms indicates a development contemporary with or subsequent to the development of the vertebrates. Revision of classification is to be expected, especially in the tapeworms, when less reliance is placed on highly variable and adaptive features such as the scolex, and when more reliance is placed on fundamental systems and their arrangement.

The absence of fossils of the Platyhelminthes makes discussion of phylogeny highly speculative. The previously mentioned resemblance of polyclads and ctenophores is not considered of phylogenetic significance by most zoologists. The view of Hadzi, that the Turbellaria gave rise to most of the unsegmented invertebrates, including the coelenterates, does not seem to have been accepted by many. A popular view is that the flatworms arose from a planula-like organism by way of the Acoela. The planula larva of coelenterates then becomes the basis for a close phylogenetic relationship with the flatworms. The general view seems to be that the flatworms have a higher level of development than the coelenterates and thus may be derived from them, or their ancestors.

Modifications for Parasitism. Within the phylum are a broad range of parasitic modifications. The cestodes may be considered the most highly modified for a parasitic existence and seem to do little damage to their normal hosts. Some features associated with the parasitic modifications encountered in the flatworms include (1) loss of the epidermis and development of a protective cuticle (Figs. 5–24 and 5–25); (2) reduction and loss of a digestive

Fig. 5-25. Cestode cuticle. Electron micrograph of *Hymenolepis citelli.* × 5,000. Courtesy of Dr. Alvin H. Rothman.)

system; (3) development of organs of attachment; (4) development of enlarged reproductive systems or egg producing capacity; and (5) tendency to complex life cycles.

The History of Our Knowledge of the Platyhelminthes. Parasitic flatworms, such as tapeworms, were well known to the ancients as inhabitants of man and domesticated animals. Trematodes were first described clearly in the sixteenth century, but it was not until the close of the seventeenth century that the hydatids of tapeworms were recognized as animals, having been considered previously as abscesses or abnormal growths. Linnaeus placed all of the invertebrates except the arthropods into one class, the Vermes, and allocated the worms to an order, the Intestina, of this class. The fundamental difference between segmented and unsegmented worms was recognized by Cuvier in 1798. In 1808 Rudolphi proposed the name Entozoa for the unsegmented worms, because at that time most of the species known were internal parasites. Rudolphi recognized five orders: (1) Nematodes, (2) Acanthocephala, (3) Trematodes, (4) Cestodes, and (5) Cystici. The term Turbellaria was coined by Ehrenberg in 1831 for the free-living species of flatworms because the beating of their cilia caused disturbances (turbellae) in the water. In 1744 Trembley published the first figure of a turbellarian in his memoir on *Hydra*. O. F. Müller and Ehrenberg founded our knowledge of the Turbellaria and Lang and von Graff have contributed more recently. In 1851 Vogt united four orders of flatworms in the class Platelmia which we now know as the phylum Platyhelminthes. Leuckart, who contributed so much to our knowledge of the parasitic worms, presents the history of the subject up to the year 1879 in his book *The Parasites of Man*. Major contributions to the knowledge of the Turbellaria have been made in recent decades by Libbie Hyman. Many workers have been active contributors to knowledge of the parasitic worms, recent important books having been contributed by Dawes on the Trematoda, by Wardle and McLeod on the tapeworms, and by Yamaguti on both groups.

References to Literature on the Platyhelminthes

BILS, R. F., and W. E. MARTIN. 1966. Fine structure and development of the trematode integument. *Trans. Am. Microsc. Soc.*, 85:78–88.

BROOKS, T. J. 1963. *Essentials of Medical Parasitology*. Macmillan, New York. 358 pp.

CHENG, T. C. 1964. *The Biology of Animal Parasites*. Saunders, Philadelphia. 727 pp.

——, C. N. SHUSTER, and A. H. ANDERSON. 1966. A comparative study of the susceptibility and response of eight species of marine pelecypods to the trematode *Himasthla quissetensis*. *Trans. Am. Microsc. Soc.*, 85:284–295.

DAWES, B. 1946. *The Trematoda*. Cambridge Univ. Press, Cambridge. 644 pp.

HYMAN, L. H. 1951. *The Invertebrates*. Vol. II. *Platyhelminthes and Rhynchocoela.* McGraw-Hill, New York. 550 pp.

——, and E. R. JONES. 1959. Turbellaria. pp. 323–365. In W. T. EDMONDSON. *Fresh-Water Biology*. 2nd ed. Wiley, New York. 1248 pp.

JACOBSON, A. L., C. FRIED, and S. D. HOROWITZ. 1966. Planarians and memory. *Nature*, **209**:599–601.

JENKINS, M. M. 1963. Bipolar planarians in a stock culture. *Science*, **142**:1187.

——, and H. P. BROWN. 1964. Copulatory activity and behavior in the planarian *Dugesia dorotocephala* (Woodworth) 1897. *Trans. Am. Microsc. Soc.*, **83**:32–40.

LEUCKART, R. 1886. *The Parasites of Man*. 771 pp.

OSCHMAN, J. L., and P. GRAY. 1965. A study of the fine structure of *Convoluta roscoffensis* and its endosymbiotic algae. *Trans. Am. Microsc. Soc.*, **84**:368–375.

ROTHMAN, A. H. 1963. Electron microscopic studies of tapeworms. *Trans. Am. Microsc. Soc.*, **82**:22–30.

SURFACE, F. M. 1907. The early development of polyclad *Planocera inquilina*. *Proc. Acad. Natur. Sci. Philadelphia*, **59**.

WARDLE, R. A., and J. A. McLEOD. 1952. *The Zoology of Tapeworms*. Univ. of Minn. Press, Minneapolis. 780 pp.

WOLFF, E. 1962. Recent researches on the regeneration of planaria. In D. RUDNICK. *Regeneration*. Ronald Press, New York. 250 pp.

YAMAGUTI, S. 1958. *Systema Helminthum*. Vol. I., *The Digenetic Trematodes of Vertebrates*. 1959. Vol. II., *The Cestodes of Vertebrates*. 1963. Vol. IV., *Monogenea and Aspidocotylea*. Wiley, New York.

Chapter VI

Phylum Aschelminthes

THE ASCHELMINTHES constitute a phylum of five diverse classes that have in common a pseudocoelom, bilateral symmetry, a cuticle, a lack of complete segmentation, a digestive tract with an anterior oral and posterior anal opening, no circulatory or respiratory systems, usually separate sexes, and usually a protonephridial system of flame cells or flame bulbs. An anterior nerve mass, which may encircle the digestive tract, gives off two or more longitudinal tracts. Nuclear numbers within species are constant.

The classes have frequently been recognized as phyla because of their great differences in general morphology. The Acanthocephala are sometimes included in this phylum, but they also show relationships to the Platyhelminthes. Because of their distinctive characteristics, they are treated as a separate phylum in the next chapter. The Priapulida have been removed for the same reason.

The body cavity and complete digestive tract represent a considerable advance over previous phyla discussed. The body cavity may be lined with a membrane, but it is never nucleated as is the lining membrane of a true coelom. The digestive tract does not have a muscular wall. The Gastrotricha are probably most like the ancestral type. The Rotifera have long fascinated microscopists with their variety and abundance in fresh water. The Nematoda are of great economic importance because of the many parasitic species of man, animals, and plants.

The following classification into two subphyla seems to accommodate the classes conveniently in this broadly limited phylum.

Phylum Aschelminthes. Unsegmented, triploblastic, bilaterally symmetrical, pseudocoelomate animals with complete digestive tract and no circulatory or respiratory system.

SUBPHYLUM I. TROCHELMINTHES. Microscopic Aschelminthes; typically with external cilia and toes of a bifurcated foot provided with adhesive glands; muscles as discrete fibers or tracts; reproduction parthenogenetic in many species; protonephridia. Marine or fresh water.

CLASS 1. GASTROTRICHA. Pharynx simple; no segmentation of cuticle, which often has scales or plates which may be spined; hermaphroditic or parthenogenetic females.

CLASS 2. ROTIFERA. Pharynx modified into a special grinding structure, the mastax; cilia typically forming an anterior ring, the corona; sexes separate or parthenogenetic females.

CLASS 3. KINORHYNCHA. With an anterior region that may be everted or inverted; no external cilia; bristly cuticle differentiated into about 13 superficial segments; sexes separate; muscles mostly longitudinal with some segmental arrangement; all marine.

SUBPHYLUM II. NEMATHELMINTHES. Aschelminthes devoid of motor cilia; round elongate bodies; only longitudinal muscles in body wall, contractile fibers in peripheral part of muscle cell, nucleus in expanded inner part; no flame cells. Many are parasitic. The unsegmented roundworms.

CLASS 1. NEMATODA. Lateral epidermal chords present and containing the excretory ducts; pharynx present; female reproductive system opens to exterior. Thousands of species.

CLASS 2. NEMATOMORPHA. Lateral epidermal chords and excretory ducts absent; pharynx undifferentiated; female reproductive system opens into intestine; intestine often degenerate; juveniles parasitic in arthropods.

1 / Class I. Gastrotricha

(1) Chaetonotus

Chaetonotus (Fig. 6–1) is one of the more common gastrotrichs encountered on aquatic vegetation or detritus and in infusions. The body, usually from 100 to 200 microns long, is divided into a *head, neck,* and *trunk* bearing two tail forks. Locomotion is by means of cilia on two ventral areas. Much of the cuticle is divided into scales, many of which bear a spine. Four groups of sensory bristles occur on the head. The tail forks (*caudal furcae*) serve as tubes for paired *adhesive glands.*

The digestive system consists of a straight tube differentiated into an anterior *pharynx* and a posterior *intestine.* The *mouth* is at the extreme anterior end, the *anus,* on the dorsal surface of the posterior end. In some species a rectum may be posterior to a constriction of the intestine.

The *protonephridia* are paired and each consists of a flame cell with a long coiled tubule which opens to the exterior of the midregion of the body. Six pairs of longitudinal strands form the muscular system. Fibers lead from a

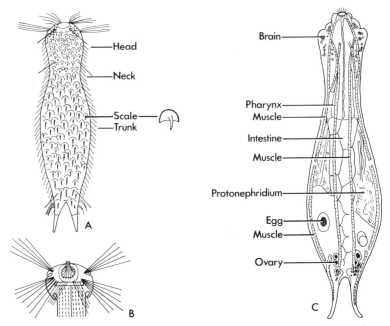

Fig. 6-1. Gastrotricha. (A) *Chaetonotus brevispinosus*, dorsal view. (B) *Polymerurus rhomboides*, ventral view of head. (C) *Chaetonotus*, showing internal organs. (A, C, after Zelinka; B, after Stokes.)

brain, looped over the pharynx, to the sides of the head and the posterior end of the body. Some gastrotrichs have pigmented eyespots.

Only parthenogenetic females are known. The *eggs* are very large, sometimes about half the length of the body; they are attached to various aquatic objects and give rise directly to the fully developed organism. The female pore is near the posterior end. The eggs may be *tachyblastic*, which proceed with development immediately, or *opsiblastic*, which undergo a period of dormancy during which they can survive a variety of unfavorable conditions.

(2) Other Gastrotricha

The approximately 2,000 species of gastrotrichs may be divided into the following two orders.

Order 1. Macrodasyoidea. Hermaphroditic; several pairs of adhesive tubes in addition to those of the tail fork; no protonephridia; all marine, but none on American shores.

Order 2. Chaetonotoidea. Only parthenogenetic females; two or four adhesive glands and tubes at the posterior; one pair of protonephridia; mostly freshwater species. *Chaetonotus* (Fig. 6–1, A and B) is a common genus, which contains about a third of the nearly 40 species of fresh-water gastrotrichs in the United States. A recent study by Sacks (1964) found that *Lepidodermella squammata* laid no more than four eggs during its entire life cycle. The eggs are laid about a day apart during the first five days of life. The life span averaged 10 days and those hatched from first eggs and last eggs of individuals seemed to live as long as those from second and third eggs.

\2 / Class II. Rotifera

(1) Epiphanes senta

Epiphanes senta (Fig. 6–2) is a commonly studied rotifier which serves to illustrate the class. The Rotifera (Rotatoria), once known as wheel animalcules, are extremely small Metazoa. They were at one time considered Infusoria. Most of them are inhabitants of fresh water, but some are marine and a few parasitic. The anatomy of *Epiphanes* is shown in Figure 6–2. The *head* is provided with *cilia*, which aid in locomotion and draw food into the

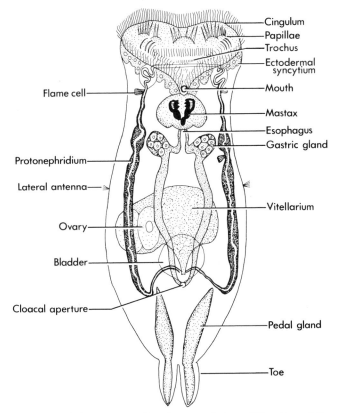

Fig. 6-2. Rotifera. *Epiphanes senta.* Female, ventral view. (After Borradaile and Potts, modified.)

mouth. The *tail* or *foot* is bifurcated and adheres to objects by means of a secretion from a *cement gland*. The body is usually cylindrical and is covered by a shell-like *cuticle*.

The Protozoa and other minute organisms used as *food* are swept by the cilia through the *mouth* into the *pharynx*, also called the *mastax* or chewing stomach. Here chitinous *jaws* (the *trophi*), which are constantly at work, break up the food. The movements of these jaws easily distinguish a living rotifer from other organisms. The food is *digested* in the glandular *stomach*. Undigested particles pass through the *intestine* into the *cloaca* and out the cloacal opening.

Two coiled tubes, which give off a number of ciliated lobules and enter a bladder, constitute the *excretory system*. The bladder contracts at intervals, forcing the contents out of the cloacal opening. Because the amount of fluid expelled by the bladder is very large, water regulation and respiration are probably also a function of this organ, the oxygen being taken into the animal with the water, which diffuses through the body wall, and the carbonic acid being cast out with the excretory fluid. The body cavity is not a true coelom.

The *sexes* of rotifers are separate. The *female* possesses an *ovary* in which the eggs arise, a *yolk gland*, which supplies the eggs with yolk, and an *oviduct*, which carries the eggs into the cloaca. From here the eggs reach the exterior through the cloacal opening. The *males* are usually smaller than the females, and often degenerate. They possess a *testis* in which the spermatozoa arise, and a *penis* for transferring the spermatozoa to the female.

Two kinds of eggs are produced by rotifers: (1) summer eggs, and (2) winter eggs. The *summer eggs*, which develop parthenogenetically, are thin-shelled, and of two sizes; the larger produce females and the smaller males. The *winter eggs*, which are fertilized, have thick shells and develop females. The winter eggs and the summer eggs that develop into males are produced by females whose eggs undergo meiosis. If the egg is unfertilized a male is produced, if the egg is fertilized it develops into a female. Thus, males have only half the chromosomes in their nuclei that female rotifers have. This is shown in Figure 6–3.

Constancy of Nuclear Numbers. Many rotifers exhibit *eutely*, the phenomenon of each somatic organ having a characteristic number of nuclei that is constant for the species. In most rotifers the number of nuclei is from 900 to 1,000. The following numbers of nuclei have been reported from some groups of nuclei in *Epiphanes senta*. Epidermis, 280; pedal glands, 19 each; muscular system, 104; brain, 183; other nervous tissue, 97; digestive tract lining, 159; gastric glands, 6 each; yolk gland, 8; oviduct, 3; protonephridium, 14 each. Six nuclei in a gastric gland and eight nuclei in a yolk gland have proven to be common to most species of rotifers examined. Birky and Field (1966) have found that species of *Asplanchna*, a common planktonic genus, are exceptions to the rule and that variation is subject to environmental control.

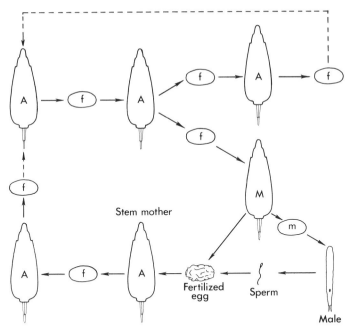

Fig. 6-3. Diagram showing the alternation of generations in a rotifer, such as *Lecane inermis*. The most common type of individual, the "amictic" female (A), reproduces exclusively by diploid parthenogenesis. Its eggs (*f*) develop invariably into females, which are usually amictic, so that multiplication by diploid parthenogenesis may continue for many generations (as indicated by the long, broken-lined arrows). But the daughters of the amictic female may be "mictic" (*M*). Their eggs are haploid, and develop parthenogenetically (*m*) into males, or, if fertilized, produce amictic females, the "stem mothers," with which the cycle begins anew. (After Miller.)

Cells of which various organs are constituted do not vary greatly in size within the individuals of a species. Thus, variations in the size of the body or of an organ are generally considered to be due to differences in the number of cells. In adult rotifers the cells are generally fused into a syncytium and thus the number of nuclei represents the approximate number of cells an equivalent cellular tissue would have. In many animals, as in *Epiphanes*, it has been shown that certain organs are almost invariably made up of a definite and constant number of cells or nuclei and in some animals the cell or nuclear number of the entire somatic tissue is constant.

In the differentiated somatic cells of such an animal the power of mitotic cell division appears to be lost; for example, no regeneration occurs in the rotifer, *Stephanoceros* (Fig. 6–4, I), if its arms are injured.

Cell or nuclear constancy occurs in species in which there is determinate cleavage of the egg. Apparently partial constancy is more frequent than complete constancy. In four genera of Acanthocephala, however, all of the somatic tissues have a constant number of cells although the number may differ in different species. The nematode worm, *Oxyuris curvula*, has a

Fig. 6-4. Types of rotifers and their jaws. (A) *Proales werneckii.* (B) *Monommata longiseta.* (C) *Mytilina spinigera.* (D) *Brachionus pala.* (E) *Floscularia ringens.* (F) *Trochosphaera solstitialis.* (G) *Rotaria citrinus.* (H) *Philodina roseola.* (I) *Stephanoceros fimbriatus.* (J) *Conochilus unicornis.* (K) *Seison annulatus.* (L) *Collotheca proboscidea.* (M) Jaws of *Asplanchnopus myrmeleo.* (N) Jaws of *Asplanchna priodonta.* (O) Jaws of *Harringia eupoda.* (K) Seisonida. (G, H) Bdelloida. (A–F, I, J, L) Monogononata. (From Jennings, after various authors.)

constant number of cells (412) in the excretory and nervous systems and in the connective tissue, but a variable number in other organs. The number of muscle cells in the body wall of seven different species belonging to the genus

Oxyuris is the same for all, namely 65. Similarly the cells in the ommatidia of the compound eye of arthropods are not only constant in number but also constant in their location and physiological interrelations. Cell or nuclear constancy may occur also among the germ cells. For example, in the fly, *Miastor*, a definite number of primordial germ cells, and later, of ova, develop in each individual. Many other instances of cell or nuclear constancy are known among the tunicates, insects, annelids, nematodes, turbellarians, trematodes, etc.

(2) Other Rotifera

The *corona*, or anterior crown of cilia found on most rotifers has many variations in different species. The primitive type, much like *Epiphanes*, was thought to have an anterior circle of cilia, the *trochus*, and another circle just behind the trochus, the *cingulum*. Between the two rings is a ciliated buccal field enclosing the mouth. One line of evolutionary development probably gave rise to a lobed trochus (Fig. 6–5, D) found in the suborder Flosculariacea. Further separation of the trochus into two disks (Fig. 6–5, E) is found in the Bdelloida. Some think the trochal disks developed from papillae in the buccal field. In the Collothecacea the anterior has lost the typical ciliation and only a few bristles may remain.

Rotifers are abundant in the plankton of fresh water. They are even more abundant on the surfaces of aquatic plants and debris. They reach their greatest abundance in numbers in the wet interstices of sandy beaches (Pennak, 1953). They are important primary consumers in aquatic ecosystems.

Williams (1966) found that five genera of ploimate rotifers, *Keratella*, *Polyarthra*, *Brachionus*, *Synchaeta*, and *Trichocerca*, were commonly abundant in collections of planktonic rotifers in some major waterways of the United States. They outnumbered other metazoans 30 to 1 but were nearly

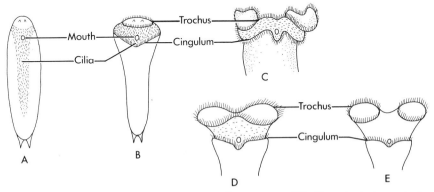

Fig. 6-5. Presumed derivation of the rotifer corona. (A) Hypothetical, ventrally ciliated ancestor. (B) Basic ciliation of a rotifer. (C) *Hexarthra*, with reduced buccal field. (D) Lobed floscularian corona. (E) Trochal disks of the bdelloid type. (Modified from Hyman and Edmondson, after de Beauchamp.)

absent in the winter. More than one genus commonly shared the dominance at one time, although only one species from a genus tended to be among the dominants.

Classification of Rotifers

Rotifers are microscopic in size, frequently with a superficial segmentation. They possess a mastax in the pharynx, the trophi (Fig. 6–4, M, N, and O) of which are often important in species identification. A crown of cilia (the corona) is usually at the anterior end, and the tail is frequently jointed with toes at the posterior end. Three orders are as follows.

Order 1. Seisonida. These rotifers are parasitic on marine crustacea. The corona is greatly reduced; the body is long, narrow, and ringed; the neck is much elongated; and the elongated foot has a terminal perforated disk with which it attaches itself to its host. All species belong to the genus *Seison* (Fig. 6–4, K).

Order 2. Bdelloida. Fresh-water species that swim with the corona or creep like a leech or both. Two ovaries occur in these rotifers. Behind the corona is a dorsal proboscis. The body is usually cylindrical and without a lorica; it is composed of rings that may be drawn together like the sections of a telescope. *Rotaria* (Fig. 6–4, G) and *Philodina* (Fig. 6–4, H) are very common bottom-dwelling rotifers that frequently occur in infusions. The corona bears two wheels of cilia on separate retractile lobes (Fig. 6–5, E). Two posterior spurs make it difficult to distinguish the three toes of *Rotaria* or the four toes of *Philodina*. *Philodina roseola* has two eyes behind the proboscis and a slender, rose-colored body that may cause the bottom of shallow ponds to appear red when they are abundant. Many species of this order are able to withstand dessication and come to life when placed in water, after existing for months in a dried condition.

Order 3. Monogononata. Rotifers with one gonad. Three suborders are quite distinct.

Suborder 1. Ploima. Planktonic or swimming rotifers with normal corona (Figs. 6–2 and 6–5, C). *Epiphanes senta* has already been described. *Keratella* has a sculptured lorica with one or two posterior spines and three pair of anterior spines, there is no foot. *Brachionus* (Fig. 6–4, D) and *Platyias* also are loricate but have a foot, the foot is retractable in *Brachionus*. *Polyarthra* has 12 cuticular paddles along the sides and attached at the anterior. *Trichocerca* is asymmetrical due to a twisted lorica. *Monostyla* has one long toe, which projects from the fused dorsal and ventral plates of the lorica. *Lecane* is similar but has two toes. *Synchaeta* lacks a lorica but has four anterior spines. *Asplanchna herricki* is a large species, saclike in form, and without foot or anus, waste products being cast out through the mouth. It thrusts its forceps-like jaws out of the mouth and seizes other animals with them. The plankton of the Great Lakes sometimes contains enormous numbers of this and related species. The simplest of all rotifers belong to the genus *Proales* (Fig. 6–4, A). They are small and cylindrical, with a short foot and toes, and without a tail; the corona is a uniformly ciliated area and does not possess portions bearing longer cilia.

Suborder 2. Flosculariacea.   Rotifers that have a large corona with two parallel rows of cilia around the outer edge, the inner row being larger than the outer. Between these two rows is usually a groove, often lined with fine cilia, along which food particles are carried to the mouth. The jaws are of the peculiar malleo-ramate type. The species may be solitary or colonial, free-swimming or attached. *Floscularia ringens* (Fig. 6–4, E) has a large corona with four large lobes, lives in a tube formed of spherical pellets and is common on water plants. *Conochilus unicornis* (Fig. 6–4, J) is a free-swimming, pelagic species, living in small colonies in which each individual occupies a separate, transparent tube. *Sinantherina* has a heart-shaped corona and forms visible colonies, either floating or attached; *Lacinularia* is similar, but embedded in a gelatinous mass.

Suborder 3. Collothecacea.   The adult males and young rotifers belonging to this order are free-swimming, but the adult females are mostly solitary and attached to water plants by a stalk, which is the modified foot. They live in a transparent tube and usually possess a lobed corona that is much expanded and has the mouth in the center. The cilia at the edge of the corona are often long and do not beat actively but are moved about so as to entangle prey. In these forms the digestive tract is modified for dealing with the large animals captured by the corona. *Collotheca ornata* (Fig. 6–4, L) has a corona with five knobbed lobes, a foot about twice as long as the body but no eyes. *Stephanoceros fimbriatus* (Fig. 6–4, I) also has a corona with five lobes; these are very long and slender and their cilia are long and nonvibratile. *Cupelopagis vorax* (Fig. 6–6) is a large rotifer, lacking vibratile cilia, that feeds on small organisms that blunder into its retractible, funnel-like anterior.

Fig. 6-6. Rotifera. *Cupelopagis vorax*, a highly modified collothecacean that uses a funnel to trap food organisms rather than using ciliary currents. (A) Funnel retracted. (B) Funnel extended. (C) Lateral view.

\3 / Class III. Kinorhyncha

This group of about 100 species of microscopic, marine, spiny, and superficially segmented animals have their mouth situated on a protrusible mouth cone. The segmentation is superficial and is not thought to be truly metameric. It is likely that they arose from the gastrotrich stem close to the rotifer line. The Priapulida are thought to have arisen from the Kinorhyncha by some zoologists. A close relationship with the nematodes is also claimed.

Thirteen segments (or *zonites*) form the slightly elongate, tapering body. Some internal structures reflect the external segmentation, namely the muscles and the ventral nerve, which has ganglia in the segments of the trunk. The digestive tract (Fig. 6–7, B) is a straight tube with the retractable mouth cone opening through a narrowed esophagus into the stomach-intestine. Several small glands are associated with these portions. A short rectum opens through a posterior anus. Paired protonephridia of the flame cell type open on the eleventh segment. Sexes are separate and the paired gonads open on the last segment. The cuticle is molted as juvenile kinorhynchs grow, and segments are added at the posterior until the adult stage is reached. Kinorhynchs live primarily in marine bottom muds and are of no special economic importance. Higgins (1965) is a leading investigator of the Kinorhyncha. Further study of the Kinorhyncha may clarify their relationship to the nematodes and priapulids.

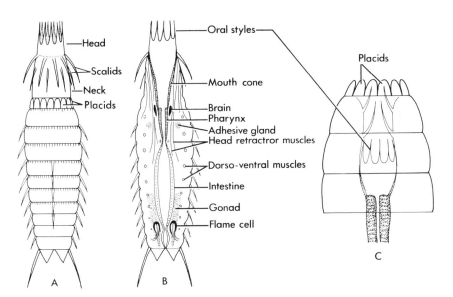

Fig. 6-7. Kinorhyncha. Generalized diagram of anatomy. (A) External, with mouth cone extended. (B) Internal. (C) Anterior with mouth cone retracted.

4 / Class IV. Nematoda

The Nematoda are called unsegmented roundworms (along with the Nematomorpha and Acanthocephala), to distinguish them from the flat-worms and segmented annelids. They are long, slender animals usually with a smooth and glistening surface and tapering somewhat toward one or both ends. Roundworms are very widely distributed and occur in large numbers, both as regards species and individuals, in soil, fresh water and salt water, and as parasites in plants and animals. It has been estimated that the top six inches of an acre of arable soil contains thousands of millions of nemas. In size, they range from about 0.5 mm to over 1 meter in length. One can recognize most of them easily because of their peculiar movements. They whip about by contortions of their entire body in a dorso-ventral plane without making any forward progress unless solid particles are present for the body to lash against. As a rule, the free-living nemas are slighted in courses in zoology because they are mostly small and not of medical interest. How-ever, they present the morphological and physiological characteristics of the phylum in certain respects better than do the parasitic species, which are modified more or less for their mode of life.

(1) Turbatrix (Anguillula) aceti—The Vinegar Eel

The vinegar eel, *Turbatrix aceti*, is a favorable free-living nematode for study because it is easily procured at any time of the year in cider vinegar, can be examined in the living condition, and can be fixed and stained easily. It is visible to the naked eye when held before a bright light and exhibits characteristic nematode movements. Heating for a minute kills and straightens vinegar eels, and staining with Delafield's haematoxylin in 70 per cent alcohol reveals the internal organs.

The worms are cylindrical, the anterior end being slightly narrowed and the posterior end tapering to a fine point. The female is about 2 mm in length and 0.05 mm in breadth and the male about 1.4 mm in length and 0.03 mm in breadth. The *cuticle* is transparent and transversely striated. The *mouth* is a pore at the anterior end; it opens into a cone-shaped *buccal capsule* about 0.01 mm long. The posterior portion of the buccal capsule is provided with one dorsal and two ventro-lateral *teeth*. The *pharynx*, in which the buccal capsule is partly embedded, consists of an anterior thick portion 0.1 mm in length, followed by a narrow neck 0.05 mm in length which leads to a mus-cular bulb 0.02 mm in diameter in which is a valvular apparatus. The *ex-cretory pore* is difficult to find; it is on a level with the anterior end of the bulb. Just in front of the bulb, the *nerve ring* crosses the pharynx. The *intestine* is a straight tube, about 0.02 mm in diameter in the female and smaller in the male; it extends from the pharynx to the *rectum*, which is short, narrow, and straight and opens into the *cloaca*.

The *male reproductive organs* consist of a testicular tube, a seminal vesicle, a genital pore, a pair of spicules, and an accessory piece. The *testicular tube* forms a loop arising about 0.3 mm from the ano-genital pore, extending forward about 0.1 mm and then bending back upon itself to the *genital pore* which opens into the cloaca. It contains reproductive cells in two or three rows near its origin but these form a single row from near the bend to the posterior end. A portion of the tube near the posterior end is modified into a thin-walled *seminal vesicle* in which spermatozoa may be seen. This joins the rectum to form a short cloaca. Near the opening of the cloaca to the outside is a pair of *curved spicules* about 0.37 mm long and an accessory piece, which is a curved plate shaped somewhat like the keel of a boat. The muscles that extend the spicules are conspicuous. Five pairs of *papillae* are present near the cloacal opening; one postanal, dorsal pair; two preanal, central; one adanal, ventral; and one postanal, ventral.

The *female reproductive organs* comprise an ovarian tubule, a seminal receptacle, a uterus, a vagina, and vulva. The *ovarian tubule* arises posterior to the middle of the body, runs forward dorsally about 0.5 mm where it joins the *uterus*, which runs backward ventrally to the vagina, which opens to the outside through the slit-like *vulva* near the middle of the body. An oval sac extending posteriorly from the vulva is probably a *seminal receptacle*. The ovarian tubule contains a single row of germ cells; these are fertilized near the bend where they become oval in shape and soon begin to segment. A varied number of *eggs* may be present in the uterus but usually about two ovoid and three vermiform embryos may be observed. The thin egg membrane ruptures in the uterus and the young are born in an active condition, that is, the vinegar eel is viviparous. The fertilized eggs hatch in about eight days, and the larvae, which are 0.2 mm long when hatched, become mature in about four weeks. Males and females are equal in number; they may live for 10 months or more and one female may produce as many as 45 larvae. The male may be recognized by the blunter posterior and (as in most aschelminths) smaller size than in the female.

(2) Ascaris lumbricoides

External Features. *Ascaris lumbricoides* is the common roundworm parasitic in the intestine of man. Roundworms morphologically indistinguishable from this species occur in pigs, but these have been shown to be physiologically different and not infective to man. The sexes are separate. The female, being the larger, measures from 5 to 11 inches in length and about one fourth of an inch in diameter. The *body*, when alive, may be milk-white or somewhat reddish-yellow and has a characteristic sheen; it has a dorsal and a ventral narrow white stripe running its entire length and a broader *lateral line* is present on either side. The *cuticle* is smooth and marked with fine striations. The *mouth* opening is in the anterior end and is surrounded by one dorsal

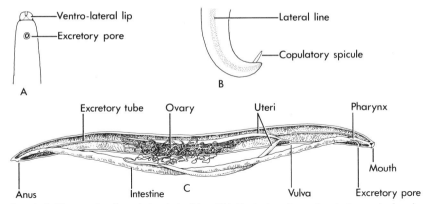

Fig. 6-8. Nematoda. *Ascaris lumbricoides*. (A) Ventral surface of anterior end of male. (B) Lateral view of posterior end of male. (C) Dissection of female to show internal organs. (A, B, original; C, from Woodruff.)

and two ventral *lips*; these are finely toothed and bear *papillae*, the dorsal lip two and each ventral lip one. Near the posterior end is the *anal opening*, from which, in the male, extends two spicules or *penial setae* of use during copulation. Many ventral preanal and postanal *papillae* are also present in the male. The male can be distinguished from the female by the presence of a bend in the posterior part of the body. In the female, the genital opening, the *vulva*, is located about one third the length of the body from the anterior end.

Internal Anatomy.   If an animal is cut open along the dorsal line (Fig. 6–8), it will be found to contain a straight *alimentary canal*, and certain other organs, lying in a central cavity, the pseudocoel. The alimentary canal is very simple, since the food is taken from material already digested by the host whose intestine the worm inhabits. It opens at the posterior end through the *anus*, which is not present in members of the phyla already discussed. A small *buccal vestibule* opens into the muscular *pharynx*, from 10 to 15 mm long, which draws the fluids into the long nonmuscular intestine through the walls of which the nutriment is absorbed. The walls are lined with microvilli (in the pig ascaris, Kessel *et al.*, 1961), which have an ultrastructural resemblance to cilia. They form a tightly packed "brush-border" (Fig. 6–10) with no known motor function. They are now thought to be absorptive or secretory structures. Just before the anal opening is reached, the intestine gradually becomes smaller; this portion is known as the *rectum*. The rectum opens through the *anus* in the female and into the *cloaca* in the male.

The *excretory system* consists of two longitudinal canals one in each lateral line; these open to the outside by a single pore situated near the anterior end in the ventral body wall.

A ring of *nervous tissue* surrounds the pharynx and gives off two large nerve cords, one dorsal, the other ventral, and a number of other smaller strands and connections.

The *male reproductive organs* are a single coiled threadlike *testis*, from which a *vas deferens* leads to a wider tube, the *seminal vesicle*; this is followed by the short muscular *ejaculatory duct* which opens into the cloaca. In the *female* lies a Y-shaped reproductive system. Each branch of the Y consists of a coiled threadlike *ovary* which is continuous with a larger canal, the *uterus*. The uteri of the two branches unite into a short muscular tube, the *vagina*, which opens to the outside through the *genital aperture* or *vulva*. *Fertilization* takes place in the uterus. The egg is then surrounded by a shell of chitin, and passes out through the genital pore. The genital tubules of a female worm may contain as many as 27 million eggs at one time and each mature female lays about 200,000 eggs per day. Because the fertilized eggs in the uterus undergo the early cleavage divisions and have only a few large chromosomes, sections of *Ascaris* uterus are frequently used for the beginning study of mitosis.

The relations of the various organs to one another, as well as the structure of the body wall, and the character of the coelom, are shown in Figure 6–9, which is a transverse section of a female specimen of *Ascaris lumbricoides*. The body of the worm should be considered as consisting of two tubes, one, the

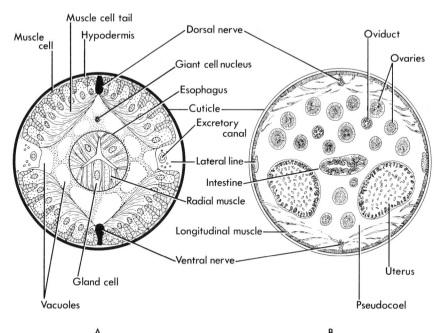

A   B

Fig. 6-9. *Ascaris.* (A) Cross-section through region of esophagus. (B) Cross-section through midregion of a female. (A, after Borradaile and Potts, modified; B, original.)

Lumen of intestine

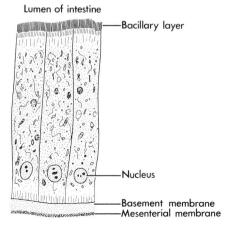

—Bacillary layer

Fig. 6-10. *Ascaris* intestine. Three cells of intestinal wall showing bacillary layer, or "brush border" of cilia-like microvilli, lining the intestine. (Diagrammatic.)

—Nucleus

—Basement membrane
—Mesenterial membrane

intestine, lying within the other, the body wall; between them is a cavity, the pseudocoel, in which lie the reproductive organs.

The *body wall* is composed of several layers, an outer chitinous cuticle, a thin layer of hypodermis just beneath it, and a thick stratum of longitudinal muscle fibers, mesodermal in origin, lining the coelom. Thickenings of the hypodermis form the dorsal, ventral, and lateral lines. In each of the last-named lines lies one of the longitudinal excretory tubes. The nerve cords are also embedded in the body wall.

The *intestine* consists of a single layer of columnar cells bearing the microvilli within (Fig. 6–10).

The pseudocoel of *Ascaris* differs from the coelom of the higher animals in several respects. Typically the coelom is a cavity in the mesoderm lined by an epithelium; the excretory organs open into it, and the reproductive cells originate from its walls. In *Ascaris* the pseudocoel is lined only by the mesoderm of the body wall, there being no mesoderm surrounding the intestine. Furthermore, the excretory organs open to the exterior through the excretory pore, and the reproductive cells are not derived from the coelomic epithelium. The body cavity of *Ascaris*, therefore, differs structurally and functionally from that of a true coelom, but nevertheless is similar in many respects.

Life Cycle. Maturation, fertilization, and the phenomena concerned with the early differentiation of germ cells and somatic cells in *Ascaris* eggs have for many years served to illustrate these processes in animals in general. The eggs of *Ascaris* segment after they leave the body. They are very resistant and may remain alive in the soil for months. Embryos are formed under favorable conditions in about two weeks. Infection with *Ascaris* results from ingesting embryonated eggs. The eggs are usually carried to the mouth either with food or water or by accidental transfer of soil containing such ova. They do not regularly hatch in the stomach but pass to the small intestine where they begin to hatch within a few hours after ingestion. Formerly it was believed that the larvae upon hatching settled down in the small intestine and there developed directly into the adult stage. Investigations have shown, however, that the larvae of this parasite leave the intestine immediately after hatching and then follow a definite path of migration through the tissues of the host, afterward returning to the intestine to grow into mature worms.

The newly hatched larvae burrow into the wall of the intestine and enter the lymphatic vessels or the venules. If the larvae enter the lymphatics they are carried to the mesenteric lymph nodes and from there may reach the circulation either by entering the blood capillaries and passing into the portal circulation, or pass into the thoracic duct and from there to the right side of the heart. If the portal circulation is entered the larvae are carried to the liver where they pass from the interlobular veins to the intralobular veins. From the liver they are carried to the right side of the heart and then to the lungs. Within the lungs they break into the alveoli where some further development and growth takes place, after which they pass on to the intestine by way of the trachea, esophagus, and stomach. This journey through the host's tissues requires about 10 days. They become mature worms in the intestine in about $2\frac{1}{2}$ months.

Relations of Ascaris to Man. Ascarids are pathogenic to man. When large numbers of larvae pass through the lungs inflammation is set up and generalized pneumonia may result. The adults may be present in the intestine in such large numbers as to produce intestinal obstruction and nervous symptoms may appear as a result of the secretion of toxic substances by the worms. Fortunately several drugs are available which easily remove the worms; the best of these are piperazine citrate and hexyl resorcinol. Ascariasis is essentially a children's disease in the United States, but a high percentage of adults in many other countries are infected. Studies in this country have shown that the infestations were particularly severe in families where the children were allowed to pollute the soil near the houses. Under these conditions the soil contains large numbers of embryonated eggs which find their way into the children's mouths on dirty hands. Infection can be prevented easily by enforcing sanitary practices.

(3) Other Nematoda

The many species of nematodes are thought to number in the hundreds of thousands. The differences between species are in minor features that do not warrant separation above the order level. The tremendous numbers of very similar species have made it difficult, even for specialists on the Nematoda, to arrive at a satisfactory classification. Seventeen superfamilies are noted below. Only the first eight superfamilies contain free-living species.

Free-Living Nematodes. Roundworms that are not parasitic are more abundant and more widely distributed on the earth's surface than most zoologists realize. They live in almost every conceivable type of environment, such as in wet sand or mud, aquatic vegetation, in standing or running water, in the soil, the sea, tap water, fruit juices, and in moist places almost everywhere.

If all the matter in the universe except the nematodes were swept away, our world would still be dimly recognizable, and if, as disembodied spirits, we could then investigate it, we should find its mountains, hills, vales, rivers, lakes, and oceans represented by a film of nematodes. The location of towns would be decipherable, since for every massing of human beings there would be a corresponding massing of certain nematodes. Trees would still stand in ghostly rows representing our streets and highways. The location of the various plants and animals would still be decipherable, and, had we sufficient knowledge, in many cases even their species could be determined by an examination of their erstwhile nematode parasites (Cobb).

Free-living nematodes are mostly small, a large specimen being only 1 cm in length. The eggs may withstand dessication, a fact which no doubt is responsible in part for their wide distribution, since they may be carried about by the wind as well as by currents of water, birds and other animals, and by man. They feed on other nematodes and on microorganisms. Most species are transparent but some have pigment granules in the intestinal cells which give them a yellowish or brownish appearance. Colored eye spots may also be present.

The body is covered by a transparent noncellular coat, the cuticula, beneath which is a cellular layer, the subcuticula or hypoderm, which secretes the cuticula. The cuticula is shed about four times during the growth of the larva and the lining of the mouth, pharynx, and rectum are shed at the same time. Within the cells of the hypoderm are longitudinal contractile fibers. The hypoderm is in many nematodes thickened along the center of the lateral and dorsal and ventral surfaces thus dividing the body wall into four quadrants. The thickenings on the sides are called lateral lines. The digestive system is simple. The mouth is at the anterior end, usually surrounded by lips or papillae (Fig. 6–11). Teeth may be present for rasping the tissue of plants or animals on which the nematodes feed. The buccal cavity is tubular, funnel-shaped, or expanded into a cup-shaped capsule adapted for sucking. The pharynx is either a thin-walled tube, or thick and muscular, and usually possesses a bulb or valvular apparatus where it joins the intestine. The intestine is a straight tube of columnar epithelial cells. It decreases in size at the posterior end in the female, becoming the rectum. In the male the intestine and genital duct open into a cloaca. The anal opening is on the ventral surface near the posterior end.

The excretory organ is a unicellular gland, the renette, located in the body cavity near the union of pharynx and intestine. A nerve ring surrounds the pharynx. Certain species possess a pair of pigmented eye spots, one on either side of the pharynx. Cephalic, caudal, and terminal setae, probably organs of

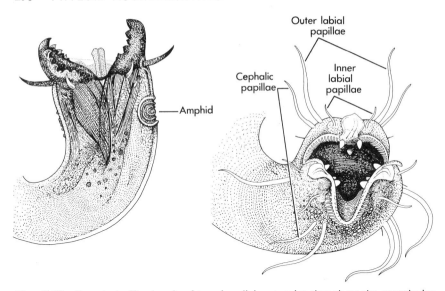

Fig. 6-11. Nematoda. The heads of two free-living species that show the complexity of structure of certain nemas. (After Cobb.)

touch, taste, or smell, occur on free-living but not on the parasitic species. A pair of laterally situated cephalic organs known as *amphids* (Fig. 6–11), probably sensory in nature, also occur on free-living nemas. The free-living stages of certain parasitic nematodes also possess sensory organs. No circulatory system is present, circulation being accomplished by the fluid in the body cavity in which currents are set up by the movements of the worm. The sex organs are, in general, similar to those of *Turbatrix* already described.

1. Superfamily Enoploidea. Marine nematodes with papillae and bristles on the head; a pair of sensory slits on the head in addition to the amphids; pharynx typically a simple straight tube. As with most free-living nematodes, a group of caudal glands are present. These are adhesive in function and are probably homologous to the pedal glands of rotifers and gastrotrichs.

Metoncholaimus pristiurus (Fig. 6–12), found in marine mud of Atlantic coastal regions, is a good example of a free-living marine nematode. It has six lips surrounding the mouth. Each lip bears a papilla. The amphids are lateral and shield-shaped. The male has a ventral row of 10 papillae on the tail as well as numerous bristles and a small preanal papilla. Two slender spicules can be protracted to aid in copulation or retracted. The testes are paired. The female has a single ovary from which eggs pass through the oviduct to the uterus where fertilization occurs. Up to 40 eggs are stored in a single row in the uterus. They are laid before segmentation occurs. A *demanian system*, peculiar to this nematode and others in the same family, occurs in the female as a system of tubes in contact with uterus and intestine and

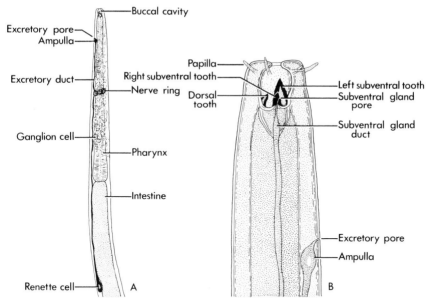

Fig. 6-12. Nematoda. *Metoncholaimus pristiurus.* (A) Anterior end. (B) Lateral view of head. (After Chitwood.)

opening through a pore near the anus. It is thought to be an accessory reproductive structure. Also characteristic of the family (Oncholaimidae) is a large mouth cavity containing one to three teeth (Fig. 6–12, B).

2. Superfamily Dorylaimoidea. Buccal cavity containing a hollow protrusible spear mounted on the pharynx and used when sucking juices from plant and animal food organisms; common in soil and fresh-water. *Xiphinema index* is a dorylaimid, which has modified cilia in sensory structures (Roggen *et al.*, 1966). The definite presence of ciliary structures in nematodes removes one of the most formidable objections to the use of the Phylum Aschelminthes as a natural, phylogenetic group.

3. Superfamily Mermithoidea. Long, slender juveniles are parasites of insects or other terrestrial and fresh-water invertebrates; no buccal cavity; pharynx long and passing through *stichocytes* (cells of the stichosome, a pharyngeal gland); adults do not feed, but live on food stores acquired during the parasitic juvenile stage. The larva has a dorylaimid type of spear on the pharynx. *Agameris decaudata*, a parasite of grasshoppers, leaves its posterior larval half behind when it actively penetrates its young grasshopper host. Other species may infect after the egg stage is ingested.

4. Superfamily Chromadoroidea. Spiral amphids; ornamented cuticle; primarily marine; pharynx with a posterior bulb; usually with teeth in the buccal cavity. The families Draconematidae and Epsilonematidae are marine and have "stilt bristles" near the posterior end of the body.

5. Superfamily Araeolaimoidea. Four large cephalic bristles posterior to the labial papillae; loop-shaped or spiral amphids; cuticle without ornamentation.

6. Superfamily Monhysteroidea. Circular amphids; mostly marine. *Cylindrolaimus* is a genus of soil and fresh-water nematodes with the buccal capsule in the shape of a long tube.

7. Superfamily Demoscolecoidea. Marine; thick-bodied; amphids semicircular; buccal cavity reduced; head distinct from body; four cephalic papillae.

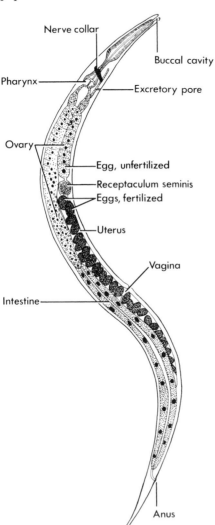

Fig. 6-13. Nematoda. *Rhabditis.* Mature female. (After Maupas, modified.)

8. Superfamily Rhabditoidea. Pharynx with two expanded regions, or bulbs; amphids reduced; no caudal glands; phasmids present (the only group containing free-living species with phasmids); a large group of mostly terrestrial species. *Turbatrix aceti* has been previously discussed. *Rhabditis* (Fig. 6–13) is a large genus containing both free-living and parasitic forms.

The family Tylenchidae contains species with a buccal stylet. *Heterodera* commonly lives in galls on the roots of plants. *Criconema* (*Iota*) has marked annulations of the cuticle bearing posteriorly projecting scales in eight rows.

Parasitic Nematoda. Only two of the preceding superfamilies contained parasites of animals, none of which were vertebrates. The remaining superfamilies all contain parasites of vertebrates. No free-living species occur in them although some may have a developmental stage outside the host. Life cycles require an intermediate host in some species. Phasmids occur in all but the superfamilies Trichuroidea and Dioctophymoidea. *Phasmids* are paired cuticular glands near the caudal end. They are of unknown significance and are microscopic. Some of the superfamilies bear a close relationship to free-living superfamilies. This is especially true of the Rhabdiasoidea and Rhabditoidea.

9. Superfamily Rhabdiasoidea. Parasites of vertebrates; structure much as in the Rhabditoidea; pharyngeal bulb reduced.

Rhabdias bufonis is a common lung nematode in frogs and other amphibians.

Strongyloides stercoralis is a common human parasite especially in the moist tropics. Its life cycle includes a female stage that lives in the human intestine and lays eggs that give rise to male and female larvae. These rhabditiform larvae pass out in the feces and form a free-living generation. They may become infective larvae or develop into sexually mature adults. The offspring of these are filariform larvae, which are infective to man. They may be swallowed but usually penetrate the skin of bare feet. They are carried in the blood stream to the lungs, break out into the trachea, migrate through the epiglottis into the digestive tract, and become localized in the ileum.

10. Superfamily Oxyuroidea. Parasites of vertebrates, or, in a few cases, of invertebrates; small slender worms; one or two bulbs on pharynx.

This superfamily contains the pinworm of man, *Enterobius vermicularis* (Fig. 6–14, G), and a similar species in horses. The human pinworm (female) measures from 9 to 12 mm in length, is world-wide in distribution and lives in the adult stage in the upper part of the large intestine. Children are often infected, sometimes over 5,000 worms being present in a single child. The female worms creep out of the rectum, usually at night, causing intense itching. They lay their eggs at once. The infected person scratches the anal region thereby contaminating the hands, especially the fingernails, and the eggs are then conveyed to the mouth and swallowed, thus increasing the infection. Piperazine salts are effective drugs for treatment. *Oxyuris equi*

Fig. 6-14. Nematoda. (A) *Heterakis gallinae*, from the cecum of fowls; about one-half natural size. (B) *Wuchereria bancrofti*, microfilariae. (C) *Loa loa*, microfilariae. (D) *Trichinella spiralis*, the trichina worm, young larva. (E) *Gongylonema pulchrum*, anterior end. (F) *T. spiralis*, the trichina worm, male. (G) *Enterobius vermicularis*, female; the pinworm of man. (H) *Trichuris ovis*, whipworm, from sheep and cattle. (After various authors.)

resembles the pinworm of man; it causes anal pruritus in horses, asses, and mules.

Heterakis contains species that live in birds and mammals. Of particular importance is *Heterakis gallinae* (Fig. 6–14, A) which lives in the cecum of barnyard and wild fowls. Eggs, which are passed in the feces of infected birds, are swallowed and the young that hatch from them in the small intestine move on into the ceca. They do not seriously injure the fowls but are of great economic importance since they carry with them a protozoan parasite, *Histomonas meleagridis*, which is the causative agent of the disease of turkeys known as blackhead.

11. Superfamily Ascaroidea. This group of large nematodes are parasites in the digestive tract of vertebrates. *Ascaris lumbricoides* (Fig. 6–8) from man

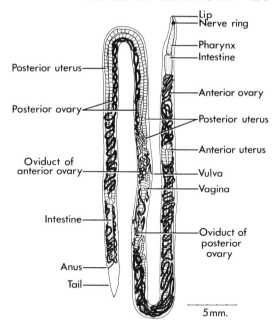

Fig. 6-15. Nematoda. The chicken nematode, *Ascaridia galli*, female. Digestive and reproductive organs. The uterus is distinguished from the other organs by crossed lines. (After Ackert, modified.)

has already been described. *Ascaridia galli* (Figs. 6–15 and 6–16) is the common round worm of chickens, living in the small intestine.

Toxocara canis is the common ascarid of dogs being especially prevalent in puppies. Dogs become infected by swallowing the eggs. The larvae migrate through the body as do those of *Ascaris lumbricoides* in man. Dogs acquire

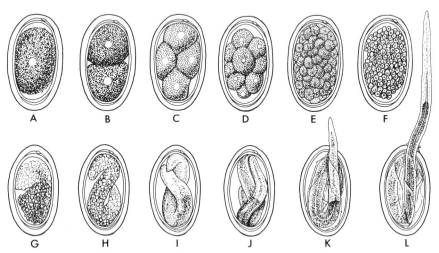

Fig. 6-16. Nematoda. Development of the egg of the chicken nematode, *Ascaridia galli*. (A) Fertilized egg. (B) Two-cell stage. (C) Four-cell stage. (D) Early morula stage. (E, F) Late morula stages. (G) "Tadpole" stage. (H, I) Vermiform stages. (J) Coiled embryo = "embryonated egg." (K, L) Young worm hatching. (After Ackert.)

an immunity as a result of the infection, and after 3 or 4 months the worms are cast out and susceptibility to further infection is lost.

12. Superfamily Strongyloidea. Posterior of the male expanded into a bursa supported by muscular rays. All are parasites of vertebrates, commonly in the intestine. Many interesting and economically important species belong to this superfamily. Five families will be mentioned here. The family Strongylidae contains many parasites of domesticated animals. *Strongylus vulgaris* is the most important round worm of horses and other Equidae and is world-wide in distribution but especially prevalent in warm countries. It lives in the cecum or colon attached by the mouth to the mucosa, from which it sucks blood. Loss of blood results in anemia. The eggs of *Strongylus* are deposited in the feces where they give rise to infective larvae. These, when ingested by a horse, migrate to the posterior mesenteric artery where an aneurysm is produced: they then move on to the cecum where they become

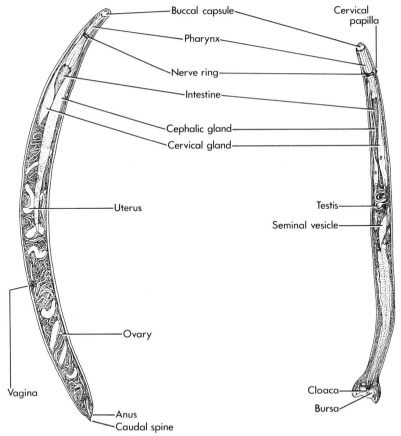

Fig. 6-17. *Ancylostoma duodenale*, the Old World Hookworm, female (left) and male (right). (After Loos.)

encysted in the submucosa; and finally they break out into the lumen, attach themselves to the mucosa, and develop into adults.

The nodular worm of sheep and goats, *Esophagostomum columbianum*, also belongs to this family. The young worms encyst in the wall of the intestine forming nodules. Later they break out into the lumen and become adults. Diarrhea and emaciation result from infection and the intestines are not usable for sausage casings.

Syngamus trachea in the family Syngamidae is a slender red worm, which occurs in the trachea of fowls and wild birds and causes gapes. Infection results from the ingestion of infective larvae that hatch from eggs passed in the feces or coughed up by infected birds. The larvae penetrate the wall of the esophagus, migrate to the lungs, where they become mature, and later move into the trachea to the wall of which they attach themselves by the buccal capsule. Fowls suffer from catarrh and from abscesses where the worms are attached.

The hookworms belong to the family Ancylostomidae. The hookworm of the Old World is *Ancylostoma duodenale* (Fig. 6–17). Other species of this genus occur in the intestine of various species of carnivores including the dog, cat, tiger, lion, and wolf. The hookworm of the New World is *Necator americanus* which lives in man and pig. Other species of *Necator* have been reported in chimpanzees. The larvae of the hookworm develop in moist earth and usually find their way into the bodies of human beings by boring through the skin of the foot. In localities where the hookworm is prevalent, many of the people go barefoot. The larval hookworms enter the veins and pass to the heart; from the heart they reach the lungs, where they make their way through the air passages into the windpipe, and thence into the intestine. The adults attach themselves to the walls of the intestine and feed upon the blood of their host (Fig. 6–18, C). In the case of the dog hookworm and probably also of the human hookworm, blood is continuously being sucked into the body of the worm and expelled from the anus in the form of droplets consisting mainly of red corpuscles. Calculations indicate the possibility that a single worm may withdraw blood from the host at the rate of 0.8 cc in 24 hours (Wells, 1931). When the intestinal wall is punctured, a small amount of poison is poured into the wound by the worm. This poison prevents the blood from coagulating, and therefore results in a considerable loss of blood, even after the worm has left the wound. The victims of the hookworm are anemic, and also subject to tuberculosis because of the injury to the lungs. It is estimated that 2,000,000 persons in 1930 were afflicted by this parasite in the United States. Hookworm disease can be cured by hexylresorcinol or tetrachlorethyl. The most important preventive measure is the disposing of the human feces in rural districts, mines, brickyards, etc., in such a manner as to avoid pollution of the soil, thus giving the eggs of the parasites contained in the feces of infected human beings no opportunity to hatch and develop to the infectious larval stage.

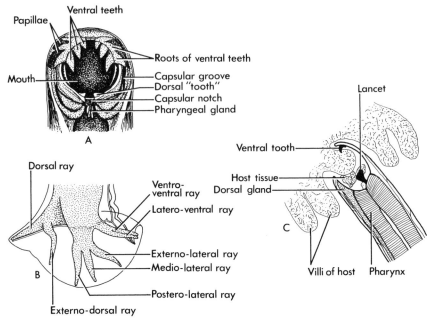

Fig. 6-18. Hookworm. (A) Buccal capsule of *Ancylostoma caninum*, the dog hookworm. (B) Bursa of *A. duodenale*, the human hookworm. (A, from Chandler; B, C, after Loos, modified.)

Ancylostoma braziliensis is a parasite common in cats and dogs in various countries including the southern United States. Under favorable conditions the infective larvae of this species may penetrate the skin of man through which it migrates parallel to the surface forming a tortuous path and causing the condition known as creeping eruption. Ethyl acetate on cotton and carbon dioxide snow have been found to be effective methods of treatment. Another species of hookworm living in cats and dogs is *A. caninum*. It is cosmopolitan in distribution and very pathogenic to puppies.

The species in the family Metastrongylidae are much less important. *Dictyocaulus filaria* is the thread lung worm of sheep, goats, cattle, etc. Its eggs hatch in the lungs and the larvae migrate through the trachea into the alimentary canal from which they escape from the mouth in the saliva or from the anus in the feces. The larvae, which become infective in about 10 days, crawl to the tip of blades of grass with which they may be ingested by herbivorous animals. They establish themselves in the lungs causing a catarrhal condition.

To the family Trichostrongylidae belong several interesting parasites of lower animals. *Haemonchus contortus* is one of the commonest parasites of domestic sheep throughout the world, and also occurs in other ruminants. It lives principally attached to the wall of the fourth stomach. The eggs are deposited in the feces of the host and the infective larvae crawl to the tip of blades of grass where they may be ingested by grazing animals. The infection results in anemia. *Heligmosomum muris* is a species of trichostrongyl parasitic in wild rats in the United States that may be obtained easily for study.

13. Superfamily Spiruroidea. Parasites of vertebrates' digestive tracts, respiratory cavities, and eyes; one or more intermediate arthropod hosts; no pharyngeal bulb; usually with two lateral lips by mouth. *Thelazia* is a parasite in the tear ducts and eyelids of various vertebrates and occasionally man. *Oxyspirura mansoni*, the "eyeworm" of chickens, uses a cockroach as an intermediate host. Larvae escape from an ingested roach in the chickens crop and migrate to the eye region. *Habronema megastoma* lives in the stomach of the horse and is prevalent in the southern United States. It produces nodules or tumors in the stomach and is transmitted by the house fly. *Adruenna strongylina* is a worm that forms tumors in the stomach wall of pigs in this country. *Gongylonema scutatum* (Fig. 6–14, E) inhabits the mucosa of the esophagus of sheep, cattle, and goats. The intermediate hosts are dung beetles.

14. Superfamily Dracunculoidea. Parasites in the connective tissue or coelom of vertebrates; vulva in posterior half of female, but usually atrophied.

Dracunculus medinensis, the guinea worm, belongs to this superfamily. It is a common human parasite in tropical Africa, Arabia, and India, that has been known for centuries and is probably the "fiery serpent" mentioned by Moses (Numbers, XXI). The adult female, which may reach a length of over three feet, is located usually in the subcutaneous tissue of the arm, leg, and shoulders. The young larvae are discharged from the worm and escape through an opening in the human skin; if they reach water and chance to encounter the fresh-water crustacean *Cyclops* they burrow into it and metamorphose in the body cavity. Man becomes infected by swallowing the *Cyclops* in drinking water. The method of extracting the worm that has been practiced for hundreds of years is to roll it up on a stick gradually, a few turns each day, until the entire worm has been drawn out.

15. Superfamily Filarioidea. Parasites of the body fluids and tissues of vertebrates; transmitted by arthropods; vulva of female near the anterior end; slender worms. *Wuchereria bancrofti* (Fig. 6–14, B) is a species of the Filariidae that lives in man and is widely spread in tropical countries. The larvae of this species are about $\frac{1}{100}$ inch long. During the daytime they live in the lungs and larger arteries, but at night they migrate to the blood vessels in the skin. Mosquitoes, which are active at night, suck up these larvae with the blood of the infected person. The larvae develop in the mosquito's body, becoming about $\frac{1}{20}$ inch long, make their way into the mouth parts of the insect, and enter the blood of the mosquito's next victim. From the blood they enter the lymphatics and may cause serious disturbances, probably by obstructing the lymph passages. This results in a disease called elephantiasis. The limbs or other regions of the body swell up to an enormous size, but there is very little pain. Treatment is difficult. The disease may be fatal. Infection with this parasite is common in man especially in the West Indies, South

America, and West and Central Africa. Formerly common in Charleston, S.C., the worms having been introduced probably by Negro slaves from Africa.

Another interesting species of the family Filariidae is the eye worm, *Loa loa* (Fig. 6–14, C), of West Africa. It migrates around the body through the subdermal connective tissue, sometimes across the eyeball. No severe pathological lesions are produced. The transmitting agents are mango flies of the genus *Chrysops*. Among other species in this family are *Onchocerca volvulus*, which occurs also in West Africa and produces subdermal nodular swellings; *Dirofilaria immitis*, which may be present in tangled masses in the right ventricle of the dog's heart; *Setaria equina*, a frequent parasite of the peritoneal cavity of horses and other Equidae; and species that are common in birds, especially crows and English sparrows, in whose blood large numbers of the microfilariae may be present.

16. Superfamily Trichuroidea.   Parasites of vertebrates; slender pharynx embedded in stichosome; anterior usually narrower than posterior; phasmids lacking. Two important human parasites belong to this order. Trichinosis, caused by one, is unusual for a parasitic disease in that it is more common in the United States than in any other region.

Trichinella spiralis (Figs. 6–19 and 6–14, D, F) causes the disease of human beings, pigs, and rats called trichinosis. The parasites enter the human body when inadequately cooked meat from an infected pig is eaten. The larvae soon become mature in the human intestine, and each mature worm deposits probably about 10,000 young. These young (Fig. 6–14, D) are either placed directly into the lymphatics by the female worms or burrow through the intestinal wall; they encyst in muscular tissue in various parts of the body (Fig. 6–19). As many as 15,000 encysted parasites have been counted in a single gram of muscle. Pigs acquire the disease by eating offal or infected

A   B   C

Fig. 6-19. *Trichinella spiralis.* (A) Larvae among muscle fibers, not yet encysted. (B) A single larva encysted. (C) Piece of pork, natural size, containing many encysted worms. (After Leuckart.)

rats. In a few countries pork is inspected for this and other parasites by government agents.

The whipworm, *Trichuris trichiura*, lives in the cecum and appendix of man. Its body is drawn out anteriorly into a long slender whiplike process (Fig. 6–14, H). There is no intermediate host. The eggs escape in the feces and ripen outside of the body. Ripe eggs when swallowed hatch in the intestine and the larvae become located in the cecum. Whipworms injure the host very little. *Capillaria hepatica* occurs in the liver and *Trichosomoides crassicauda* in the urinary bladder of rats. These species may be found of value as examples of round worms for laboratory study.

17. Superfamily Dioctophymoidea. The few worms of this group lack phasmids, are parasites of the digestive tract, kidneys, and body cavity of birds and mammals, and the larvae develop in an intermediate host. *Dioctophyme renale* is the largest known nematode and may reach a length of over three feet. It is most frequently encountered in the kidney of the dog, which is gradually consumed by the worm. Renal colic and failure of the infected kidney to function are symptoms. Fish are thought to be the intermediate hosts.

5 / Class V. Nematomorpha

The Nematomorpha or Gordiacea resemble the Nematoda in general body features. The muscle cells especially indicate the close relationship. Major differences from the Nematoda are the lack of lateral lines and the presence of only a ventral epidermal chord in most. These opaque-bodied worms are usually referred to as horsehair snakes (Fig. 6–20) and are erroneously supposed to arise from horsehairs. Sexes are separate; in both sexes the intestine and genital ducts open into a cloaca; spicules are absent in the male; the body cavity is lined with epithelium; the ova escape into the body cavity and thence into the oviducts; and the alimentary canal is atrophied in the sexually mature worms. The eggs are laid in the water in long strings where the adults live. The larvae that hatch from the eggs penetrate into a young mayfly or

Fig. 6-20. *Gordius*, twining around a water plant and laying eggs. *A*, clump and string of eggs. (After von Linstow.)

some other aquatic insect; they escape in some unknown way from this host and find their way into a second host, usually a beetle, cricket, or grasshopper; in the body cavity of the second host the larvae continue their development eventually passing out into the water where they become sexually mature. Because the adults live only in water, those that survive probably emerge from terrestrial insects, which constitute their second intermediate hosts, that chance to become drowned in watering troughs and small pools frequently formed after a rain. *Gordius aquaticus* (Fig. 6–20) is a cosmopolitan species; *Paragordius varius* is common in North America; and *Nectonema agile* lives as a parasite in marine crustaceans at Woods Hole, Mass., and elsewhere.

Two orders are recognized: the Gordioidea with fresh-water and terrestrial species; and the Nectonematoidea with the marine genus, *Nectonema*.

6 / Aschelminthes in General

Cell or nuclear constancy is a phenomenon demonstrated in the Aschelminthes. Like organs of adults of the same species contain the same number of cells or nuclei in most instances investigated. The microscopic size of most organisms in the phylum made such determinations possible. This phenomenon is probably correlated with their lack of regenerative ability. Because regenerative abilities are common in other major phyla, it is one indication that considerable divergence has occurred from the ancestral stock from which more advanced phyla developed. The resemblance of a highly modified rotifer, *Trochosphaera* (Fig. 6–4, F), to the trochophore larvae of annelids and mollusks had led some zoologists to think rotifers may be an important ancestral group in the phylogeny of invertebrates. Hyman (1951) states the reasons for denying this assumption.

Axenic culture, or culture in the absence of all other species of organisms, has been achieved with a few nematodes and a rotifer. Thus, the Aschelminthes are one of the few phyla with considerable axenic studies already done. The great economic importance of the nematodes makes further axenic nutritional studies of importance in developing some types of control.

Ecology. Many interesting examples of interaction between organism and environment occur in the Aschelminthes. Morphological differences develop in some rotifers under changed environmental conditions. The production of sexual females in rotifers seems to be environmentally controlled.

The presence of nematodes will induce the development of nematode trapping devices on some species of fungi (Pramer, 1964). Attempts to capitalize on this reaction in controlling phytoparasitic nematodes has not yet met with much success.

Similar species from all classes of Aschelminthes except the Kinorhyncha can be found widely distributed in fresh waters of the world. The ability to withstand desiccation of eggs or other stages has probably been an important factor in the wide dispersal of fresh-water species. Although no fossils are known for the Aschelminthes, the group is undoubtedly quite old and thus time is also a factor contributing to their wide dispersal.

The numerical importance of rotifers in fresh-water plankton communities merits increased study of their role as primary consumers in lakes.

Parasitic Nematodes.   Between the free-living nematodes and those spending all their life cycle in hosts are many degrees and types of parasitism. Some are parasites only as juveniles, others as adults. The plant parasites may be external or internal parasites, are usually of small size, and are the cause of great agricultural loss. Nematodes of animals are usually larger, some reaching several feet in length, and are also the cause of severe agricultural losses. Nematodes of man may do little damage to the host when only a few parasites are present. Any tissue damage done may serve as the avenue of infection by other organisms. Because even asymptomatic infections are dangerous as a source of infection for others, treatment of all infected individuals is desirable. Diagnosis of infection with a particular intestinal nematode parasite of man is based on identification of the eggs or larvae in the feces.

The eggs of roundworms are distinctive in size and shape and of importance in the identification of species, especially of those that live in man (Fig. 6–21). They may be discharged either before or during segmentation, or with the embryo fully developed. In a few species the embryos hatch within the uterus of the female worm and are then brought forth viviparously. The embryonic development is simple and much alike in all species. The larvae upon hatching have the main characteristics of nematodes but are not sexually developed. Many parasitic species have certain adaptive larval characters which are subsequently lost. In the course of its development, the worm undergoes about four moults with the adult stage following after the fourth or last moult. Among the parasitic species some of these moults may take place within the egg before hatching, during its free existence, while within the tissue of an intermediate host, or within the tissues of the definitive host.

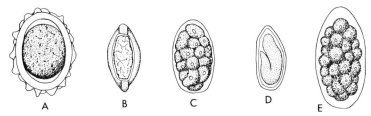

Fig. 6-21. Nematoda. Eggs of species that live in man. (A) *Ascaris lumbricoides*. (B) *Trichuris trichiura*. (C) *Ancylostoma duodenale*. (D) *Enterobius vermicularis*. (E) *Trichostrongylus orientalis*. (After Cort.)

Fig. 6-22. The germ track in *Ascaris*. Stages in early cleavage showing the chromatin-diminution process in all cells except the stem cell. (From Boveri.)

Of interest is that ascarid embryos can develop in the presence of substances lethal to most other organisms. The protection enabling such development to occur comes, not from the egg shell, but, from a thin lipid membrane.

The Germ Track in Nematodes. A classical study tracing the lineage of the germ cells, or reproductive cells was done with *Parascaris equorum* (*Ascaris megalocephala*). The first cleavage division of the egg results in two daughter cells, each containing two long chromosomes (Fig. 6–22, A). In the second division the chromosomes of one cell divide normally and each daughter cell receives one half of each (B). The chromosomes of the other cell behave differently; the thin middle portion of each breaks up into granules (A) which split, half going to each daughter cell, but the swollen ends (B) are cast off into the cytoplasm. In the four-cell stage there are consequently two cells with the full amount of chromatin and two with a reduced amount. This inequality in the amount of chromatin results in different-sized nuclei (C); those with entire chromosomes are larger than those that have lost the swollen ends. In the third division one of the two cells with the two entire chromosomes loses the swollen ends of each; the other (D) retains its chromosomes intact. A similar reduction in the amount of chromatin takes place in the fourth and fifth divisions and then ceases. The single cell in the 32-cell stage, that contains the full amount of chromatin has a larger nucleus than the other 31 cells and gives rise to all of the germ cells, whereas the other cells are for the production of somatic cells only. It is likely that any animal having this type of chromatin diminution will have very limited or no regenerative power.

References to Literature on the Aschelminthes

BIRKY, C. W., and B. FIELD. 1966. Nuclear number in the rotifer *Asplanchna*: intraclonal variation and environmental control. *Science*, **151**:585–587.

BRUNSON, R. B. 1959. Gastrotricha. In W. T. EDMONDSON. *Fresh-Water Biology*. Wiley, New York. 1,248 pp.

——. 1963. Aspects of the natural history and ecology of the Gastrotricha. In E. DOUGHERTY. *The Lower Metazoa*. Univ. Calif., Berkeley. 478 pp.

CHITWOOD, B. G., and D. G. MURPHY. 1964. Observations on two marine monhysterids—their classification, cultivation, and behavior. *Trans. Am. Microsc. Soc.*, **83**:311–329.

COBB, N. A. 1915. Nematodes and their relationships. *Yearbook, U.S. Dept. Agric.*, 1914:457–490.

GOODEY, T. 1951. *Soil and Freshwater Nematodes.* Wiley, New York. 390 pp.

HIGGINS, R. P. 1965. The homalorhagid Kinorhyncha of Northeastern U.S. coastal waters. *Trans. Am. Microsc. Soc.*, **84**:65–72.

HYMAN, L. H. 1951. *The Invertebrates.* Vol. III. *Acanthocephala, Aschelminthes, and Entoprocta.* McGraw-Hill, New York. 572 pp.

KESSEL, R. G., *et al.* 1961. Cytological studies on the intestinal epithelial cells of *Ascaris lumbricoides suum. Trans. Am. Microsc. Soc.*, **80**:103–118.

PENNAK, R. W. 1953. *Fresh Water Invertebrates of the United States.* Ronald, New York. 769 pp.

PRAMER. D. 1964. Nematode-trapping fungi. *Science*, **144**:382–388.

PRAY, F. A. 1965. Studies on the early development of the rotifer *Monostyla cornuta* Muller. *Trans. Am. Microsc. Soc.*, **84**:210–216.

ROGGEN, D. R., D. J. RASKI, and N. O. JONES. 1966. Cilia in nematode sensory organs. *Science*, **152**:515–516.

SACKS, M. 1964. Life history of an aquatic gastrotrich. *Trans. Am. Microsc. Soc.*, **83**:358–362.

THORNE, G. 1961. *Principles of Nematology.* McGraw-Hill, New York. 553 pp.

WELLS, H. S. 1931. Observations on the blood-sucking activities of the hookworm, *Ancylostoma caninum. J. Parasitol.*, **17**:167–182.

WILLIAMS, L. G. 1966. Dominant planktonic rotifers of major waterways of the United States. *Limnol. and Oceanog.*, **11**:83–91.

YAMAGUTI, S. 1962. *Systema Helminthum.* Vol. III. *The Nematodes of Vertebrates.* Wiley, New York. 1,274 pp.

YORKE, W., and P. MAPLESTONE. 1926. *The Nematode Parasites of Vertebrates.* 548 pp. (Reprinted, 1962, by Hafner, New York.)

Chapter VII

Minor Phyla

T HE MESOZOA, Acanthocephala, Rhynchocoela, Priapulida, Ectoprocta, Entoprocta, Brachiopoda, Phoronidea, Sipunculida, Chaetognatha,
Pogonophora, and Hemichordata are phyla discussed in this chapter that
contain relatively few species or are not at present considered important in
the phylogeny of major groups of invertebrates. They are of minor economic
importance. Some could well be appended to other phyla, but all are distinct
groups that differ sufficiently so that recent classifications by many zoologists
have listed them as independent phyla. Other groups that could also be considered in this chapter are the Ctenophora, which are so obviously related to
the Coelenterata that they were treated in the chapter following them; the
Archiannelida, Echiuroidea, and Myzostomaria, which are treated with the
Annelida; and the Onychophora, Pentastomida, Pycnogonida, and Tardigrada, which are treated as arthropodan groups. All of the preceding have
been treated as independent phyla in some classifications but the relationship
to the major phyla with which they are treated here seems clear although they
are distinctive groups.

Phylogeny. The many classification schemes proposed in the past usually
have tried to reflect the groupings that were thought to have occurred phylo-
genetically. Because the development of groups is hidden in the past, major
divisions of the animal kingdom have been variously based on morphological, physiological, and developmental features. Symmetry, metamerism,
coelom development, and type of cleavage in the egg are some of more
commonly used criteria for establishing relationships. Although none of the
many schemes warrant complete acceptance at this time, the student should
be familiar with the considerations involved.

Symmetry. A major dichotomy of the animal kingdom into the Radiata and Bilateria is sometimes proposed. Symmetry is a major feature of considerable stability, but it also tends to modification adaptive to the environment. Thus, sessile animals with radial symmetry seem to have a selective advantage over sessile bilateral forms. A basic bilateral symmetry appears to occur with a motile way of life. Spherical symmetry is almost restricted to planktonic forms. Thus, symmetry is a risky base for a truly phylogenetic classification.

Metamerism. The serial repetition of similar structures is used for major groupings into those with no segments, few segments, and many segments, respectively, the Ameria, Oligomeria, and Polymeria, which are the invertebrate metazoan phyla of Hadzi (1963). Although his views merit further investigation, they have not had wide acceptance, probably because of his unpopular attempt to derive the Coelenterata from the Turbellaria. One problem in the use of metamerism as the criterion is the presence of metamerism in one group of mollusks (*Neopilina*) only. A reduction in segmentation has occurred in numerous arthropods. Such reduction could well have occurred in other groups in separate lines, and thus the Ameria and Oligomeria are likely polyphyletic groups.

Coelom. Absence of a coelom, presence of a pseudocoel, or presence of a true coelom are features given considerable weight in most phylogenetic schemes. Method of coelom formation is of importance also. The fact that a coelom may form by different methods such as budding off from the enteron, or developing from a split in the mesoderm is an indication that a coelom may have arisen in different lines and just be an adaptation to increased size.

Structural Level. Division of the Metazoa into diploblastic and triploblastic grades of organization is not considered of great phylogenetic significance, because the diploblastic phylum, Coelenterata, has only two cell layers in species that are thought to have undergone a reduction in the level of development. The vast majority of metazoans are clearly triploblastic.

Early Embryology. Early cleavage divisions with either a radial, indeterminate type of development or a spiral, determinate type of development provides a major dichotomy in the metazoans. One objection is the variation in embryology that can occur within a single phylum. As previously mentioned, the method of formation of the coelom in the embryo is given considerable significance. Similarity of larval types is often thought to be significant.

Comparative Biochemistry. Insufficient data have been accumulated, tabulated, and analyzed to make comparative biochemistry contribute significantly to an understanding of phylogeny as it may well do in the future.

Comparative Morphology. Structural similarities have always been, and will continue to be, important criteria for determining relationships. Gross appearance can often be a reflection of the ecology of the organism as indicated under symmetry. The lophophorate invertebrates may have lophophores as a consequence of their sessile, filter-feeding habits. Such structures as flame cells and their modification are more likely to be indicative of a relationship. Absence of a structure may not indicate a wide phylogenetic separation from other organisms having the structure. For example, subterranean species often lack eyes and pigmentation found in very closely related surface-dwelling species. The relationship of form and function has brought about many cases of convergent evolution. Bivalved shells have developed independently in at least three phyla, the Brachiopoda, Mollusca, and Arthropoda.

In general, gross types of similarities and differences in the categories discussed are of use in determining relationships at the phylum level. Groups of characteristics are likely to have greater validity than single features as indices of relationships. As we proceed to lower and closer taxonomic relationships, the characteristics of use become more specific until at the species level even structure size may be significant.

The sequence of phyla within this chapter approximates one of increasing complexity. The same procedure has been followed in the arrangement of chapters in the book. Such a linear sequence does not show a phylogenetic pattern, because such a pattern would be branching and not linear. Thus, the arrangement in the sequence is arbitrary as must all alleged phylogenetic

An Outline of the Invertebrate Phyla

I. Unicellular, or all somatic cells alike	Protozoa
II. Multicellular (Metazoa)	
A. stereoblastula grade construction	Mesozoa
B. cellular grade construction (Parazoa)	Porifera
C. tissue grade construction (Eumetazoa, in part)	Coelenterata, Ctenophora
D. organ-system grade construction (Eumetazoa, in part)	
1. acoelomate	Platyhelminthes, Rhynchocoela
2. pseudocoelomate	Aschelminthes, Entoprocta, Acanthocephala
3. coelomate	
a. protostomes (spiral, determinate cleavage)	
(1) lophophorate protostomes	Ectoprocta, Phoronidea, Brachiopoda
(2) schizocoelous protostomes	Mollusca, Priapulida, Sipunculida, Annelida, Arthropoda
b. deuterostomes (radial, indeterminate cleavage ; enterocoelous)	Chaetognatha, Pogonophora, Hemichordata, Echinodermata, Chordata

schemes be with presently available knowledge. All phylogenetic relationships are not equally speculative. The relationship of annelids and arthropods is close and well documented. Others are highly enigmatic, for example, the chaetognaths are often put on a branch with the echinoderms and chordates, but there are some grounds for putting them near nematodes. Perhaps it only means that the phyla have diverged less than we think. The incompleteness of the fossil record means that phylogeny is likely to remain one of the most fascinating puzzles of nature.

The arrangement of phyla in An Outline of the Invertebrate Phyla incorporates some of the groupings popular among American zoologists. Other arrangements are proposed by some zoologists. Although this grouping of phyla does not account for all relationships satisfactorily, it is useful as a base for discussion.

1 / Phylum Mesozoa

The Mesozoa are small parasites of the kidneys of cephalopods and body spaces of other marine invertebrates. Less than a hundred species are known.

Morphology.   The vermiform body (Fig. 7–1) consists of a layer of ciliated cells surrounding one or more *axial cells*. There are no spaces or organs. The reproductive cells develop from the axial cell. Length is less than one

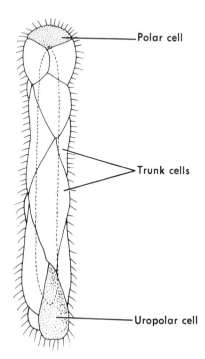

Fig. 7-1. A dicyemid mesozoan. *Pseudicyema truncatum.* Position of axial cell indicated by broken line. (Modified from several authors after Whitman.)

Polar cell

Trunk cells

Uropolar cell

centimeter. The surface or *somatic cells* may be differentiated at the anterior into a *polar cap* of smaller cells where the mesozoan adheres to the host cells.

Reproduction. Both asexual and sexual reproduction occur, although the complete life cycle is not known for the Dicyemida. In the dicyemids the asexual individuals are known as *nematogens*, which eventually produce *rhombogens*, which have somatic cells bulging with nutrients. The sexual *infusorigens* develop within the rhombogen and after self-fertilization ciliated larvae escape from the host. Orthonectids have a vegetative, amoeboid plasmodium within which the sexual individual develops as a ball of cells. As these balls mature as sexual individuals, they escape from the host and sexual reproduction occurs in the water. The sexual adult resembles the dicyemid rhombogen but has a greater number of cells internally and the somatic cells are more numerous and arranged in rings.

Classification. Two orders of Mesozoa are known. Mesozoa are thought by some zoologists to be degenerate trematodes based largely on life cycle similarities. Other relationships have been postulated also, including the view, as the name Mesozoa implies, that they represent a stepping stone from the Protozoa to the Metazoa. The complex life cycle and parasitic nature make this seem unlikely.

Order 1. Dicyemida. Parasites in the kidneys of cephalopods; few axial cells; polar cap; three genera; e.g., *Dicyema typus* from the octopus.

Order 2. Orthonectida. Internal parasites of marine flatworms, annelids, mollusks, and echinoderms; asexual amoeboid stage; ciliated adult with ringed appearance; often many axial cells; e.g., *Rhopalura ophiocomae* from the brittle star.

2 / Phylum Acanthocephala

The spinyheaded worms (Fig. 7–2) belong to this phylum. They live in the intestine of vertebrates attached to the wall by a protrusible proboscis usually covered with recurved hooks. The immature stages develop in arthropods such as insects and crustaceans.

Morphology. The adults vary in length from several millimeters to over 50 cm. An alimentary canal is not present at any stage in their life cycle, although one or two *ligament sacs* running the length of the animal are thought to represent the entoderm derivatives. A thin cuticle, often spiny, covers the syncytial epidermis, which has three layers, the innermost thick and penetrated by lacunae. A layer of circular muscles and an inner layer of longitudinal muscles are between the epidermis and the pseudocoelomate

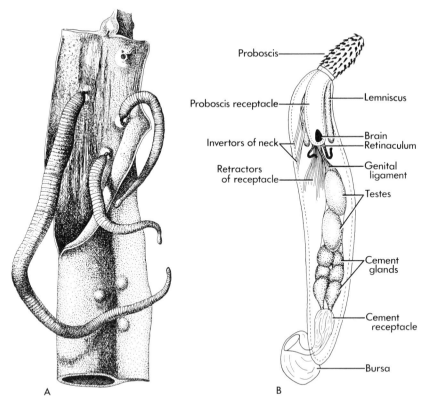

Fig. 7-2. Acanthocephala. (A) *Macracanthorhynchus hirudinaceus* clinging to the intestinal wall of a pig. The two small worms are males, and the larger is a female. (B) A male specimen of the genus *Acanthocephalus* showing internal organs. (A, after Brumpt; B, after Van Cleave.)

body cavity. The anterior spiny *proboscis* is attached by a neck region to a *proboscis receptacle* into which the proboscis can be withdrawn. Special muscles move the proboscis. Two large glandular structures, the *lemnisci*, are thought to provide and receive fluid moved during extension and retraction of the proboscis. The *cerebral ganglion* (brain) is on the ventral surface of the proboscis receptacle. Several nerves connect to the brain. A few acanthocephalans have an excretory system of the flame cell type. Sexes are separate, and the complex reproductive systems are closely associated with the ligament sacs.

Life Cycles.   After copulation and fertilization a modified spiral cleavage occurs. If ingested by the proper invertebrate host the larva hatches from the egg and penetrates the gut wall to develop into a juvenile worm in the host hemocoel. Some worms are capable of re-encapsulating in another host if ingested by one that is not a suitable final host. Thus, more than two hosts may be present in the life cycle. Some species normally have more than two hosts in the life cycle.

Host-Parasite Relationship. Acanthocephalans are most common in fishes and seem to cause few or no symptoms in them. Because the proboscis can penetrate the intestinal lining of the host it is a potential avenue for other infections. One specimen has been reported to be fatal in the robin and a few more in some other birds. One juvenile stage is known to prevent ovarian function in the crustacean host so that an immature stage is maintained in the host. Perhaps this increases the length of life of the intermediate host and the probable success of reaching a final host. Of interest is the apparent dependence of the worm on the host for digestion of lipids, although enzymes useful for the digestion of other substances are present in the worm.

The juvenile worm becomes encapsulated in the intermediate arthropod host. Second intermediate, or transport hosts, are commonly fish or invertebrates in which the juvenile will re-encapsulate when the first host is eaten. Ordinarily, no growth occurs while in the transport host.

Phylogeny. Because they are parasitic roundworms covered with a cuticle the spiny-headed worms have sometimes been considered closely related to the nematodes. The type of muscular system present makes relationship to the Aschelminthes doubtful, though not impossible. The muscular system resembles that of the flatworms and the proboscis shows some similarities to the rostellum of the cestodes. However, the pseudocoelomate condition does not support a relationship with the Platyhelminthes. Thus, as with most phyla, the origin of the phylum is not clear.

Sufficient resemblance between all species of the Acanthocephala is present so that no classes and only three orders are recognized.

Order 1. Archiacanthocephala. Small proboscis hooks concentrically arranged; excretory system present; parasites of terrestrial birds and mammals; intermediate hosts are terrestrial arthropods. Examples are *Macracanthorhynchus hirudinaceus* (Fig. 7–2, A) cosmopolitan in pigs, and *Moniliformis moniliformis* in small mammals. Both species have been reported from man.

Order 2. Palaeacanthocephala. Proboscis hooks alternating in radial rows; no excretory system; parasites of fishes, amphibians, aquatic birds, and marine mammals; first intermediate hosts are crustaceans. *Acanthocephalus* (Fig. 7–2, B) has numerous species in fish and amphibians; *Echinorhynchus salvelini* occurs in lake trout and *Arhythmorhynchus brevis* in the bittern.

Order 3. Eoacanthocephala. Proboscis hooks arranged radially; no excretory system; parasites of fishes and reptiles; first intermediate hosts are aquatic arthropods. *Neoechinorhynchus emydis* is found in turtles in the United States.

3 / Phylum Rhynchocoela

The Rhynchocoela or Nemertinea are a group of several hundred mostly marine bottom-dwelling worms. They are flattened and have a ciliated epidermis that contains rhabdites in a few species. The lack of a coelom and the presence of rhabdites add to the evidence that they share a common ancestry with the Platyhelminthes.

Morphology (Fig. 7–3).   The most important anatomical features of the nemertines (Fig. 7–3) are the presence of (1) a long proboscis, which lies in a proboscis sheath just above the digestive tract, and may be everted and used as a tactile, protective, and defensive organ; (2) a blood vascular system consisting usually of a median dorsal and two lateral trunks; and (3) an alimentary canal with both mouth and anal openings. The blood vascular

Fig. 7-3. Nemertinea. *Tetrastemma.* General view of internal organs. (From Hatschek.)

Proboscis pore
Ciliated groove
Brain
Lateral nerve
Lateral vessel
Dorsal vessel
Proboscis sheath
Nephridial pore
Nephridium
Accessory stylet
Stylet
Proboscis
Dorsal vessel
Retractor muscle
Anus

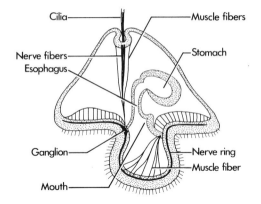

Fig. 7-4. Pilidium larva of a nemertine. (After Salensky.)

system is here encountered for the first time. Nemertines possess a mesoderm and nervous and excretory systems, which do not differ markedly from those of the flatworms. The proboscis sheath may represent the coelom, but this is not certain.

Ecology. Nemertines feed on other animals, both dead and alive. They live, as a rule, coiled up in burrows in the mud or sand, or under stones, but some of them frequent patches of seaweed. Locomotion is effected by the cilia which cover the surface of the body, by contractions of the body muscles, or by the attachment of the proboscis and subsequent drawing forward of the body. *Cerebratulus* swims actively like a leech.

A variety of invertebrates have nemertines that live with them commensally. No truly parasitic species are known. Although the majority are shallow marine-bottom dwellers a few are found in fresh water and a few terrestrial species occur in the tropics. They reach considerable depths in the ocean and a few are pelagic in the ocean.

Reproduction. Sexes are separate in most species of nemertines. The eggs undergo a determinate type of spiral cleavage. Eventually a peculiar larval stage called the *pilidium* (Fig. 7–4) is usually passed through. This resembles a helmet with cilia on the surface and a long tuft of cilia at the apex. The adult develops from this larva by the formation of ectodermal invaginations which surround the alimentary canal. This invaginated portion escapes from the *pilidium* and grows into the adult nemertine.

Several species of nemertines reproduce during the summer by spontaneous fragmentation (autotomy) followed by the regeneration of each of the 2 to 20 or more fragments into complete worms (Fig. 7–5). This type of reproduction is inhibited by cold weather in the autumn at the time when the sex cells are beginning to develop. Nemertines of these species possess remarkable powers of regeneration since, if, for example, an individual of *Lineus socialis* 100 mm in length is cut into as many as 100 pieces, each piece will regenerate a minute worm within 4 or 5 weeks. These minute worms may again be cut

Fig. 7-5. *Lineus socialis*, reproduction by fission. (A) Mature worm. (B) Worm divided by fission into nine pieces. (C) Reconstruction of these pieces into complete worms. (From Coe.)

into pieces that regenerate and these may in turn be cut up and so on until miniature worms less than $\frac{1}{200,000}$ the volume of the original worm result (Fig. 7–6).

The Rhynchocoela may be divided into four orders.

Order 1. Paleonemertini. The species in this order possess a proboscis free from stylets, and cerebral ganglia and lateral nerves in the ectoderm or

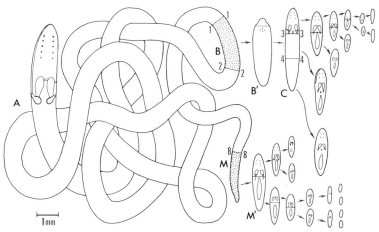

Fig. 7-6. *Lineus socialis*, regeneration. (A) Normal worm. (B, B′) Section cut from body and its appearance after twelve days. (C) Same, after thirty days, cut in planes 3-3 and 4-4. Successive cuttings and regenerations indicated by arrows. (M, M′) Similar experiments and results on posterior end of body. (From Coe.)

between the two layers of muscles. *Tubulanus pellucida* is a marine species that lives below low water among annelid tubes and has been reported from Long Island and Vineyard Sounds and California. *Cephalothrix linearis* is another marine species living on both our Atlantic and Pacific coasts and in Europe.

Order 2. Heteronemertini. There are no stylets on the proboscis and the lateral nerve cords lie between layers of circular and longitudinal muscles. *Lineus ruber* (Fig. 7–6) has a long filiform body; is green, brown, or reddish; has a row of from four to eight eyes on either side of the head; and lives under stones in shallow water on our eastern coast, Alaska, and Europe. *Cerebratulus* is a well-known genus with representatives in all seas. *C. lacteus* may reach a length of several yards, is flesh colored, has a white proboscis, and lives in the sand near low-water mark from Florida to Maine. Both genera are represented on our Pacific Coast.

Order 3. Hoplonemertini. The proboscis in this group bears one or more stylets and the lateral nerves are in the muscle layers. The genus *Tetrastemma* (Fig. 7–3) is widespread and contains many species, mostly unisexual. They are small and possess four eyes. *T. candidum* is slender, about 2 cm long, white, green, or yellow, and lives among algae between tide lines on our eastern coast and in Europe. *Prostoma rubrum* is a fresh-water species resembling *Tetrastemma*, but is about 18 cm long, is yellow or reddish, and has three pairs of eyes.

Order 4. Bdellonemertini. Commensal nemertines lacking stylets on the proboscis; mouth anterior to brain; only one genus, *Malacobdella*. *M. grossa* is broad, has a sucker at the posterior end, and lives in the branchial chamber of pelecypod mollusks, such as *Mya* and *Venus*, on both sides of the North Atlantic.

4 / Phylum Priapulida

This phylum contains only six species of wormlike marine animals of moderate size. The mouth is centered in an eversible spiny proboscis. Bulbs of the flame cells have a single flagellum. The body wall and intestine are both provided with circular and longitudinal muscles. Many other features show striking similarities to the kinorhynchs of the Aschelminthes. They have previously been considered members of that phylum as well as the annelids and echinoderms at different times. Shapeero (1961) reports that the lining of the coelom is nucleated and thus they differ too much from the aschelminthes to be included with them. *Priapulus caudatus* occurs in both northern oceans. The pharynx is muscular and provided with numerous teeth, and the anus is located at the posterior end near a caudal appendage of hollow vesicles. The surface of the trunk of the body is warty or spiny. It lives in the mud or sand in shallow water with the anterior end projecting into the water.

5 / Phylum Entoprocta

This phylum of about 60 species was previously included with the Ectoprocta in the Bryozoa or Polyzoa. Lack of a true coelom and the inclusion of the anus within the nonretractile lophophore in the Entoprocta is the reason most recent classifications list them as a separate phylum.

The *lophophore* is a crown of ciliated tentacles, found in this and the next three phyla, which provides an advantageous filter feeding mechanism for these sessile animals. The cilia-lined digestive tract consists of a mouth, esophagus, stomach, intestine, rectum, and anus. The epidermis secretes a cuticle over much of the body or *calyx*. Between the epidermis and the digestive tract the body is filled with a gelatinous substance containing a few cells. The body is attached to the substrate by a *stalk*. The main ganglionic mass, the gonads, and the pair of flame cells are located above the stomach (Fig. 7-7, A). Muscle fibers are very sparse. The tentacles of the lophophore can be bent inward to cover the area within the lophophore.

Some species are dioecious and others hermaphroditic. *Loxosoma davenporti* is a solitary species that bears buds; it is about 2 mm long; has from 22 to 26 tentacles; and possesses a mammary organ in the vestibule to which developing embryos are attached. It is a marine species abundant in Vineyard Sound. *Pedicellina cernua* is a colonial, marine species, the zooids of which arise from a creeping, branching stolon. It attaches itself to shells and algae in shallow water along the Atlantic coast of the United States and Europe.

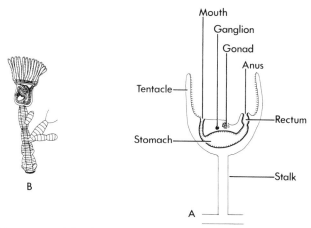

Fig. 7-7. Entoprocta. (A) Diagram of arrangement of digestive tract. (B) *Urnatella gracilis*. (B, after Leidy.)

Urnatella gracilis (Fig. 7–7, B) is a colonial species that lives on the underside of stones in running fresh water in the eastern and central states. Its zooids, which are few in number, arise from a common disk and form long stalks, which are jointed and form branches.

6 / Phylum Ectoprocta

The Ectoprocta or Bryozoa are sessile, colonial, lophophore-bearing animals that live in secreted cases. The individuals are barely visible to the unaided eye. The majority of them live in the sea, but a few inhabit fresh water. *Bugula* is a common marine genus which shows the principal characteristics of the group.

The soft parts constituting the *polypide* lie within the true *coelomic cavity* bounded by the body wall or *zooecium*. The *mouth* lies in the midst of a crown of *ciliated tentacles* (Fig. 7–8, A) called the *lophophore*, which serve to draw food particles into the body. The U-shaped *alimentary canal* consists of a ciliated *esophagus*, a *stomach*, and an *intestine*, which opens by means of an anus lying just outside the lophophore. One *retractor muscle* serves to draw the polypide into the zooecium. The *funiculus* is a strand of mesodermal tissue attached to the base of the stomach. There are no circulatory nor excretory organs.

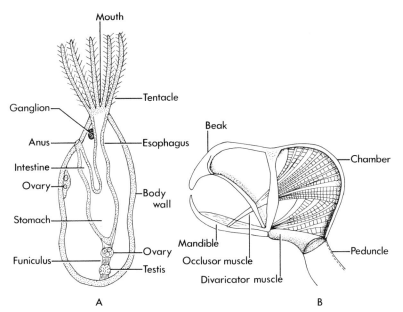

Fig. 7-8. Ectoprocta. (A) Diagram showing the structure of a single individual. (B) An avicularium of *Bugula*. (After Hincks.)

Both an *ovary* and a *testis* are present in each individual; they may be found attached to the funiculus or the body wall. The *eggs* are probably fertilized in the coelom and then develop in a modified portion of the zooecium called the *ooecium*. The larvae of some Bryozoa resemble a trochophore.

Certain members of *Bugula* colonies are modified into structures called *avicularia* (Fig. 7–8, B). These have jaws that probably protect the colony from the attacks of small organisms and prevent the larvae of other animals from settling upon it. The latter function is accomplished in some genera by whiplike zooids called *vibracula*.

Classification. The members of both classes of Ectoprocta are sessile, lophophore-bearing animals, of small size, living in secreted cases; true coelom; anus opens outside the lophophore; lophophore rectractable; no excretory organs; no special respiratory or circulatory structures; hermaphroditic and unisexual species occur; asexual reproduction by budding is common to all and large branching and encrusting colonies are formed by this means; many species.

Fig. 7-9. Ectoprocta. Phylactolaemata. (A) *Plumatella punctata*. (B) *Pectinatella magnifica*. (C) *Plumatella*, statoblast. (D) *Cristatella mucedo*. (E) *C. mucedo*, statoblast. (A, B, after Kraepelin; D, E, after Allman.)

Class I. Phylactolaemata

Phylactolaemata are fresh-water species that have an oval or horseshoe-shaped lophophore, a sort of lip, called the epistome, projecting over the mouth and statoblasts usually provided with marginal air cells which float them on the surface of the water. *Plumatella repens* (Fig. 7–9, A) forms a much-branched, creeping or erect colony and produces elongated statoblasts. *Cristatella mucedo* (Fig. 7–9, D) forms an elongate, creeping gelatinous colony, with zooids on the upper surface, and produces circular statoblasts with two rows of marginal hooks (Fig. 7–9, E). These statoblasts are buds with a hard chitinous shell that arise from the funiculus and give rise to new colonies after the death of the parent or a period of drought. *Pectinatella magnifica* (Fig. 7–9, B) forms rosette-shaped groups of associated colonies which may build up a thick gelatinous base. It has from 60 to 84 tentacles, and black, circular statoblasts with one row of from 10 to 22 marginal hooks. *Fredericella sultana* forms a colony of intertwining branches. It has a lophophore that is oval, and produces dark brown, elliptical statoblasts without a float. According to their structure and function statoblasts receive various names such as floatoblasts, spinoblasts, and sessoblasts.

Class 2. Gymnolaemata

Gymnolaemata are mostly marine species that have a circular lophophore without an epistome.

Order 1. Ctenostomata. Zooecium fleshy or membranous; aperture closed by a folded membrane when the lophophore is retracted; no ooecia or avicularia. *Alcyonidium hirsutum* forms yellowish brown or reddish colonies that are often encrusting, with conical projections on the surface between which are the orifices.

Order 2. Cheilostomata. Zooecium rectangular; aperture closed by an operculum (lid or flap) when the lophophore is retracted; ovicells (ooecia), avicularia, and vibracula may be present; zooecium may be calcified. *Membranipora pilosa* (Fig. 7–10, B) is a common species near Woods Hole. It forms, usually, encrusting, calcareous colonies, each zooid having a thickened margin with from 4 to 12 spines and below this a long or short corneous spine. *Bugula* also belongs to this order.

Order 3. Cyclostomata. Zooecium tubular, calcified; no operculum or membrane closing aperture; no avicularia. *Crisia* (Fig. 7–10, A) belongs to this order.

Ectoprocta in General. The bryozoans were once thought to be plants. The mosslike appearance of *Bugula* colonies, with their sessile, arborescent

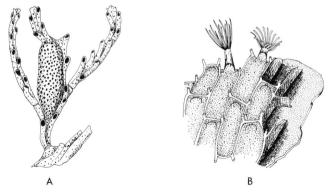

A   B

Fig. 7-10. Ectoprocta. Gymnolaemata. (A) *Crisia maxima*, zooecium and ovicell. (B) *Membranipora membranacea*. (From Johnson and Snook.)

habit makes this understandable. The present trend is to consider the Entoprocta and Ectoprocta as separate phyla, although a leading bryozoologist, the late Mary Rogick, favored retaining them in a single phylum (Rogick, 1959).

Marine species are numerous and common, their fossil record extends back to the Cambrian. Fresh-water species are less numerous and more uniform in structure, although colonies may show considerable variability under different conditions. The cosmopolitan *Plumatella repens* is the most abundant and common fresh-water species (Bushnell, 1965). The asexual reproductive bodies, or statoblasts, are an important aid to the widespread distribution of fresh-water species. Statoblasts may survive passage through the digestive tract of birds.

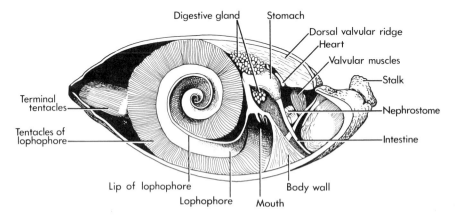

Fig. 7-11. Brachiopoda. Longitudinal section of *Waldheimia*. (After Lister, from Shipley and MacBride.)

7 / Phylum Brachiopoda

The Brachiopoda are marine animals living within a calcareous bivalve *shell* (Fig. 7–12). They are usually attached to some object by a stalk, called the *peduncle* (Fig. 7–11). Because of their shell they were for a long time regarded as mollusks. The valves of the shell, however, are dorsal and ventral instead of lateral as in the bivalve mollusks. Within the shell (Fig. 7–11) is a conspicuous structure called the *lophophore*, which consists of two coiled ridges, called arms; these bear ciliated tentacles. *Food* is drawn into the *mouth* by the lophophore. A true *coelom* is present, within which lie the *stomach, digestive gland*, and the *heart*.

The group Brachiopoda is extremely old, and, although found in all seas today, brachiopods were formerly more numerous in species and of much greater variety in form than at present. Some of them, for example *Lingula*

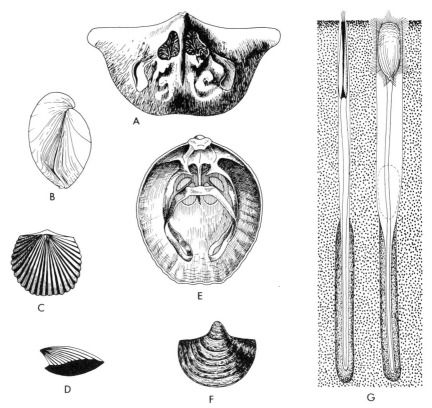

Fig. 7-12. Brachiopoda. (A) *Productus giganteus:* Carboniferous limestone; interior of dorsal valve. (B) *Terebratula semiglobosa:* upper Chalk; lateral view. (C, D) *Orthis calligramma:* Ordovician. (E) *Waldheimia:* interior of dorsal valve showing brachial skeleton. (F) *Micromitra labradorica:* Lower Cambrian; ventral valve. (G) *Lingula anatifera* in their tubes in the sand; the dotted line in the right tube indicates the position of the body when retracted. (A–F, from Woods, after various authors; G, after Francois.)

(Fig. 7–12, G), are apparently similar to fossil forms found recently in pre-Cambrian rocks, perhaps a billion years old.

Two classes of brachiopods may be recognized according to whether or not the valves of the shell are joined together by a hinge.

Class 1. Inarticulata or Ecardines

An inarticulate brachiopod has a shell without a hinge. There is an alimentary canal with an anus. No internal skeleton is present. Three families with about 32 living and 400 fossil species mostly paleozic, belong to this order. *Lingula* (Fig. 7–12, G) has already been mentioned. *Glottidia albida* occurs on our Pacific coast from low water to a depth of 60 fathoms. It has a smooth, white shell about 30 mm long, and a stout peduncle about 45 mm long. *Crania anomala* lives at a depth of about 100 fathoms in the West Indies. The shell is brown, about 18 mm long and 22 mm broad, and fastened by the ventral valve to a rock. No peduncle is present.

Class 2. Testicardines or Articulata

An articulate brachiopod has a shell with a hinge and an internal skeleton. No anus is present. The three families in this order contain about 80 living and 2,200 fossil species. *Terebratulina septentrionalis* has a yellowish or whitish, thin, semitransparent shell that is broadly oval in shape. *Waldheimia floridana* has a gray or brownish-white shell that is triangular in shape.

8 / Phylum Phoronidea

The species in this group, about 15 in all, belong to the genera *Phoronis* (Fig. 7–13) and *Phoronopsis*. They are small, marine animals of sedentary habit that live in tubes. The larva, called an actinotrocha, is free-swimming and resembles a trochosphere. The adults are unsegmented, coelomate, and hermaphroditic. They possess a horseshoe-shaped lophophore, an epistome, two excretory organs, and a vascular system. *Phoronis architecta* occurs in sand flats near the low-water mark in North Carolina. It lives in a straight tube about 13 cm long and 1 mm broad; is flesh colored; and has about 100 tentacles. *Phoronopsis pacifica* is about 9 cm long and 2 mm broad, has about 190 tentacles, and lives on the Pacific coast of North America.

This phylum and the previous three all possess lophophores. Major differences in other features such as the coelom, excretory system, and other systems are usually considered valid for distinction being made at the phylum level.

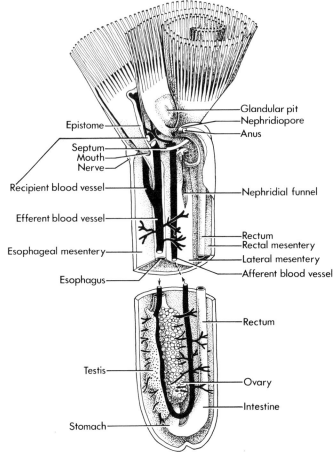

Fig. 7-13. Phoronidea. *Phoronis*, diagram to show the structure of one half of the lophophore and the main internal organs. (From Benham.)

9 / Phylum Sipunculida

The Sipunculida (Fig. 7–14) are considered definite relatives of the Annelida on the basis of an annelid type of nervous system, nephridia, and embryology. The complete lack of segmentation indicates a great divergence from the annelids and thus phylum rank is warranted.

The approximately 250 species are all marine-bottom dwellers, although larval stages are sometimes planktonic for as long as a month. Sipunculida are unsegmented with only one pair of nephridia, a large coelom, and an anus on the dorsal surface near the anterior end. They live in the sand or bore into coral rock and are capable of slow, creeping locomotion. The anterior part of the body can be drawn into the larger posterior portion and is therefore called the introvert. Tentacles are usually present at the anterior end. *Phascolosoma*

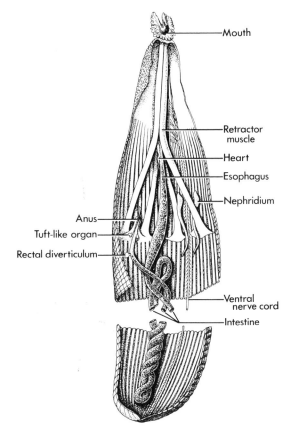

Fig. 7-14. Sipunculida. *Sipunculus nudus,* with introvert and head fully extended, laid open by an incision along the right side to show the internal organs. The spindle-muscle is seen overlying the rectum. (From Shipley.)

gouldi is about 18 cm long, and has a smooth skin and many tentacles in several rows. *Phascolion strombi* uses a snail shell for protection, closing the entrance with a plug of sand, through a hole in which the introvert may be protruded.

10 / Phylum Chaetognatha

The Chaetognatha are marine animals which swim about near the surface of the sea. The best-known genus is *Sagitta,* the arrowworm. Figure 7–15 shows most of the anatomical features of *Sagitta hexaptera.* The body consists of three regions, head, trunk, and postanal tail. Lateral and caudal fins are present. There is a distinct coelom, an alimentary canal with mouth, intestine, and anus, a well-developed nervous system, two eyes, and other sensory organs. The mouth has a lobe on either side provided with bristles which are used in capturing the minute animals and plants that serve as food. The members of the group are hermaphroditic. There is no circulatory or

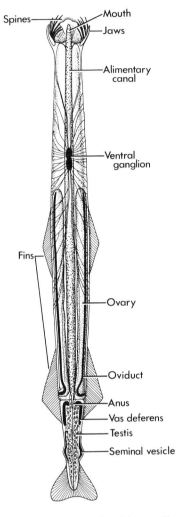

Spines — Mouth
Jaws

Alimentary canal

Ventral ganglion

Fins

Ovary

Oviduct

Anus
Vas deferens
Testis
Seminal vesicle

Fig. 7-15. Chaetognatha. *Sagitta hexaptera,* ventral view. (After O. Hertwig, modified.)

excretory system in this small phylum of about 50 species. Radial, indeterminate cleavage and type of coelom formation have been used to link this phylum with deuterostomes such as the echinoderms and chordates. Adult anatomy, however, shows considerable resemblance to the aschelminths, hence their phylogenetic position remains problematic.

Sagitta bipunctata is a pelagic species capable of vertical migration through many fathoms. *Eukrohnia hamata* has a slender body with a single lateral fin on either side. *Pterosagitta draco* has a broad body with a single pair of lateral fins and an integumentary expansion along the sides. All these species are cosmopolitan in their distribution.

Sagitta elegans is common in North Atlantic coastal waters and *S. serratodentata* in surface waters of warmer oceans.

Chaetognaths are important members of the plankton of the oceans. Species distribution seems to be determined by temperature.

11 / Phylum Pogonophora

The Pogonophora are a recently discovered group of long, slender, solitary, tube-dwelling invertebrates from the deep ocean bottoms. Although discovered this century, they are very widespread in the deeper oceans and recently have been found in somewhat shallow water near the coast of Florida. The most peculiar feature of these free-living animals is the complete lack of a digestive tract.

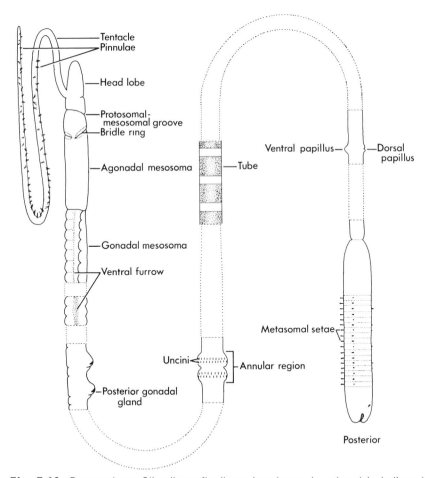

Fig. 7-16. Pogonophora. *Siboglinum fiordicum,* length greatly reduced in indicated areas. (Modified after Webb.)

General Morphology. The long cylindrical body (Fig. 7–16) seldom exceeds 1 millimeter in diameter but the length may exceed $\frac{1}{3}$ meter. They live in a secreted proteinaceous and chitinous tube, which usually has many ringlike thickenings evident. The tubes are thought to have a vertical orientation in the bottom mud. Recent discoveries by Webb (1964) indicate that the body regions (Fig. 7–18) described in earlier works were based on incomplete specimens. A short anterior *protosoma* bears one, a few, or many *tentacles*. Beneath this is a short *agonadal mesosomal region* followed by a very long *trunk*. About midway down the trunk is an *annular region* of two raised belts studded with uncini. The *uncini* are minute, toothed, hard structures that probably aid this region as holdfast structures. The long preannular portion has a metameric region at the anterior with paired rows of papillae bounding the *ventral furrow*. A variable number of several types of papillae are distributed over the rest of the trunk. At the extreme lower or posterior end is a setae-bearing region thought to be the true *metasoma*, only recently discovered.

Internally the coelom has several divisions. A concentration of nervous tissue occurs in the protosoma. Two vessels, probably afferent and efferent, from the blood vascular system supply each tentacle. Nephridial structures are present. Sexes are separate, but reports of the position of the gonads vary. In *Siboglinum fiordicum* the oviducts open anterior to the first postgonadal gland and spermatophores leave the genital papillae at the anterior end of the metameric region.

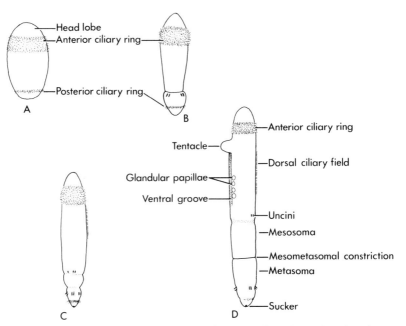

Fig. 7-17. Pogonophora. Larval differentiation. (A–D) early to late larval stages. (Modified after Webb.)

Development. Cleavage is holoblastic and unequal. No blastopore is formed. The larva has an anterior and posterior ciliary ring (Fig. 7–17). The great length of the organism is achieved by elongation of the mesosoma.

Pogonophora in General. Many questions remain unanswered about the pogonophorans. The method of nutrition may involve external digestion within the tube or within a chamber formed by the tentacles. Tentacular gland cells support this assumption. A possibility not yet explored is that nutrition is partly saprophytic through the posterior embedded in the organic ooze and that the tentacles also function as gills.

The phylogenetic position is puzzling, although most zoologists seem to assign them a position near the deuterostomes (echinoderms, hemichordates, and chordates). However (Foucart, *et al.*, 1965), the presence of chitin has been reported in their tubes. Chitin is not present in the deuterostomes in general. Several workers think a two tentacled arrangement is primitive and a horseshoe-shaped base has been reported at one stage. Thus, a possible relationship to the lophophorate phyla cannot be eliminated.

It seems possible the pogonophorans are extremely long lived. If the tubes are oriented in a vertical position (tubes are often three times the length of the organism), they may grow upward as the ocean ooze slowly accumulates. It seems unlikely that they are pushed into the ooze as formed, because tubes formed when the animal breaks through the side of the tube with its posterior

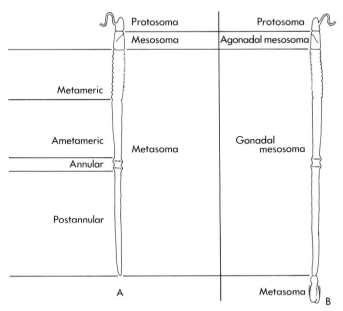

Fig. 7-18. Pogonophora body regions. (A) After Ivanov. (B) As revised by Webb following discovery of the posterior extremity. (Modified after Webb.)

are thinner and without annulations. Thus, the tubes and their length could indicate extreme ages for invertebrates.

Classification into two orders is generally accepted.

Order 1. Athecanephria. Nephridiopores lateral; pericardial sac; one or several tentacles. *Siboglinum* (Fig. 7–16) is a genus of about 10 species, each with a single tentacle.

Order 2. Thecanephria. Nephridiopores medial; no pericardial sac; several to many tentacles, often fused to some extent. In *Lamellisabella* the tentacles are fused into a cylinder, *Spirobrachia* may have over 200 tentacles that are fused and spiralled at the base.

12 / Phylum Hemichordata

This phylum of wormlike animals of shallow ocean bottoms is considered closely related to the chordates. The body (Fig. 7–19) is divided into three regions, an anterior *protosome*, a *mesosome*, and a *metasome*, each with a coelomic compartment. Most species have *gill slits* opening from the pharynx

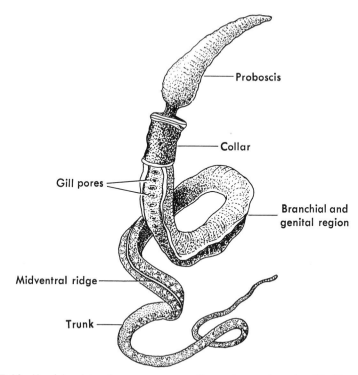

Proboscis

Collar

Gill pores

Branchial and genital region

Midventral ridge

Trunk

Fig. 7-19. Hemichordata. An acorn worm, *Saccoglossus kowalevskii*. (From Lang after Spengel.)

through the body wall of the anterior metasome. A circulatory system is present as well as a complete digestive tract. The brain occurs in the mesosome and the main nerve tracts are in middorsal and midventral positions. A complex of tubules between heart and peritoneum and thought to be excretory structures are in some species. No notochord is found, a diverticulum of the buccal cavity was once erroneously described as one. In species with indirect development a *tornaria larva* is produced that resembles the bipinnaria larvae of some echinoderms. Cleavage is holoblastic and radial.

Two classes of adult hemichordates are described. A third class, Planctosphaeroida, is known only from larvae.

Class I. Enteropneusta

Solitary hemichordates; medium length to long worms; mesosome forms a noticeable collar; many gill slits; straight digestive tract; the acorn worms. Ex. *Balanoglossus.*

Class II. Pterobranchia

Colonial; with secreted tubes; small to microscopic; U-shaped digestive tract; with tentacles, bearing resemblance to lophophore.

Order 1. Rhabdopleurida. Members of colony connected by a black stolon; two tentacle-bearing arms. Ex. *Rhabdopleura.*

Order 2. Cephalodiscida. Members of colony not connected by a stolon; four or more tentacle-bearing arms. Ex. *Cephalodiscus.*

An extinct class of animals, the Graptolita, were colonial forms secreting tubes resembling the Pterobranchia tubes and thus are often included with the Hemichordata. Some include them with the Hydrozoa.

References to Literature on the Minor Phyla

BUSHNELL, J. H. 1965. On the taxonomy and distribution of freshwater Ectoprocta in Michigan. *Trans. Am. Microsc. Soc.,* **84**:231–244, 339–358, 529–548.

CHENG, T. C. 1964. *The Biology of Animal Parasites.* Saunders, Philadelphia. 727 pp.

FOUCART, M. F., S. B. GREGOIRE, and C. JEUNIAUX. 1965. Composition chimique du tube d'un pogonophore (*Siboglinum* sp.) et des formation squelettiques de deux pterobranches. *Sarsia,* **20**:35–41.

GRANT, G. C. 1963. Investigations of inner continental shelf waters off lower Chesapeake Bay. Part IV. Descriptions of the Chaetognatha and a key to their identification. *Chesapeake Sci.,* **4**:107–119.

HADZI, J. 1963. *The Evolution of the Metazoa.* Macmillan, New York. 499 pp.

HYMAN, L. H. 1940. *The Invertebrates.* Vol. I. Mesozoa, pp. 233–247. Vol. II. Rhynchocoela, pp. 459–531. Vol. III. Acanthocephala, pp. 1–52; Priapulida, pp. 183–197; Entoprocta, pp. 521–554. Vol. V. Chaetognatha, pp. 1–71; Hemichordata, pp. 72–207; Pogonophora, pp. 208–227; Phoronida, pp. 228–274; Ectoprocta, pp. 275–515; Brachiopoda, pp. 516–609; Sipunculida, pp. 610–696. McGraw-Hill, New York.

IVANOV, A. V. 1963. *Pogonophora.* Consultants Bureau, New York. 479 pp.

ROGICK, M. D. 1959. Bryozoa. In W. T. EDMONDSON. *Fresh-Water Biology.* Wiley, New York. 1,248 pp.

SHAPEERO, W. 1961. Phylogeny of Priapulida. *Science,* **133**:879–880.

———. 1962. The epidermis and cuticle of *Priapulus caudatus* Lamarck. *Trans. Am. Microsc. Soc.,* **81**:352–355.

WEBB, M. 1963. *Siboglinum fiiordicum* sp. nov. (Pogonophora) from the Raune-fjord, Western Norway. *Sarsia,* **13**:33–49.

———. 1964. The posterior extremity of *Siboglinum fiordicum* (Pogonophora). *Sarsia,* **15**:33–36.

———. 1964. The larvae of *Siboglinum fiordicum* and a reconsideration of the adult body regions (Pogonophora). *Sarsia,* **15**:57–68.

Chapter VIII

Phylum Annelida

A NNELIDS differ from the other groups of "worms" in possessing the following complex of characteristics: (1) the body is divided into a linear series of similar segments (also called metameres or somites) visible externally because of grooves that encircle the body, and internally because of partitions called septa; (2) the body cavity between the alimentary canal and body wall is a true coelom; (3) there is a single preoral segment, the prostomium; (4) the nervous system consists of a pair of dorsal preoral ganglia, the brain, and a pair of ventral nerve cords with typically a pair of ganglia in each segment; (5) typically a nonchitinous cuticle on the surface of the body supplied with chitinous bristles or setae.

Five classes may be recognized in the phylum as follows:

CLASS I. POLYCHAETA. Marine annelids with many setae situated on fleshy lateral outgrowths, the parapodia; conspicuous segments; intersegmental septa; a large coelom; usually a well-developed head, bearing appendages; sexes separate; and a free-swimming trochophore larva. Ex. *Nereis virens, Amphitrite ornata, Arenicola cristata.*

CLASS II. OLIGOCHAETA. Mostly terrestrial and fresh-water annelids with no parapodia and few setae; conspicuous segments; intersegmental septa; a large coelom; no distinct head with appendages; hermaphroditic; no trochophore larva. Ex. *Lumbricus terrestris, Tubifex tubifex.*

CLASS III. ARCHIANNELIDA. Small marine annelids without parapodia; usually with a tonguelike buccal structure; trochophore larva. Ex. *Polygordius appendiculatus.*

CLASS IV. HIRUDINEA. Leeches. Annelids usually dorsoventrally flattened, with a prostomium and 32 body segments; two suckers, one surrounding the mouth and the other at the posterior end; no setae nor parapodia;

hermaphroditic; coelom small because of growth of mesenchyme cells. Ex. *Hirudo medicinalis, Macrobdella decora.*

CLASS V. ECHIUROIDEA. Marine annelids with well-developed prostomium; evidence of segmentation usually absent. Ex. *Echiurus.*

1 / Class I. Polychaeta

(1) Nereis virens*—A Clamworm

The clamworm, *Nereis virens*, is a common annelid living in burrows in the sand or mud of the seashore at tide level. The burrows are sometimes two feet deep and are kept from collapsing by a lining of mucus, which holds together

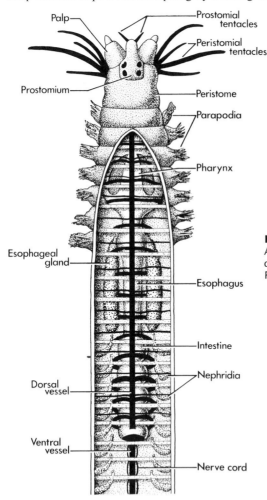

Fig. 8-1. *Nereis*, the clamworm. Anterior end of the body with dorsal body wall removed. (After Parker and Haswell, modified.)

---

* *Nereis virens,* sometimes referred to as *Neanthes virens,* is in the genus *Nereis,* subgenus *Neanthes,* according to Pettibone (1963).

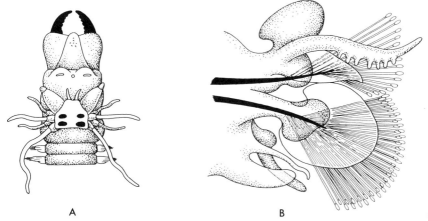

Fig. 8-2. *Nereis,* the clamworm. (A) Head with jaws and pharynx protruded in the position assumed when grasping food. (B) A parapodium showing two acicula (in black), many locomotor setae, and several flattened respiratory gills. (From Newman, after Leukart.)

the grains of sand. By day the clamworm rests in its burrow, but at night it extends its body in search of food, or may leave the burrow entirely.

External Features.   The body is flattened dorso-ventrally and may reach a length of over 30 cm. The *head* is distinct (Figs. 8–1 and 8–2). Above the mouth is the *prostomium* which bears a pair of terminal *tentacles*, two pairs of simple *eyes*, and, on either side, a thick *palp*. The first true segment is the *peristomium*; from each side of this arise four tentacles or *cirri*. The crustaceans and other small animals that serve as food are captured by a pair of strong chitinous *jaws* which are everted with part of the pharynx when *Nereis* is feeding. Behind the head are a variable number of segments each bearing a fleshy outgrowth on either side, the *parapodia* (Fig. 8–2). These are used as locomotor organs, in addition to undulations of the body that are effective in swimming. New segments are added near the posterior end; here and near the anterior end the parapodia are not as well developed as elsewhere. The peristomium and posterior terminal segment are free from parapodia. Each parapodium consists of a dorsal blade, the *notopodium*, and a ventral blade, the *neuropodium*. The notopodium has a thin, vascular, dorsal lobe, respiratory in function, and bears a dorsal *cirrus* and a bundle of long *setae*, one of which, the *aciculum*, is entirely internal, very thick, and attached to muscles within the body. The neuropodium also bears a cirrus and a similar bundle of setae with an aciculum. The posterior terminal segment bears a pair of ventral cirri that extend posteriorly, and the *anus*.

Body Wall (Fig. 8–3).   This consists of an outer *cuticle*, which is secreted by the cells of the *hypodermis* just beneath it, and several *muscular layers* under the hypodermis. The first are circular muscles; then come two dorsal and two ventral bands of longitudinal muscles; and also a layer of

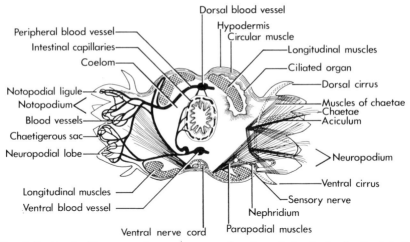

Dorsal blood vessel
Hypodermis
Circular muscle
Longitudinal muscles
Ciliated organ
Dorsal cirrus
Muscles of chaetae
Chaetae
Aciculum
Neuropodium
Ventral cirrus
Sensory nerve
Nephridium
Parapodial muscles

Peripheral blood vessel
Intestinal capillaries
Coelom
Notopodial ligule
Notopodium
Blood vessels
Chaetigerous sac
Neuropodial lobe
Longitudinal muscles
Ventral blood vessel
Ventral nerve cord

Fig. 8-3. *Nereis.* Diagrammatic transverse section through the body. On the left the chief constituents of the vascular system are represented; on the right side the setae (chaetae) and their muscles, as well as the distribution of the lateral nerve, etc., are shown. (From Benham.)

oblique muscles. These muscles are covered within by a layer of *peritoneal epithelium*.

Coelom. The body cavity between the body wall and the intestine is a coelom (Fig. 8–3). It is divided into chambers by transverse *septa*, which correspond to the limits of the segments. Perforations in the septa beneath the intestine allow fluid to pass from one chamber to the next. The coelom is lined with peritoneal epithelium.

Digestive System (Fig. 8–1). The *mouth* opens into the *pharynx* which forms a sort of proboscis when protruded (Fig. 8–2, A). This is accomplished by protractor and retractor muscles. The pharynx leads into a slender *esophagus* which has a *digestive gland* on either side opening into it. Following the esophagus is a straight *stomach-intestine* extending to the anus.

Circulatory System (Fig. 8–1). The blood is contained in contractile tubes, the blood vessels. There is a *dorsal vessel*, that lies between the two dorsal longitudinal muscle bands, which carries blood anteriorly, and a *ventral vessel* beneath the intestine which carries blood posteriorly. In each segment the two longitudinal vessels are connected on either side by right and left transverse vessels From these arise two dorsal and two ventral branchial vessels that form networks of capillaries in the dorsal and ventral lobes of the parapodia.

Excretory System. Every segment except the peristomium and the anal segment contains a pair of *nephridia* (Figs. 8–1 and 8–4, A). Each nephridium opens into the coelomic cavity by means of a *ciliated funnel*; passes posteriorly

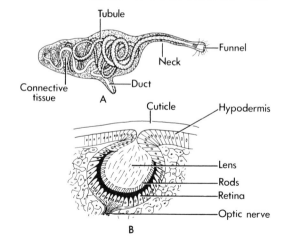

Fig. 8-4. *Nereis*. (A) Nephridium. (B) Eye. (A, after
Goodrich; B, after Andrews.)

through the septum into the following segment, where it forms a coiled tube;
and opens at the base of a parapodium on the ventral surface through a
nephridiopore. The parapodia serve as respiratory organs.

Nervous System (Fig. 8–5). Above the pharynx in the head is a pair of
supra-pharyngeal ganglia that constitute the *brain*. This is connected with a
pair of *subpharyngeal ganglia* by a *circumpharyngeal commissure* on either side

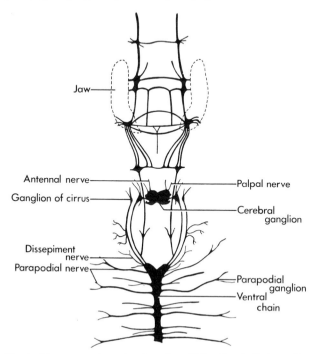

Fig. 8-5. *Nereis*. Nervous system, head region. (After Turnbull, from Petrunkevitch.)

that form a ring around the pharynx. Following this is a *ventral nerve cord* with a pair of ganglia in each segment. The brain gives off an optic nerve to each eye, a palpal nerve to each palpus and a tentacular nerve to each group of tentacles. The peristomial tentacles receive nerves from small ganglia connected with the circumpharyngeal commissure. Several dorsal and ventral ganglia around the pharynx, that are connected with one another and with the brain, constitute the *visceral nervous system*. From each of the ganglia of the ventral nerve chain arise three pairs of nerves, one pair to the parapodia, one to the anterior segment, and one to the muscles of the segment.

Reproductive System. The sexes are separate. No well-defined *gonads* are present, but during the breeding season ova or spermatozoa arise from the wall of the coelom in each segment except near the anterior end. At this time the worm is externally differentiated into two regions, an anterior *atoke* and a posterior *epitoke*, which contains the gonads. When thus specialized the worm is called a heteronereid. The gametes leave via the nephridiopores and fertilization occurs in the open water. Trochophore larvae develop from the fertilized eggs.

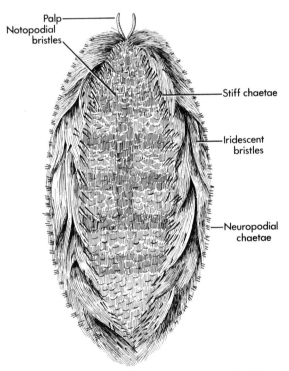

Fig. 8-6. Polychaeta. *Aphrodite aculeata*, the "sea mouse." (From Benham, after Regne Animal.)

(2) Other Polychaeta

The principal characteristics of the Polychaeta are exhibited by *Nereis virens*. Many variations from this type occur, some of which are noted below. The orders and a few of the more important families and their commoner representatives are as follows.

Order 1. Errantia. Free-swimming; segments of body similar except at anterior and posterior ends; parapodia with acicula.

FAMILY 1. APHRODITIDAE (Fig. 8–6). Back partly or entirely covered with scales, which usually alternate with slender cirri. *Lepidonotus squamatus* has 12 pairs of scales (elytra); is dark brown and about 3 cm long; and lives under stones near the tide lines along the New England shore.

FAMILY 2. SYLLIDAE. Short, slender worms usually with long slender dorsal cirri; asexual budding common. *Autolytus cornutus* (Fig. 8–7, C) is pinkish and about 15 mm long. Asexual budding results in a linear row of offspring each of which acquires a head before separating from the parent.

FAMILY 3. NEREIDAE. For example, *Nereis virens*, already described.

FAMILY 4. EUNICIDAE. Slender worms of various lengths, with usually branching gills arising from the parapodia near the anterior end; proboscis with complicated jaw apparatus, and generally a parchment-like tube. *Eunice schemacephala* is known as the palolo worm which lives in coral rock in the Gulf of Mexico and the West Indies. Swarming occurs in July within three days of the full moon. At that time the epitokes break free of the atokes and

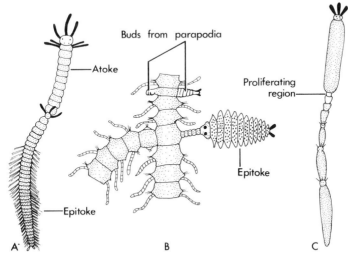

Fig. 8-7. Polychaeta. Asexual reproduction. (A) *Syllis*, with the posterior region forming a reproductive individual. (B) *Syllis*, showing branching of the asexual stock and budding of reproductive individuals from parapodia. (C) *Autolytus*, with a chain of reproductive individuals budded off successively from a proliferating region. (After Borradaile and Potts, modified.)

Fig. 8-8. Polychaeta. *Chaetopterus.* Dorsal view of anterior end. (After Borradaile and Potts, modified.)

swim to the surface at night. Gametes are freed by ruptures of the epitokes about sunup.

Order 2. Sedentaria.   Tube-dwelling; head small or much modified; parapodia simple and without acicula; branchiae localized to a definite region.

FAMILY 1. CHAETOPTERIDAE.   Filter feeders, which utilize secreted mucous bags to strain food particles from water circulated through their tube. Typically with a vertical tube and well-developed palps for ejecting large particles (Barnes, 1965). *Chaetopterus* (Fig. 8–8) lives in a U-shaped, parchment-like tube; the worm may be 15 cm long and has considerable variation in the morphology of the segments and parapodia in different parts of the body; palps are poorly developed.

FAMILY 2. TEREBELLIDAE (Fig. 8–9).   Long worms living in burrows or tubes; head with many long tentacular filaments, respiratory in function; usually several pairs of branching gills on segments just back of head; parapodia small. *Amphitrite ornata* is pinkish; up to 30 cm long; and lives in a strong tube.

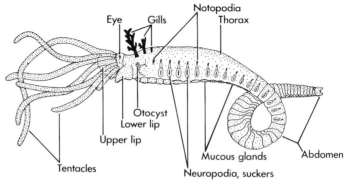

Fig. 8-9. Polychaeta. Family Terebellidae. Side view of a young worm removed from its tube. (After Wilson, modified.)

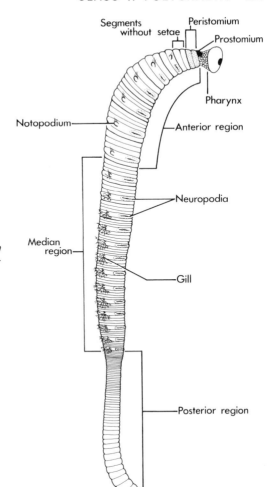

Segments without setae
Peristomium
Prostomium
Pharynx
Notopodium
Anterior region
Neuropodia
Median region
Gill
Posterior region

Fig. 8-10. Polychaeta. *Arenicola marina*. Side view. (After Ashworth, modified.)

FAMILY 3. ARENICOLIDAE. Contains the lugworms. *Arenicola marina* (Figs. 8–10 and 8–11) has a head without tentacles and a proboscis without jaws; the parapodia are rudimentary; branching gills are present above the parapodia of the middle segments of the body. It reaches a length of 20 cm, and lives in deep burrows in the sand.

FAMILY 4. SABELLIDAE. Worms with palps modified into semicircular feathered gills; parapodia rudimentary; living in membranous tubes. *Sabella microphthalma* is greenish-yellow and about 5 cm long; the gill filaments are provided with minute eye spots; the tubes often encrust oyster shells.

FAMILY 5. SERPULIDAE. These worms live in calcareous tubes; have prostomial palps modified into semicircular feathered gills and dorsal gill filaments that serve as an operculum to close the opening to the tube. *Hydroides hexagonus* has usually purplish-brown gills; lives in a contorted tube

Septa

Notopodial muscles

Nephridium
Nephrostome

Esophageal pouch

Notopodial muscles

Ventricle

Auricle

Afferent vessel

Efferent vessel

Doral vessel
Ventral vessel

Lateral vessel
Subintestinal
vessel

Ventral nerve cord

Dorsal vessel

Septa

Fig. 8-11. Polychaeta. *Arenicola marina*. Dissection to show internal organs. (After Ashworth, modified.)

encrusted on shells, etc.; and is about 75 mm long. *Spirorbis spirorbis* lives in a coiled tube, often forming a flat spiral, that is encrusted on seaweeds, etc.

Order 3. Myzostomaria. These polychaetes are highly modified as adults for a parasitic existence on or within echinoderms, especially crinoids. The body is externally unsegmented, flat, and oval or discoidal in shape (Fig. 8–12). Five pairs of parapodia armed with acicula and hooks are present on

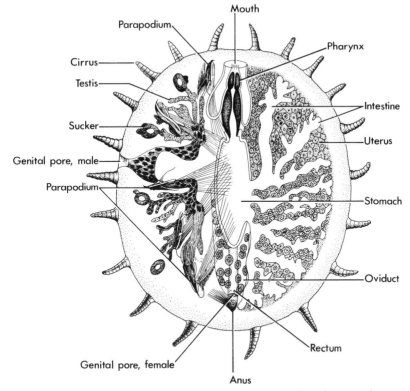

Fig. 8-12. *Myzostoma cirriferum*. The organs are supposed to be seen by transparency. On the right side the more dorsal organs are shown and on the left, those lying more ventrally. (After Lang and v. Graff.)

the ventral surface, and around the edge are usually 10 pairs of cirri. Alternating with the parapodia are normally four pairs of suckers.

The digestive system consists of a mouth on the ventral surface near the anterior end, which opens into a retractile pharynx provided with a bulbous musculosus; next comes a short esophagus, then the stomach, from which a number of ceca arise, and a straight intestine which ends in the anus on the ventral surface near the posterior end. The coelom is greatly reduced by parenchymous tissue. There is no circulatory system except a series of spaces filled with coelomic fluid. No special respiratory system is present. In most species there is one pair of nephridia. The nervous system is well developed and of the ladder type. The worms are normally protandric hermaphrodites, functioning first as males and then as females. A trochophore larva develops from the egg.

Myzostoma cubanum is a parasite of crinoids in the West Indies. It is about 1.7 mm in diameter and has well-developed parapodia but no suckers. *Myzostoma glabrum* is a species that attaches itself to the oral plates of the crinoid, *Antedon rosacea*. It is nearly circular in outline and about 4 mm long.

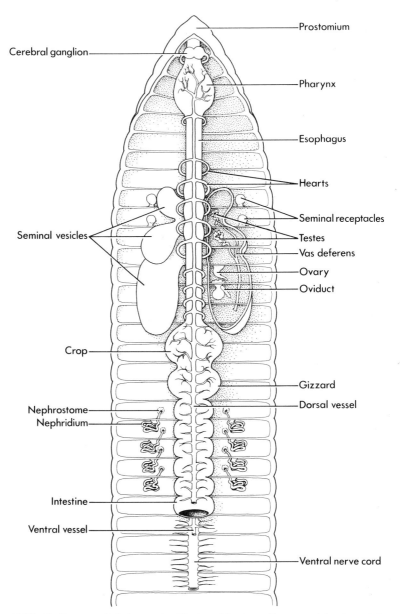

Fig. 8-13. Earthworm. Anterior part with dorsal body wall removed to show internal organs, diagrammatic. Dorsal wall of seminal vesicles and underlying seminal capsule have been removed on the right side to show gonads. Internal musculature not shown, nephridia are shown in only a few segments.

2 / Class II. Oligochaeta

(1) Lumbricus terrestris—An Earthworm

The common earthworm, or "night crawler," *Lumbricus terrestris*, or one of its near relatives, is usually used as a type in introductory courses. It illustrates the principal characteristics of the advanced members of the class Oligochaeta so its description will serve for review and reference. Figure 8–13 shows many of the features seen in the usual dorsal dissection.

External Features. The body of *Lumbricus* is cylindroid, and varies in length from about 6 inches to 1 foot. The *segments*, of which there are over 100, are easily determined externally because of the grooves extending around the body. At the anterior end a fleshy lobe, the *prostomium* (Fig. 8–19), projects over the *mouth*; this is not considered a true segment. It is customary to number the segments with Roman numerals, beginning at the anterior end, because both external and internal structures bear a constant relation to them. Segments XXXI or XXXII to XXXVII are swollen in mature worms, forming a saddle-shaped enlargement, the *clitellum*, of use during reproduction. Every segment except the first and last bears four pairs of chitinous bristles, the *setae* (Fig. 8–14); these may be moved by retractor and protractor muscles, and are renewed if lost. The setae on segment or *somite* XXVI are, in mature worms, modified for reproductive purposes.

The body is covered by a thin, transparent *cuticle* secreted by the cells lying just beneath it. The cuticle protects the body from physical and chemical injury; it contains numerous *pores* (Fig. 8–15) to allow the secretions from unicellular glands to pass through, and is marked with fine *striae*, causing the surface to appear iridescent.

A number of *external openings* of various sizes allow the entrance of food into the body, and the exit of feces, excretory products, reproductive cells, etc. (1) The *mouth* is a crescentric opening situated in the ventral half of the first somite (Fig. 8–19); it is overhung by the prostomium. (2) The oval *anal aperture* lies in the last somite. (3) The openings of the sperm ducts or *vasa deferentia* are situated one on either side of somite XV. They have swollen lips; a slight ridge extends posteriorly from them to the clitellum. (4) The openings of the *oviducts* are small, round pores one on either side of somite XIV; eggs pass out of the body through them. (5) The openings of the *seminal receptacles* appear as two pairs of minute pores concealed within the grooves which separate somites IX and X, and X and XI. (6) A pair of *nephridiopores* (Fig. 8–16), the external apertures of the excretory organs, open on every somite except the first three and the last. They are usually situated immediately anterior to the outer seta of the inner pair. (7) The body cavity or *coelom* communicates with the exterior by means of *dorsal pores* located middorsally at the anterior of somites posterior to VII or VIII.

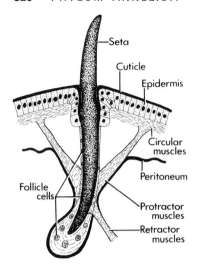

Fig. 8-14. Earthworm, *Lumbricus*. Histology of seta and surrounding tissue. (After Stephenson, modified.)

Internal Anatomy (Fig. 8–13). If a specimen is cut open from the anterior to the posterior end by an incision passing through the body wall a trifle to one side of the middorsal line, a general view of the internal structures may be obtained. The body is essentially a double tube (Fig. 8–16), the body wall constituting the outer, the straight alimentary canal, the inner; between the two is a cavity, the coelom. The external segmentation corresponds to an internal division of the coelomic cavity into compartments by means of partitions, called *septa*, which lie beneath the grooves. The alimentary canal passes through the center of the body, and is suspended in the coelom by the partitions. Septa are absent between somites I and II, and incomplete between somites III and IV, and XVII and XVIII. The walls of the coelom are lined with an epithelium, termed the *peritoneum*. The coelomic cavity is filled with

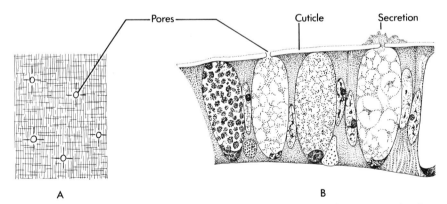

Fig. 8-15. *Lumbricus.* (A) Superficial view of the cuticle showing pores and striae. (B) Vertical section of a bit of epidermis showing four mucous cells in different stages of secretion. Mucus is passing through one of the two pores in the cuticle. (B, from Dahlgren and Kepner.)

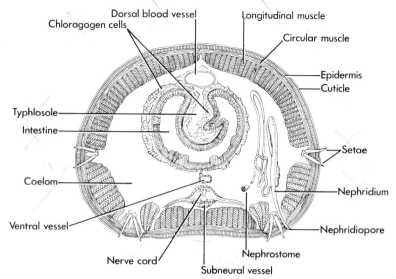

Dorsal blood vessel
Chloragogen cells
Longitudinal muscle
Circular muscle
Epidermis
Cuticle
Typhlosole
Intestine
Setae
Coelom
Nephridium
Ventral vessel
Nephridiopore
Nerve cord
Nephrostome
Subneural vessel

Fig. 8-16. *Lumbricus.* Transverse section through the middle region of the body. (From Woodruff.)

a colorless fluid, which flows from one compartment to another when the body of the worm contracts, thus producing a sort of circulation. In somites IX to XVI are the reproductive organs; running along the upper surface of the alimentary canal is the dorsal blood vessel; and just beneath it lie the ventral blood vessels and nerve cord.

The coelomic fluid in the various compartments also serves as a *hydrostatic skeleton* for the earthworm. The opposing action of circular and longitudinal muscles (Fig. 8–16) of the body wall is mediated through hydraulic action of the body fluid. Thus, extension of the worm is accomplished by contraction of the circular muscles. Loss of much body fluid causes a great loss of mobility.

Digestive System. The *alimentary canal* (Fig. 8–13) consists of (1) a *mouth cavity* or *buccal pouch* in somites I to III, (2) a thick muscular *pharynx* lying in somites IV and V, (3) a narrow, straight tube, the *esophagus* which extends through somites VI to XIV, (4) a thin-walled enlargement, the *crop* or *proventriculus*, in somites XV and XVI, (5) a thick muscular-walled *gizzard* in somites XVII and XVIII, and (6) a thin-walled *intestine* extending from somite XIX to the *anal aperture*. The intestine is not a simple cylindrical tube; but its dorsal wall is infolded, forming an internal longitudinal ridge, the *typhlosole* (Fig. 8–16). This increases the digestive surface. Surrounding the alimentary canal and dorsal blood vessel is a layer of *chloragogen cells*. The functions of these cells are somewhat comparable to those of the liver of higher animals as centers of glycogen and fat synthesis and storage. Three pairs of *calciferous glands* lie at the sides of the esophagus in segments X to XII; they produce calcium carbonate, which they excrete into the digestive tract when the component ions are overly abundant in the body fluids.

The *food* of the earthworm consists principally of pieces of leaves and other vegetation, particles of animal matter, and soil. This material is gathered at night. At this time the worms are active; they crawl out into the air, and, holding fast to the tops of their burrows with their tails, explore the neighborhood. Food particles are drawn into the buccal cavity by suction produced when the pharyngeal cavity is enlarged by the contraction of the muscles which extend from the pharynx to the body wall.

Fig. 8-17. *Lumbricus.* Diagrams showing the arrangement of the blood vessels. (A) Longitudinal view of the vessels in somites VIII, IX, and X. (B) Transverse section of same region. (C) Longitudinal view of the vessels in the intestinal region. (D) Transverse section through the intestinal region. (From Bourne, after Benham.)

In the pharynx, the food receives a secretion from the pharyngeal glands; it then passes through the esophagus to the crop, where it is stored temporarily. In the meantime the secretion from the calciferous glands in the esophageal walls is added, neutralizing the acids. The gizzard is a grinding organ; in it the food is broken up into minute fragments by being squeezed and rolled about. Solid particles, such as grains of sand, which are frequently swallowed, probably aid in this grinding process. The food then passes on to the intestine, where most of the digestion and absorption takes place.

Circulatory System. The *blood* of the earthworm is contained in a complicated system of tubes which ramify to all parts of the body. A number of these tubes are large and centrally located; these give off branches which likewise branch, finally ending in exceedingly thin tubules, the *capillaries*. The *blood* consists of a plasma in which are suspended a great number of colorless cells, called corpuscles. Its red color is due to a pigment termed *hemoglobin*, which is dissolved in the plasma. In vertebrates the hemoglobin is located in the blood corpuscles.

There are *five longitudinal blood vessels* connected with one another and with various organs by branches, more or less regularly arranged. These are shown in Figure 8–17, and are as follows: (1) the dorsal or supraintestinal vessel, (2) the ventral or subintestinal trunk, (3) the subneural trunk, (4) two lateral neural trunks, (5) five pairs of hearts in segments VII to XI, (6) two intestino-tegumentary vessels (in A and B) arising in segment X and extending to the esophagus, integument, and nephridia in segments X to VI, (7) branches from the ventral trunk to the nephridia and body wall (D), (8) parietal vessels connecting the dorsal and subneural trunks in the intestinal region, (9) branches from the dorsal trunk to the intestine (in C), (10) a typhlosolar vessel connected by branches with the intestine and dorsal trunk, and (11) branches from the ventral vessel to the nephridia and body wall (in D).

The dorsal trunk (Fig. 8–18) and hearts determine the direction of the blood flow, since they furnish the power by means of their muscular walls. Blood is forced forward by wavelike contractions of the dorsal trunk, beginning at the posterior end and traveling quickly anteriorly. These contractions are said to be *peristaltic*, and have been likened to the action of the fingers in the operation of milking a cow. *Valves* in the walls of the dorsal trunk prevent the return of blood from the anterior end. In somites VII to XI the blood passes from the dorsal trunk into the hearts, and is forced by them both forward and backward in the ventral trunk. Valves in the heart also prevent the backward flow. From the ventral trunk the blood passes to the body wall and nephridia. Blood is returned from the body wall to the lateral-neural trunks. The flow in the subneural trunk is toward the posterior end, then upward through the parietal vessels into the dorsal trunk. The anterior region receives blood from the dorsal and ventral trunks. The blood

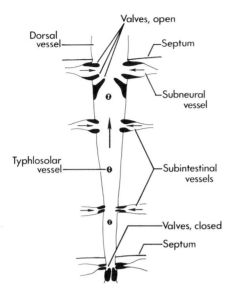

Valves, open

Dorsal vessel

Septum

Subneural vessel

Typhlosolar vessel

Subintestinal vessels

Valves, closed

Septum

Fig. 8-18. Earthworm, *Lumbricus.* Diagram of dorsal blood vessel to show connections and valves. (After Johnston.)

carried to the body wall and integument receives oxygen through the cuticle, and is then returned to the dorsal trunk by way of the subneural trunk and the intestinal connectives. Because of its proximity to the subneural trunk, the nervous system receives a continuous supply of the freshest blood.

Respiration. The earthworm possesses no respiratory system, but obtains oxygen and gets rid of carbon dioxide through the moist outer membrane. Many capillaries lie just beneath the cuticle, making the exchange of gases easy. The oxygen is combined with the hemoglobin.

Excretory System. Most of the excretory matter is carried outside of the body by a number of coiled tubes, termed *nephridia* (Fig. 8–16), a pair of which are present in every somite except the first three and the last. A nephridium occupies part of two successive somites; in one is a ciliated funnel, the *nephrostome*, which is connected by a thin ciliated tube with the major portion of the structure in the somite posterior to it. Three loops make up the coiled portion of the nephridium. The cilia on the nephrostome and in the nephridium create a current which draws solid waste particles from the coelomic fluid. Glands in the coiled tube take waste matter, principally ammonia and urea, from the blood, and the current in the tube carries it out through the *nephridiopore.* Most salts are removed before the fluid is excreted.

Nervous System. The nervous system is concentrated. There is a bilobed mass of nervous tissue, the *brain* or *suprapharyngeal ganglion*, on the dorsal surface of the pharynx in segment III (Fig. 8–19). This is connected by two *circumpharyngeal connectives* with a pair of *subpharyngeal ganglia* which lie just beneath the pharynx. From the latter the *ventral nerve cord* (Figs. 8–13

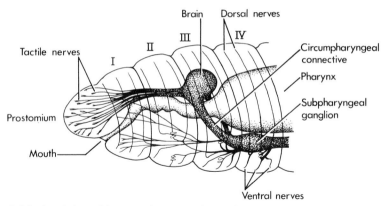

Fig. 8-19. *Lumbricus.* Diagram of the anterior end to show the arrangement of the nervous system. (From Shipley and MacBride.)

and 8–16) extends posteriorly near the ventral body wall. The ventral nerve cord enlarges into a ganglion in each segment and gives off three pairs of nerves in every segment posterior to IV. Each ganglion really consists of two ganglia fused together. Near the dorsal surface of every ganglionic mass are three longitudinal cords, the giant fibers (Fig. 8–21). The brain and nerve cord

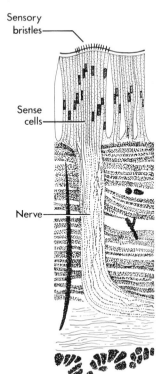

Fig. 8-20. *Lumbricus.* Tactile nerve endings in the integument. (From Dahlgren and Kepner.)

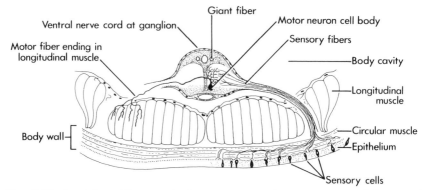

Fig. 8-21. *Lumbricus.* Diagram of primary sensory and motor neurons of the ventral nerve cord, showing their connections with the skin and the muscles to form a simple reflex arc. (After Parker, from Woodruff.)

constitute the *central nervous system*; the nerves that pass from and to them represent the *peripheral nervous system* (Fig. 8–20).

The nerves of the peripheral nervous system are either efferent or afferent. *Efferent* nerve fibers (Fig. 8–21) are extensions from cells in the ganglia of the central nervous system. They pass out to the muscles or other organs, and, because impulses sent along them give rise to movements, the cells of which they are a part are said to be *motor nerve cells*. Some have fibers that exert an excitatory effect whereas others have an inhibitory effect. The *afferent* fibers originate from epidermal nerve cells that are sensory in function, and extend into the ventral cord. The two types may have synaptic connections, or be connected synaptically by *interneurons*, which also send processes to ganglia of neighboring segments.

Neurosecretory substances have been found in the brain of *Lumbricus*. These secretions are thought to function much like hormones. Some seem to regulate salt and water balance (Kamemoto, *et al.*, 1966).

Sense Organs. The sensitiveness of *Lumbricus* to light and other stimuli is due to the presence of a great number of *epidermal sense organs*. These are groups of sense cells connected with the central nervous system by means of nerve fibers and communicating with the outside world through *sense hairs* which penetrate the cuticle. More of these sense organs occur at the anterior and posterior ends than in any other region of the body.

Reproduction. Both male and female sexual organs occur in a single earthworm. Figure 8–13 shows diagrammatically the position and shape of the various structures. The *female system* consists of: (1) a pair of *ovaries* in segment XIII; (2) a pair of *oviducts* which open by a ciliated funnel in segment XIII, enlarge into an *egg sac* in segment XIV, and then open to the exterior; and (3) two pairs of *seminal receptacles* or *spermathecae*, in somites IX and X.

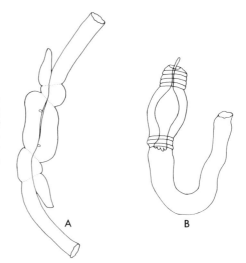

Fig. 8-22. *Lumbricus.* (A) The anterior segments of two copulating earthworms. Slime tubes encircle the pair from the 8th to the 33rd segment. (B) Cocoon, freshly deposited, surrounded by one half of a slime tube. (After Foot.)

The *male organs* are (1) two pairs of glove-shaped *testes* in segments X and XI, (2) two *vasa deferentia* which lead from ciliated funnels to the exterior in segment XV, and (3) three pairs of *seminal vesicles* in segments IX, XI, and XII, and two central reservoirs.

Self-fertilization does not take place, but spermatozoa are transferred from one worm to another during a process called *copulation*. Two worms come together, as shown in Figure 8–22, A; slime tubes are formed, and then a bandlike *cocoon* is secreted about the clitellar region. Eggs and spermatozoa are deposited in the cocoon, but fertilization does not occur until the cocoon is slipped over the head (Fig. 8–22, B).

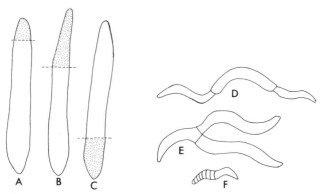

Fig. 8-23. *Lumbricus.* (A) Head end of five segments regenerated from the posterior piece of a worm. (B) Tail regenerated from the posterior piece of a worm. (C) Tail regenerated from an anterior piece of a worm. (D) Union of three pieces to make a long worm. (E) Union of two pieces to make a double-tailed worm. (F) Anterior and posterior pieces united to make a short worm. The dotted portions represent regenerated material. (From Morgan.)

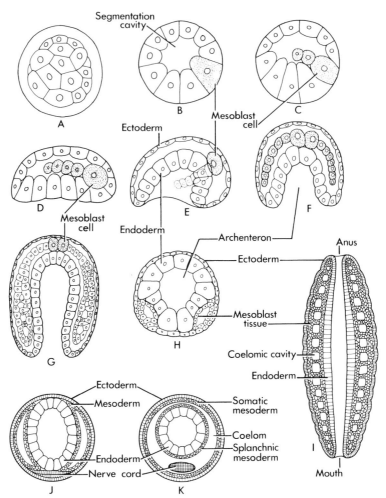

Fig. 8-24. *Lumbricus.* Diagrams of stages in development. (A) Blastula (surrounded by a membrane). (B) Section of a blastula showing blastocoel and one of the primary cells (pole cells) of the mesoderm. (C) Later blastula with developing mesoderm bands. (D) Start of gastrulation. (E) Lateral view of gastrula showing invagination, which as it proceeds leaves the mesoderm bands on either side of the body as indicated by the cells represented with dotted outline. (F) Section of E, along the line, to show pole cells, mesoderm bands and enteric cavity. (G) Later stage showing cavities in the mesoderm bands. (H) The same as G, in cross-section. (I) Diagram of a longitudinal section of a young worm after formation of mouth and anus. (J) The same in cross-section. (K) Later stage in cross-section. (From Woodruff, after Sedgwick and Wilson.)

The *eggs* of the earthworm are *holoblastic*, but cleavage is unequal. A hollow blastula is formed, and a gastrula is produced by invagination. The mesoderm develops from two of the blastula cells, called *mesoblasts*. These cells divide, forming two *mesoblastic bands*, which later become the epithelial lining of the coelom. The embryo escapes from the cocoon as a small worm in about two or three weeks. Stages in the development of an earthworm are shown and explained in Figure 8–24.

Regeneration and Grafting. Earthworms have considerable powers of regeneration and grafting. Some of the results of experiments along this line are shown in Figure 8–23. A posterior piece may regenerate a head of five segments (A) or in certain cases a tail (B). Such a double-tailed worm slowly starves to death. An anterior piece regenerates a tail (C). Three pieces from several worms may be united so as to make a long worm (D); two pieces may fuse, forming a worm with two tails (E); and an anterior piece may be united with a posterior piece to make a short worm (F). In all these experiments the parts were held together by threads until they became united.

Ecology. Darwin (1881) has contributed greatly to the understanding of the importance of earthworms in soil formation. More recent information on the subject has been assembled by Rodale (1961). They improve the soil by burrowing through it and increasing its porosity while mixing organic and inorganic materials and making some of the inorganic materials available to the plants. An interesting side effect of some species voiding their earth containing feces on the surface has been the gradual burial of such things as abandoned Indian cities in Central America.

The accumulation of insecticide residues in earthworms feeding on leaf litter from sprayed trees and the subsequent death of robins feeding on the worms has caused a great rise in public appreciation for ecology following its publicity through Rachael Carson's book, *Silent Spring*.

(2) Other Oligochaeta

The principal characteristics of the Oligochaeta are exhibited by *Lumbricus terrestris*. Many variations from the type occur as may be seen from the brief descriptions of some of the more common representatives as follows.

Order 1. Plesiopora. Small oligochaetes in which the vasa deferentia open to the exterior in the segment behind the one containing the testes. Two suborders may be noted, the Plesiothecata in which the seminal receptacles are in or near the segments containing the gonads, and the Prosothecata containing only the family Enchytraeidae in which the seminal receptacles are far in advance of the segments containing the gonads. The Plesiothecata are primarily aquatic, and reproduction by fission is very common among them (Fig. 8–25).

FAMILY 1. AEOLOSOMATIDAE. Fresh-water worms; microscopic in size; four bundles of setae in each segment; reproduction by asexual division. *Aeolosoma hemprichi* (Fig. 8–25) is 1 mm long and spotted with red oil globules in the integument; lives among algae; and consists of from 7 to 10 segments.

Fig. 8-25. Oligochaeta. (A) *Aeolosoma* dividing transversely. (B) Photo shows fission region of one of the Naididae. (Drawing after Lankester.)

FAMILY 2. NAIDIDAE. Aquatic, mostly in fresh water; small; transparent; two to four bundles of setae on each segment, the ventral setae forked; reproduction principally by transverse division, long chains of offspring formed. *Nais elinguis* (Fig. 8–26) is light brown; 2 to 4 mm long; with 15 to 37 segments; head distinct; often among algae. *Stylaria lacustris* is 25

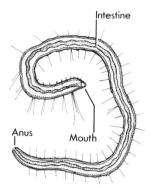

Fig. 8-26. Oligochaeta. *Nais*. (After Leunis.)

mm long; has a long, tentacle-like prostomium and 25 segments. *Dero digitata* is reddish; lives in tubes in ponds; has ciliated branchial appendages at posterior end; and consists of about 48 segments. *Chaetogaster limnaei* may be free-living or attached to or in the liver of fresh-water snails (*Lymnaea* or *Planorbis*); it is colorless; and has two bundles of ventral hooked setae on each segment.

FAMILY 3. TUBIFICIDAE. Fresh- and brackish-water species living in tubes; slender; with four bundles of setae on each segment; no asexual reproduction by transverse division. *Tubifex tubifex* is reddish and about 4 cm long; it occurs in patches on muddy bottoms where the posterior end of the body, which protrudes from the tube, is waved back and forth. *Limnodrilus hoffmeisteri* resembles *Tubifex* but lacks hair setae in the dorsal bundles of setae. It is probably the most common tubificid worm found in organically polluted waters.

FAMILY 4. ENCHYTRAEIDAE. Both terrestrial and aquatic species; four bundles of hairlike setae in each segment; usually whitish in appearance; up to 25 mm long. *Enchytraeus albidus* is milk-white, slender, and about 25 mm long; it has from 53 to 69 segments, and the setae are nearly straight and of equal length; it lives under débris along the seashore.

Order 2. Prosopora. Oligochaetes with the opening of the vasa deferentia on the same segment containing the testes.

FAMILY 1. LUMBRICULIDAE. Free-living aquatic species; four pairs of setae per segment; usually reddish. *Lumbriculus variegatus* has a terminal fork on all the setae.

FAMILY 2. BRANCHIOBDELLIDAE. All species epizoic on crayfishes; with sucker at the posterior end of the body; no setae present; one dorsal and one ventral chitinous jaw. *Cambarincola philadelphica* is 10 mm long; the dorsal and ventral jaws are dissimilar; it lives principally on the ventral surface of the crayfish. Branchiobdellids are thought to be commensals of the crayfish and feed upon algae and other available food particles.

Order 3. Opisthopora. Earthworms and a few other oligochaetes with the opening of the vasa deferentia one or usually several segments behind the segment bearing the testes; large; many segments; reproduction sexual.

FAMILY 1. LUMBRICIDAE. Common earthworms. *Lumbricus terrestris* has already been described as the type of this class *Eisenia foetida* lives in manure and is pink with a dark ring on each segment. *Allolobophora caliginosa* is a common garden worm found in the soil and may be pink, blue, yellow, or gray. These three species are common in such widely separated areas as the United States, England, and New Zealand.

FAMILY 2. MEGASCOLECIDAE. Terrestrial, some species aquatic; many tropical species. *Diplocardia communis* is a North American species that lives in the soil, is flesh colored, and about 30 cm long. The Asian *Pheretima* has been introduced into the United States. The giant earthworm of Australia, *Megascolides*, is said to exceed 3 meters in length. This family of very large worms has provided excellent material for experimental studies of nerve impulse transmission and other physiological problems.

3 / Class III. Archiannelida

This class contains six genera of annelids of which *Polygordius* is the best known. *Polygordius* (Fig. 8–27, A) is a marine worm living in the sand. It is

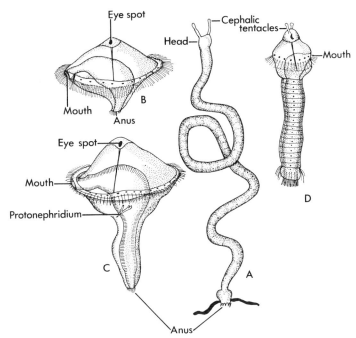

Fig. 8-27. Archiannelida. *Polygordius appendiculatus.* (A) Dorsal view. (B) Trochophore larva. (C) and (D) Stages in development of trochophore into the worm. (After Fraipont, from Bourne.)

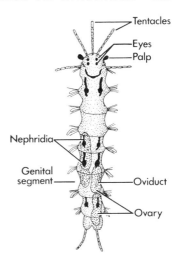

Fig. 8-28. Archiannelida. *Nerilla.* Dorsal view of female. (After Goodrich, modified.)

about 4 cm long, and only indistinctly segmented externally. The prostomium bears a pair of tentacles. The mouth opening is in the ventral part of the first segment, and the anal opening in the last segment. A pair of ciliated pits, one on either side of the prostomium, probably serve as sense organs.

Internally *Polygordius* resembles the earthworm. The coelom is divided into compartments by septa. The internal organs are repeated so that almost every segment possesses coelomic cavities, longitudinal muscles, a pair of nephridia, a pair of gonads, a section of the alimentary canal, and part of the ventral nerve cord. The development of *Polygordius* includes a trochophore stage (Fig. 8–27, B). The adult develops from the trochophore by the growth and elongation of the anal end. This elongation becomes segmented and by continued growth transforms into the adult.

Some authorities think the archiannelids are not primitive, but are specialized in the direction of simplification and reduction, and represent modifications from several groups of polychaetes. Others think they represent remnants of the ancestral annelid stock. In either event, the genera may be arranged in a series beginning with *Polygordius* and ending with forms close to the Polychaeta (e.g., *Nerilla*, Fig. 8–28).

4 / Class IV. Hirudinea

(1) Hirudo medicinalis—The Medicinal Leech

The animals included in this class are commonly called *leeches*. They are usually flattened dorso-ventrally, but differ externally from the flatworms (Platyhelminthes, Chap. V) in being distinctly segmented. The external segmentation, does not correspond exactly to the internal segmentation

Mouth

Posterior
sucker

Fig. 8-29. *Hirudo medicinalis,* the medicinal leech.
(From Shipley and MacBride.)

because there are a variable number of external rings, or *annuli* (from 1 to
14) to every segment, e.g., usually five in the medicinal leech, *Hirudo* (Fig.
8-29), and its allies, and three in *Glossiphonia.* Anatomical features that distinguish the Hirudinea from other Annelida are (1) the presence of a definite
number of segments (33 and a prostomium, based on the larval number of
ganglia), (2) two suckers, one found around the mouth and the other at the
posterior end, and (3) the absence of setae (except in one genus). They are
hermaphrodites.

Hirudo medicinalis, the medicinal leech (Fig. 8-29), is usually selected as an
example of the class. It is about four inches long, but is capable of great con-

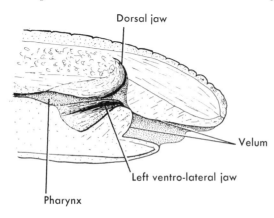

Dorsal jaw

Velum

Left ventro-lateral jaw

Pharynx

Fig. 8-30. Gnathobdellida.
Dissection showing jaws of
leech.

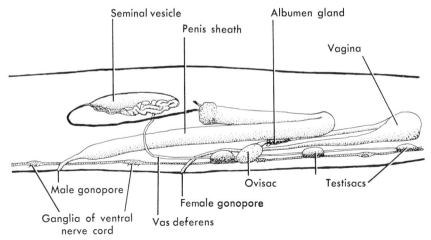

Fig. 8-31. Gnathobdellida. Diagrammatic, lateral view of the main features of the reproductive system. Right members of paired organs are omitted.

tractions and elongation. The *suckers* are used as organs of attachment, and during locomotion are alternately fastened to and released from the substratum, the animal looping along like a measuring-worm. Leeches are also able to swim through the water by undulating movements.

The *alimentary tract* (Fig. 8–32) is fitted for the digestion of the blood of vertebrates, which forms the principal food of some leeches. The *mouth* (Fig. 8–30) lies in the anterior sucker and is provided with three *jaws* armed with chitinous teeth for biting. The blood flow caused by the bite of a leech is difficult to stop, since a secretion from glands opening near the jaws prevents coagulation. Blood is sucked up by the dilation of the muscular *pharynx*. The short *esophagus* leads from the pharynx into the *crop*, which has 11 pairs of lateral branches. Here the blood is stored until digested, presumably by the action of symbiotic bacteria. A leech is able to ingest three times its own weight in blood, and, since it may take as long as 9 months to digest this amount, meals are few and far between. The *intestine* leads from the crop and stomach to the rectum which opens through the *anus* on the dorsal surface of the posterior sucker. The absorbed food passes into the *blood vessels* and the *coelomic cavities*, and is carried to all parts of the body. The coelom is usually small because of the development of the *botryoidal tissue* (Fig. 8–34), which is homologous to the chloragogen tissue of the oligochaetes. The spaces in the body which are not filled up by this tissue are called sinuses, and in many species contain a fluid very much like true blood. Reduction of the blood circulatory system with the assumption of much of its function by the coelomic spaces has been a general trend of leech specialization.

Respiration is carried on at the surface of the body, oxygen being taken into, and carbon dioxide given off by, many blood capillaries in the skin. Waste

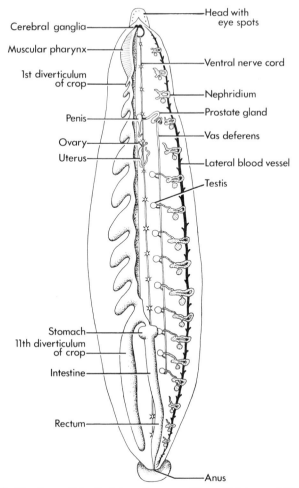

Cerebral ganglia

Muscular pharynx

1st diverticulum of crop

Penis

Ovary

Uterus

Stomach

11th diverticulum of crop

Intestine

Rectum

Head with eye spots

Ventral nerve cord

Nephridium

Prostate gland

Vas deferens

Lateral blood vessel

Testis

Anus

Fig. 8-32. *Hirudo medicinalis*, internal organs. (From Shipley and MacBride.)

products are extracted from the blood and coelomic fluid by seventeen pairs of *nephridia* (Fig. 8–32) which resemble those of the earthworm (Fig. 8–16), but frequently lack the internal opening.

Leeches are *hermaphroditic* (Fig. 8–31), but the eggs of one animal are fertilized by spermatozoa from another leech. The *spermatozoa* arise in the nine pairs of segmentally arranged *testes* (Fig. 8–32): they pass into the *vas deferens*, then into a convoluted tube called the *epididymus*, where they are fastened into bundles called *spermatophores*, and are finally deposited within the body of another leech by means of the muscular *penis*. The *eggs* arise in the *ovaries* of which there is a single pair; they pass into the *oviducts*, then into the *uterus*, and finally out through the *genital pore* ventrally situated in segment XI. *Copulation* and the formation of a *cocoon* are similar to these processes in the earthworm.

(2) Other Hirudinea

Hirudo medicinalis (Figs. 8–29 and 8–32) has served to illustrate the principal characteristics of this class. The leeches are also known as "blood suckers," although not all leeches feed on blood. Some are predators on small invertebrates which they swallow whole. Variations from the type described are indicated in the following descriptions.

Order 1. Acanthobdellida. Setae present on anterior end of body; no anterior sucker; parasitic on fish. Includes only the single genus, *Acanthobdella*, which differs so from other leeches it is sometimes separated into its own subclass. Found only in Eurasia.

Order 2. Rhynchobdellida. Both suckers present; no setae; without jaws; proboscis can be protruded from mouth; blood colorless; segments usually of three or four, rarely five, rings; fresh-water and salt-water species.

FAMILY 1. PISCICOLIDAE. Mostly marine leeches (Fig. 8–33, A). A few fresh-water species, mostly parasites of fish. Body long; more than three annuli on each segment; suckers pedunculate. *Piscicola* contains species parasitic on a variety of fish. *Cystobranchus verrilli* possesses 11 pairs of brownish or purplish papiliform gill-vesicles along the sides of the body, these are larger and more evident on preserved leeches than those of *Piscicola*.

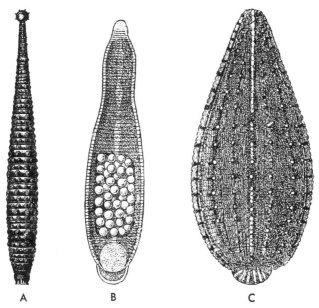

A   B   C

Fig. 8-33. Leeches. (A) *Pontobdella muricata*, a green-colored marine species that attacks rays and sharks. (B) *Helobdella algira*, a species that transmits trypanosomes to frogs. Ventral view showing eggs. (C) *Placobdella catenigera*, a species that transmits hemogregarines to tortoises. (A, after Bourne; B, C, after Brumpt.)

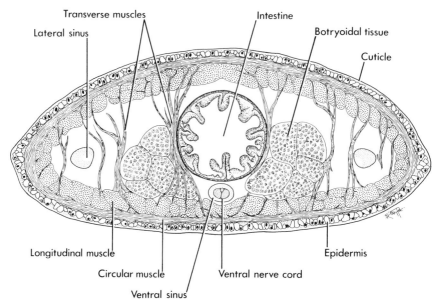

Transverse muscles Intestine
Lateral sinus Botryoidal tissue
Cuticle
Longitudinal muscle Epidermis
Circular muscle Ventral nerve cord
Ventral sinus

Fig. 8-34. Leech. Cross-section showing principal features of the midregion.

FAMILY 2. GLOSSIPHONIIDAE. Fresh-water species; each segment with three annuli; usually very flat and broad near the posterior; anterior sucker fused with the body; posterior sucker distinct. *Placobdella parasitica* occurs under stones or attached to turtles. The body is broad, flat, and greenish or yellowish. *Helobdella stagnalis* is a very active, small species that feeds on snails. It can be recognized by a small brownish plate on the dorsal surface of segment VIII and the general grayish or pinkish color. *Hemiclepsis marginata* attacks frogs and toads. It is greenish with longitudinal stripes. Glossiphonid leeches are very commonly found with eggs or young in a pouch-like area on the ventral surface (Fig. 8–33, B). Undulations by the parent leech insure an adequate supply of oxygen for the developing leeches.

Order 3. Gnathobdellida. Leeches mostly with jaws; no proboscis present; red blood; fresh-water and terrestrial species.

Suborder 1. Gnathobdellae. Jaws with teeth present.

FAMILY 1. HIRUDINIDAE. Each segment with five rings; three toothed jaws; five pairs of eyes. *Hirudo medicinalis* has been described. *Haemopis marmoratis*, the horse leech, is about 10 cm long; it lives in mud near fresh water and feeds principally on worms, snails, etc., occasionally sucking blood. *Macrobdella decora* is very common in fresh water and sucks blood avidly from frogs, fish, cattle, man, etc., although it also eats other small animals. It is easily recognized by its orange ventral surface.

FAMILY 2. HAEMADIPSIDAE. Terrestrial leeches of the tropics and subtropics, especially South East Asia; membraneous fold around suckers;

blood feeders. Found in moist areas where they will extend from the tips of vegetation to attach to passing mammals by pointing their anterior sucker toward warm objects moving by them.

Suborder 2. Pharyngobdellae. Leeches with three muscular ridges in place of jaws. Represented principally by the family Erpobdellidae, the worm leeches. These leeches lack teeth and are not blood feeders but are carnivores that feed on small invertebrates. *Erpobdella punctata* is common in ponds and streams. It has three pairs of eyes; is about 8 cm long; and is brownish-black with four rows of black spots along the dorsal surface.

5 / Class V. Echiuroidea

The class Echiuroidea is sometimes considered as a separate phylum. The members show relationships with the Sipunculida and Annelida. They are included here because of their annelid type nervous system; nephridia, several pair in some; circulatory system; setae; and trochophore larvae. The prostomium is well developed as a proboscis which is used for locomotion, for capturing prey, and as an organ of sense. Sexes are separate. All are marine-bottom dwellers. *Urechis caupo*, the "innkeeper," is an interesting west coast species that lives and feeds in a U-shaped burrow. It uses a mucous net to gather food in a manner much as did *Chaetopterus*. When it swallows the net, any lost particles are quickly seized by one of the commensals living with it in the burrow. The scale worm, *Hesperonoe adventor* lives only in association with *Urechis*. Other commensals usually encountered with *Urechis* include a

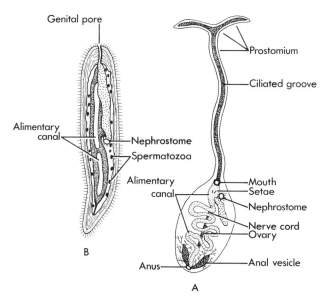

Fig. 8-35. Echiuroidea. *Bonellia viridis.* (A) Female. (B) Male from nephridium of female. (After Spengler, modified.)

pea crab, goby fish, and a small clam. One reason *Urechis* is a favorable source of material for embryological studies is that eggs and sperm can be removed from them during most of the year. *Urechis* has some peculiarities found also in some distant phyla: a siphon parallels part of the intestine, the posterior portion of the intestine becomes engorged with water taken in through the anus for respiration, and the circulatory system is aided by ciliary circulation of coelomic fluid (as well as by peristaltic movements) although the blood vascular system is reduced.

The other echiuroids possess an annelid-type closed blood vascular system. *Echiurus pallasi* possesses a spoon-shaped proboscis and 22 body rings. In *Thalassema melitta* the proboscis is somewhat pointed. This species often occurs in sand-dollar shells. *Bonellia viridis* (Fig. 8–35) is supplied in the female with a very long proboscis, which is bifurcated at the end; the male is a small turbellarian-like ciliated organism that lives in the segmental organ of the female.

6 / Annelids in General

Morphology. Three morphological characteristics of the Annelida are especially worthy of notice: (1) metamerism, (2) the coelom, and (3) the trochophore stage in development.

Metamerism. The segmentation of the body as exhibited in annelids is called *metamerism*, and is here encountered for the first time. This type of structure is of considerable interest, because the most successful groups in the animal kingdom, the Arthropoda and Vertebrata, have their parts metamerically arranged. How this condition has been brought about is still doubtful, but many theories have been proposed to account for it. According to one view the body of a metameric animal has evolved from that of a nonsegmented animal by transverse fission. The individuals thus produced remained united end to end and gradually became integrated both morphologically and physiologically so that their individualities were united into one complex individuality. Some zoologists maintain that the segmental arrangement of organs such as nephridia, blood vessels, and reproductive organs has been caused by the division of a single ancestral organ, and not by the formation of new organs as the fission theory demands.

True metamerism, as exhibited by annelids, should not be confused with the *pseudometamerism* of the tapeworms (Fig. 5–19). The proglottids of the tapeworms are individuals budded off from the posterior end of the scolex and differ from one another only in the degree of development. The tapeworm may be considered a row of incomplete individuals. Annelids add new segments by budding from the front of the last segment (the *pygidium*) and thus have the oldest segments at the anterior end, as do other segmented animals.

The Coelom. The coelom has already been defined as a cavity in the mesoderm lined by an epithelium; into it the excretory organs open, and from its walls the reproductive cells originate.

The importance of the coelom should be clearly understood, since it has played a prominent role in the progressive development of complexity of structure. The appearance of this cavity between the digestive tract and body wall brought about great physiological changes and is correlated with the origin of nephridia for transporting waste products out of the body, and of genital ducts for the exit of eggs and spermatozoa. The coelom also affected the distribution of nutritive substances within the body, since it contains a fluid which takes up material absorbed by the alimentary canal and carries it to the tissues. Excretory matter finds its way into the coelomic fluid and thence out of the body through the nephridia.

So important is the coelom considered by most zoologists that the Metazoa are frequently separated into two groups: (1) the Acoelomata without a coelom, and (2) the Coelomata with a coelom. The Porifera, Coelenterata, and Ctenophora are undoubtedly Acoelomata. Likewise the Annelida, Echinodermata, Arthropoda, Mollusca, and Chordata are certainly Coelomata. The Aschelminthes and a number of other groups with a body cavity having a different development are grouped in the (3) Pseudocoelomata, or those with no epithelium lining the cavity in the mesoderm.

The Trochophore. The term *trochophore* has been applied to the larval stages of a number of marine animals. The description and figures of the development of *Polygordius* (Fig. 8–27) are sufficient to indicate the peculiarities of this larva.

Many other marine annelids pass through a trochophore stage during their life history; those that do not are supposed to have lost this step during the course of evolution.

Because a trochophore also appears in the development of animals belonging to other groups, for example, Mollusca, Nemertinea, and Bryozoa, and resembles very closely certain Rotifera, the conclusion has been reached by some embryologists that these groups of animals are all descended from a common hypothetical ancestor, the trochozoan. Strong arguments have been advanced both for and against this theory.

Physiology. Among the interesting modifications encountered among various annelids are a variety of adaptations with respiratory value. These include (1) *gills*, especially in the polychaetes; (2) *behavioral patterns*, such as the undulations of the posterior of tubificid worms under conditions of low dissolved oxygen; (3) presence of *respiratory pigments*, which increase the oxygen carrying capacity of the blood; and (4) the *ability to respire anerobically* for short periods by utilizing stored glycogen. The blood vascular system is also very important in the respiration of the organism.

Locomotion varies considerably. In the polychaetes, parapodia of opposite sides are out of phase and accompanying undulations of the body are lateral in forms such as *Nereis*. In oligochaetes and leeches opposite sides are in phase in their movements. Forms such as *Lumbricus* have waves of alternate contraction and extension of segments which travel the length of the animal. Leeches swim by undulating in a dorso-ventral plane or creep by bending and straightening in the same plane while alternately attaching and releasing anterior then posterior suckers. The *hydrostatic skeleton* is essential to locomotion. Also of great importance in coordinating these locomotor movements is the structure and function of the nervous system. The latter topic is thoroughly reviewed by Bullock and Horridge (1965) and is discussed more concisely by Dales (1963). *Aeolosoma* and some others glide smoothly along propelled by cilia.

Neurosecretion is of considerable importance in the regeneration of *Nereis*. Neurosecretory cells are localized in the brain of annelids. Their secretions reach the site of action via the blood stream and thus function as endocrine substances. Thus, a tail-less, brain-less nereid will not regenerate a tail well, but will if brain tissue is implanted although neuronal connections are not reestablished. Neurosecretions have been demonstrated to inhibit metamorphosis in some polychaetes but are required for the development of mature sperm in *Hirudo*. They are important in the regulation of salt and water balance in *Lumbricus*.

Ecology.   Aside from their role in the food chain and energy cycle, which is considerable in some habitats, annelids have a great role to play in the physical modification of soils and shallow marine bottom deposits. Many species pass large tonnages of substrate through their collective alimentary canals while relocating it within or upon the surface of each acre over a period of a year. The agricultural value of land is usually enhanced in the process. Tube-building polychaetes may stabilize drifting marine bottoms and provide a habitat for a different biological community than would otherwise occur there.

Accumulation and transfer of pesticides via earthworms has been of importance in indicating the hazards which may affect man if he carelessly pollutes his environment.

Interrelations and Phylogeny of the Annelids.   The polychaetes appear to be the simplest of the annelids, other than the enigmatic Archiannelida. Polychaetes show a range in structure of nephridia including those with flame cell elements, their gonads show less specialization in structure, and they are marine animals. The oligochaetes probably arose from the polychaetes or their ancestral stock and adaptation for burrowing resulted in reduced head specialization, loss of parapodia, and reduction of setae. The Oligochaeta and Hirudinea show close relationships in their reproductive structures and habits, and *Acanthobdella* is of somewhat intermediate morphology. The Aeolosomatidae have been considered to be archiannelids by some and the Branchiobdellidae were formerly included with the leeches although most recent classifications include both in the Oligochaeta. The

Echiuroidea possess sufficient annelid characteristics to justify their inclusion in this phylum. They seem to have evolved from the Polychaeta but have lost many of the features of this class, probably as a result of their sedentary mode of life.

The History of Our Knowledge of the Annelida.   The annelids were by early zoologists included with other worms in the group Vermes but were separated by Cuvier in 1798 from the unsegmented worms and designated by Lamarck the Annelids. This group was sometime later (1820) divided by Savigny into four subdivisions, (1) the Nereideae, (2) the Serpuleae, (3) the Lumbricineae, and (4) the Hirudineae. The terms Polychaeta and Oligochaeta we owe to Grube (1851).

References to Literature on the Annelida

BELL, A. W. 1962. Enchytraeids (Oligochaeta) from various parts of the world. *Trans. Am. Microsc. Soc.*, **81**:158–178.

BARNES, R. D. 1965. Tube-building and feeding in chaetopterid polychaetes. *Biol. Bull.*, **129**:217–233.

BULLARD, R. W. 1964. Animals in aquatic environments: annelids and molluscs. In *Handbook of Physiology*. Section 4: Adaptation to the Environment, pp. 683–695. Am. Physiol. Soc., Washington.

BULLOCK, T. H., and G. A. HORRIDGE. 1965. *Structure and Function in the Nervous System of Invertebrates*. W. H. Freeman, San Francisco. 2 vols., 1,719 pp.

CARSON, R. 1962. *Silent Spring*. Houghton Mifflin, Boston. 368 pp.

CHAPMAN, G. 1958. The hydrostatic skeleton in the invertebrates. *Biol. Rev.*, **33**:338–371.

DALES, R. P. 1963. *Annelids*. Hutchinson, London. 200 pp.

DARWIN, C. 1881. *The Formation of Vegetable Mould through the Action of Worms*. 1898 printing. Appleton, New York. 326 pp.

GOODNIGHT, C. J. 1959. Oligochaeta. In W. T. EDMONDSON. *Fresh-Water Biology*, pp. 522–537. 2nd ed. Wiley, New York. 1,248 pp.

GORDON, D. C. JR. 1966. The effects of the deposit feeding polychaete *Pectinaria gouldii* on the intertidal sediments of Barnstable Harbor. *Limnol. and Oceanog.*, **11**:327–332.

HARTMAN, O. 1959. Polychaeta. In W. T. EDMONDSON. *Fresh-Water Biology*, pp. 538–541. 2nd ed. Wiley, New York.

KAMEMOTO, F. I., K. N. KATO, and L. E. TUCKER. 1966. Neurosecretion and salt and water balance in the Annelida and Crustacea. *Am. Zoologist*, **6**:213–219.

MANN, K. H. 1962. *Leeches (Hirudinea)*. Pergamon Press, New York.

MOORE, J. P. 1959. Hirudinea. In W. T. EDMONDSON. *Fresh-Water Biology*, pp. 542–557. 2nd ed. Wiley, New York.

PETTIBONE, M. H. 1963. Marine Polychaete Worms of the New England Region. *Bull.* 227, Part 1. U.S. Nat. Mus., Washington. 356 pp.

RODALE, R. 1961. *The Challenge of Earthworm Research*. Soil and Health Foundation, Emmaus, Penna. 102 pp.

Chapter IX

Phylum Mollusca

T HE PHYLUM Mollusca includes the snails, slugs, clams, oysters, octopods, and nautili. They exhibit primitive bilateral symmetry, are unsegmented, and many of them possess a shell of calcium carbonate. Mussels, clams, snails, and squids do not appear at first sight to have much in common, but a closer examination reveals several structures possessed by all. One of these is an organ called the *foot*—which the snail (Fig. 9–1, A) uses for creeping over surfaces, the clam (B) generally for plowing through mud, and the squid (C) for seizing prey. In each animal there is a space called the *mantle cavity* between the main body and an enclosing envelope, the *mantle*. The *anus* opens into the mantle cavity.

The mollusks are divided into five classes according to their symmetry and the characters of the foot, shell, mantle, gills, and nervous system.

Definition. Phylum Mollusca: clams, snails, squids, octopods. Triploblastic, bilaterally symmetrical animals; anus and coelom present; no segmentation; shell usually present; the characteristic organ is a ventral muscular foot.

CLASS I. AMPHINEURA, the chitons, with bilateral symmetry, often a shell of eight transverse calcareous plates, and many pairs of gill filaments.

CLASS II. GASTROPODA, the snails, slugs, whelks, etc., with asymmetry and usually a spirally coiled shell.

CLASS III. SCAPHOPODA, the elephants'-tusk shells, with tubular shell and mantle.

CLASS IV. CEPHALOPODA, the squids, cuttlefishes, octopods, and nautili, with bilateral symmetry, a foot divided into arms provided with suckers, and a well-developed nervous system concentrated in the head.

CLASS V. PELECYPODA, the clams, mussels, oysters, and scallops, usually with bilateral symmetry, a shell of two valves, and a mantle of two lobes.

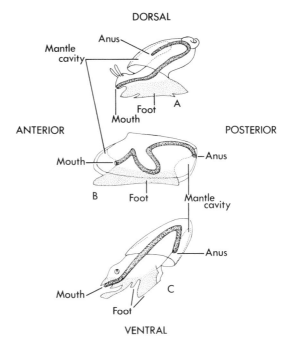

Fig. 9-1. Diagrams of three types of mollusks. (A) A prosobranch gastropod. (B) A pelecypod. (C) A cephalopod. Compare the form of the foot and its regions and the relations of the visceral hump to the anteroposterior and dorsoventral axes. (From Shipley and MacBride, after Lankester.)

1 / Class I. Amphineura

(1) Neopilina galatheae

Neopilina galatheae (Fig. 9–2) is one of very few living members of the Monoplacophora. Fossil members are known from Cambrian rocks. The similarity of the shell to limpet shells made them appear closely related to the gastropods until the soft parts of the living animal were discovered. *Neopilina* is a deep-sea mollusk of special interest, because it illustrates the primitive occurrence of metamerism in mollusks. This strengthens the concept of a close phylogenetic connection between annelids and mollusks that had been suspected prior to the discovery of *Neopilina* in 1952. Metamerism, or the serial repetition of homologous structures, in this genus is probably ultimately derived from a segmented form ancestral to annelids and mollusks.

External Features. The single, bilaterally symmetrical *shell* is low, somewhat patelliform, and exogastrically coiled. The largest specimen known is 37 mm long, 35 mm wide and 13 mm high. *Neopilina* appears somewhat chiton-like from the ventral surface (Fig. 9–2). The central circular *foot* is separated from the encircling mantle by a *pallial groove*, which contains five pairs of lamellated gills with a ciliated epithelium. The head is inconspicuous with two small pre-oral tentacles and two oral tentacle tufts around the *mouth*.

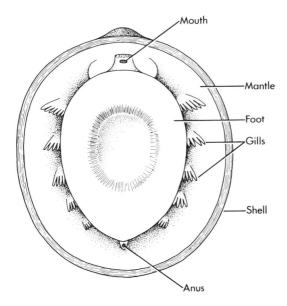

Fig. 9-2. *Neopilina.* Ventral view. (Modified from several authors after Lemche.)

Anterior to the mouth is a velar ridge with two flaps. Unpaired anterior and posterior lips border the mouth. A feeding furrow extends between velar ridge and tentacle tufts. At the opposite, and posterior, end is the *anus.*

Internal Features. Aside from the metameric appearance of some structures, *Neopilina* presents rather generalized molluscan anatomy.

Alimentary Canal. Behind the oral cavity is the *pharynx,* which contains a *radula.* Radulae are usually chitinous, tooth-bearing ribbons borne on a tonguelike structure, the *odontophore.* They are found in all classes of mollusks except the Pelecypoda. In *Neopilina* the radula extends from a sheath to act against a radular plate on the opposite side of the pharynx. The *esophagus* leads from the pharynx to the *stomach.* The stomach contains a *crystalline style.* This peculiar molluscan feature is found in a variety of mollusks and is usually embedded in a ciliated style sack, which rotates the style thus pulling in a mucous food ribbon. The *intestine* contains six coils in contrast to the straight intestine of other amphineurans. A *rectum* leads from intestine to anus.

Systems Showing Metamerism. The *muscular system* is complex. The foot retractors show a segmental type arrangement. The metameric condition of *Neopilina* is also evident in the six pair of *nephridia,* which are located in the pallial fold. The nephridia open to the coelomic spaces by nephrostomes, and the nephridiopores are near the bases of the gills. Two pair of nephridia also serve as reproductive ducts. The circulatory system shows some evidence of metamerism in that there are efferent gill vessels from the five metamerically arranged gills. These vessels lead to two pair of *atria,* which fill the single pair of *ventricles.* Other mollusks have only a single ventricle. The ventricles of *Neopilina* are on opposite sides of the rectum. This position makes it likely that the pelecypod heart with its perirectal ventricle has arisen from the monoplacophoran type by fusion of the ventricles around the rectum. This tends to substantiate the primitive molluscan nature of *Neopilina*. Blood is pumped from the ventricle via the dorsal aorta to hemocoelic spaces and vascular sinuses.

The *nervous system* is similar to that of the chitons. There is a *circum-oral nerve ring*. The main nerves are lateral nerve cords and pedal nerve cords. Paired *statocysts* are located in the body wall behind the tentacle tufts. The *reproductive system* consists primarily of gonads located between intestine and foot. Sexes are separate. The gonads contain cavities in addition to two sets of coelomic cavities. Reproductive products escape via two pair of nephridia.

Ecology. *Neopilina* was trawled up from very cold water (2°C) on a soft bottom at a 3,570 meter depth along with a varied catch of fish, echinoderms, crustaceans, and mollusks as well as a few annelids, coelenterates, and sponges. Their food seems to consist of radiolarians and other materials of the bottom.

Although very few specimens of *Neopilina* have been obtained, a very complete account of their anatomy is found in Lemche and Wingstrand (1959).

(2) Other Amphineura

This class contains fewer than a thousand species of marine mollusks that usually live on the bottom near the shore. Chitons are the most commonly encountered amphineurans. Their shell consists of eight separate plates (Fig. 9–3). Otherwise there is a general correspondence to *Neopilina* as is shown by

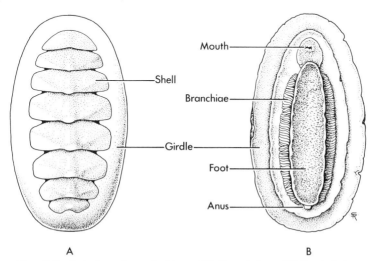

Fig. 9-3. Polyplacophora. A chiton. (A) Dorsal view. (B) Ventral view.

comparison with the following general description of a chiton. The body (Fig. 9–3) is elongated and bilaterally symmetrical with the *mouth* at one end and the *anus* at the other end. The *head*, which is sheltered by the mouth, is usually not well developed and lacks both tentacles and eyes. The dorsal surface is occupied by the *mantle*, in which calcareous spicules are embedded and sometimes a continuous covering of plates (Fig. 9–3) with a surrounding scaly girdle. A narrow *mantle cavity* extends along the sides of the body; that part of the mantle that forms this cavity is known as the *girdle*. The *foot* is flat. A *radula* (Fig. 9–4) is usually present. The *nervous system* consists of a circumesophageal ring and two pairs of longitudinal cords, which innervate the foot (pedal) and mantle (pallial). No definite ganglia are present, but the nerve cords are supplied with ganglion cells. In the chitons the valves of the shell are pierced by branching canals through which nerves reach the surface of the mantle where they connect with sense organs called shell eyes.

The *alimentary canal* (Fig. 9–4) extends in a straight line from the mouth to the anus; ducts from mucous, salivary, and hepatic glands open into it.

Fig. 9-4. Amphineura. *Proneomenia gerlachei.* (A) Right half of anterior part of body, left-side view. (B) Right half of posterior part of body, left-side view. (From Cooke.)

There is a heart near the posterior end, an aorta, and two large sinuses. The blood is, of course, oxygenated in the gills. Two kidneys are present; each possesses a duct that opens outside the body near the posterior end and a duct that opens into the pericardium. The eggs usually give rise to trochophore larvae. Chitons occur as fossils in the Cambrian Period.

The Amphineura may be divided into three orders.

Order 1. Monoplacophora.   The only living representatives are *Neopilina*, which has been described, and several related species. A single shell.

Order 2. Polyplacophora.   Polyplacaphora are known as chitons. They are elliptical in outline, have a flat foot which occupies the entire ventral surface, and a convex dorsal surface characterized by a series of eight transverse overlapping calcareous plates. The mantle groove contains from 4 to 80 pairs of ctenidia-like gills. Chitons creep about slowly on the sea bottom giving preference to smooth stones. The overlapping valves of the shell allow them to bend the body and even to roll up into a ball. They feed chiefly on algae. The sexes are separate.

Chaetopleura apiculata is a chiton that is common in shallow water along the Atlantic coast from Cape Cod to Florida. It is oval in shape and about 17 mm long and 10 mm broad. *Chiton tuberculatus* is common in the West Indies. It is about 8 cm long and 0.5 cm broad. *Amicula stelleri*, the giant Pacific Coast chiton, may reach 30 cm.

Order 3. Aplacophora.   The name Solenogastres is also used for this order. They are often wormlike in appearance; the shell is absent; the foot is reduced or lost; the radula may be reduced or absent; the gills are located in the cloaca. Certain species live among corals and hydroids and eat these polyps, and other species feed on protozoans and other minute organisms. This order is believed by some zoologists to be more closely allied with the primitive worms, such as the Archiannelida, than with the mollusks. *Neomenia carinata* is a species living in the North Atlantic; it has a short, thick body about 2.5 cm long; is covered with spicules; but lacks a radula. *Chaetoderma nitidulum* occurs in the Gulf of Maine and elsewhere; it is slender and wormlike, being about 25 mm long and only 2 mm broad.

2 / Class II. Gastropoda

(1) Helix pomatia—A Terrestrial Snail

External Features.   The body of a snail consists of a *head, neck, foot,* and *visceral hump*, as shown in Figure 9–5. The *head* bears two pairs of *tentacles*: (1) a short anterior pair containing the olfactory nerves, and (2) a longer pair containing the *eyes*. The *mouth* is in front and below the tentacles; beneath

Fig. 9-5. *Helix.* Side view with shell removed to show internal organs. (Modified after Root.)

the mouth is the opening of the pedal *mucous gland.* The *foot* is broad and flat; it is a muscular organ of locomotion with a mucous-secreting integument (Fig. 9–6). Both the foot and head may be withdrawn into the *shell.*

The *spiral shell* encloses the visceral hump, consisting of parts of the digestive, circulatory, respiratory, excretory, and reproductive systems. The *mantle* lines the shell, and is thin except where it joins the foot; here it forms a thick collar, which secretes most of the shell. An opening beneath this collar is the *respiratory aperture* leading into the mantle cavity. The *anus* opens just back of this aperture. The *genital pore* is on the side of the head.

**Anatomy and Physiology.   *Digestion.*   The general anatomy of a snail is shown in Figure 9–5. The *digestive organs* include a *buccal mass, esophagus, salivary glands, crop, stomach, digestive glands, intestine, rectum,* and *anus.*

The *food* is chiefly, if not entirely, vegetation, such as lettuce. This is scraped up by a horny jaw or *mandible* and devoured after being rasped into fine particles by a band of teeth termed the *radula* (Fig. 9–7). The radula and the cartilages and muscles that move it backward and forward constitute the buccal mass. The *salivary glands,* which lie one on either side of the crop, pour their secretion by means of the *salivary ducts* into the buccal cavity, where it is mixed with the food.

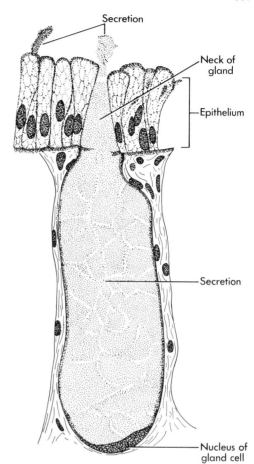

Fig. 9-6. Mucous cell from the edge of the mantle of a terrestrial snail. (From Dahlgren and Kepner.)

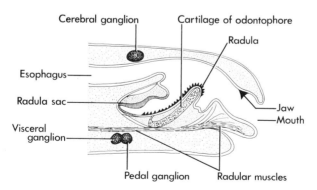

Fig. 9-7. *Helix*, a snail. Vertical longitudinal section through head. (After Meisenheimer, modified.)

The *esophagus* leads to the *crop*, and from here the food enters the *stomach*. The two *digestive glands* occupy a large part of the visceral hump. They secrete enzymes such as amylase, which converts starch into glucose, and are comparable to the pancreas in vertebrate animals. This secretion enters the *stomach* and aids in digestion. Additional digestive secretions are supplied by cells lining the stomach and intestine and by symbiotic bacteria. The latter seem to be essential for digestion of cellulose and chitin. Absorption takes place chiefly in the *intestine*, and the feces pass out the *anus*.

Circulation and Respiration.   The *blood* of the snail consists of a colorless plasma containing corpuscles and serves to transport nutriment, oxygen, and waste products from one part of the body to another. The heart lies in the *pericardial cavity*. The muscular *ventricle* forces the blood through the blood vessels by rhythmical pulsations. One large *aorta* arises at the apex of the ventricle; this gives rise at once to a *posterior branch*, which supplies chiefly the digestive gland, stomach, and ovotestis, and an *anterior branch*, which carries blood to the head and foot. The blood passes from the arterial capillaries into *venous capillaries* and flows through these into *sinuses*. *Veins* lead from these sinuses to the walls of the mantle cavity, where the blood, after taking in oxygen and giving off carbon dioxide, enters the *pulmonary vein* and is carried to the single *auricle* and finally into the ventricle again.

Excretion.   The glandular *kidney* lies near the heart. Its duct, the *ureter* or *renal duct*, runs along beside the rectum and opens near the anus.

Nervous System (Figs. 9–8 and 9–9).   Most of the nervous tissue of the snail is concentrated just back of the buccal mass and forms a ring about the esophagus. There are five sets of ganglia and four ganglionic swellings. The *supraesophageal* or *cerebral ganglia* are paired and lie above the esophagus.

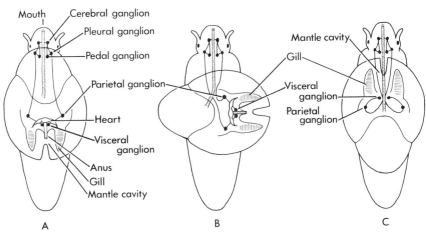

Fig. 9-8. Nervous system of Gastropoda as related to torsion. (A) Supposed ancestral condition. (B) Torsion 90°. (C) Torsion 180°. (After Naef, from Borradaile and Potts, modified.)

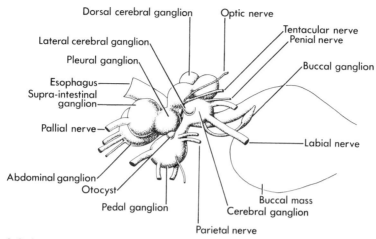

Fig. 9-9. *Lymnaea stagnalis;* central nervous system, right-side view. (From Pelseneer.)

Nerves extend anteriorly from them, ending in the two *buccal ganglia,* the two *eyes,* the two *ocular ganglionic swellings,* the two *olfactory ganglionic swellings,* and the mouth. Nerves called commissures connect the supra-esophageal ganglia with the ganglia, which lie beneath the esophagus. Here are four pairs of ganglia lying close together—the *pedal, pleural, parietal,* and *visceral.* Nerves pass from them to the visceral hump and the basal parts of the body.

Sense Organs.   Both the foot and the tentacles are sensitive to contact, and are liberally supplied with nerves. Each long tentacle bears an *eye.* These eyes are probably not organs of sight, but only sensitive to light of certain intensities. Many snails feed mostly at night, and their eyes may be adapted to dim light.

Snails possess a sense of *smell,* because some of them are able to locate food, which is hidden from sight, at a distance of 18 inches. We are not certain where the sense of smell is located, but investigators are inclined to believe that the small tentacles are the *olfactory organs.* A sense of *taste* is doubtful.

There are two organs of equilibrium (*statocysts*), one on either side of the supraesophageal ganglia. They are minute vesicles containing a fluid in which are suspended small calcaerous bodies (*statoliths*). Nerves connect them with the supraesophageal ganglia.

Locomotion.   The snail moves from place to place with a gliding motion. The slime gland that opens just beneath the mouth deposits a film of slime, and on this the animal moves by means of wavelike contractions of the longitudinal muscular fibers of the foot. *Snails* have been observed to travel 2 inches per minute.

Reproduction.   Some gastropods are dioecious; others are monoecious. *Helix* is *hermaphroditic,* but the union of two animals is necessary for the

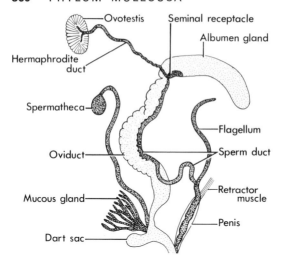

Fig. 9-10. *Helix*, a snail. Reproductive organs. (After Meisenheimer, modified.)

fertilization of the eggs, because the spermatozoa of an individual do not unite with the eggs of the same animal. The *spermatozoa* arise in the *ovotestis* (Fig. 9–10); they pass through the coiled *hermaphroditic duct* and into the *sperm duct*; they then enter the *vas deferens* and are transferred to the *vagina* of another animal by means of a cylindrical *penis*, which is protruded from the *genital pore*.

The *eggs* also arise in the *ovotestis* and are carried through the *hermaphroditic duct*; they receive material from the *albumen gland* and then pass into the *uterine canal*; they move from here down the *oviduct* into the *vagina*, where they are *fertilized* by spermatozoa transferred to the *seminal receptacle* by another snail. In almost all other land pulmonates impregnation is mutual, each animal acting during copulation as both male and female.

Helix has a dart sac that secretes a calcareous spicule, which is discharged into a potential mate. It is thought to stimulate effective copulation and thus serves as the equivalent of cupid's arrow.

(2) Other Gastropoda

The gastropods are mollusks that have become modified from the bilaterally symmetrical, unsegmented condition of their ancestors as a result of the coiling of the visceral hump and the rotation of this structure in a counterclockwise direction through an angle of 180° (Fig. 9–8). The foot is flat for creeping; the head is distinct and bears eyes and tentacles; there is usually a shell of one piece (Fig. 9–11); radulae are present; the nervous system has cerebral, pleural, visceral, and usually pedal ganglia and a visceral loop; the visceral hump is often coiled; in some species there is a trochophore larva.

Gastropods are essentially aquatic animals, although some of them live in moist places on land or have means of preventing the escape of moisture from the body such as the epiphragm of certain snails. A few are parasitic on the

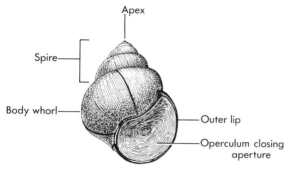

Fig. 9-11. *Viviparus*. A dextrally coiled snail showing major features of the shell and the operculum closing the aperture.

outside or inside of other animals. Both unisexual and hermaphroditic gastropods occur; most species are oviparous but a few are viviparous. Variations from the type are indicated in the following paragraphs. No classification of this group is accepted by zoologists in general; the arrangement used here includes three orders, a number of suborders, and some of the more important families.

Order 1. Prosobranchia. The large order Prosobranchia contains the majority of the gastropods, about 30,000 species, most of which are marine. The gills are in the mantle cavity anterior to the heart (hence Prosobranchia) and the visceral hump is coiled. The visceral connectives are usually twisted into a figure 8. The sexes are separate.

Suborder 1. Archaeogastropoda (Aspidobranchia). Primitive snails that have usually two gills, two auricles, and two nephridia. The gonad opens to the outside through the right nephridium.

FAMILY 1. ACMAEIDAE (Fig. 9–12, A). Limpets. Marine; shell conical, no spiral; one gill; one auricle. Ex. *Acmaea testudinalis*; common on rocks in shallow water from Cape Cod northward. *A. scabra*; common on West Coast.

A   B   C

Fig. 9-12. Archaeogastropoda. (A) *Acmaea*, a limpet. (B) *Haliotus*, an abalone. (C) *Trochus*. (A and B from Tryon.)

FAMILY 2. HALIOTIDAE (Fig. 9–12, B). Ear Shells. Marine; shell with flat spiral, very large aperture; spiral series of holes near left margin; two gills, right gill small; two auricles; two nephridia; foot very large, with epipodia projecting through holes in shell. Ex. *Haliotis rufescens*: red abalone, common along coast of California south of Cape Mendocino; abalone shells are made into jewelry, buttons, and buckles, and are used for inlaying; the shells of some tropical abalones are greatly reduced.

FAMILY 3. TROCHIDAE (Fig. 9–12, C). Marine; shell usually conical; horny operculum present; one gill. Ex. *Trochus niloticus*: shell pyramidal, of value as ornament; Indian Ocean. *Margarites obscurus*: shell conical; Long Island Sound northward.

FAMILY 4. HELICINIDAE. Terrestrial, in warm regions; shell conical; operculum oval or triangular; no gills, mantle cavity serving as lung. Ex. *Helicina orbiculata*: in the United States south of Tennessee.

Suborder 2. Mesogastropoda. Snails that have one auricle, one nephridium, and one gill; gill feathered on one side; gonad opens through a separate

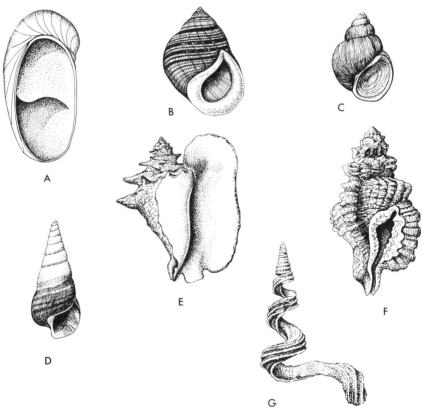

Fig. 9-13. Mesogastropoda. (A) *Crepidula.* (B) *Littorina.* (C) *Campeloma.* (D) *Pleurocera.* (E) *Strombus.* (F) *Charonia.* (G) *Vermicularia.* (A, B, E, F, from Tryon.)

duct; from several to many teeth in each row of the radula; shell usually closed with an operculum. Most of the Prosobranchia belong to this suborder of mollusks, which is the largest and also the most varied in morphology and ecological adaptations.

FAMILY 1. CAPULIDAE (Fig. 9–13, A).   Shell with inconspicuous or no spiral, but with internal shelf; operculum absent; foot broad; sedentary, attached to rocks. Ex. *Crepidula fornicata*: shell convex, with slight spiral; shelf concave, white; Nova Scotia southward, in shallow water. *C. onyx*; in clusters on West Coast mud flats.

FAMILY 2. LITTORINIDAE.   Periwinkles. Salt, brackish, and fresh water; shell conical and spiral; operculum horny; eyes at base of tentacles. Ex. *Littorina litorea* (Fig. 9–13, B): European edible periwinkle; introduced and common from Delaware Bay northward.

FAMILY 3. VIVIPARIDAE (Fig. 9–13, C).   Fresh water; cosmopolitan; shell conical; operculum horny; eyes on short stalks; viviparous. Ex. *Campeloma ponderosum*: shell thick and solid; no umbilicus (cavity in columella); aperture ovate, longer than spire; New York to Illinois southward.

FAMILY 4. PLEUROCERIDAE (Fig. 9–13, D).   Fresh water; all in North America, mostly in southern states; shell conical, elongate; operculum present; eyes sessile, at base of tentacles. Ex. *Pleurocera subulare*: long, tapering spire; Great Lakes region.

FAMILY 5. STROMBIDAE (Fig. 9–13, E).   Marine; shell usually large, solid, with large lower whorl and expanded lip; foot long, narrow, for springing; eyes at end of stalks; in warm seas. Ex. *Strombus gigas*: conch; largest mollusk in the United States; about 25 cm long; shell heavy, up to five pounds; flesh edible; shell used as horn and for making ornaments.

FAMILY 6. CYMATIIDAE (Fig. 9–13, F).   Tritons. Tropical seas. Ex. *Charonia* (*Triton*) *nodifera*: length 45 cm; shell used as war horn or shepherd's horn.

FAMILY 7. EULIMIDAE.   Shell elongate; foot long and narrow; proboscis very long; parasitic on echinoderms.

FAMILY 8. CYPRAEIDAE.   Cowries. Shell very shiny but covered by mantle in life; developing whorls of shell enclose older whorls; mantle with many sensory papillae; tropical, marine. Ex. *Zonaria spadicea*, the nut brown cowry of the southern California coast.

Suborder 3. Neogastropoda.   Snails with one auricie, one nephridium, and one gill; gill feathered on one side; typically with a pallial siphon; three or less teeth in each row of the radula; marine.

FAMILY 1. MURICIDAE (Fig. 9–14, A).   Shell rough, with rows of protuberances; central tooth of radula with three cusps; mostly tropical; food mostly other mollusks. Ex. *Urosalpinx cinereus* (Fig. 9–14, B): oyster drill; drills hole through oyster shell with radula in the proboscis; Massachusetts to Florida. *Pterynotus trialatus* of California has winglike longitudinal ridges.

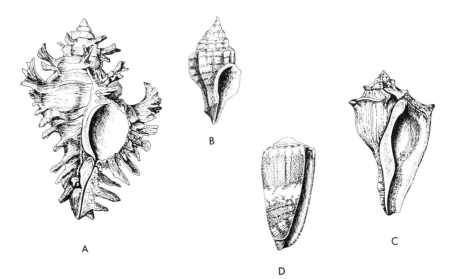

Fig. 9-14. Neogastropoda. (A) *Murex.* (B) *Urosalpinx.* (C) *Busycon.* (D) *Conus.* (A, B, and C from Tryon.)

FAMILY 2. BUCCINIDAE (Fig. 9–14, C).   Whelks. Marine. Ex. *Buccinum undatum*: New Jersey northward; used as bait for cod, and in Europe as food for man. *Busycon canaliculatum*; whelk; marine; large, heavy shell; long siphonal canal; Atlantic Coast.

Order 2. Opisthobranchia.   Sea slugs. All are marine; shell small or absent; gill when present, posterior to the heart; visceral connectives not twisted; hermaphroditic; mostly live among seaweed and under stones near shore, some pelagic; food chiefly animal; three suborders.

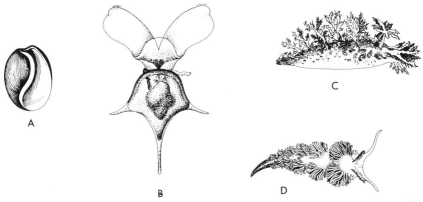

Fig. 9-15. Opisthobranchia. (A) *Haminea.* (B) *Cavolinia.* (C) *Dendronotus.* (D) *Aeolis.* (From Tryon.)

Suborder 1. Tectibranchia. Shell usually present; gills in mantle cavity.

FAMILY 1. AKERIDAE (Fig. 9–15, A). Shell external. Ex. *Haminea solitaria*: Atlantic Coast, Massachusetts to South Carolina.

FAMILY 2. APLYSIIDAE. Sea hares. Shell internal, rudimentary; body sluglike; epipodia over back; brightly colored; cosmopolitan. Ex. *Aplysia protea*: 16 cm long; Florida and West Indies.

Suborder 2. Pteropoda. Sea butterflies. Pelagic, with foot modified for swimming.

FAMILY 1. CAVOLINIIDAE (Fig. 9–15, B). Shell present; gill absent; two large epipodia (fins, hence pteropods); pelagic. Ex. *Cavolinia trispinosa*; shell with three long spines; Atlantic Coast.

FAMILY 2. CLIONIDAE. Shell and mantle absent; gill absent; foot modified as a pair of fins; proboscis usually with suckers; pelagic. Ex. *Clione limacina*: Arctic Ocean south to New York; sometimes in enormous schools which color sea; serve as food for whales.

Suborder 3. Nudibranchia. Sea slugs. Shell absent; gills present or absent.

FAMILY 1. DENDRONOTIDAE. Body long; tentacles branched; cerata (modified gills) branched in two rows on back. Ex. *Dendronotus arborescens* (Fig. 9–15, C): length, 8 cm; about 6 transparent cerata in each row; Rhode Island northward.

FAMILY 2. DORIDIDAE. Integument with spicules; mantle large; gills retractile; cosmopolitan. Ex. *Doris repanda*: gills in star-shaped group; body covered with small white tubercles; Cape Cod northward.

FAMILY 3. AEOLIDIDAE. No mantle; no spicules in integument; cerata in transverse rows along body; nematocysts in cerata from hydroids used as food. Ex. *Aeolis papillosa* (Fig. 9–15, D): 10 or 12 cerata in a row and 12 to 20 rows on each side; two pairs of cylindrical tentacles; Rhode Island northward.

FAMILY 4. ELYSIIDAE. No cerata; body ciliated. Ex. *Elysia chlorotica*: 40 mm long; bright green with white and red spots; Massachusetts to New Jersey.

Order 3. Pulmonata. Fresh-water and terrestrial snails. The characteristics of a member of this order have already been described. No gills, the mantle cavity serves as a lung; the shell is usually a simple, regular spire, sometimes rudimentary or absent; no operculum; shell closed by many land snails by temporary epiphragm of calcified slime; one or two pairs of tentacles; hermaphroditic; mostly oviparous, a few viviparous; mostly terrestrial, many in fresh water, a few marine; mostly vegetarian, a few carnivorous; many species; two suborders.

Suborder 1. Basommatrophora. Mostly in fresh water, a few terrestrial or marine; one pair of tentacles; eyes at base of tentacles; shell usually with conical spire; cosmopolitan.

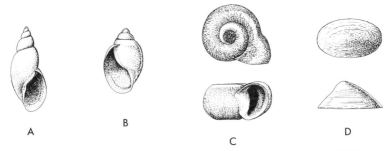

Fig. 9-16. Fresh-water Pulmonata. (A) *Lymnaea*. (*B*) *Physa*. (*C*) *Helisoma*. (D) *Ferrissia*.

FAMILY 1. LYMNAEIDAE (Fig. 9–16, A). Spire of shell acute; tentacles flattened. Ex. *Lymnaea stagnalis*: large shell with six whorls; Northern Hemisphere. There are many similar appearing species of *Lymnaea*.

FAMILY 2. PHYSIDAE (Fig. 9–16, B). Shell with large lower whorl and acute spire; tentacles filiform; cosmopolitan. Ex. *Physa gyrina* (Fig. 9–16, B): shell with five or six whorls; about 22 mm long; central states. *Aplexa hypnorum*: shell thin; body whorl not inflated; northern U.S.

FAMILY 3. PLANORBIDAE. Shell discoidal. Ex. *Helisoma trivolvis* (Fig. 9–16, C): shell sinistral and with four whorls; North America.

FAMILY 4. ANCYLIDAE (Fig. 9–16, D). Shell conical, nonspiral, with oval aperture. Ex. *Ferrissia parallelus*: river limpet; about 5 mm long; New England.

Suborder 2. Stylommatophora. Terrestrial snails; two pairs of retractile tentacles; eyes at tips of posterior tentacles; shell with conical spire, or rudi-

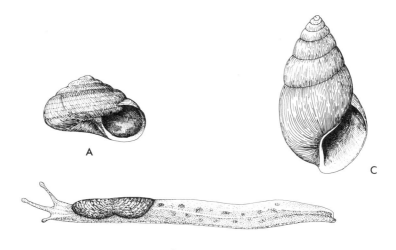

Fig. 9-17. Terrestrial Pulmonata. (A) *Triodopsis multilineata*. (*B*) *Limax*. (C) *Achatina*. (B, from Tryon.)

mentary and concealed, or absent; respiratory pore on right side; cosmopolitan.

FAMILY 1. HELICIDAE.   Shell with low, conical spire of five to seven whorls. Ex. *Helix pomatia*: French, edible snail.

FAMILY 2. POLYGYRIDAE (Fig. 9–17, A).   A large family of land snails from the temperate regions; similar to the Helicidae; with very low spire; lip usually reflected; aperture often toothed. *Polygyra, Triodopsis, Mesodon*, and *Stenotrema* are genera commonly encountered in woodlands and other moist areas of North America.

FAMILY 3. ENDODONTIDAE.   Shell conical or depressed; umbilicus open. Ex. *Anguispira alternata*: shell depressed; gregarious; eastern and Central America. *Helicodiscus parallelus*: shell disk-shaped; diameter about 4 mm; eastern states.

FAMILY 4. ACHATINIDAE (Fig. 9–17, C).   Tropical snails; long, thin shell; several species introduced in southern states. *Achatina fulica*, the giant African snail, may reach 20 cm and is a serious agricultural pest that has been introduced into several countries and Hawaii (Mead, 1961).

FAMILY 5. LIMACIDAE (Fig. 9–17, B).   Slugs; shell rudimentary concealed in mouth; nocturnal; habitat moist; mantle covers less than half of dorsal surface. Ex. *Limax maximus*: about 10 cm long; surface of body with tubercles; European species; eastern states and California. *Derocera laeve*: about 25 cm long; mantle oval; prominent tubercles on dorsal surface; introduced throughout U.S.

FAMILY 6. PHILOMYCIDAE.   Slugs; shell absent; mantle covering entire dorsal surface. Ex. *Philomycus carolinianus* about 7 cm long; eastern and central states.

3 / Class III. Scaphopoda

The Scaphopoda, or tooth shells (Fig. 9–18), are all marine mollusks of which about 12 genera and 200 living species are known; nearly 300 fossil species have also been described. The body exhibits bilateral symmetry and is enclosed in a tubular shell open at both ends. The foot is small and used for burrowing. The head is supplied with many tentacles (captacula) and contains a radula. No gills are present and the circulatory system is rudimentary. Excretory organs are paired and the duct of the right one serves as the outlet for the gametes. Sexes are separate. Development includes a trochophore, then a veliger stage. The mantle fuses ventrally to form an open cylinder.

Scaphopods are typically found in sandy ocean bottoms from one mile deep to just below low tide level. They are usually small. *Dentalium pretiosum* was used by West Coast Indians for wampum. *D. entale* is about 5 cm long by 5 mm broad and occurs from Cape Cod northward. *Dentalium* has a trilobate foot and a tapered shell. The shell of *Cadulus* is broadest near the

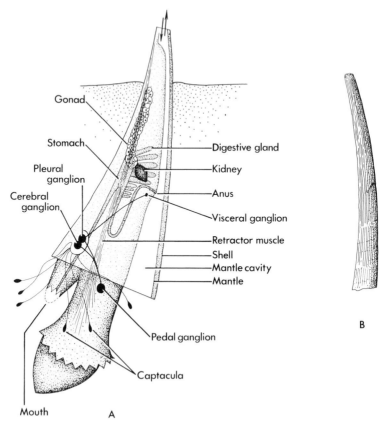

Fig. 9-18. Scaphopoda. *Dentalium* (A) Structure of specimen buried in sand, except for the end through which inhalant and exhalant currents of water pass. (B) Shell. (A, after Naef, modified from Borradaile and Potts.)

midregion of the shell. *Siphonodentalium lobatum* has an elongate vermiform foot and is only 10 mm long. It occurs in Arctic seas from New England to Europe.

4 / Class IV. Cephalopoda

(1) Loligo pealii—A Squid

Loligo pealii (Fig. 9–19) is one of the common squids found along the eastern coast of North America from Maine to South Carolina. It probably lives in deep water during the winter, but about May 1 it enters shallow water in large schools to lay its eggs. Squids are of some economic importance, because they are used as food by Chinese and Italians, and as bait for line and trawl fishing. They feed on small fish, Crustacea, and other squids, and in turn furnish food for cod and other large fish.

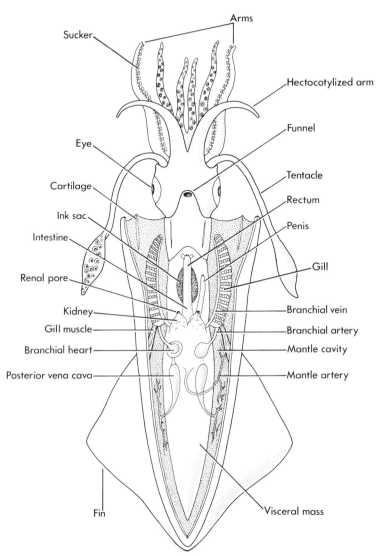

Fig. 9-19. *Loligo*, with ventral portion of mantle removed to show internal anatomy. (Modified after Root.)

Anatomy and Physiology. The body of *Loligo* is spindle-shaped. When swimming through the water the foot is anterior instead of ventral as in other classes of mollusks. The *skin* may change color rapidly; sometimes it is bluish white, at others, mottled red or brown. The color changes are produced, under nervous control, by changes in the size of *chromatophores*. The chromatophores of *Loligo* are elastic sacs filled with red or yellow pigment and changes in the amount of pigment visible result from contraction or relaxation of muscles. Squids are more heavily pigmented on the functionally dorsal surface. In that respect they resemble many vertebrates which show such obliterative countershading that they blend with a uniform background when they are illuminated from above.

The *foot* consists of 10 *lobes* and a *funnel*. Eight of the lobes are *arms* and two are long *tentacles*. The inner surfaces of both arms and tentacles are provided with *suckers*. The arms are pressed together and used for steering when the squid swims, but when capturing prey the tentacles are extended, seize the victim with their suckers, and draw it back to the arms, which hold it firmly to the mouth. The *funnel* is a muscular tube extending out beyond the edge of the *mantle collar* beneath the *head*. Water is expelled from the *mantle cavity* through it. The funnel is the principal steering organ; if it is directed forward, the jet of water passed through it propels the animal backward; if directed backward, the animal is propelled forward.

A thick muscular *mantle* encloses the visceral mass and mantle cavity. It terminates anteriorly in a collar, which articulates with the visceral mass and funnel by three pairs of interlocking surfaces. Water is drawn into the mantle cavity at the edge of the collar by the expansion of the mantle and forced out through the funnel by the contraction of the mantle. On each side of the animal is a triangular finlike projection of the mantle; these *fins* may propel the squid slowly forward or backward by their undulatory movements, or may change the direction of the squid's progress by strong upward or downward strokes.

The *head* is the short region between the arms and the mantle collar; it contains two large eyes.

The *skeletal system* consists of the pen and several cartilages.* Some of the cartilages form articulations for funnel and mantle, others protect the ganglia (Fig. 9–21) or support the eye (Fig. 9–22). The *pen* is homologous with the shell of other mollusks. In *Loligo* the pen is a thin, chitinous, feather-shaped plate concealed beneath the dorsal region of the mantle.

The *muscular system* comprises the major part of mantle, foot, funnel, and fins. Large retractor muscles of the head and funnel run through the visceral mass to their origin under the pen. The mantle is mostly circular muscle.

The *respiratory* structures consist of a pair of *gills* in the mantle cavity. The gill filaments are well supplied with blood capillaries. The blood contains the respiratory pigment *hemocyanin*.

Circulation of the blood is through a closed vascular system (Fig. 9–20). Arterial blood is forced by a muscular *systemic heart* to all parts of the body by three *aortae*: (1) anterior, (2) posterior, and (3) genital. It passes from *arterial capillaries* into *venous capillaries*, and thence into the large *veins*. From these it enters the right and left *branchial hearts*, and then is forced into the *gills* through the *branchial arteries*. In the gills the blood is oxygenated and is finally carried by the *branchial veins* back to the systemic heart.

* These skeletal parts are best left to be seen during dissection of other systems.

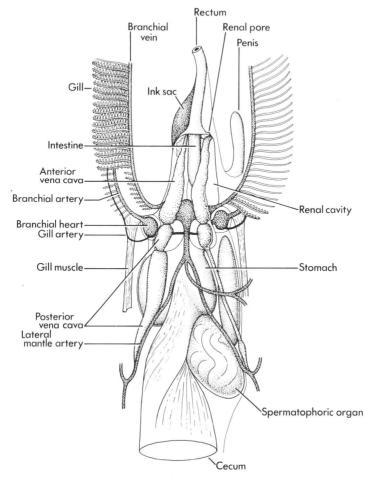

Fig. 9-20. *Loligo pealii*, male. Dissection revealing the circulatory and renal organs. (From Brooks, modified.)

The two *nephridia* or *kidneys* (Fig. 9-20) are white triangular bodies extending forward from the region of the branchial hearts and opening on either side of the intestine at the ends of small papillae.

The *digestive system* is found in the head and visceral mass. There are two powerful chitinous *jaws* in the *buccal mass*; the jaws resemble a parrot's beak and they are moved by strong muscles. A *radula* is present. Two *salivary glands* lie in the buccal mass. The third salivary gland is near the anterior end of the liver and secretes a poison, which passes through a duct to the region of the jaws. The *esophagus* leads from the buccal mass through the liver and into the stomach. The digestive gland is in two parts, the anterior liver and posterior *pancreas*. Both pass their secretions via a common duct, to the cecum. The *stomach* is muscular and mixes food and secretions from the digestive gland. Material from the stomach may pass into the intestine or into the cecum. The *cecum* is a thin-walled sac, that absorbs the digested nutrients from the food. Near its anterior is a ciliary sorting area, which removes particulate matter for elimination through the *intestine* and *rectum*. The cecum may fill up much of the visceral mass in the apex of the mantle. Because specimens are usually collected during the reproductive season, the cecum is frequently crowded into a much smaller space by the reproductive products. There is a flap on both sides of the rectum near the anus. A slim, silvery-appearing rectal gland, the *ink sac*, found above the rectum contains a dark pigment, which may be discharged from an opening just inside the anus. The ink may protect the animal in two ways. When discharged in a small cloud about the size of the cephalopod, it may divert the attention of a predator while the squid escapes. It has been found to protect the octopus from its principal enemy, the moray eel, by deadening the olfactory sense the eel uses to locate the octopus.

The *nervous system* consists of ganglia and nerves. The cerebral, pedal, visceral, suprabuccal, infrabuccal, and optic ganglia are in the head (Figs.

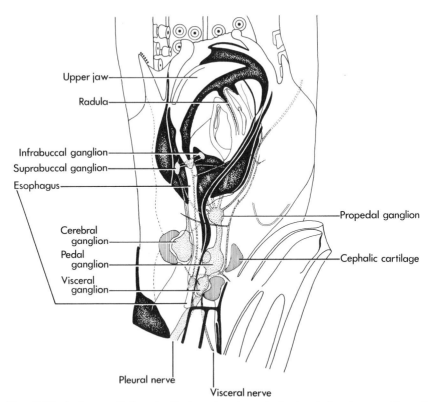

Fig. 9-21. *Loligo pealii.* Longitudinal section through the head showing ganglia and cartilages. (After Williams, from Petrunkevitch.)

9–21 and 9–22). The stellate ganglia are easily seen on both sides near the anterior junction of visceral mass and mantle. Giant nerve fibers passing from neurons in these ganglia to the circular muscles of the mantle cause simultaneous contraction of all parts of the mantle when their neurons are stimulated by giant fibers from neurons in the visceral ganglia. This is possible because larger fibers run to the more distant parts and conduction is more rapid in the larger fibers. Giant fibers from larger species of squids were the material studied for learning much of the basic information now known about nerve impulse transmission.

The *sensory organs* are two very highly developed *eyes*, two *statocysts*, and probably an *olfactory organ*. The *statocysts* are two vesicles lying side by side in the head; each contains a concretion, the *statolith*, and is probably an organ of equilibrium. The *eyes* (Fig. 9–22) are large and somewhat similar superficially to those of vertebrates. Just behind the eye, a fold projects backward under the collar and is probably olfactory.

Squids are either male or female. The *male* has a large white *testis* dorsal to the cecum. Released sperm are picked up by the *vas deferens* and transferred to the *spermatophoric* organ, a compact convoluted organ that packages the sperm into *spermatophores*. These are long slender structures, which may be seen in the thin-walled *spermatophoric sac* in which they are then stored until ejection by the *penis*. In the *female* the *ovary* and *oviduct* may be packed with eggs and fill much of the apical region of the viscera. Part of the oviduct

Fig. 9-22. Section through the eye of a cephalopod. (After Hensen, from Parker and Haswell.)

is expanded into a thick-walled *oviducal gland*. Before eggs are layed they are coated with secretions from the large *nidamental glands* located very conspicuously in the ventral part of the visceral mass. The function of the smaller accessory nidamental glands is not known. The horseshoe organ is located on the buccal membrane of the female and may serve as a seminal receptacle. The lower left arm of the male (hectocotylized arm) is used to remove spermatophores from the penis for transfer to the female. The eggs are deposited in clusters on the bottom and develop directly into small squids.

(2) Other Cephalopoda

The cephalopods are marine mollusks known as squids, devilfish, cuttlefish, octopods, and nautili. About 150 genera contain living representatives;

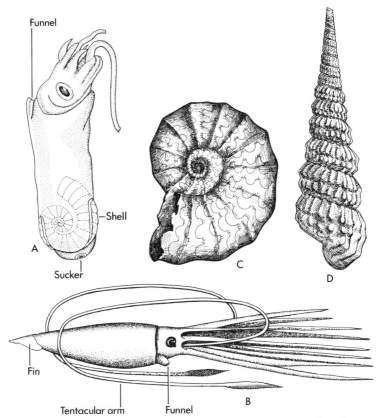

Fig. 9-23. Cephalopoda; living and fossil types. (A) Decapoda. *Spirula peronii*, a living species containing a spiral, chambered shell almost completely covered by the mantle. (B) Decapoda. *Architeuthis princeps;* the largest living invertebrate. (C) Tetrabranchia. *Ceritites nodosus*, a Triassic ammonite with shell removed so as to reveal the sutures. (D) Tetrabranchia. *Turrilites costatus*, an uncoiled ammonite from the Lower Chalk. (A, after Owen, from Cooke; B, after Verrill; C, D, from Woods.)

most of the species in the class are known only as fossils. The most striking differences between cephalopods and other mollusks are their ability to move about rapidly and their aggressive, carnivorous habits. The body is bilaterally symmetrical. The head is well developed and contains a radula and large, often complex, eyes. Part of the foot has grown around the head and gives rise to mobile, prehensile tentacles, and the other part forms the muscular funnel, or siphon through which water is expelled from the mantle cavity. The mouth lies in the midst of the tentacles. One or two pairs of gills are present in the mantle cavity. The typical cephalopod possesses a chambered shell and lives in the last and largest, chamber, but most of the living representatives are either without a shell or have one that is reduced and internal. Certain species of squids possess luminous organs that contain symbiotic, luminous bacteria; these are not transmitted from mother to offspring but enter the organs from outside each generation.

Many fossil cephalopods are now extinct. One group, the Ammonoidea, resembled *Nautilus* but had complex sutures where the septa joined the outer shell (Fig. 9–23, C). Another group, the Belemnoidea, had internal shells. The belemnites are thought to be ancestral to all living cephalopods except *Nautilus*.

The living Cephalopoda may be classified in two subclasses as follows.

Subclass 1. Nautiloidea (Tetrabranchia) (Figs. 9–23, C and D; 9–24). Calcareous shell, closely coiled; tentacles numerous and without suckers; eyes simple; no chromatophores; no ink sac; two pairs of gills and two pairs of

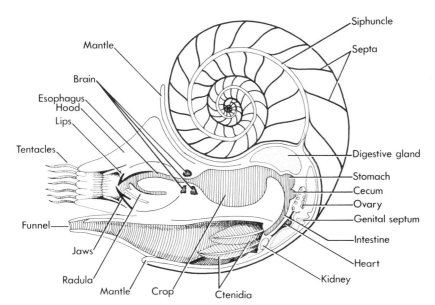

Fig. 9-24. *Nautilus pompilius.* Dissection of the "pearly nautilus" showing chambered shell and anatomy of the animal. (From Borradaile and Potts.)

nephridia. The only family that contains living representatives is the Nautilidae with one genus. Ex. *Nautilus pompilius*: pearly nautilus (Fig. 9–24); shell coiled in flat spiral; many chambers formed by curved septa; a slender tube, the siphuncle, passes through chambers near center; shell up to 25 cm in diameter; edible; Pacific and Indian Oceans.

Subclass 2. Coleoidea (Dibranchia). Shell absent or reduced and internal, calcareous or horny, not coiled; one pair of gills; one pair of nephridia; from 8 to 10 tentacles, with suckers or hooks; eyes complex; chromatophores and ink sac present; two suborders.

Suborder 1. Decapoda. Shell present, chitinous or calcareous, internal, reduced; 10 tentacles, one pair long with suckers near distal end, four pairs short with suckers along entire length.

FAMILY 1. SPIRULIDAE. An exception to other members of order, because shell is partly external and loosely coiled. Ex. *Spirula peroni* (Fig. 9–23, A): white shell; 25 mm in diameter; Caribbean Sea.

FAMILY 2. SEPIIDAE. Shell calcareous; body oval; one pair narrow fins; cosmopolitan. Ex. *Sepia officinalis*: about 20 cm long; Europe; edible.

FAMILY 3. SEPIOLIDAE. Shell chitinous, straight (called a pen); body short and broad; fins large, rounded; eyes with cornea. Ex. *Rossia sublevis*: about 46 mm long; pinkish, spotted; Cape Cod northward.

FAMILY 4. LOLIGINIDAE. Body long; fins near posterior end; eyes with cornea. Ex. *Loligo pealii*: common squid of the East Coast; *L. opalescens*: common squid of the West Coast.

FAMILY 5. ARCHITEUTHIDAE. Body long, cylindrical; fins near posterior end; eyes without cornea; cosmopolitan. Ex. *Architeuthis princeps* (Fig. 9–23, B): giant squid; body up to 6 meters long; total length including arms, over 50 feet; largest living invertebrate; deep sea.

Fig. 9-25. Octopoda. *Argonauta pacifica*, a paper nautilus, with its egg case. (From Johnson and Snook.)

Fig. 9-26. Octopoda. An octopus.

Suborder 2. Octopoda.   Shell absent (except in *Argonauta*); eight arms.

FAMILY 1. ARGONAUTIDAE (Fig. 9–25).   Shell of female thin, spiral, without septa, serves as an egg case; male small. Ex. *Argonauta argo*: paper nautilus; Atlantic Ocean.

FAMILY 2. OCTOPODIDAE (Fig. 9–26).   Devilfishes; body globose; head very large. Ex. *Octopus bairdi*: sea polyp; body about 75 mm long; arms about 10 cm long; Cape Cod northward. *O. apollyon* of the Pacific Coast attains a weight of over 100 pounds. Octopuses can swim by jet propulsion as does the squid although they typically live in crevices on the bottom.

5 / Class V. Pelecypoda

(1) Anodonta—A Fresh-Water Mussel

External Features (Fig. 9–27).   Mussels, or clams, usually lie almost entirely buried in the muddy or sandy bottom of lakes or streams. They burrow and move from place to place by means of the *foot*, which can be extended from the anterior end of the shell. Water loaded with oxygen and

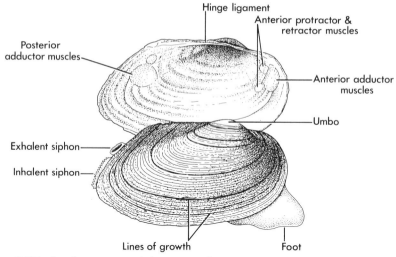

Posterior adductor muscles

Hinge ligament

Anterior protractor & retractor muscles

Anterior adductor muscles

Umbo

Exhalent siphon

Inhalent siphon

Lines of growth

Foot

Fig. 9-27. *Anodonta;* external features, soft parts extended from shell, and inner markings of shell. (From Shipley and MacBride.)

food material is drawn in through a slitlike opening at the posterior end, called the *ventral siphon,* and excretory substances and feces along with deoxygenated water are carried out through a smaller *dorsal siphon.*

The Shell. The shell consists of two parts, called *valves,* which are fastened together at the dorsal surface by an elastic ligamentous hinge. In a nearly related genus, *Unio,* the valves articulate with each other by means of projections called teeth, but these are almost entirely atrophied in *Anodonta.* A number of concentric ridges appear on the outside of each valve; these are called *lines* of *growth,* and, as the name implies, represent the intervals of rest between successive periods of growth. The small area situated dorsally toward the anterior end is called the *umbo;* this is the part of the shell with which the animal was provided at the beginning of its adult stage. The umbo is usually eroded by the carbonic acid in the water.

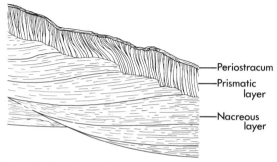

Periostracum

Prismatic layer

Nacreous layer

Fig. 9-28. *Unio.* Vertical section of shell. The periostracum is formed of the organic material, conchiolin. The other layers are principally calcium carbonate. (From Woods.)

The *structure* of the *shell* is easily determined (Fig. 9–28). There are three layers: (1) an outer thin, horny layer, the *periostracum*, which is secreted by the edge of the mantle—it serves to protect the underlying layers from the carbonic acid in the water, and gives the exterior of the shell most of its color; (2) a middle portion of crystals of calcium carbonate, called the *prismatic layer*, which is also secreted by the edge of the mantle; and (3) an inner *nacreous layer* (mother-of-pearl), which is made up of many thin lamellae secreted by the entire surface of the mantle, and produces in the light an iridescent sheen.

Anatomy and Physiology (Figs. 9–29 and 9–30). *General Account.* The valves of the shell are held together by two large *transverse muscles*, which must be cut in order to gain access to the internal organs. These muscles are situated one close to either end near the dorsal surface; they are called *anterior adductors*, and *posterior adductors*. As the shell grows, they migrate outward from a position near the umbo, as indicated by the faint lines in Figure 9–27. When these muscles are cut, or when the animal dies, the shell gapes open, the valves being forced apart by the elasticity of the *ligamentous dorsal hinge*, which is stretched when the shell is closed.

The two folds of the dorsal wall of the mussel which line the valves are called the *mantle* or *pallium*. The mantle flaps are attached to the inner surface of the shell along a line shown clearly in Figure 9–27. The space between the mantle flaps containing the two pairs of *gill plates*, the *foot*, and the *visceral mass*, is called the *mantle cavity*.

Digestion. The *food* of the mussel consists of organic material carried into the mantle cavity with the water that flows through the ventral siphon. The *mouth* lies between two pairs of triangular flaps, called *labial palps*. The *cilia* (Fig. 9–33, B) on these palps drive the food particles into the mouth. A short *esophagus* leads from the mouth to the *stomach*. On either side of the stomach

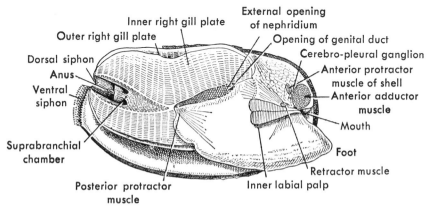

Fig. 9-29. *Anodonta mutabilis*, right side, with mantle cut away and right gills folded back. (After Hatschek and Cori, from Shipley and MacBride.)

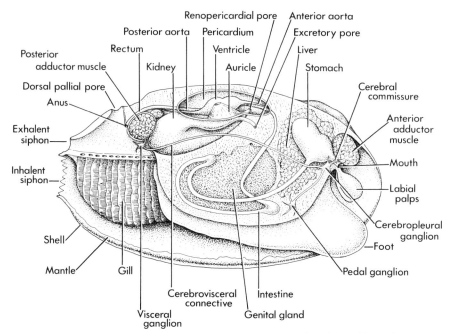

Fig. 9-30. Longitudinal section of a fresh-water clam with right gills and part of visceral mass removed to show internal organs.

is a lobe of a glandular mass called the *digestive gland* or *liver*; a digestive fluid is secreted by the liver and is carried into the stomach by ducts, one for each lobe.

The food is mostly digested and partly absorbed in the stomach; it then passes into the *intestine*, by whose walls it is chiefly absorbed. The intestine coils about in the basal portion of the foot, then passes through the *pericardium*, runs over the posterior adductor muscle, and ends in an *anal papilla*. The feces pass out of the anus and are carried away by the current of water flowing through the dorsal siphon.

Circulation.   The circulatory system comprises a heart, blood vessels, and spaces called sinuses. The *heart* (Fig. 9–30) lies in the *pericardium*. It consists of a *ventricle*, which surrounds part of the intestine, and a pair of *auricles*. By its contractions the ventricle drives the blood forward through the *anterior aorta* and backward through the *posterior aorta*. Part of the blood passes into the mantle, where it is oxygenated, and then returns directly to the heart. The rest of the blood circulates through numerous spaces in the body and is finally collected by a vessel called the *vena cava*, which lies just beneath the pericardium. From here the blood passes into the kidneys, then into the *gills*, and finally through the auricles and into the ventricle. Nutriment and oxygen are carried by the blood to all parts of the body, and carbon dioxide and other waste products of metabolism are transported to the gills and kidneys.

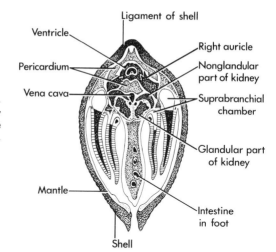

Fig. 9-31. *Anodonta.* Diagrammatic section showing especially the gills hanging down into the mantle cavity. (After Howes, from Shipley and MacBride.)

Respiration.   The respiratory organs of the mussel are the *gills* or *branchiae* or *ctenidia*. A pair of these hang down into the mantle cavity on either side of the foot (Fig. 9–31).

Each *gill* is made up of two plates or lamellae (Fig. 9–32), which lie side by side and are united at the edges except dorsally. The cavity between the lamellae is divided into vertical *water tubes* by partitions called *interlamellar junctions*. Each lamella consists of a large number of *gill filaments*, each supported by two *chitinous rods*, and covered with *cilia*. Openings, called *ostia*, lie between the gill filaments, and blood vessels are present in the interlamellar junctions and filaments.

Water is drawn through the ostia into the water tubes by the cilia which

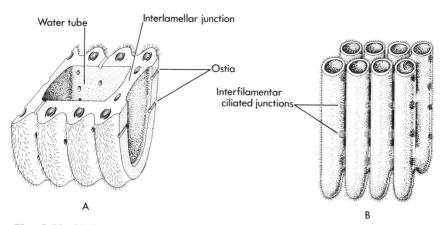

Fig. 9-32. Gill filaments. (A) Eulamellibranch type of gill with filaments fused laterally and lamellae joined by partitions. (B) Filibranch type of gill with filaments joined loosely by ciliated junctions.

cover the gill filaments; it flows dorsally into the *suprabranchial chamber* (Fig. 9-31); from here it enters the dorsal mantle cavity and passes out through the dorsal siphon. The blood which circulates through the gills discharges carbon dioxide into the water and takes oxygen from it. Respiration also takes place through the surface of the mantle. There are no respiratory pigments in the blood.

Excretion. The organs of excretion are two U-shaped *kidneys* or *nephridia* lying just beneath the pericardium, one on either side of the vena cava (Fig. 9-30). Each kidney consists of a ventral glandular portion into which the pericardium opens by a ciliated slit and a dorsal thin-walled bladder, which opens to the exterior through the *renal aperture.* Some excretory matter is probably driven into the kidney from the pericardium by cilia, and other excretory matter is taken from the blood by the glandular portion. These waste products of metabolism are carried out of the body through the dorsal siphon.

Nervous System. There are only a few ganglia in the body of the mussel. On each side of the esophagus is a so-called *cerebropleural ganglion* (Fig. 9-30), connected with its fellow by a nerve called the *cerebral commissure,* which passes above the esophagus. From each cerebropleural ganglion a nerve cord passes ventrally, ending in a *pedal ganglion* in the foot. The two pedal ganglia are closely joined together. Each cerebropleural ganglion also gives off a *cerebrovisceral connective,* which may be enclosed by the kidneys and leads to a *visceral ganglion.*

Sensory Organs. Fresh-water mussels are not well provided with sensory organs. A small vesicle, the *statocyst,* containing a calcareous concretion, the *statolith,* lies a short way behind the pedal ganglia. It is an organ of equilibrium (Fig. 9-33, A). A thick patch of yellow epithelial cells covers each visceral ganglion and is known as an *osphradium.* The functions of the osphradia are not certain. They probably test the water that enters the mantle

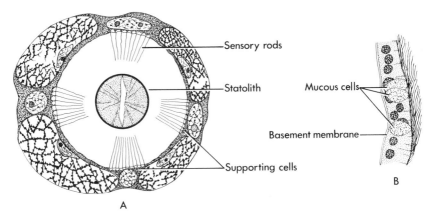

Fig. 9-33. (A) Statocyst of *Sphaerium.* (B) Ciliated epithelium of *Mya.* (From Dahlgren and Kepner.)

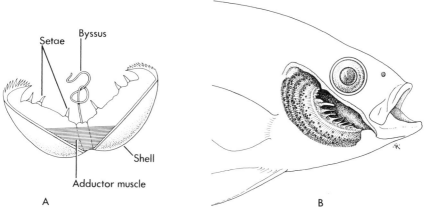

Fig. 9-34. (A) A young mussel or glochidium. (B) The gills of a fish in which are embedded many young mussels forming "blackheads." (A, after Balfour; B, after Lefever and Curtis.)

cavity. The edges of the mantle are provided with *sensory cells*; these are especially abundant on the ventral siphon, and are sensitive to contact and light.

Reproduction. Mussels are usually either male or female; a few are hermaphroditic. The *reproductive organs* are situated in the foot (Fig. 9–30). They are paired bunches of tubes and open just in front of the renal aperture on each side. The *spermatozoa* are carried out through the dorsal siphon of the male and in through the ventral siphon of the female. The eggs pass out of the genital aperture and come to lie in various parts of the gills according to the species. The spermatozoa enter the gill of the female with the water and fertilize the eggs. That portion of the gill in which the eggs develop is termed the *marsupium*.

The *eggs* undergo complete but unequal segmentation. Blastula and gastrula stages are passed through, and then a peculiar larva known as a *glochidium* is produced (Fig. 9–34). The glochidium has a shell consisting of two valves, which are hooked in some species; these may be closed by a muscle when a proper stimulus is applied. A long, sticky thread called the *byssus* extends from the center of the larva, and bunches of *setae* are also present.

In *Anodonta* the eggs are fertilized usually in August, and the glochidia that develop from them remain in the gills of the mother all winter. In the following spring they are discharged, and, if they chance to come in contact with the external parts of a fish, this *contact stimulus* causes them to seize hold of it by closing the valves of their shell. The valves cut through the soft tissues of the host, but merely clasp the firmer, deeper organs, such as blood vessels and fin rays. Cells of the host lying near the glochidium migrate toward and completely enclose the partly buried organism. The glochidium probably chemically stimulates the skin of the fish to grow around it, forming the well-known "worms" or "blackheads." While thus embedded the glochidium undergoes a stage of development (metamorphosis), during which the foot, muscles, and other parts of the adult are formed. The glochidium is nourished by tissue severed from the host at the time of attachment, and by the disintegrated larval muscle and larval mantle. Other nutriment consists of transuding tissue juices absorbed from the host. After a *parasitic life* within the tissues of the fish from 3 to 12 weeks the young mussel is liberated and takes up a free existence. The liberation of the glochidium is due largely to its own efforts. The injured host tissue is rapidly repaired. Some fishes possess a natural, or racial immunity to infestation with glochidia; others are known to acquire immunity. In the former, many glochidia are destroyed by cytolysis and invasion of the cells of the host. In both cases glochidia are shed, prematurely, at about the second day.

In most other mussels the eggs are fertilized during the late spring and summer, and the glochidia are discharged before the middle of September. The glochidium of *Unio* is smaller than that of *Anodonta* and is usually hookless. It does not as a rule become permanently attached to the fins, operculum, or mouth as in *Anodonta*, but usually lodges on the gill filaments of the fish.

One result of the parasitic habit of larval mussels is the *dispersal of the species* through the migrations of the fish. Only in this way can we account for the rapid colonization of certain streams by mussels, because the adult plows its way through the muddy bottom very slowly.

(2) Other Pelecypoda

This class, for which the term Lamellibranchia is also used, contains the bivalve mollusks, such as the clams, mussels, oysters, scallops, cockles, and ship worms. About four fifths of the more than 10,000 species are marine; the rest live in fresh water. The body typically exhibits bilateral symmetry, is compressed laterally, and is completely covered by a bilobed mantle. The mantle secretes the shell, which usually consists of two valves hinged together dorsally and separated ventrally. The head is absent as well as tentacles and radula. The foot is usually wedge-shaped and adapted for burrowing. There are usually two gills on either side of the mantle cavity; these are covered with cilia, which help carry minute particles of food to the mouth as well as create a current of fresh water through the mantle cavity. The sexes are usually separate and there are trophophore and veliger larval stages in marine species. The Pelecypoda usually are divided into orders according to the characteristics of their gills. The mussel used as an example of the class has served to illustrate many of their characteristics; variations from this are indicated in the following account of the orders and a few of the families.

Order 1. Protobranchia. Marine. The gills are not lamellar but consist of two rows of short, flat leaflets projecting into the mantle cavity; the foot has a creeping surface with sometimes a fringed margin.

FAMILY 1. NUCULIDAE.   Valves of shell equal in size, oval or triangular; hinge with many teeth; oral palps large; cosmopolitan. Ex. *Nucula proxima*: shell 10 mm long; in shallow water; South Carolina northward. *Yoldia limatula*: shell about 5 cm long; North Carolina northward, Pacific Coast, Europe.

FAMILY 2. SOLEMYIDAE.   Valves of shell equal in size, long, semi-cylindrical, open at ends; foot long and slender; oral palps long. Ex. *Solemya velum*: about 25 mm long; North Carolina northward.

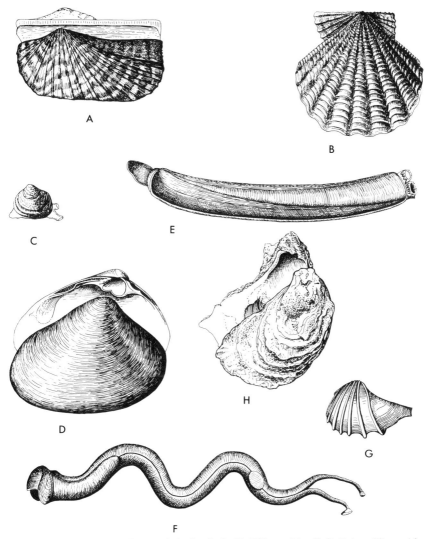

Fig. 9-35. Pelecypoda. Types of shells: A–B, H, Filibranchia; C–F, Eulamellibranchia; G, Septibranchia. (A) *Arca*. (B) *Pecten*. (C) *Sphaerium*. (D) *Mactra*. (E) *Ensis*. (F) *Teredo*. (G) *Cuspidaria*. (H) *Crassostrea*. (A–G, from Tryon.)

Order 2. Filibranchia. Marine. The gills consist of two rows of long filamentous leaflets hanging down into the mantle cavity on either side; the two lamellae of each gill are usually not joined by partitions; the foot is poorly developed; a byssus is present consisting of tough strings secreted by the foot and of use for purposes of attachment.

FAMILY 1. ARCIDAE (Fig. 9–35, A). Shell oval, with radial corrugations; valves equal. Ex. *Arca pexata*: shell thick; umbo directed obliquely forward; about 35 corrugations; Florida northward.

FAMILY 2. MYTILIDAE. Mussels; valves equal, long; umbo near or at anterior end; foot cylindrical; attached by byssus. Ex. *Mytilus edulis*: edible mussel; umbo at anterior end; North Carolina and San Francisco northward. *Modiolus modiolus*: horse mussel; umbo near anterior end; burrow in gravel; New Jersey northward and San Francisco northward.

FAMILY 3. PECTINIDAE (Figs. 9–35, B and 9–36). Scallops; valves with a wing on either side of umbo, and with radiating ribs; muscle near center of body. Ex. *Pecten irradians*: common scallop; wings large; twenty radiating ribs; Cape Cod southward. *Pecten aequisulcatus* of California similar to *P. irradians*. *Pecten magellanicus*: giant scallop; New Jersey northward. Scallops have numerous eyes and the ability to swim short distances.

FAMILY 4. OSTREIDAE. Oysters; valves unequal, irregular and variable; one adductor muscle; adults sessile; marine. *Ostrea lurida* is the West Coast oyster. *Crassostrea virginica* (Fig. 9–35, H) is the common oyster of the East Coast. It is found in shallow, brackish-water areas. Oyster fishermen return empty shells to the oyster beds so that the planktonic larva will have a suitable place to settle and develop. The adult shell has calcium carbonate in the form of calcite as its principal component whereas most mollusk shells have the calcium carbonate as aragonite.

Order 3. Eulamellibranchia. Fresh water and marine. The two gills on each side have the filamentous leaflets connected so as to form two lamellae (Fig. 9–32); siphons present; foot large; byssus small or absent. This order contains most of the lamellibranchs.

FAMILY 1. UNIONIDAE. Fresh-water clams or mussels; shell large; valves equal; umbo anterior to center; eggs usually carried in outer gill of each pair; glochidia develop from eggs; about one thousand species. Ex. *Lampsilis ventricosa*: pocketbook clam; shell used for making buttons. *Anodonto grandis*: central states. *Elliptio dilatatus*: Mississippi Valley, etc. *Amblema costata*: blue foot clam; shell used for making buttons; Mississippi Valley, etc.

FAMILY 2. SPHAERIIDAE (Fig. 9–35, C). Fresh-water or brackish water; shell small, oval; foot elongate, flattened; eggs hatch in inner gill of each pair; many species. Ex. *Sphaerium occidentale*: umbo median; about 7 mm long. *Pisidium abditum*: umbo posterior to middle of shell; about 4 mm long.

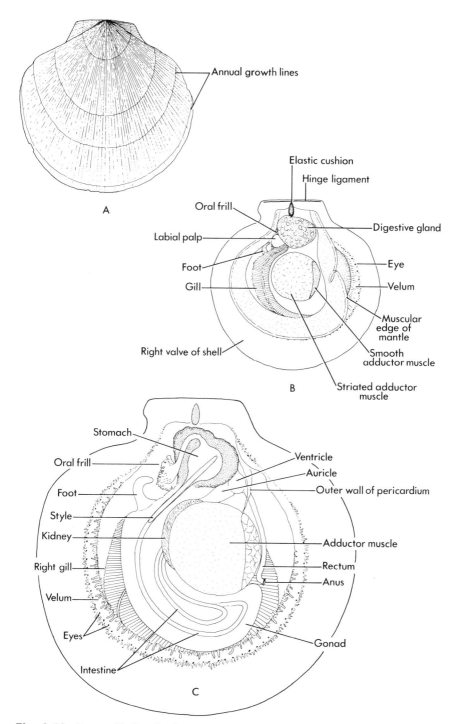

Fig. 9-36. *Pecten.* Shell and soft parts of the scallop. (A) Outer surface of left valve. (B) View with left valve removed. (C) Internal anatomy.

A

B

Fig. 9-37. Some symbionts of pelecypods. (A) Valve of *Pecten*, with numerous epizoic barnacles, polychaetes, and ectoproctans. (B) Photo of *Tridacna* boring in coral rock beside a colony of brain coral. *Tridacna* is exposing its mantle with enclosed photosynthetic zooanthellae to light. Although the giant clam is anchored hinge down, the soft parts have rotated to the position normal to clams with the hinge uppermost.

FAMILY 3. CORBICULIDAE. This family of fresh-water clams has a general resemblance to the Sphaeriidae, but most are larger and native to Asia. *Corbicula* has been introduced into some streams of this country where it has become a pest because it has a planktonic veliger stage not found in our native fresh-water bivalves. The larva may settle in water intake pipes in large numbers and, with growth, clog the pipes.

FAMILY 4. TRIDACNIDAE. Marine; the giant clams of coral reefs. *Tridacna* (Fig. 9–37), the largest of pelecypods, lives hinge down in a hole it has bored in coral. It is a plankton feeder but presumably gets considerable nutriment from zooanthellae growing in its exposed mantle. It may reach a length of over five feet and weigh several hundred pounds.

FAMILY 5. MACTRIDAE (Fig. 9–35, D). Marine; shell large, triangular. Ex. *Mactra solidissima*: giant clam; 15 cm long; edible.

FAMILY 6. VENERIDAE. Marine; shell thick. Ex. *Venus mercenaria* (Fig. 9–38): hard-shell clam or quahog; 11 cm long; edible; source of wampum of the Indians.

FAMILY 7. MYIDAE. Marine; shell not pearly; burrowing habit. Ex. *Mya arenaria*: soft-shell clam; 10 cm long; edible.

FAMILY 8. SOLENIDAE (Fig. 9–35, E). Marine; shell thin, long, narrow; foot large, cylindrical. Ex. *Ensis directus*: razor clam; 15 cm long and 25 mm high.

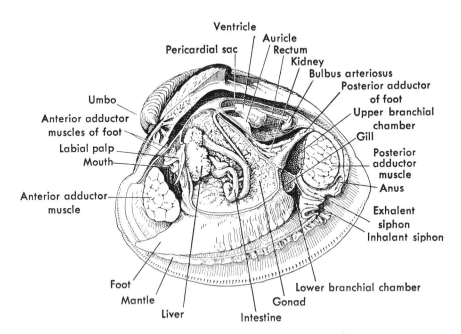

Fig. 9-38. *Venus mercenaria*, the hard-shell clam or quahog. Dissection showing organs revealed when left valve, mantle, and gills are removed. (From Woodruff.)

FAMILY 9. TEREDIDAE (Fig. 9–35, F).   Marine; vermiform; burrow in wood or clay. Ex. *Teredo navalis*: ship worm; tube about 25 cm long and 8 mm in diameter; shell 6 mm long and 2 mm broad. At Woods Hole, Massachusetts, *Teredo navalis* breeds from May 10 to October 10. The eggs remain in the mother's gills for about 3 weeks during cleavage and early larval development. A free-swimming veliger results. The trochophore is nonmotile.

Order 4. Septibranchia.   Marine. The gills are absent and a perforated septum divides the mantle cavity horizontally into two chambers.

FAMILY 1. CUSPIDARIIDAE (Fig. 9–35, G).   Valves of shell small and almost equal in size; siphons short, fused together. Ex. *Cuspidaria pellucida*: right valve smaller than left, about 12 mm long; umbo anterior to center; deep water; Massachusetts northward.

6 / Mollusks in General

The mollusks are a large, successful group of invertebrates with many marine, fresh-water, and terrestrial species. Most are free-living filter feeders or grazers, but numerous predatory and parasitic mollusks exist. They are an economically important group supplying food and some other materials, damaging crops, and serving as intermediate hosts for trematodes. They show considerable diversity and include the largest invertebrate, the squid, and other cephalopods which are among the most complex of invertebrates.

Mollusks and chordates both probably arose from their ancestral stocks in Precambrian times with forms much simpler than exist today. Thus, parallels in functional features of the nervous system demonstrate the selective values of a highly developed nervous system are of sufficient importance to cause a functional convergence in this feature of the two phyla. There is evidence that the octopus has both a long-term and a short-term memory. Memory seems more closely related to the amount of brain tissue left after surgery than on the presence of specific cells (Boycott, 1965). Both characteristics are also thought to apply to man. The general similarity of the eyes has already been cited. That eyes of such complexity are new developments in both groups is indicated by the different position of nerve fibers serving the retinal cells in the two phyla.

Interrelations and Phylogeny of the Mollusca.   The Amphineura appear to be the most primitive class in the phylum and to have changed the least from the ancestral condition. The modifications of the other classes have taken place in various directions. The Gastropoda became a short, creeping type with a spiral, visceral hump revolved through an angle of 180°. The Pelecypoda seem to be derived from the Monoplacophora as indicated by the

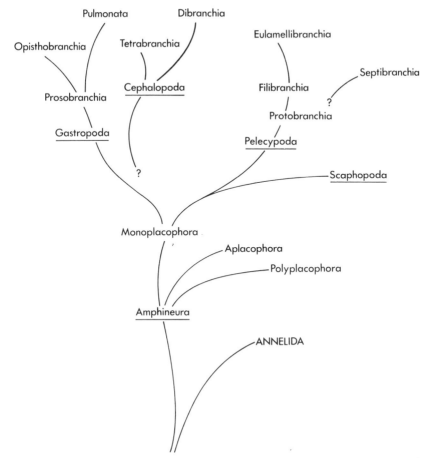

Fig. 9-39. Diagram indicating one view of the presumed relationships of the main groups of mollusks.

Ordovician fossil, *Babinka* (McAlester, 1964); they became flattened laterally and developed a large bilobed mantle that secreted a shell of two valves, a large mantle cavity containing gills, and a burrowing foot in place of the creeping type. The Cephalopoda have become free-swimming animals, with the foot modified into prehensile tentacles, and with the brain and sense organs highly developed. Trochophore larvae among both mollusks and annelids indicate that these may be derived from the same ancestral type. This is supported by the presence of metamerism in *Neopilina*. The general relationships of the mollusks are indicated in Figure 9–39.

Reproduction.   Sexes are usually separate although hemaphroditism is common. A number of unusual reproductive phenomena have evolved in different groups. The peculiar dart sac of *Helix* has already been noted. The hectocotylized arm of the squid derives its name from the fragment of the male arm found in the mantle cavity of the female in some species following its separation when transferring sperm. The fragment was first thought to be a parasite and given the name *Hectocotylus*. The cephalopods package their sperm in complex packets, the spermatophores. In some pelecypods the sperm are released in *Volvox*-like balls. Gastropods may form spermatozeugma in which small sperm which will fertilize the eggs are carried on the surface of a large motile cell which may also give them some nourishment. In some species the eggs hatch within the female, others lay them in distinctive masses or shed them into the water.

Embryology. Mollusks and annelids correspond remarkably closely in their embryonic development. As in the flatworm, *Holoplana* (Fig. 5–23), and in representatives of other phyla, a definite cell lineage has been worked out in a number of species. One of the most interesting results obtained is the fact that the quartets that are destined to give rise to definite parts of the embryo and adult have similar values in the flatworms, annelids, and mollusks. There are many variations of a minor type but the first three quartets of micromeres given off by the macromeres form the entire ectoblast of the larva. The first quartet in annelids and mollusks give rise to the pretrochal ectoblast and the second and third to the posttrochal ectoblast. In some cases, as in the Turbellaria, the ectoblastic quartets may give rise to mesoblast cells. Three of the macromeres (4A, 4B, and 4C), after three quartets have been given off, are entirely endoblastic; the fourth (4D) is the primary endoblast. It divides into two equal teloblasts from which arise the mesoblastic bands that develop into the coelomic wall and much of the muscular system (Fig. 9–40).

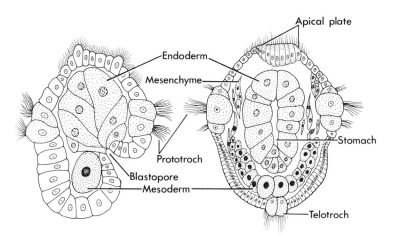

Fig. 9-40. *Patella coerulea.* Sections of young larvae. (A) Sagittal section of early stage. (B) Frontal section of veliger larva. (After Patten.)

Growth. Many leave a record of annual growth on their shells where heavy dark lines on the periostracum indicate the slow growth of winter. From this it has been established that some fresh-water clams reach an age of one hundred years. The giant *Tridacna* reaches its large size by rapid growth, as much as by long life, reaching a length of half a meter in nine years (Bonham, 1965). Nothing is known of the age reached by the giant squid, the largest living invertebrate, although the extremely rare sporadic abundance of it may indicate a very long slow growth if, as in some cephalopods, egg laying is followed by death.

The History of Our Knowledge of the Mollusca. Mollusks were well known to the ancients because of their conspicuous shells, and constituted an important article of diet of primitive people. At first the group included a number of types of animals that possessed a superficial resemblance to the mollusks because of their shells, for example, the Brachiopoda, Tunicata, and Cirripedia. When the larval stages of the Cirripedia were studied it was found that they really belonged to the Crustacea. Investigations of the Tunicata revealed their chordate nature and vertebrate affinities. Finally the Brachiopoda were excluded but placed near the Mollusca in the group Molluscoidea. Cuvier (1795) recognized three subdivisions of the Mollusca, (1) Gastropoda, (2) Cephalopoda, and (3) Acephala. They were included by Linnaeus as one of the four divisions of the Vermes. Many workers have made significant contributions to our knowledge of the mollusks in modern times, among these may be mentioned Thiele, Yonge, Lemche, Clench, van der Schalie, Baker, Tryon, and Pilsbry.

References to Literature on the Mollusca

ARNOLD, J. M. 1965. Normal embryonic stages of the squid, *Loligo pealii* (Lesueur). *Biol. Bull.*, **128**:24–32.

BONHAM, K. 1965. Growth rate of giant clam *Tridacna gigas* at Bikini Atoll as revealed by radioautography. *Science*, **149**:300–302.

BOYCOTT, B. 1965. Learning in the octopus. *Sci. Am.*, **212**:42–50.

BROWN, F. A., H. M. WEBB, and F. H. BARNWELL. 1964. A compass directional phenomenon in mud-snails and its relation to magnetism. *Biol. Bull.*, **127**:206–220.

BURCH, J. B. 1962. *How to Know the Eastern Land Snails*. Brown, Dubuque. 214 pp.

CAMPBELL, J. L. 1965. The structure and function of the alimentary canal of the black abalone, *Haliotis cracherodii* Leach. *Trans. Am. Microsc. Soc.*, **84**:376–395.

CLENCH, W. J. 1959. Mollusca. In W. T. EDMONDSON. *Fresh-Water Biology*, pp. 1117–1160. 2nd ed. Wiley, New York. 1248 pp.

DAZO, B. C. 1965. The morphology and natural history of *Pleurocera acuta* and *Goniobasis livescens* (Gastropoda: Cerithiacea: Pleuroceridae). *Malacologia*, 3:1–80.

EDGAR, A. L. 1965. Observations on the sperm of the pelecypod *Anodontoides ferussacianus* (Lea). *Trans. Am. Microsc. Soc.*, **84**:228–230.

GALTSOFF, P. S. 1964. The American Oyster. *Fish. Bull.*, Vol. 64. U.S. Dept. Interior. 480 pp.

GHISELIN, M. T. 1965. Reproductive function and the phylogeny of opisthobranch gastropods. *Malacologia*, **3**:327–378.

HERRINGTON, H. B. 1962. A revision of the Sphaeriidae of North America (Mollusca: Pelecypoda). *Misc. Publ. Mus. Zool.*, No. 118. Univ. Mich. 74 pp. + 7 Pl.

HYMAN, L. H. 1967. *The Invertebrates: Mollusca I (Vol. VI)*. McGraw-Hill, New York. 792 pp.

JONES, E. C. 1963. *Tremoctopus violaceus* uses *Physalia* tentacles as weapons. *Science*, **139**:764–766.

KEEN, A. M. 1963. *Marine Molluscan Genera of Western North America: An Illustrated Key*. Stanford Univ. Press, Stanford. 126 pp.

KOHN, A. J. 1959. The ecology of *Conus* in Hawaii. *Ecol. Monog.*, **29**:47–90.

LANE, C. E. 1961. The Teredo. *Sci. Am.*, **204**:132–142.

LANE, F. W. 1960. *Kingdom of the Octopus*. Sheridan House, New York, 300 pp.

LEMCHE, H., and K. G. WINGSTRAND. 1959. The anatomy of *Neopilina galatheae* Lemche, 1957. *Galathea Report*, **3**:9–72, +56 Pl.

MCALESTER, A. L. 1964. Transitional Ordovician bivalve with both monoplacophoran and lucinacean affinities. *Science*, **146**:1293–1294.

MCCRAW, B. M. 1961. Life history and growth of the snail, *Lymnaea humilis* Say. *Trans. Am. Microsc. Soc.*, **80**:16–27.

MEAD, A. R. 1961. *The Giant African Snail: A Problem in Economic Malacology*. Univ. Chicago Press, Chicago. 257 pp.

MORTON, J. E. 1958. *Molluscs*. Hutchinson, London. 232 pp.

RAVEN, C. P. 1958. *Morphogenesis: The Analysis of Molluscan Development*. Pergamon Press, New York. 311 pp.

STENZEL, H. B. 1964. Oysters: composition of the larval shell. *Science*, **145**:155–156.

TASAKI, I., and M. LUXORO. 1964. Intracellular perfusion of Chilean giant squid axons. *Science*, **145**:1313–1314.

WELLS, M. J. 1962. *Brain and Behavior in Cephalopods*. Stanford Univ. Press, Stanford. 171 pp.

WILBUR, K. M., and C. M. YONGE. 1964. *Physiology of Mollusca*, Vol. I. Academic Press, New York. 473 pp.

YOUNG, J. Z. 1961. Learning and discrimination in the octopus. *Biol. Rev.*, **36**:32–96.

Chapter X

Phylum Arthropoda

THE ARTHROPODS comprise the largest phylum in the animal kingdom, surpassing in number of species all the other phyla combined. They may be said to be the dominant animals on the earth at the present time, if the numbers of different species and numbers of individuals are accepted as criteria of dominance. To the phylum belong the lobsters, crabs, water fleas, barnacles, millipedes, centipedes, scorpions, spiders, mites, and insects. The most important characteristic common to all of these is the possession of jointed appendages. They exhibit bilateral symmetry; consist of a linear series of segments, on all or some of which is a pair of appendages; are covered with a chitinous exoskeleton, which is flexible at intervals to provide movable joints; possess a nervous sytem of the annelid type; have a coelom, which is small in the adult, the body cavity being a hemocoel filled with blood; and are free from cilia.

Regional specialization into groups of segments (*tagmata*) with a common function such as those forming the head or thorax or abdomen have occurred in arthropods. The jointed, chitinous exoskeleton has been an important factor in the success of this phylum by contributing to the protection and efficient locomotion of its members. Problems of growth and respiration caused by an effective exoskeleton have been averted by molting and the development of trachea, gills and other modifications in various groups.

A brief classification of the phylum is presented below. Smaller divisions are given under each class.

Excluded from the classification are an extinct group of paleozic fossils, the trilobites. They may be considered as a separate subphylum, the Trilobitomorpha.

SUBPHYLUM 1. MANDIBULATA.   Typically with mandibles and antennae.
   CLASS 1. CRUSTACEA.   Ex. Lobster, crab, barnacle, sow bug.

CLASS 2. INSECTA. Ex. Grasshopper, honeybee, fruit fly.
CLASS 3. CHILOPODA. Ex. Centipede.
CLASS 4. DIPLOPODA. Ex. Millipede.
CLASS 5. PAUROPODA. Ex. *Pauropus.*
CLASS 6. SYMPHYLA. Ex. *Scutigerella.*

SUBPHYLUM 2. ONYCHOPHORA. Only slight development of oral appendages. With several annelid-like characteristics.
CLASS 1. ONYCHOPHORA. Ex. *Peripatus.*

SUBPHYLUM 3. CHELICERATA (ARACHNOIDEA). Typically with chelicerae and pedipalps as head appendages; no antennae; usually a cephalothorax and abdomen; four pairs of legs on most species.
CLASS 1. MEROSTOMATA. Ex. *Xiphosura.*
CLASS 2. ARACHNIDA. Ex. Spider, scorpion, mite.
CLASS 3. PYCNOGONIDA. Ex. Sea spiders.
CLASS 4. TARDIGRADA. Ex. *Macrobiotus.*
CLASS 5. PENTASTOMIDA. Ex. *Linguatula.*

1 / Class I. Crustacea

(1) The Crayfish

Crayfishes inhabit fresh-water lakes, ponds, and streams. The genera *Procambarus, Cambarus,* and *Orconectes* are common in the Central and Eastern United States. Pacific Coast crayfishes are in the genus *Pacifastacus.* The lobster is so nearly like the crayfish in structure that the anatomical portion of this chapter may be applied also in large part to this animal. In Europe the most common crayfish is *Astacus fluviatilis,* a species made famous by Huxley's classical work *The Crayfish.*

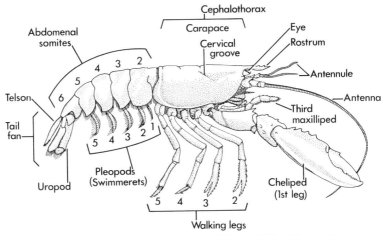

Fig. 10-1. External features of a lobster. (After Calman.)

External Features (Figs. 10–1 and 10–3).   *Exoskeleton.*   The outside of the body of the crayfish is covered by an extremely hard chitinous *cuticle* impregnated with lime salts. This exoskeleton is thinner and flexible at the joints, allowing movement.

Regions of the Body.   The body of the crayfish consists of two distinct regions, an anterior rigid portion, the *cephalothorax*, and a posterior series of segments, the *abdomen*. The entire body is segmented, but the joints have been obliterated on the dorsal surface of the cephalothorax.

Structure of a Segment.   A typical segment is shown in cross section in Figure 10–5. It consists of a convex dorsal plate, the *tergum*, a ventral transverse bar, the *sternum*, plates projecting down at the sides, the *pleura*, and smaller plates between the pleura and the basis of the limb, the *epimera*.

Cephalothorax.   The cephalothorax consists of segments I–XIII, which are enclosed dorsally and laterally by a cuticular shield, the *carapace*. An indentation, termed the *cervical groove*, runs across the middorsal region of the carapace, and obliquely forward on either side, separating the *cephalic* or

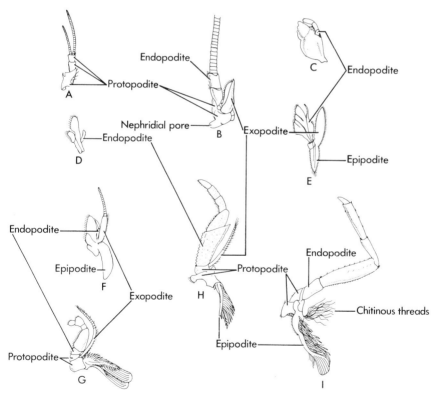

Fig. 10-2. Appendages of crayfish as seen from the ventral side. (A) First antenna. (B) Second antenna. (C) Mandible. (D) First maxilla. (E) Second maxilla. (F) First maxilliped. (G) Second maxilliped. (H) Third maxilliped. (I) Fourth leg. (From Kerr.)

head region from the posterior *thoracic* portion. The anterior pointed extension of the carapace is known as the *rostrum*. Beneath this on either side is an *eye* at the end of a movable peduncle. The *mouth* is situated on the ventral surface near the posterior end of the head region. It is partly obscured by the neighboring appendages. The carapace of the thorax is separated by *branchiocardiac grooves* into three parts, a median dorsal longitudinal strip, the *areola*, and two large convex flaps, one on either side, the *branchiostegites*, which protect the gills beneath them.

Abdomen. In the abdomen there are six segments, and a terminal extension, the *telson*, bearing on its ventral surface the longitudinal anal opening. Whether or not the telson is a true segment is still in dispute; we shall adopt the view that it is not. The first abdominal segment (XIV) is smaller than the others and lacks the pleura. Segments XV–XIX are like the type described above.

Appendages. With the possible exception of the first abdominal segment in the female, every segment of the body bears a pair of jointed appendages. These are all variations of a common type, consisting of a basal segment, the *protopodite*, which bears two branches, an inner *endopodite*, and an outer *exopodite*. Beginning at the anterior end, the appendages are arranged as follows (Fig. 10–2). In front of the mouth are the *antennules*, and the *antennae*; the mouth possesses a pair of *mandibles*, behind which are the first, and the second *maxillae*; the thoracic region bears the first, the second, and the third *maxillipeds*, the *pinchers* or *chelipeds*, and four other pairs of *walking legs*; beneath the abdomen are six pairs of *swimmerets*, some of which are much modified. The accompanying Descriptive Table of the Appendages of the Crayfish gives brief descriptions of the different appendages, and shows the modifications due to differences in function (see pages 400–402).

Three kinds of appendages can be distinguished in the adult crayfish; (1) the *foliaceous*, e.g., the second maxilla, (2) the *biramous*, e.g., the swimmerets, and (3) the *uniramous*, e.g., the walking legs. All of these appendages have doubtless been derived from a single type, the modifications being due to the functions performed by them. The biramous type probably represents the condition from which the other types developed. The uniramous walking legs, for example, pass through a biramous stage during their embryological development. Again, the biramous embryonic maxillipeds are converted into the foliaceous type by the expansion of their basal segments.

General Internal Anatomy (Fig. 10–3). The body of the crayfish contains all of the important systems of organs characteristic of the higher animals. The coelom is not a large cavity but is restricted to the cavities of the reproductive organs. Certain of the organs are metamerically arranged, e.g., the *nervous system*; others like the *excretory organs*, are concentrated into a small space. The systems of organs and their functions will be presented in

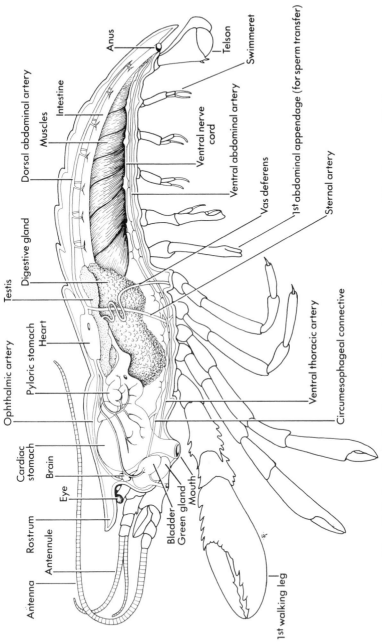

Fig. 10-3. Longitudinal section of a lobster showing internal organs. (After Root modified.)

Descriptive Table of the Appendages of the Crayfish

Appendage	Protopodite	Exopodite	Endopodite	Function
I. Antennule	3 segments: statocyst in basal segment	many-jointed filament	many-jointed filament	tactile; chemical; equilibration
II. Antenna	2 segments; excretory pore in basal segment	broad, thin, dagger-like lateral projection	a long many-jointed "feeler"	tactile; chemical
III. Mandible	2 segments; a heavy jaw and basal segment of palp	absent	small; 2 distal segments of palp	crushing food
IV. 1st Maxilla	2 thin lamellae extending inward	absent	a small outer lamella	
V. 2d Maxilla	2 bilobed lamellae	dorsal half of plate, the scaphognathite	1 segment; small, pointed	creates current of water in gill chamber
VI. 1st Maxilliped	2 thin segments extending inward; a broad plate, the epipodite extending outward	a long basal segment bearing a many-jointed filament	small; 2 segments	chemical; tactile; holds food
VII. 2d Maxilliped	2 segments; a basal coxopodite bearing a gill, and a basipodite bearing the exopodite and endopodite	similar to VI	5 segments; the basal one long and fused with the basipodite	similar to VI

VIII. 3d Maxilliped	similar to VII	similar to VI	similar to VII, but larger	similar to VI
IX. 1st Walking Leg (Chela, Cheliped, or Pincher)	2 segments; coxopodite, and basipodite	absent	5 segments, the terminal two forming a powerful pincher	offense and defense; aids in walking; tactile
X. 2d Walking Leg (Pereiopod)	similar to IX	absent	as in IX, but not so heavy	walking; prehension; toilet implements
XI. 3d Walking Leg	similar to IX; coxopodite of female contains genital pore	absent	similar to X	similar to X
XII. 4th Walking Leg	similar to IX	absent	similar to X, but no pincher at end	walking
XIII. 5th Walking Leg	similar to IX; coxopodite of male bears genital pore	absent	similar to XII	walking; cleaning abdomen and eggs
XIV. 1st Abdominal (1st Pleopod or Swimmeret)				reduced in female; in male, protopodite and endopodite fused together forming an organ for transferring sperm
XV. 2d Abdominal (2d Pleopod or Swimmeret)	in female 2 segments	in female many-jointed filament	in female like exopodite but longer	in female as in XVI, in male modified for transferring sperm to female

Descriptive Table of the Appendages of the Crayfish (Continued)

Appendage	Protopodite	Exopodite	Endopodite	Function
XVI. 3d Abdominal (3d Pleopod or Swimmeret)	2 segments	many-jointed filament	like exopodite but longer	creates current of water; in female used for attachment of eggs and young
XVII. 4th Abdominal (4th Pleopod or Swimmeret)	2 segments	as in XVI	as in XVI	as in XVI
XVIII. 5th Abdominal (5th Pleopod or Swimmeret)	as in XVII	as in XVI	as in XVI	as in XVI
XIX. 6th Abdominal (Uropod)	1 short, broad segment	flat oval plate divided by transverse groove into two parts	flat oval plate	swimming

the following order: (1) digestive, (2) vascular, (3) respiratory, (4) excretory, (5) nervous, (6) sense organs, (7) muscular, and (8) reproductive.

Digestive System.   The alimentary canal of a crayfish consists of the following parts.

1. The *mouth* opens on the ventral surface between the jaws.

2. The *esophagus* is a short tube leading from the mouth to the stomach.

3. The *stomach* is a large cavity divided by a constriction into an anterior *cardiac* chamber and a smaller posterior *pyloric* chamber. In the stomach are a number of chitinous ossicles of use in chewing the food, and collectively known as the *gastric mill.* The most important of these are (a) a median cardiac ossicle, (b) a median urocardiac ossicle, (c) two lateral pterocardiac ossicles, (d) a pair of lateral zygocardiac ossicles, (e) a pyloric ossicle, and (f) a prepyloric ossicle. The ossicles are able to move one upon another, and, being connected with powerful muscles, are effective in grinding up the food. On either side of the pyloric chamber enters a duct of the digestive glands, and above is the opening of the small cecum.

At certain times two calcareous bodies, known as *gastroliths*, are present in the lateral walls of the cardiac chamber of the stomach. Their function is not certain, but is probably the storage of the calcareous matter used in hardening the exoskeleton.

4. The *intestine* is a small tube passing posteriorly near the dorsal wall of the abdomen, and opening to the outside through the *anus* on the ventral surface of the telson.

The *digestive glands*, or "liver," are situated in the thorax, one on either side. Each consists of three lobes composed of a great number of small tubules. The glandular epithelium lining these tubules produces a secretion which passes into the *hepatic ducts* and thence into the pyloric chamber of the stomach.

Nutrition.   *Food.*   The food of the crayfish is made up principally of living animals such as snails, tadpoles, insect larvae, small fish, and frogs; but decaying organic matter is also eaten. Not infrequently crayfishes prey upon others of their kind. They feed at night, being more active at dusk and daybreak than at any other time. Their method of feeding may be observed in the laboratory if a little fresh meat is offered to them. The maxillipeds and maxillae hold the food while it is being crushed into small pieces by the mandibles. It then passes through the esophagus into the stomach. The coarser parts are ejected through the mouth.

Digestion.   In the cardiac chamber of the stomach, the food is ground up by the ossicles of the gastric mill. When fine enough, it passes through the *strainer* which lies between the two divisions of the stomach. This strainer consists of two lateral and a median ventral fold which bear hairlike setae, and allow the passage of only liquids or very fine particles. In the pyloric chamber, the food is mixed with the secretion from the digestive glands brought in by way of the hepatic ducts. From the pyloric chamber the dissolved food passes into the intestine by the walls of which the nutritive fluids are absorbed. Undigested particles pass on into the posterior end of the intestine, where they are gathered together into feces, and egested through the anus.

Circulatory System. *The Blood.* The blood into which the absorbed food passes is an almost colorless liquid in which are suspended a number of amoeboid cells, the *blood corpuscles* or amoebocytes. The principal *functions* of the blood are the transportation of food materials from one part of the body to another, of oxygen from the gills to the various tissues, of carbon dioxide to the gills, and of urea to the excretory organs. If a crayfish is wounded, the blood, on coming in contact with the air, thickens, forming a clot. It is said to *coagulate.* This clogs the opening and prevents loss of blood. The chelipeds and other walking legs of the crayfish have a breaking point near their bases. When one is injured the animal may break the limb at this point and lessen the blood flow, since only a small space is present in the appendage at this particular spot, and coagulation, therefore, takes place very quickly.

Blood Vessels (Figs. 10–3, 10–4, and 10–5). The principal blood vessels are a heart, seven main arteries, and a number of spaces called sinuses.

Heart. The *heart* is a muscular-walled, saddle-shaped sac lying in the *pericardial sinus* in the median dorsal part of the thorax. It may be considered as a dilation of a dorsal vessel resembling that of the earthworm. Six elastic *ligaments*, two anterior, two posterior, and two running along the ventral border of each lateral surface, fasten it to the walls of the pericardial sinus.

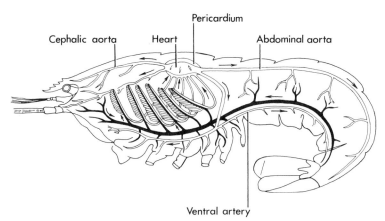

Fig. 10-4. Circulatory system of a lobster. (After Gegenbaur.)

Three pairs of valvular apertures, called *ostia*, one dorsal and two lateral, allow the blood to enter from the surrounding sinus.

Arteries. Five arteries arise from the anterior end of the heart:

1. The *ophthalmic* artery is a median dorsal tube passing forward over the stomach, and supplying the cardiac portion, the esophagus, and head.

2, 3. The two *antennary* arteries arise one on each side of the ophthalmic artery, pass forwards, outwards, and downwards, and branch, sending a gastric artery to the cardiac part of the stomach, arteries to the antennae, to the excretory organs, and to the muscles and other cephalic tissues.

4, 5. The two *hepatic* arteries leave the heart below the antennary arteries. They lead directly to the digestive glands.

A single dorsal abdominal artery arises from the posterior end of the heart.

6. The *dorsal abdominal artery* is a median tube leading backwards from the ventral part of the heart, and supplying the dorsal region of the abdomen. It branches near its point of origin, giving rise to the *sternal* artery; this leads directly downward, and, passing between the nerve cords connecting the

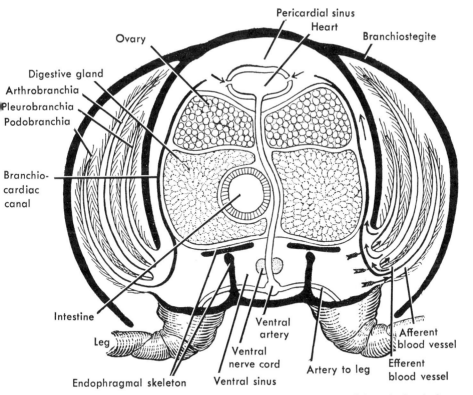

Fig. 10-5. Diagrammatic cross-section through the thorax of a crayfish at the level of the sternal artery. The arrows indicate the direction of blood flow. (From R. W. Hegner, *College Zoology*, 5th ed., 1947.)

fourth and fifth pairs of thoracic ganglia (see Fig. 10–3) divides into two arteries. One of these, the *ventral thoracic* artery, runs forward beneath the nerve chain, and sends branches to the ventral thoracic region, and to appendages III to XIII; the other, the *ventral abdominal* artery, runs backward beneath the nerve chain, and sends branches to the ventral abdominal region and to the abdominal appendages.

Sinuses. The blood passes from the arteries into spaces lying in the midst of the tissues, called sinuses. The pericardial sinus has already been mentioned. The thorax contains a large ventral blood space, the *sternal sinus,* and a number of *branchio-cardiac canals* extending from the bases of the gills to the pericardial sinus. A *pervisceral sinus* surrounds the alimentary canal in the cephalothorax.

Blood Flow (Fig. 10–5). The heart, by means of rhythmical contractions, forces the blood through the arteries to all parts of the body. Valves are present in every artery where it leaves the heart; they prevent the blood from flowing back. The finest branches of these arteries, the *capillaries,* open into spaces between the tissues, and the blood eventually reaches the sternal sinus. From here it passes into the *efferent channels* of the gills and into the gill filaments, where the carbonic acid in solution is exchanged for oxygen from the water in the branchial chambers. It then returns by way of the *afferent gill channels,* passes into the branchio-cardiac sinuses, thence to the pericardial sinus, and finally through the ostia into the heart. The valves of the ostia allow the blood to enter the heart, but prevent it from flowing back into the pericardial sinus.

Respiratory System (Fig. 10–5). Between the branchiostegites and the body wall are the branchial chambers containing the gills. At the anterior end of the branchial chamber is a channel in which the *scaphognathite* of the second maxilla (Fig. 10–2) moves back and forth, forcing the water out through the anterior opening. Water flows in through the posterior opening of the branchial chamber.

Gills. There are two rows of gills, named according to their points of attachment. The outermost, the *podobranchiae,* are fastened to the coxopodites of certain appendages and the inner double row, the *arthrobranchiae,* arise from the membranes at the bases of these appendages. In *Astacus* there is a third row, the *pleurobranchiae,* attached to the walls of the thorax. The number and arrangement of these gills are shown in the accompanying table. The podobranchiae consist of a basal plate covered with delicate setae and a central axis bearing a thin, longitudinally folded corrugated plate on its distal end, and a feather-like group of *branchial filaments.* The arthrobranchiae have a central stem on either side of which extends a number of filaments, causing the entire structure to resemble a plume. Attached to the base of the first maxilliped is a broad thin plate, the *epipodite,* which has lost its branchial filaments.

The Number and Position of the Gills of the Crayfish

Segment	Podobranchiae	Arthrobranchiae		Total Number
		Anterior	Posterior	
VI	0 (*ep.*)	0	0	0 (*ep.*)
VII	1	1	0	2
VIII	1	1	1	3
IX	1	1	1	3
X	1	1	1	3
XI	1	1	1	3
XII	1	1	1	3
	6 (*ep.*)	6	5	17 (*ep.*)

Excretory System.   The excretory organs are a pair of rather large bodies, the "*green glands*" (Fig. 10–3), situated in the ventral part of the head anterior to the esophagus. Each green gland consists of a green glandular portion, a thin-walled dilation, the bladder, and a duct opening to the exterior through a pore at the top of the papilla on the basal segment of the antenna.

Nervous System (Fig. 10–3).   The morphology of the nervous system of the crayfish is in many respects similar to that of the earthworm. The *central nervous system* includes a dorsal ganglionic mass, the *brain*, in the head, and two *circumesophageal connectives* passing to the *ventral nerve cord*, which lies near the median ventral surface of the body.

Brain.   The brain is a compact mass larger than that of the earthworm, and supplies the eyes, antennules, and antennae with nerves.

Ventral Nerve Cord.   The ganglia and connectives of the ventral nerve cord are more intimately fused than in the earthworm, and it is difficult to make out the double nature of the connectives, except between segments XI and XII, where the sternal artery passes through. Each segment posterior to VII possesses a ganglionic mass, which sends nerves to the surrounding tissues. The large subesophageal ganglion in segment VII consists of the ganglia of segments III–VII fused together. It sends nerves to the mandibles, maxillae, and first and second maxillipeds.

The *visceral nervous system* consists of an anterior visceral nerve which arises from the ventral surface of the brain, is joined by a nerve from each circumesophageal connective, and, passing back, branches upon the dorsal wall of the pyloric part of the stomach, sending a *lateral nerve* on each side to unite with an *infero-lateral nerve* from the *stomatogastric ganglion*.

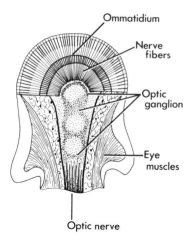

Fig. 10-6. Crayfish. Eye in longitudinal section. (After Borradaile and Potts, modified.)

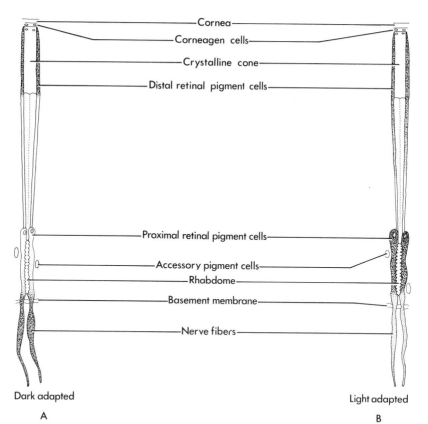

Dark adapted

A

Light adapted

B

Fig. 10-7. *Cambarus*. Longitudinal sections of two crayfish ommatidia showing the arrangement of retinal pigment under light adapted (B) and dark adapted (A) conditions. (After Bennitt and Merrick.)

Sense Organs.   *Eyes.*   The eyes of the crayfish are situated at the end of movable stalks which extend out, one from each side of the rostrum (Fig. 10–3). The external convex surface of the eye is covered by a modified portion of the transparent cuticle, called the *cornea.* This cornea is divided by a large number of fine lines into four-sided areas, termed *facets.* Each facet is but the external part of a long visual rod known as an *ommatidium.*

Sections (Fig. 10–6) show the compound eye to be made up of similar ommatidia lying side by side, but separated from one another by a layer of dark pigment cells. The average number of ommatidia in a single eye is 2,500.

Two ommatidia are shown in Figure 10–7. Beginning at the outer surface, each ommatidium consists of the following parts: (a) a *corneal* facet, (b) two *corneagen* cells which secrete the cornea, (c) a *crystalline cone* formed by four cone cells, or *vitrellae,* (d) two *retinular cells* surrounding the cone, (e) seven retinular cells which form a *rhabdom* consisting of four *rhabdomeres,* and a number of *pigment cells.* Fibers from the *optic nerve* enter at the base of the ommatidium and communicate with the inner ends of the retinular cells.

Vision.   The *eyes* of the crayfish are supposed to produce an *erect mosaic* or "*apposition image*"; this is illustrated in Figure 10–8 where the ommatidia are represented by a–e and the fibers from the optic nerve by a'–e'. The rays of light from any point a, b, or c, will all encounter the dark pigment cells surrounding the ommatidia and be absorbed, except the ray which passes directly through the center of the cornea as d or e; this ray will penetrate to the retinulae, and thence to the fibers from the optic nerve. The sum of similar events involving all the ommatidia presumably provides a mosaic image. This method of image formation is especially well adapted for recording motion, since any change in the position of a large object affects the entire 2,500 ommatidia.

When the pigment surrounds the ommatidia (Fig. 10–7, B), vision is as described above; but it has been found that in dim light the pigment migrates partly toward the outer and partly toward the basal end of the ommatidia (Fig. 10–7, A). When this occurs the ommatidia no longer act separately, but a combined image is thrown on the retinular layer. The erect "*superposition image*" thus formed is probably a strong image with little detail.

A reflecting pigment is present in the eyes of certain crustaceans which consists of amorphous guanin and forms a reflecting layer below the

Fig. 10-8. Diagram of part of a compound eye which serves to explain mosaic vision. (After Lubbock.)

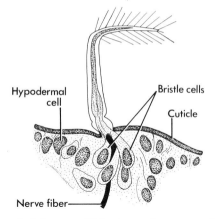

Hypodermal cell

Bristle cells

Cuticle

Nerve fiber

Fig. 10-9. Sensory hair from the statocyst of a shrimp, *Palaemonetes*. (After Prentiss; from Dahlgren and Kepner.)

rhabdomes. This layer increases the efficiency of the eye at low light intensities.

Hormones have been obtained from the eye stalk of many crustaceans. One brings about contraction of chromatophores in Crustacea. It produces melanophore expansion in frog tadpoles and melanophore contraction in fishes.

Statocysts. The statocysts of the crayfish are chitinous-walled sacs situated one in the basal segment of each antennule. In the base of the statocyst is a ridge, called the *sensory cushion*, and three sets of *hairs*, over 200 in all, each innervated by a single nerve fiber (Fig. 10–9). Among these hairs are a number of large grains of sand, the *statoliths*, which are placed there by the crayfish. Beneath the sensory cushion are *glands* which secrete a substance for the attachment of the statoliths to the hairs.

The statocyst for many years was considered an auditory organ, and it may possibly function as such, though later investigations have proven that it is primarily an organ of *equilibration*. The contact of the statoliths with the statocyst hairs determines the orientation of the body while swimming, because any change in the position of the animal causes a change in the position of the statoliths under the influence of gravity. When the crayfish changes its exoskeleton in the process of molting, the statocyst is also shed. Individuals that have just molted, or have had their statocysts removed, lose much of their powers of orientation. Perhaps the most convincing proof of the function of equilibration is that furnished by the experiments of Kreidl. This investigator placed shrimps, which had just molted and were therefore without statoliths, in filtered water. When supplied with iron filings, the animals filled their statocysts with them. A strong electromagnet was then held near the statocyst, and the shrimp took up a position corresponding to the resultant of the two pulls, that of gravity and of the magnet.

Muscular System. The principal muscles in the body of the crayfish are situated in the abdomen, and are used to bend that part of the animal forward upon the ventral surface of the thorax, thus producing backward locomotion in swimming. Other muscles extend the abdomen in preparation for another stroke. Figure 10–3 shows a longitudinal section of a crayfish. The powerful flexor muscles of the abdomen are shown. In the dorsal region are the less powerful extensor muscles. Other muscles of considerable size are situated within the tubular appendages, especially the chelipeds. A comparison of the skeleton and muscles of the crayfish with those of man is interesting. The skeleton of the crayfish is external and tubular, except in the ventral part of the thorax (Fig. 10–5). The muscles are internal, and attached to the inner surface of the skeleton. In man, on the other hand, the skeleton is internal and the muscles external.

Reproductive System. Crayfishes are normally *dioecious*, there being only a few cases on record where both male and female reproductive organs were found in a single specimen.

Male Reproductive Organs. The male organs (Fig. 10–10, A) consist of a *testis* and two *vasa deferentia* which open through the coxopodites of the fifth pair of walking legs. The testis lies just beneath the pericardial sinus (Fig. 10–3). It is a soft white body possessing two anterior lobes and a median posterior extension. The vasa deferentia are long coiled tubes.

Spermatogenesis. The primitive germ cells within the testis pass through two maturation divisions, and then metamorphose into spermatozoa. These are flattened spheroidal bodies when enclosed within the testis or vas deferens, but if examined in water or some other liquid they are seen to uncoil, finally becoming star-shaped.

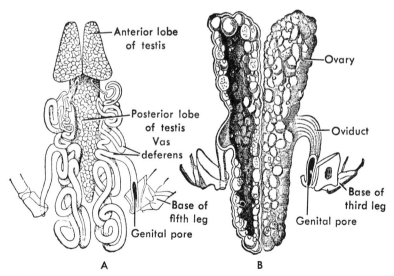

Anterior lobe
of testis

Ovary

Posterior lobe
of testis
Vas
deferens

Oviduct

Base of
third leg

Base of
fifth leg

Genital pore

Genital pore

A   B

Fig. 10-10. Reproductive organs of the crayfish. (A) Male. (B) Female. (From Shipley and MacBride.)

The spermatozoa remain in the testis and vasa deferentia until copulation takes place. As many as two million spermatozoa are contained in the vasa deferentia of a single specimen.

Female Reproductive Organs (Fig. 10–10. B). The *ovary* resembles the testis in form, and is similarly located in the body (Fig. 10–3). A short *oviduct* leads from near the center of each side of the ovary to the external aperture in the coxopodite of the third walking leg.

Oogenesis. The primitive germ cells in the walls of the ovary grow in size, become surrounded by a layer of small cells, the follicle, which eventually break down, allowing the eggs to escape into the central cavity of the ovary. At the time of laying, the ova pass out through the oviduct.

Breeding Habits. The details of copulation, egg laying, and the larval stages of crayfishes have been derived from observations of several different species.

The principal events in the reproduction of crayfishes may be enumerated as follows:

(1) Copulation, during which the spermatozoa are transferred from the vasa deferentia of the male to the seminal receptacle of the female; (2) egg laying; (3) the embryonic development of the eggs; (4) hatching; (5) the growth of the young crayfishes.

Copulation. Copulation in crayfishes, in most cases, takes place in September, October, or November of the first year of their lives, that is, when they are about 4 months old. A second copulating season is passed through at the end of the second summer, when the animals are about 17 months old, and a third copulating season occurs at the end of the third summer. At these times a male approaches a female, grasps her by her cephalic appendages, and, after a struggle, turns her over on her back. He then stands over her and transfers spermatozoa to the seminal receptacle. During this process, the spermatozoa flow out of the openings of the vasa deferentia, pass along the grooves on the first abdominal appendages of the male, and enter the seminal receptacle. Here they are stored during the winter. The *seminal receptacle* is a cavity in a fold of cuticle lying between the sterna of the segments bearing the fourth and fifth pairs of walking legs.

Egg Laying. The eggs are laid at night during the month of April. First the ventral side of the abdomen is thoroughly cleaned of all dirt by the hooks and comblike bristles near the end of the fifth pair of walking legs. A clear slime or *glair* is secreted by *cement glands* situated chiefly on the basal parts of the uropods, and on the endopodites of the other abdominal appendages. This milky glair gradually covers the swimmerets. The female then lies on her back, and an apron-like film of glair is constructed between the ends of the uropods and telson, and the bases of the second pair of walking legs. The eggs emerge from the openings of the oviducts in the bases of the third pair of walking legs, flow posteriorly, and become attached to the hairs on the swimmerets by strings of a substance no doubt secreted by the cement glands. This is brought about by the turning of the animal first on one side and then on the other a number of times. From 100 to over 600 greenish eggs are laid by a single female, depending upon the size and age of the animal. After the eggs are laid the crayfish rights herself, the apron of glair breaks down, and the abdomen is extended.

Fertilization. The method of fertilization has never been discovered. It is supposed that as the eggs are laid they pass over the opening of the seminal receptacle, and are then penetrated by the spermatozoa which were placed there by the male the preceding autumn.

Embryology. While the eggs are developing they are protected by the abdomen of the female, and are *aerated* and kept free from dirt by the waving of the swimmerets back and forth.

As already noted, the eggs of the crayfish are attached to the swimmerets of the mother by a glutinous secretion. They die if removed, although those of the lobster do not. All the eggs carried by one crayfish are in the same stage of development at the same time. Embryonic development is slow, several months being required. Most of the egg consists of *yolk*, which greatly interferes with cleavage (Fig. 10–11, A). The *fusion nucleus* lies within the yolk in a little island of cytoplasm. The nuclei that arise from it migrate to the periphery (B) and the egg then divides into incomplete columnar *blastomeres* called *primary yolk pyramids*, each with a single nucleus at the outer end (C). This *blastula* is not hollow but has a *blastocoel* filled with yolk globules, and a single layer of cells at the periphery which constitute the *blastoderm*. On one side of the egg the blastoderm cells increase in number and become columnar thus forming a *ventral plate*. Five thickenings of the ventral plate are recognizable (D); these are two *cephalic lobes* from which the eyes and cerebral ganglia will develop, two *thoraco-abdominal rudiments*, and one *endodermal disk* at the anterior end of which mesoderm cells are destined to arise. An invagination at the anterior end of the endodermal disk indicates the beginning of *gastrulation*.

Further changes in the ventral plate result in what is known as the *Nauplius* stage as illustrated in Figure 10–11, E. At this time the following rudiments are recognizable: two cephalic lobes with cerebral rudiments in the center; three pairs of outgrowths, which develop into the first and second antennae and the mandibles; the upper lip or labium; the crescent-shaped mouth; and the anus in the center of the thoraco-abdominal disk.

As development continues the thoraco-abdominal disk grows out into a long forked process, which bends underneath the egg toward the anterior end as shown in Figure 10–11, F. The following pairs of rudiments may now be seen: optic lobes, optic ganglia, cerebral ganglia, antennal ganglia, first antennae, second antennae, mandibles, first and second maxillae, first, second, and third maxillipeds, and first to fifth walking legs. The abdominal

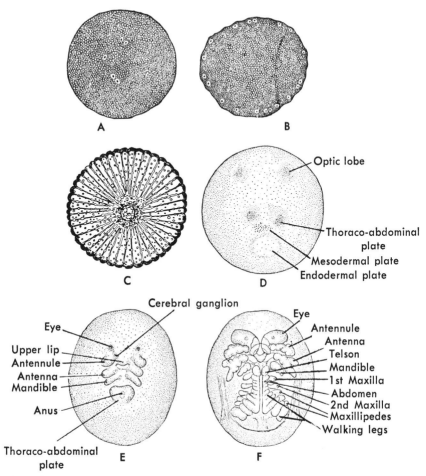

Fig. 10-11. Stages in the embryology of the crayfish. (A) Egg with a few cleavage nuclei. (B) Nuclei arranged near the surface. (C) Egg divided into yolk pyramids. (D) Embryo beginning to form. (E) Embryo in nauplius stage. (F) Older embryo. (After Reichenbach.)

segments with the telson at the end are less distinct; the labium is a triangular outgrowth; and the fold that becomes the carapace is now visible.

The time of the various stages in development is as follows: First week, cleavage; second week, embryo formation; third through fifth weeks, nauplius stage and further development prior to hatching. Hatching time is from the fifth to eighth week, depending upon temperature.

Hatching. In hatching, the egg capsule splits and the larva emerges head foremost. The helpless young crayfish would drop away from the mother at once but for a thread extending from its telson to the inner surface of the egg capsule.

Soon the larva possesses strength enough to grasp the egg string with its claws. The telson thread then breaks. After about 48 hours the larva passes into a *second stage*. This is inaugurated by the shedding of the first larval cuticular covering, a process known as *molting* or *ecdysis*. This casting off of the covering the body is not peculiar to the young, but occurs in adult crayfishes as well as in young and adults of many other animals. In the larval crayfish the cuticle of the first stage becomes loosened and drops off. In the meantime the hypodermal cells have secreted a new covering. Ecdysis is necessary before growth can proceed, since the chitin of which the exoskeleton is composed does not allow expansion. In adults it is also a means of getting rid of an old worn-out coat and acquiring a new one.

In the *second larval stage* the young crayfish is again supported immediately after casting off its covering by a thread extending from the new to the old telson. When the larva becomes strong enough, it grasps the old larval skin or swimmerets, and the telson thread drops off. The duration of the second larval stage is about six days.

No telson thread is present after the molt which ushers in the *third larval stage*, but the young is able at once to cling to the old cuticle. In about a week the third larvae become entirely independent of the mother, although they at first always return to her when separated. From this time on the larvae shift for themselves, growing rapidly, and molting at least four more times during the first summer. The first winter no growth nor molts occur. There are four or five molts the second summer, three or four in the third summer, and perhaps one or two in the fourth summer. The life of a single individual extends over a period of about three or more years.

Regeneration. The crayfish and many other crustaceans have the power of regenerating lost parts, but to a much more limited extent than such animals as *Hydra* and the earthworm. Experiments have been performed upon almost every one of the appendages as well as the eye. The second and third maxillipeds, the walking legs, the swimmerets, and the eye have all been injured or extirpated at various times and subsequently renewed the lost parts. Many species of crayfish of various ages have been used for these experiments. The growth of regenerated tissue is more frequent and rapid in young specimens than in adults.

The new structure is not always like that of the one removed. For example, when the annulus containing the sperm receptacle of an adult is extirpated, another is regenerated, but, although this is as large as that of the adult, it is comparable in complexity to that of an early larval stage. A more remarkable phenomenon is the regeneration of an apparently functional (tactile) antennalike organ in place of a degenerate eye which was removed from the blind crayfish, *Orconectes pellucidus testii*. In this case a nonfunctional organ was replaced by a functional one of a different character. The regeneration of a new part which differs from the part removed is termed *heteromorphosis*.

Autotomy. Perhaps the most interesting morphological structure connected with the regenerative process in the crayfish is the definite breaking point near the bases of the walking legs. If the chelae are injured, they are broken off by the crayfish at the breaking point. The other walking legs, if injured, may be thrown off at the free joint between the second and third segments. A new leg, as large as the one lost, develops from the end of the stump remaining. This breaking off of the legs at a definite point is known as *autotomy*, a phenomenon that also occurs in a number of other animals. The breaking point in decapod crustaceans is in the base of the ischium. The leg is flexed by the autotomizer muscle until the ischium comes in contact with the coxa. Continued pull of the autotomizer muscle separates the leg at the breaking point. The muscles are not damaged and the valve and diaphragm prevent haemorrhage. Autotomy results when the leg is stimulated by some harmful agent or may be brought about in certain instances by injury to a ventral ganglion or by a strong general stimulus. Immediately after the leg has been thrown off, a membrane of ectoderm cells covers the canal through which the nerve and blood passed; five days later regeneration begins by an outward growth of the ectoderm cells which lined the exoskeleton. An interesting point in this new growth is that the muscles of the regenerated part are probably produced by ectoderm cells, whereas in the embryonic development of the crayfish the muscles are supposed to arise from the mesoderm.

The power of autotomy is of advantage to the crayfish, since the wound closer more quickly if the leg is lost at the breaking point.

As in the earthworm, the *rate of regeneration* depends upon the amount of tissue removed. If one chela is amputated, a new chela regenerates less rapidly than if both chelae and some of the other walking legs are removed.

Behavior. When at rest, the crayfish usually faces the entrance to its place of concealment, and extends its antennae. It is thus in a position to learn the nature of any approaching object without being detected. Activity at this time is reduced to the movements of a few of the appendages and the gills; the scaphognathites of the second maxillae move back and forth baling water out of the forward end of the gill chambers; the swimmerets are in constant motion creating a current of water; the maxillipeds are likewise kept moving; and the antennae and eye stalks bend from place to place.

Crayfishes are more active at nightfall and at daybreak than during the remainder of the day. At these times they venture out of their hiding places in search of food, their movements being apparently all utilitarian and not for spontaneous play or exercise.

Locomotion. Locomotion is effected in two ways, walking and swimming. Crayfishes are able to walk in any direction, forward usually, but also sidewise, obliquely, or backward. In walking, the fourth pair of legs are most effective and bear nearly all of the weight of the animal; the fifth pair serve as props, and to push the body forward; the second and third pairs are less efficient for walking, since they are modified to serve as prehensile organs, and as toilet implements. Swimming is not resorted to under ordinary conditions, but only when the animal is frightened or shocked. In such a case the crayfish extends the abdomen, spreads out the uropods and telson, and, by sudden contractions of the bundles of flexor abdominal muscles, bends the abdomen and darts backwards. The swimming reaction apparently is not voluntary, but is almost entirely reflex.

Equilibration. The crayfish either at rest or in motion is in a state of unstable equilibrium, and must maintain its body in the normal position by its own efforts. The force of gravity tends to turn the body over. From a large number of experiments it has been proven that the statocysts are the organs of equilibration. The structure of these organs has been described. The contact of the statoliths with the statocyst hairs furnishes the stimulus which causes the animal to maintain an upright position.

When placed on its back, the crayfish has some difficulty in righting itself. Two methods of regaining its normal position are employed. The usual method is that of raising itself on one side and allowing the body to tip over by the force of gravity. The second method is that of contracting the flexor abdominal muscles which causes a quick backward flop, bringing the body right side up.

Senses and Their Location. The sense of *touch* in crayfishes is perhaps the most valuable, since it aids them in finding food, avoiding obstacles, and in many other ways. It is located in specialized hairs on various parts of the body. *Vision* in crayfishes is probably of minor importance, since the compound eyes are almost useless in recognizing form, and are of real value only in detecting moving objects. No reactions to *sound* have ever been observed in crayfishes, and apparently they do not hear, although tactile reflexes may simulate reaction to sound. In aquatic animals it is so difficult to distinguish between reactions of *taste* and *smell* that these senses are both included in the term *chemical sense*. The end organs of this sense are distributed all over the body.

Reactions to Stimuli. *Contact.* The crayfish has tactile receptors on all surface areas. Receptors are concentrated on extremities, ventral surface, and mouth parts. The antennae are usually considered the special organs of touch, but experiments seem to prove that they are not so sensitive as other parts of the body. The tactile hairs are plumed, and supplied by a single nerve. *Positive* reactions to contact are exhibited by crayfishes to a marked degree, the animals seeking to place their bodies in contact with a solid object, if possible. The normal position of the crayfish when at rest under a stone is such as to bring its side or dorsal surface in contact with the walls of its hiding place. This, no doubt, is of distinct advantage, since it forces the animal into a place of safety.

Light. Light of various intensities in the majority of cases causes the crayfish to retreat. Individuals prefer colored lights to white, having a special liking for red. Negative reactions to light play an important role in the animal's life, since they influence it to seek a dark place where it is concealed from its enemies.

Chemicals. The reactions of the crayfish to food are due in part to a chemical sense. All surfaces seem sensitive to chemicals. The anterior appendages, however, are the most sensitive, especially the outer ramus of the antennule. *Positive reactions* result from the application of food substances. For example, if meat juice is placed in the water near an animal, the antennae move slightly and the mouth parts perform vigorous chewing movements. The meat causes activity and, if the food is touched, localization of the food. Acids, salts, sugar, and other chemicals produce a sort of *negative reaction* indicated by scratching the carapace, rubbing the chelae, or pulling at the part stimulated.

Habit Formation. It has been shown by certain simple experiments that crayfishes are able to learn habits and to modify them. They learn by experience, and modify their behavior slowly or quickly, depending upon their familiarity with the situation. Proprioceptors as well as external sensory receptors are factors in habit formation.

(2) Asellus

The water sowbug or water slater, *Asellus* (Fig. 10–12), is a common member of the order Isopoda in many shallow streams and ponds of the Northern

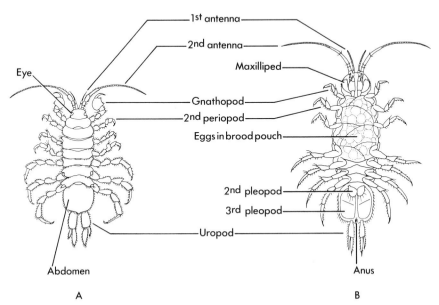

Fig. 10-12. *Asellus communis.* (A) Dorsal view of male. (B) Ventral view of female. (A, from Van Name, after Harger; B, from Van Name.)

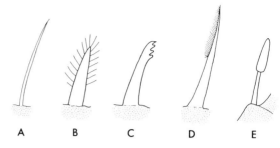

Fig. 10-13. Setae of *Asellus*. (A) Simple tactile seta from leg. (B) Plumose seta from first maxilla. (C) Spinose seta from first maxilla. (D) Pectinate seta from maxilliped. (E) Olfactory seta from first antenna. (Not to same scale.)

Hemisphere. Comparison with the crayfish will show a form that has a similar number of segments organized in different functional groupings.

External Anatomy. *Asellus* tapers to a narrow small head with sessile eyes and two pair of uniramous antennae. The first pair of antennae bear a number of olfactory setae (Fig. 10–13, E). The mandibles bear a three-jointed palp, cutting teeth and a molar process. A spine row prevents escape of food being ground by the molar process (Fig. 10–15). Two pair of maxillae posterior to the mandibles aid in food handling.

There are eight thoracic appendages as in the crayfish. Only the first forms a food-handling maxilliped that can be considered a mouthpart. The segment it is borne on is fused with the head. The following seven thoracic segments are separate and each bears a pair of legs.

The first pair of legs is more specialized than the rest. It has a terminal segment (dactyl) that can fold against the segment bearing it (propod). In

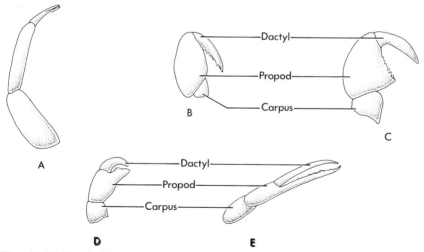

Fig. 10-14. Terminal three segments of crustacean appendages showing varying levels of chela development. (A) Fourth leg of female *Asellus communis*, no chelate function. (B) Gnathopod of female *A. communis*. (C) Gnathopod of female *Colubotelson thomsoni*. (D) Cheliped of the crab, *Planes minuta*. (E) Cheliped of *Portunus pelagicus*. (D and E modified from Hale.)

Pharynx

Molar process

Spine row

Incisor process

Fig. 10-15. Section through mandibles of an aquatic isopod showing opposing action of right and left cutting (incisor) and grinding (molar) processes. An inwardly directed spine row prevents escape of food materials being ground by the molar processes.

some related species the side of the propod is expanded to form a more efficient grasping organ. Comparison of these types with the chelae of a crayfish show how the pincer has probably formed by even greater growth of the lateral surface of the propod (Fig. 10–14). This simple illustration, although it involves different thoracic appendages, indicates how a simple modification can change the functional ability of an appendage. Thus, part of the success of the arthropods has been due to the presence of many segments with similar appendages, which have undergone individual modifications selected to fill the needs of their diverse ways of life.

The abdominal segments form a unit bearing five pair of pleopods and a terminal pair of branched uropods. The female has only four pair of pleopods and the first pair is greatly reduced. The second pair of pleopods in the male is used for sperm transfer. The third pair bears a protective cover for the remaining pair. The uropods seem to have a sensory function and are held poised like a pair of posterior antennae.

Internal Anatomy. The stomach contains a gastric mill and receives two pairs of long digestive glands. The intestine is straight and tubular.

The heart lies in a blood sinus in the posterior thoracic region. In the head are a prominent pair of maxillary glands which are thought to be excretory organs. As with other arthropods there is a supraesophageal ganglion with circumesophageal connectives to the subesophageal ganglion. Smaller ganglia are located along the ventral nerve cord.

Fig. 10-16. *Asellus* egg showing the appendage which is an early developmental feature that is lost after hatching of the embryo.

Reproduction.   *Asellus* belongs to a large group of crustaceans that carry their eggs in a temporary brood pouch. The pouch is formed by platelike expansions (*oostegites*) from the coxal segments of the first four pairs of legs (Fig. 10–12, B). The male carries the female with his fourth legs prior to fertilization. Fertilization occurs as soon as the posterior half of the female exoskeleton is shed. After fertilization the anterior half of the exoskeleton is shed and the brood pouch is fully developed. Eggs are rapidly deposited in it.

A peculiarity of the embryology of *Asellus* eggs is the growth of an appendage (Fig. 10–16) that seems an aid for respiration by the embryo. The appendage disappears from its dorsal, thoracic attachment shortly after hatching. The young isopod resembles the adult but has one less pair of legs. *Asellus*, with the egg appendage, hatches in about two weeks. This contrasts with a six months incubation period in a southern hemisphere isopod (Fig.

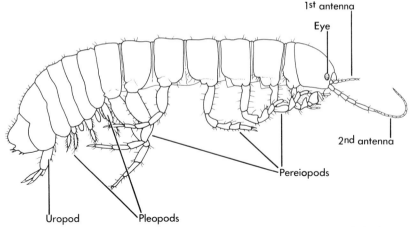

Fig. 10-17. *Colubotelson thomsoni.* A representative of a group of fresh-water isopods which are nearly the ecological equivalents of *Asellus* in the Southern Hemisphere. (From Engemann, 1963.)

10–17), which lacks the appendage. It seems that the appendage is one of several factors enabling *Asellus* to develop quite rapidly.

Ecology. *Asellus* is a detritus feeder. They reach greatest abundance in mildly polluted waters. Sometimes large aggregations of them occur. The latter phenomenon led W. C. Allee, one of the leading early ecologists in this country, to investigate many facets of their behavior. The isopod forms an important item in the diet of many game fish. Since it feeds on the abundant decaying organic matter, or detritus, found in its habitat and can be fed upon by useful food fishes it serves as an efficient link in the food chain.

(3) Other Crustacea

The Crustacea are arthropods most of which live in the water and breathe by means of gills. The body is divided into head, thorax, and abdomen, or the head and thorax may be fused, forming a cephalothorax. The head usually consists of five segments fused together; it bears two pairs of antennae (feelers), one pair of mandibles (jaws), and two pairs of maxillae. The thorax bears a variable number of appendages, some of which are usually locomotory. The abdominal segments are generally narrow and more mobile than those of the head and thorax; they bear appendages which are often reduced in size.

Hormones in crustaceans have been investigated in a number of the *Decapoda*. Secretions originating in nerve cells of the brain and X-organ move along neurons and accumulate in the sinus gland of the eyestalk (Fig. 10–18). The secretions, or hormones, are involved in regulation of such things as

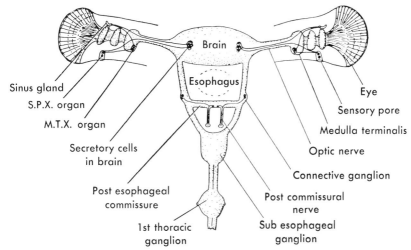

Fig. 10-18. Diagram of the front part of the nervous system of a decapod, to show the location of some important centers of hormone secretion. (From J. Green. *A Biology of Crustacea.* Copyright 1961 by H. F. & G. Witherby Ltd. London.)

color changes, molting and related physiological changes. A Y-organ in one of the head appendages is also involved in regulation of molting.

Circadian rhythms have been observed most extensively in *Uca*, the fiddler crab. Circadian rhythms are cyclic changes that approximate a day in length. Because *Uca* has such cyclic changes in coloration that persist when it is placed in a constant environment it is said to have a "biological clock." Such changes presumably involve cyclic physiological or metabolic rhythms that develop in phase with cyclic events in nature and are somewhat regulated by the external environment. Studies of such rhythms have become increasingly important with the increased speed of transportation. Perhaps studies of such invertebrates will help develop safe methods of resetting "biological clocks" of statesmen flown to different time zones so they can negotiate at peak efficiency during resting hours of their homeland.

A special type of such cyclic rhythms especially common in planktonic and pelagic crustaceans are the *vertical migrations* normally regulated by light. Forms exhibiting such activity include cladocerans, copepods, euphausids, and decapods. The movement is typically up into or toward surface waters in the evening hours and back down into deeper waters at other times except for some upward movement around dawn. In shallow fresh water lakes it may involve a vertical movement of only a few meters whereas some larger crustaceans in the ocean undertake daily vertical migrations of nearly a thousand meters.

Ecology.   Crustaceans are very important members of aquatic ecosystems. The food value of shrimps, crabs, and lobsters is well known. Of even greater importance are such planktonic genera as *Calanus, Daphnia*, and *Cyclops*. They harvest smaller plankton organisms, including the photosynthetic forms, and serve as food organisms for many larger animals. The marine copepod, *Calanus finmarchicus*, is perhaps the most abundant animal in the world. Other crustaceans are important as scavengers and predators.

Isopods are the only crustaceans to achieve much success on land. They are frequently the dominant invertebrate detritus feeder in the litter layer of forests and grasslands.

Classification. The diversity of the crustaceans necessitates a somewhat complex classification. The more important orders are briefly described in the following pages. The term Entomostraca is no longer used in classification, although it is still useful to designate an odd mixture of subclasses including the small crustaceans once thought to be insect-like.

Subclass I. Branchiopoda

Branchiopoda are free-swimming crustaceans with flattened, leaflike thoracic appendages that are respiratory in function. There is usually a carapace.

Order 1. Cephalocarida. An order of few species first reported in 1955. Hermaphroditic, marine mud-dwellers; carapace covers the head region; two

Fig. 10-19. Cephalocarida. *Hutchinsoniella macracantha* with the nearest known relatives of the Cephalocarida, *Lepidocaris rhyniensis* (with antennae showing), a Devonian fossil. (From Sanders, 1957; *Lepidocaris*, from Sanders after Scourfield.)

ovisacs, each with one egg, carried on the genital segment; abdomen of ten segments. Sanders (1957) proposes these as the closest living relatives of the primitive crustacean stock. Ex. *Hutchinsoniella macracantha* (Fig. 10–19) from Long Island Sound.

Order 2. Anostraca.   Body elongate; eyes stalked; thoracic segments many, no carapace. Ex. *Eubranchipus vernalis* (Fig. 10–20, D): fairy shrimp; pinkish; fresh-water pools, especially in spring; eastern North America. *Artemia salina*: brine shrimp; western U.S.

Order 3. Notostraca (Fig. 10–20, A).   Body elongate; eyes sessile; thoracic segments many; carapace broad, shield-shaped. Ex. *Apus lucasanus*: about 4 cm long; in fresh water; western U.S.

Order 4. Conchostraca.   Body enclosed in carapace in the form of a bivalve shell; eyes sessile; antennae large, biramous. Ex. *Estheria morsei* (Fig. 10–20 B); shell about 12 mm long; central and western United States.

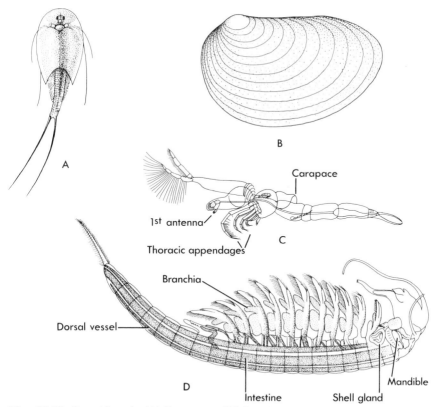

Fig. 10-20. Branchiopoda. (A) Notostraca. (B) Conchostraca. *Estheria*. (C) Cladocera. *Leptodora*. (D) Anostraca. *Branchipus*. (B, after Sars; C, after Smith; D, after Sedgwick.)

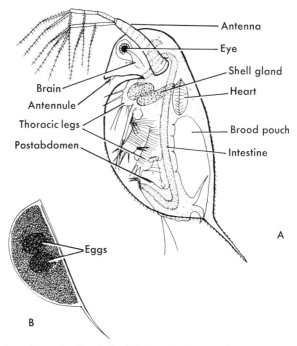

Antenna

Eye

Shell gland

Heart

Brain

Antennule

Brood pouch

Thoracic legs

Postabdomen

Intestine

A

Eggs

B

Fig. 10-21. Branchiopoda. *Daphnia.* (A) Female. (B) Ephippium containing fertilized eggs. (A, after Claus.)

Order 5. Cladocera.   Bivalve carapace usually covers the body but not the head; eyes sessile; antennae large, biramous; four to six thoracic segments. Ex. *Daphnia pulex* (Fig. 10–21): water flea; reddish; sharp caudal spine; ventral beak large; America. *Simocephalus vetulus*: no caudal spine; America. *Leptodora hyalina* (Fig. 10–20, C): shell small; abdomen terminated by two claws; antennae large in male.

Subclass II. Ostracoda

Free-swimming crustaceans with a bivalve carapace; compound eyes present or absent; two or less thoracic, nonphyllopod appendages; mandibular palp, usually biramous.

Order 1. Myodocopa.   Marine; second antennae biramous, one branch large, the other small; deep notch in anterior margin of shell. Ex. *Sarsiella zostericola*: three eyes present; notch in shell (antennal sinus) absent in female; eastern United States.

Order 2. Podocopa (Fig. 10–22).   Mostly in fresh water; second antennae uniramous; no notch in anterior margin of shell. Ex. *Eucypris virens*: in fresh water; shell covered with short hairs; one median eye; second antennae with

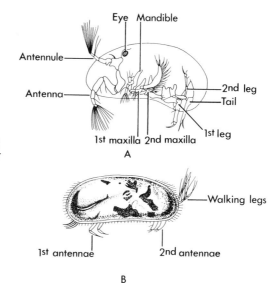

Fig. 10-22. Ostracoda. (A) *Cypris*. (B) *Candona*. (A, after Zender; B, after Baird.)

five natatory bristles; parthenogenetic; no males known; cosmopolitan. *Loxoconcha impressa*: marine; Vineyard Sound.

Subclass III. Mystacocarida

Microscopic; marine; in the interstitial water of sandy beaches; four pair of thoracic legs. The single order Mystacocarida contains only one genus, *Derocheilocaris*. Considered close relatives of the Copepoda.

Subclass IV. Copepoda

Free-swimming or parasitic; compound eyes and carapace absent; typically with six pairs of thoracic appendages; marine and fresh water. About eight orders. Free-living species are in the first three orders below.

Order 1. Calanoida. Body distinctly divided into an anterior metasome and a narrow posterior urosome; first antennae approximately as long as body; females with a single egg sac. Ex. *Calanus finmarchicus*: marine; yellow or red; pelagic in North Atlantic; important as fish food. *Diaptomus sanguineus*: in fresh water; bright red; about 2 mm long; in pools in spring; North America.

Order 2. Cyclopoida. Body tapers to a narrow urosome; first antennae no longer than metasome; two egg sacs carried laterally by the female. Ex. *Cyclops viridis* (Fig. 10–23, A): usually greenish; small ponds; United States and Europe. *Ergasilus versicolor*: parasitic on gills of bullhead and catfish.

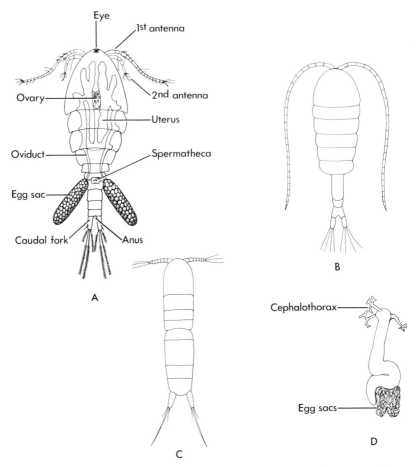

Fig. 10-23. Copepoda. (A) *Cyclops*, dorsal view of female showing cyclopoid body type. (B) Calanoid body type, diagrammatic. (C) Harpacticoid body type, diagrammatic. (D) *Lernaea*, parasite of fish (haddock). (A, after Hartog; D, after Scott.)

Order 3. Harpacticoida. Urosome not distinctly narrower than metasome; first antennae no longer than head segment; female with one medial egg sac; typically from surface of bottom sediments in shallow water. Ex. *Cantho-camptus assimilis*; ponds and ditches; North America.

Order 4. Lernaeoida. Parasitic; segments usually not evident. Ex. *Lernaea branchialis* (Fig. 10–23, C): body of fertilized female, wormlike, twisted; two convoluted egg sacs; on gills of codfish, etc.

Subclass V. Branchiura

Parasitic on marine and fresh-water fishes; no egg sacs; body flattened; five pair of thoracic appendages. Sometimes considered an order of the Copepoda. Order of the same name as the subclass. Ex. *Argulus laticauda*

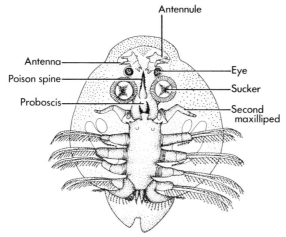

Fig. 10-24. Brachiura. *Argulus,* ventral view of female. (After Wilson.)

(Fig. 10–24): fish louse; suckers flank a hollow spine used to penetrate host tissues; about 6 mm long; on eel, flounder, etc.

Subclass VI. Cirripedia

Sessile as adults; no compound eyes in adult; carapace enclosing body; mostly hermaphroditic.

Order 1. Thoracica. Barnacles; marine; body surrounded by calcareous shell; six pairs of biramous thoracic legs. Ex. *Lepas anatifera* (Fig. 10–25, A and B): goose barnacle; body attached by short stalk; shell of five thin plates; cosmopolitan. *Balanus balanoides* (Fig. 10–25, C and D): rock barnacle; shell thick, closed by two hinged plates; stalk absent; both coasts of U.S.

Order 2. Acrothoracica. Parasitic; no calcareous shell; body covered by large mantle. Ex. *Alcippe lampas*: males, small, legless, and attached to females; bores into *Natica* shells containing hermit crabs: Woods Hole, Mass.

Order 3. Rhizocephala. Parasitic; no appendages, alimentary canal nor segmentation in adult; attached by stalk with roots penetrating tissue of host. Ex. *Sacculina carcini* (Fig. 10–26): parasitic on decapod crustaceans degenerating into a sac lying on the ventral surface between the thorax and abdomen.

Subclass VII. Malacostraca

Lobsters, crayfish, crabs, etc.: mostly large crustaceans; usually five segments in the head, eight in the thorax, and six in the abdomen; gastric mill in the stomach. Twelve orders are usually placed in five divisions or superorders. Two orders, the Spelaeogriphacea and Thermosbaenacea are known

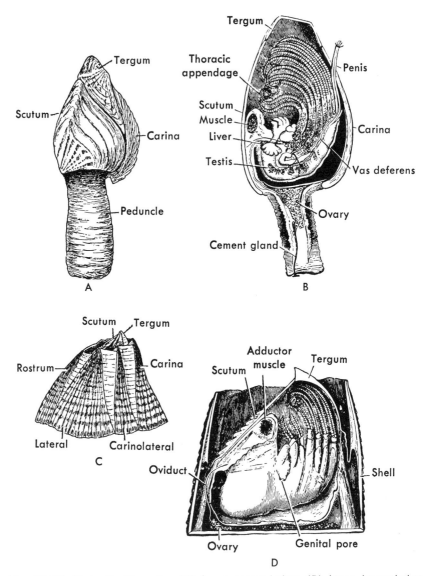

Fig. 10-25. Cirripedia. Thoracica. (A) *Lepas*, external view. (B) *Lepas*, internal view. (C) *Balanus*, external view. (D) *Balanus*, internal view. (A, B, after Darwin; C, D, after Claus.)

only from one or a few rare species from caverns and hot springs; they are omitted from the following account. The division Phyllocarida contains the Nebaliacea, forms with a large carapace. The division Syncarida contains only the Anaspidacea. The division Pericarida is very large and contains the Mysidacea, Cumacea, Tanaidacea, Isopoda, and Amphipoda. The Pericarida

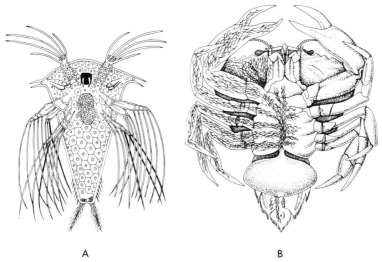

Fig. 10-26. Cirripedia. Rhizocephala. *Sacculina*. (A) Nauplius larva. (B) Adult attached like a sac to the undersurface of the abdomen of a crab and sending "roots" throughout the crab's body for extracting nourishment. (After Leuckart.)

have little or no carapace and are the only crustaceans with oostegites forming a brood pouch. The division Eucarida is also very large; it contains only the Euphausiacea and Decapoda, which have the carapace covering the thorax. The division Hoplocarida contains only the Stomatopoda.

Order 1. Nebaliacea (Fig. 10–27, A).   Primitive marine Malacostraca with seven abdominal segments; stalked eyes; thorax with eight pairs of leaflike gills. Ex. *Nebalia bipes*: body slender, compressed; eggs carried by setae on the thoracic appendages of female.

Order 2. Anaspidacea.   Fresh water; no carapace; a tail fan. Ex. *Anaspides tasmaniae* (Fig. 10–27, B): from ponds in Tasmania.

Order 3. Mysidacea (Fig. 10–27, C).   Carapace covers almost entire thorax; eyes stalked; thoracic appendages all biramous. Ex. *Mysis stenolepis*: body elongate, cylindrical; abdomen bends between first and second segments; Atlantic Coast of North America.

Order 4. Cumacea (Fig. 10–28, A).   Carapace does not cover entire thorax; eyes sessile; no tail fan. Ex. *Diastylis quadrispinosus*: a spine on each side of carapace; New Jersey northward. Cumaceans inhabit the bottom sand and mud; all are marine.

Order 5. Tanaidacea.   Small, marine, bottom-dwelling crustaceans. Usually in burrows or tubes. Isopod-like but carapace covers first two

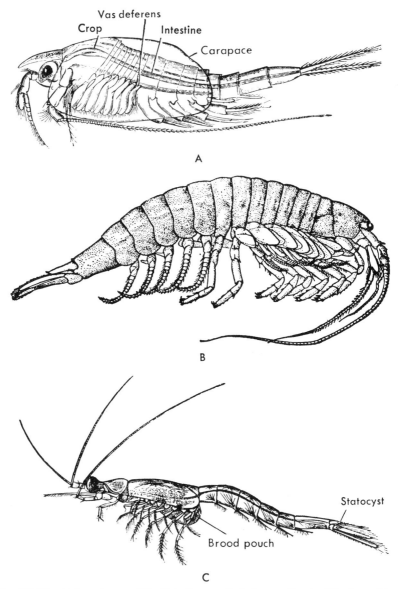

Fig. 10-27. Malacostraca. (A) Nebaliacea; *Nebalia geoffroyi*. (B) Anaspidacea; *Anaspides tasmaniae*. (C) Mysidacea; *Mysis oculata*. (A, after Claus; B, after Woodward; C, after Sars.)

thoracic segments; strongly developed chelae on first leg. Ex. *Apseudes* (Fig. 10–28, C).

Order 6. Isopoda. Marine, fresh water, terrestrial, or parasitic; eyes sessile; body usually flattened dorso-ventrally.

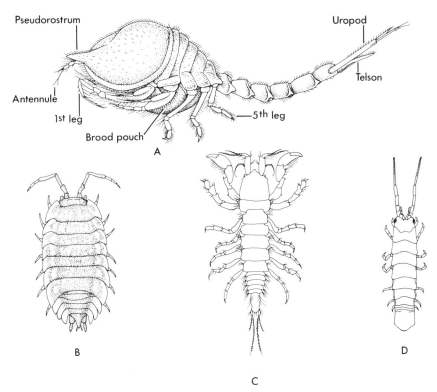

Fig. 10-28. Malacostraca. (A) Cumacea; *Diastylis goodsiri*. (B) Isopoda; *Oniscus asellus*. (C) Tanaidacea; *Apseudes australis*. (D) Isopoda; *Idothea rectilinea*. (A, after Sars; B, after Smith; C, after Hale; D, after Johnson and Snook.)

Suborder 1. Flabellifera. Uropods flattened and forming part of a tail fan; all marine. Ex. *Limnoria lignorum*: bores in submerged wooden structures causing considerable damage.

Suborder 2. Valvifera. Marine, uropods form a protective cover for the pleopods. Ex. *Idothea rectilinea* (Fig. 10–28, D): about 2 cm; California.

Suborder 3. Asellota. Uropods styliform abdominal segments usually fused. Ex. *Asellus communis* (Fig. 10–12): common among vegetation in fresh water of the United States.

Suborder 4. Phreatoicidea. Uropods styliform; abdominal segments separate; fresh water in the Southern Hemisphere. Ex. *Colubotelson thomsoni* (Fig. 10–17): montane pools; Tasmania.

Suborder 5. Epicarida. Uropods styliform; parasitic on other crustaceans; mostly marine. Ex. *Probopyrus pandalicola*: parasitic in the gill chamber of *Palaemonetes vulgaris*, a shrimp that sometimes moves up into streams of the United States.

Suborder 6. Oniscoidea. Pleopods adapted for air breathing; most species terrestrial. Ex. *Oniscus asellus* (Fig. 10–28, B): sow bug; under stones, logs,

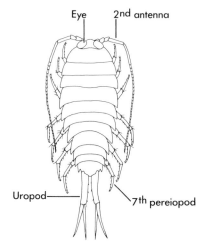

Fig. 10-29. Isopoda. *Ligia exotica*. Dorsal view of female. (After Van Name.)

bark etc.; introduced into the northern United States from Europe. *Ligia exotica* (Fig. 10–29): one of many similar species common on marine beaches of the world.

Order 7. Amphipoda. Mostly marine; usually laterally compressed; eyes sessile; no carapace; no tail fan. Ex. *Talorchestia longicornis*: beach flea; body large; two large eyes; on sand beaches; Cape Cod to New Jersey. *Gammarus fasciatus* (Fig. 10–30, A): in fresh-water ponds and streams; eastern United States. *Caprella geometrica* (Fig. 10–30, B): body elongate, slender; on seaweeds and hydroids; Cape Cod to Virginia.

Order 8. Euphausiacea. Filter-feeding; pelagic; marine crustaceans. None of the thoracic appendages are developed as maxillipeds. Ex. *Euphausia pacifica*: 25 mm; common off southern California.

Order 9. Decapoda. Lobsters, crayfish, shrimps, crabs. This order contains over 8,000 species of comparatively large and familiar crustaceans. The

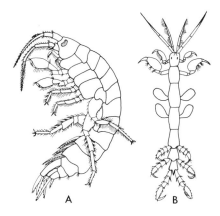

Fig. 10-30. Malacostraca. Amphipoda. (A) *Gammarus fasciatus*. (B) *Caprella geometrica*. (From Paulmier.)

carapace covers the entire thorax; three pairs of maxillipeds; five pairs of thoracic walking legs, the first pair usually larger and with pinching claws (chelae); mostly marine.

Fig. 10-31. Malacostraca. Decapoda. (A) *Palaemonetes vulgaris*, the prawn. (B) *Pagurus*, the hermit crab, in snail shell. (C) *Pagurus*, removed from snail shell. (D) *Callinectes sapidus*, the edible or blue crab. (E) *Uca crenulata*, the fiddler crab. (A, from Davenport; B, after Emerton; C, after Cuvier; D, after Rathbun; E, after Johnson and Snook.)

Suborder 1. Natantia. Shrimps and prawns. Pleopods adapted for swimming; rostrum long; body typically long and round or laterally compressed. Ex. *Crago septemspinosus*: edible shrimp; eastern coast. *C. nigricauda*: blacktail shrimp; Pacific Coast. *Palaemonetes vulgaris* (Fig. 10–31, A): prawn; eastern coast.

Suborder 2. Reptantia. Lobsters, crayfish, and crabs. Usually dorso-ventrally flattened; first pair of legs usually chelipeds; rostrum not markedly keeled if present. Divided into three sections.

Section Macrura contains species with a well-developed, extended abdomen. Ex. *Homarus americanus*: lobster; marine. *Orconectes virilis*: crayfish; central states.

Section Anomura contains species with the abdomen bearing uropods and flexed under the thorax or soft and extended asymmetrically. Ex. *Emerita talpoida*: sand crab; both coasts. *Pagurus longicarpus* (Fig. 10–31, B, C): small hermit crab; East Coast. *P. hirsutiusculus*: blue and white banding on legs; west coast.

Section Brachyura contains the true crabs. Uropods are usually lacking on the abdomen which is reduced and tightly flexed under the thorax. Ex. *Libinia emarginata*: spider crab; Atlantic Coast. *Cancer irroratus*: rock crab; edible; northeast coast. *C. magister*; edible crab; Pacific Coast. *Callinectes sapidus* (Fig. 10–31, D; 10–32): blue or edible crab; southeast coast. *Uca pugnax*: fiddler crab; East Coast. *U. crenulata*: fiddler crab (Fig. 10–31, E); California.

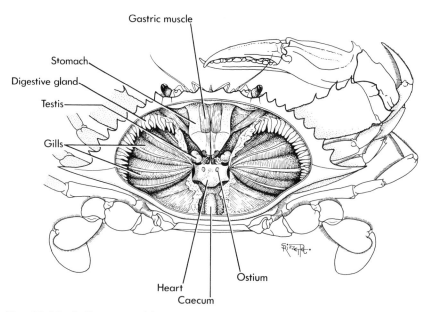

Fig. 10-32. *Callinectes sapidus,* carapace removed to show arrangement of internal organs.

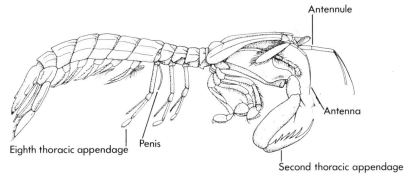

Fig. 10-33. Malacostraca. Stomatopoda. *Squilla mantis*, male. (After Calman.)

Order 10. Stomatopoda (Fig. 10–33).   Marine; body elongate with broad abdomen; carapace covering three of seven thoracic segments; stalked eyes; gills on first five pairs of abdominal appendages; second pair of maxillipeds very large and subchelate. Ex. *Squilla empusa*: body up to 25 cm long; in burrows in mud near shore; edible; eastern coast. *Pseudosquilla biglowi*: similar to *Squilla*; south California coast.

2 / Class II. Insecta

The insects are treated separately in the next chapter. This is done because of the large size of the class, to emphasize their importance, and as a convenience for varied course coverage modified for various curricular systems. Their general features are (a) three body regions—*head, thorax*, and *abdomen*; (b) one pair of antennae; (c) mouth parts—mandibles, maxillae, and labium; (d) usually two pair of wings; and (e) three pair of thoracic legs.

3 / Class III. Chilopoda

The Chilopoda are called centipedes (Fig. 10–35). The body is flattened dorso-ventrally, and consists of from 15 to 173 segments, each of which bears one pair of legs except the last two and the one just back of the head. The latter bears a pair of poison claws called maxillipeds, with which insects, worms, mollusks, and other small animals are killed for food. The antennae are long consisting of at least twelve segments.

The internal anatomy of a common centipede is shown in Figure 10–34. The alimentary canal is simple; into it open the excretory organs—two Malpighian tubules. The tracheae are branched as in insects and open by a pair of stigmata in almost every segment. The reproductive organs are

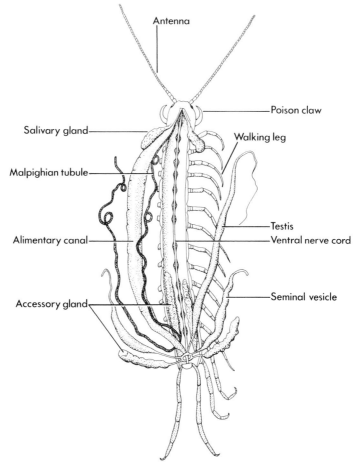

Fig. 10-34. Chilopoda. *Lithobius forficatus*, dissected to show the internal organs. (After Vogt and Jung, after Sedgwick.)

connected with several accessory glands. Eggs are usually laid. Those of *Lithobius* are laid singly and covered with earth.

The centipedes are swift-moving creatures. Many of them live under the bark of logs, or under stones. The genera *Lithobius*, *Geophilus*, and *Scutigera* are common. The poisonous centipedes of tropical countries belong to the genus *Scolopendra*. They may reach a foot in length, and their bite is painful and even dangerous to man. Fossil Chilopoda have been found in amber of oligocene age. Four of the families in this class are as follows:

FAMILY 1. GEOPHILIDAE (Fig. 10–35, A). Body long, with over 31 segments; eyes absent; antennae with 14 segments; young leave egg with full number of segments and legs. Ex. *Geophilus rubens*: about 45 mm long; 47 to 53 pairs of legs; eastern and central states.

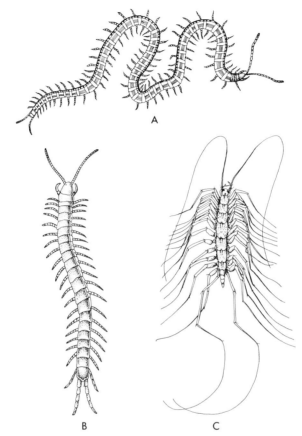

Fig. 10-35. Chilopoda. (A) Geophilidae; *Geophilus longicornis*. (B) Scolopendridae; *Scolopendra morsitans*. (C) Scutigeridae; *Scutigera forceps*. (B, from Claus; C, from Herrick.)

FAMILY 2. SCOLOPENDRIDAE. Body long, with 21 to 23 segments; eyes present or absent; antennae with 17 to 31 segments; young leave egg with full number of segments and legs. Ex. *Scolopendra morsitans* (Fig. 10–35, B): 21 pairs of legs; eyes present; cosmopolitan. *Scolopocrytops sexspinosa*: 23 pairs of legs; eyes absent; United States.

FAMILY 3. LITHOBIIDAE. Body with legs on 15 segments; maxillary palp with three segments; young leave egg with seven pairs of legs. Ex. *Lithobius forficatus* (Fig. 10–34): body about 3 mm long; antennae with 33 to 43 segments; America, Europe.

FAMILY 4. SCUTIGERIDAE. Body short, with about 15 segments; 15 pairs very long legs, last pair longest; antennae very long. Ex. *Scutigera forceps* (Fig. 10–35, C): about 25 mm long; last pair of legs about 50 mm long; United States.

4 / Class IV. Diplopoda

The Diplopoda are called millipedes (Fig. 10–37). The body is subcylindrical, and consists of from about 25 to more than 100 segments, according to the species. Almost every segment bears two pairs of appendages (Fig. 10–36), and has probably arisen by the fusion of two segments. One or both pairs of legs on the seventh segment of the male are modified as copulatory organs. The mouth parts are a pair of mandibles and a pair of maxillae. One pair of short antennae and either simple or aggregated eyes are usually present. There are olfactory hairs on the antennae and a pair of scent glands in each segment, opening laterally. The scent glands, or *repugnatorial glands*, of some have a toxic secretion containing hydrocyanic acid. Some can discharge the secretion nearly a meter. The secretions of some tropical species have caused blindness in children. The breathing tubes (tracheae) are usually unbranched; they arise in tufts from pouches which open just in front of the legs. The heart is a dorsal vessel with lateral ostia; it gives rise to arteries in the head. The two or four excretory organs are threadlike tubes (Malpighian tubules), which pour their excretions into the intestine.

The millipedes move very slowly in spite of their numerous legs. Some of them are able to roll themselves into a spiral or ball. They live in dark, moist places and feed principally on decaying vegetable matter but sometimes on living plants and may thus be destructive. The sexes are separate, and the eggs are laid in damp earth. The young have few segments and only three pairs of legs when they hatch, and resemble apterous insects. Other segments are added just in front of the anal segment. Fossil millipedes have been discovered in geological formations as far back as the Devonian and Upper Silurian. Three of the families in this class are as follows:

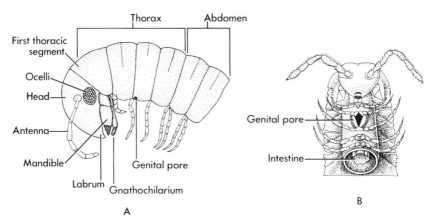

Fig. 10-36. Diplopoda. (A) *Julus terrestris*, side view of anterior end. (B) *Polydesmus complanatus*, ventral view of anterior end. (A, after Borradaile and Potts; B after Latzel.)

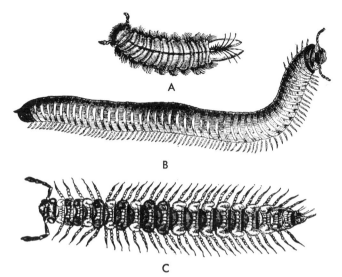

Fig. 10-37. Diplopoda. (A) Polyxenidae; *Polyxenus lagurus.* (B) Julidae; *Julus nemorensis.* (C) Polydesmidae; *Polydesmus collaris.* (From Koch.)

FAMILY 1. POLYXENIDAE (Fig. 10–37, A). Body small; integument soft; each segment with tuft of bristles on either side; maxillae leglike; no copulatory feet in male. Ex. *Polyxenus fasciculatus*: about 2.5 mm long; 13 pairs of legs; Long Island and southern states.

FAMILY 2. JULIDAE (Fig. 10–37, B). Integument hard; maxillae form a plate; two pairs of copulatory feet on seventh segment of male. Ex. *Julus virgatus*: body with 30 to 35 segments; 50 to 60 pairs legs; no legs on third segment; body about 12 mm long.

FAMILY 3. POLYDESMIDAE (Fig. 10–37, C). Body with 19 to 22 segments; first pair of legs on seventh segment of male, copulatory. Ex. *Polydesmus serratus*: body about 37 mm long; male with 30, female with 31 pairs of legs; eastern and central states.

5 / Class V. Pauropoda

The Pauropoda, Symphyla, Diplopoda, and Chilopoda are sometimes grouped together in one class, the Myriapoda. However, one large group, the Chilopoda, resembles the insects more than the other large group, the Diplopoda; and the two smaller groups the Pauropoda and Symphyla have certain characteristics in common with the Diplopoda. It seems advisable, therefore, to consider these groups as separate classes. The first three (Pauropoda, Symphyla, and Diplopoda) are sometimes combined into a superclass, the Progoneata, characterized by reproductive organs that open to the outside near the anterior end of the body, and the Chilopoda and Insecta into a

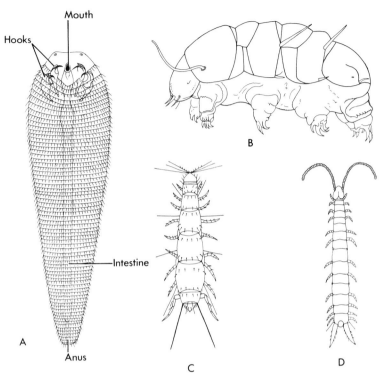

Fig. 10-38. (A) Pentastomida; *Linguatula serrata*. (B) Tardigrada; *Echiniscus spinulosus*. (C) Pauropoda; *Pauropus huxleyi*. (D) Symphyla; *Scutigerella immaculata*. (A, from Sedgwick; B, after Doyere; C, D, after Latzel.)

superclass, the Opisthogoneata, with reproductive organs that open near the posterior end.

The Pauropoda are less than 2 mm in length. They prey on microscopic animals or eat decaying animal and vegetable matter. They are without eyes, heart, and special respiratory organs, and evidently breathe through the general surface of the body, as in the earthworm. The head is distinct, and the body contains 12 segments and bears nine pairs of legs. The young possess three pairs of legs when hatched. The two families in this class are the Pauropidae and Eurypauropidae. Ex. *Pauropus huxleyi* (Fig. 10–38, C): body elongate and cylindrical; 1.3 mm long; eastern and central United States, Europe. *Eurypauropus spinosus*: body broad and flat; 1.25 mm long; eastern and central United States, Europe.

6 / Class VI. Symphyla

The Symphyla are small arthropods with twelve pairs of legs. The head bears antennae, mandibles, maxillulae, maxillae, and a labium. Fewer than 100 species belong to the class. They resemble certain wingless insects in habits and appearance, but have a greater number of legs. They live in moist places and avoid light. Their food probably consists of decaying plants. Ex. *Scutigerella immaculata* (Fig. 10–38, D): head distinct; first pair of legs well developed; about 6 mm long; eastern United States, Europe. *Scolopendrella texana*: head not distinct; first pair of legs rudimentary; 2.8 mm long; Austin, Texas.

7 / Class VII. Onychophora

The Onychophora are frequently treated as a separate phylum. They share enough characteristics with the Arthropoda to be included here as the only class in a subphylum of the same name, Onychophora. The 10 genera and 70 odd species belonging to this class are all usually referred to as *Peripatus* (Fig. 10–39). They are especially interesting because they evidently separated from the main arthropodan stock at an early period and obviously exhibit both arthropod and annelid characteristics as well as peculiarities of their own. Unfortunately they are very rare and hence not available for laboratory study.

Genera thus far described and their geographical distribution include the following: (1) *Peripatus*, tropical America; (2) *Oroperipatus*, Pacific watershed of tropical America; (3) *Metaperipatus*, Chile; (4) *Paraperipatus*, New Britain, New Guinea, and Ceram; (5) *Mesoperipatus*, French Congo; (6) *Peripatopsis*, Cape Colony and Natal; (7) *Opisthopatus*, Cape Colony and Natal; (8) *Peripatoides*, Australia, Tasmania, and New Zealand; (9) *Eoperipatus*, Sumatra and Malay Peninsula; (10) *Typhloperipatus*, Tibet.

The group furnishes an excellent example of discontinuous distribution. Even in the area where a species occurs, specimens are present only in a few of the many available habitats. This seems to indicate that the class had once a continuous distribution but has disappeared throughout most of its range and is on the road to extinction.

Peripatus lives in crevices of rock, under bark and stones, and in other dark moist places and is active only at night. As the animal moves slowly from place to place by means of its legs, the two extremely sensitive antennae test the ground over which it is to travel, while the eyes, one at the base of each antenna, enable it to avoid the light. When irritated, *Peripatus* often ejects slime, sometimes to the distance of almost a foot, from a pair of glands which open on the oral papillae. This slime sticks to everything but the body of the animal itself; it is used principally to capture flies, woodlice, termites, and other small animals, and in addition is probably a weapon of defense. A pair of modified appendages serve as jaws and tear the food to pieces.

Fig. 10-39. Onychophora. *Peripatus capensis.* (After Sedgwick.)

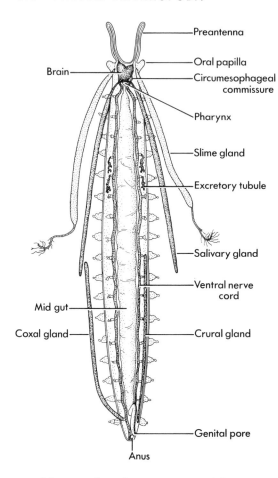

Brain—

—Preantenna

—Oral papilla

—Circumesophageal commissure

—Pharynx

—Slime gland

—Excretory tubule

—Salivary gland

—Ventral nerve cord

Mid gut—

Coxal gland—

—Crural gland

—Genital pore

Anus

Fig. 10-40. Onychophora. *Peripatus capensis.* Dissection of male. (After Balfour, modified.)

Most species of *Peripatus* are viviparous, and a single large female may produce 30 or 40 young in a year. These young resemble the adults when born, differing chiefly in size and color.

Figure 10–40 shows the principal internal organs of a male specimen. The head (Fig. 10–41, B) bears three pairs of appendages, the *antennae, oral papillae,* and *jaws,* a pair of simple *eyes,* and a ventrally placed *mouth.* The fleshly *legs* (Fig. 10–41, C) number from seventeen pairs to over forty pairs in different species; each bears two *claws.* The *anus* is at the posterior end (Fig. 10–41, A); the *genital pore* is situated between the last pair of legs; and a *nephridiopore* lies at the base of each leg. The *skin* is covered with *papillae,* each bearing a *spine*; these papillae are especially numerous on the antennae, lips, and oral papillae, and are probably *tactile.* The external rings of the body are more numerous than the internal segments.

The *digestive system* (Fig. 10–40) is very simple, consisting of a muscular *pharynx,* a short *esophagus,* a long, saccular *stomach,* and a short *intestine.*

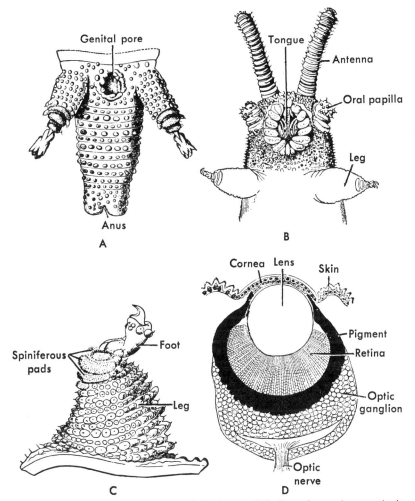

Fig. 10-41. Onychophora. Anatomy of *Peripatus*. (A) Posterior end, ventral view. (B) Anterior end, ventral view. (C) Leg, front view. (D) Eye, longitudinal section. (From Sedgwick; D, after Balfour.)

The pair of *salivary glands*, which open into the mouth cavity, are modified nephridia. The *heart* is the only blood vessel; it is a dorsal tube with paired ostia connecting it with the pericardial cavity in which it lies. The *body cavity* is a blood space, i.e., a hemocoel. The breathing organs are air tubes, called *tracheae*, which open by means of pores on various parts of the body. The excretory organs are *nephridia*, one at the base of each leg. The vesicular end of the nephridium is part of the coelom. The nervous system consists of a *brain*, dorsally situated in the head, and a pair of *ventral nerve cords*, which are connected by many transverse nerves. The sexes are separate, and the cavities of the reproductive organs are coelomic.

Peripatus is of special interest because its body exhibits certain structures characteristic of annelids and other structures found only in arthropods. It is, however, undoubtedly an arthropod. The accompanying table presents briefly these characteristics and shows in what respects it differs from other arthropods.

The Characteristics of Peripatus Arranged so as to Show the Similarity to and Differences from Arthropods and Annelids

Arthropod Characteristics	Annelid Characteristics	Structures Peculiar to Peripatus
appendages modified as jaws	paired segmentally arranged nephridia	number and diffusion of tracheal apertures
a hemocoelic body cavity	cilia in reproductive organs	single pair of jaws
no coelom around alimentary canal	chief systems of organs arranged as in annelids	distribution of reproductive organs
tracheae present	cholinergic neurons	texture of skin
character of the cuticle		simplicity and similarity of segments behind the head

8 / Class VIII. Merostomata

This class contains arthropods of the subphylum Chelicerata that have a cephalothorax (prosoma) consisting of six segments, six pair of laminate, nonlocomotor body appendages, and a terminal segment without a caudal fin but with a postanal spine or plate.

Five living species exist. They are the King, or horseshore, crabs. All belong in one order of the subclass Xiphosura. The living king crab, *Xiphosura (Limulus) polyphemus* (Fig. 10–42) is a marine animal occurring along the Atlantic Coast from Maine to Yucatan. It possesses gills but no Malpighian tubules. *Xiphosura* is a burrowing animal and lives in the sand. It may be active at night, moving by "short swimming hops, the respiratory appendanges giving the necessary impetus, whilst between each two short flights the animal balances itself for a moment on the tip of its tail." The food of *Xiphosura* consists chiefly of worms, such as *Nereis* and mollusks. These are caught while burrowing through the sand, are held by the chelicerae, and are chewed by the bases of the walking legs. In the spring the king crabs come near shore to spawn. In some respects the Xiphosura resemble fossil trilobites and the latter are placed by some students near the king crabs in the arthropod series.

The extinct trilobites (Fig. 10–42, C) are a class of arthropods placed in their own subphylum, the Trilobitomorpha. They were marine animals,

Fig. 10-42. (A) Eurypterida; *Eurypterus fischeri*. Restoration of ventral surface from an Upper Silurian fossil. 1–6, appendages of the prosoma. (B) Xiphosura; *Xiphosura polyphemus (Limulus polyphemus)* the king or horseshoe "crab" ventral view. (C) Trilobita; *Phacops*, a Devonian fossil. (A, after Holm, from Woods; B, after Shipley and MacBride modified; C, photo from a specimen courtesy of Mr. James Hodgson.)

especially abundant in the Cambrian and Silurian. One pair of antennae was present. Each segment posterior to the antennary somite bore a pair of biramous appendages each with a gnathobase. Trilobites are associated in the strata of the earth's crust with the remains of crinoids, brachiopods, and cephalopods. The best-known species. *Triarthrus becki,* occurs in the Utica shale (Lower Silurian) of New York State.

Included in the Merostomata is an extinct subclass, the Eurypterida (Fig. 10–42, A), known only from fossils from Paleozoic strata. They were scorpion-like in appearance with a small cephalothorax and an abdomen of twelve segments, the anterior six of which were provided with unbranched, platelike appendages. The largest arthropods known belonged to this order, having reached a length of over six feet. Ex. *Eurypterus, Pterygotus, Stylomurus.*

9 / Class IX. Arachnida

The Arachnida include the spiders, scorpions, mites, etc. These animals have no antennae nor true jaws; the first pair of appendages are chelicerae; and a cephalothorax, and abdomen are evident. Eleven orders are described here following a more detailed account of the spider.

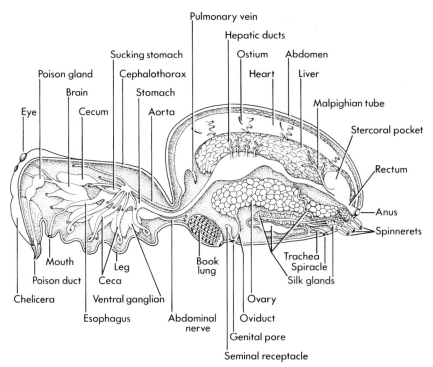

Fig. 10-43. Longitudinal section of a spider showing internal organs. (After Root.)

(1) The Spider

External Features.   The body of the spider consists of a *cephalothorax* which is undivided, and an *abdomen* which is usually soft, rounded, and unsegmented.

There are six pairs of *appendages* attached to the cephalothorax. Antennae are absent; their sensory functions are in part performed by the walking legs. The first pair of appendages are called *chelicerae*. They are in many species composed of two parts, a basal "mandible," and a terminal claw. *Poison glands* are situated in the chelicerae. The poison they secrete passes through a duct and out of the end of the chelicera; it is strong enough to kill insects and to injure large animals. The second pair of appendages are the *pedipalps*; their bases, called "maxillae," are used as jaws to press or chew the food. The pedipalps of the male are used as copulatory organs.

Following the pedipalps are four pairs of *walking legs*. This number easily distinguishes spiders from insects, since the latter possess only three pairs. Each leg consists of seven joints—(1) coxa, (2) trochanter, (3) femur, (4) patella, (5) tibia, (6) metatarsus, (7) tarsus—and is terminated by two toothed claws (Fig. 10–44, B) and often a pad of hairs which enables the spider to run on ceilings and walls. The bases of certain of the legs sometimes serve as jaws.

The *sternum* lies between the legs, and a "*labium*" is situated between the "maxillae." The *eyes*, usually eight in number, are on the front of the head (Fig. 10–44, C). The *mouth* (Fig. 10–43) is a minute opening between the bases

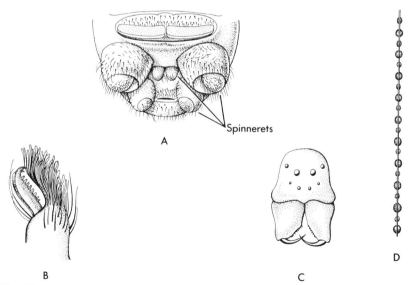

Spinnerets

A

B

C

D

Fig. 10-44. Parts of a spider's body. (A) Ventral view of posterior end of abdomen showing three pairs of spinnerets. (B) Foot showing claws and bristles. (C) Front of head showing eyes and jaws. (D) A thread from a spider's web showing adhesive droplets. (From Warburton.)

Fig. 10-45. Spider. Book lung, longitudinal section. (After MacLeod, modified.)

Air space
Leaflet
Blood space
Stigma

of the pedipalps (maxillae); it serves for the ingestion of juices only, since spiders do not eat solid food.

The *abdomen* is connected by a slender waist (*pedicel*) with the cephalo-thorax. Near the anterior end of the abdomen on the ventral surface is the *genital opening*, protected by a pair of appendages which have fused together to form a plate called the *epigynum*. On either side of the epigynum is the slitlike opening of the respiratory organs or *book lungs* (Fig. 10–45). Some spiders also possess *tracheae*, which open to the outside near the posterior end of the ventral surface (Fig. 10–43). Just back of the tracheal opening are three pairs of tubercles or *spinnerets* (Fig. 10–44, A), used for spinning threads. The *anus* lies posterior to the spinnerets.

Internal Anatomy and Physiology (Fig. 10–43). The *food* of the spider consists of juices sucked from the bodies of other animals, principally insects. Suction is produced by the enlargement of the sucking stomach, due to the contraction of muscles attached to its dorsal surface and to the chitinous covering of the cephalothorax. The *true stomach*, which follows the sucking stomach, gives off five pairs of *ceca* or blind tubes in the cephalothorax. The *intestine* passes almost straight through the abdomen; it is enlarged at a point where ducts bring into it a digestive fluid from the "*liver*," and again near the posterior end, where it forms a sac, the "stercoral pocket." Tubes, called *Malpighian tubes*, enter the intestine near the posterior end. The alimentary canal is surrounded in the abdomen by a large digestive gland or "liver." This gland secretes a fluid resembling pancreatic juice and pours it into the intestine through ducts.

The *circulatory system* consists of a heart, arteries, veins, and a number of spaces or sinuses. The *heart* is situated in the abdomen and is surrounded by the digestive glands. It is a muscular, contractile tube lying in a sheath, the pericardium, into which it opens by three pairs of ostia. It gives off posteriorly a caudal artery, anteriorly an aorta which branches and supplies the tissues in the cephalothorax, and three pairs of abdominal arteries. The *blood*, which is colorless and contains mostly amoeboid corpuscles, passes from the arteries into sinuses and is carried to the book lungs where it is aerated; it then passes to the pericardium by way of the pulmonary veins, and finally enters the heart through the ostia.

Respiration is carried on by tracheae and book lungs; the latter are peculiar to arachnids. The *book lungs*, of which there are usually two, are sacs, each containing generally from 15 to 20 leaflike horizontal shelves through which the blood circulates. Air entering through the external openings is thus brought into close relationship with the blood. Tracheae are also usually present, but do not ramify to all parts of the body as in the insects.

The *excretory organs* are the *Malpighian tubules*, which open into the intestine, and two *coxal glands* in the cephalothorax. The coxal glands are sometimes degenerate, and their openings are difficult to find; they are homologous with the green glands of the crayfish.

The *nervous system* consists of a bilobed ganglion above the esophagus, a subesophageal ganglionic mass and the nerves which arise from them. There are *sensory hairs* on the pedipalps and probably on the walking legs, but the principal sense organs are the eyes. There are usually eight *eyes* (Fig. 10–44, C), and these differ in size and arrangement in different species. Spiders apparently can see objects distinctly only at a distance of four or five inches.

The sexes are separate, and the *testes* or *ovaries* form a network of tubes in the abdomen. The spermatozoa are transferred by the pedipalps of the male to the female, and fertilize the eggs within her body. The eggs are laid in a silk cocoon, which is attached to the web or to a plant, or carried about by the female. The young leave the cocoon as soon after hatching as they can run about.

The *spinning organs* of spiders are three pairs of appendages called *spinnerets* (Fig. 10–44, A). The spinnerets are pierced by hundreds of microscopic tubes through which a fluid secreted by a number of abdominal *silk glands* (Fig. 10–43), passes to the outside and hardens in the air, forming a thread. These threads are used to build nests, form cocoons, spin webs, and for many other purposes. An *orb web*, such as is shown in Figure 10–46, is spun in the following manner. A thread is stretched across the space selected for the web; then from a point on this thread other threads are drawn out and attached in radiating lines. These threads have their strength as soon as drawn from the

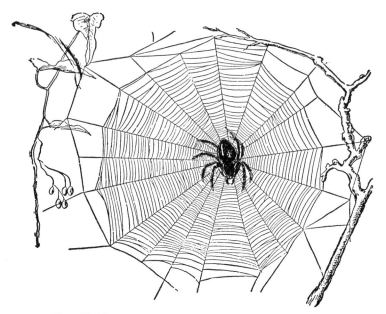

Fig. 10-46. Web of the garden spider. (After Blanchard.)

silk gland, apparently due to the orientation of the molecules as the silk is drawn out. Next a wide spiral may be placed upon the radii to temporarily hold them. A fine spiral of silk, covered with sticky droplets (Fig. 10–44, D), is then added to replace the first spiral as it is cut away. Various species of orb weavers make characteristic modifications of this basic pattern. The spider stands in the center of the web or retires to a nest at one side and waits for an insect to become intangled in the sticky thread; it then rushes out and spins threads about its prey to restrain it prior to feeding on it.

Many spiders do not spin webs, but wander about capturing insects, or lie in wait for them in some place of concealment. In this group belong the crab-spiders (Thomisidae, Fig. 10–53, D), jumping-spiders (Attidae, G, J), ground-spiders (Drassidae), and running spiders (Lycosidae, H). The cobweb spiders spin various kinds of nets for capturing insects. The tube-weavers (Agelenidae) build platforms on the grass and hide in a tube at one side.

(2) Other Arachnida

The eleven orders of living arachnids are described below.

Order 1. Scorpionida. The scorpions (Fig. 10–47) are rapacious arachnids measuring from half an inch to eight inches in length. They live in tropical and subtropical regions, hiding in crevices or in pits in the sand during the daytime, but running about actively at night. They capture insects and spiders with their pedipalpi, tear them apart with their chelicerae, and devour

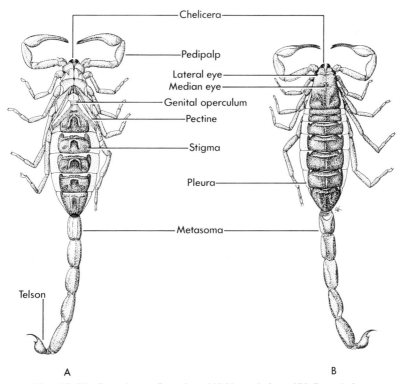

Fig. 10-47. Scorpiones. Scorpion. (A) Ventral view. (B) Dorsal view.

the pieces. Larger animals are paralyzed by the sting on the end of the tail. This sting does not serve as a weapon of defense unless the scorpion is hard pressed. Most American scorpions are relatively harmless, although *Centruroides sculpturatus* can give lethal stings.

The scorpion's body is more obviously segmented than that of most of the other arachnids. There is a *cephalothorax* (prosoma), and an abdomen of two parts—a thick anterior portion (mesosoma), and a slender tail (metasoma), which is held over the back when the animal walks. The dorsal shield of the cephalothorax bears a pair of median *eyes* and three lateral eyes on each side. The sense of sight is, however, poorly developed. On the ventral surface of the second abdominal segment are two comblike appendages called pectines; these are probably special tactile organs. *Tactile hairs* are distributed over the body, and the sense of touch is quite delicate. There are four pairs of *lung books* opening by means of *stigmata* on the undersurface of abdominal segments III–VI.

The mating activities of scorpions are very curious, and include a sort of promenade. Scorpions are viviparous. The young ride about upon the back of the female for about a week, and then shift for themselves. They reach maturity in one to five years.

Scorpions are tropical and subtropical in distribution, with a few species in the southern United States.

Order 2. Uropygi (Thelyphonida). Whip scorpions; with long slender tail, but no sting; pedipalps very large; first pair of legs long and slender. The one American species, found in the southern United States, is the largest of the order; *Mastigoproctus gianteus*: vinegar roan; about 13 cm long; emits odor of vinegar from posterior glands, which secrete formic and acetic acids.

Order 3. Palpigradi. The order Palpigradi contains a single family, Koeneniidae, of small arachnids. They possess a long segmented tail and long, slender pedipalps and legs. A few species found in a few scattered localities. Ex. *Koenenia wheeleri* (Fig. 10–48, A) about 2.5 mm long; in moist places under stones; Texas.

Order 4. Pseudoscorpionida. The pseudoscorpions (Fig. 10–48, B) resemble scorpions in general shape and in the possession of scorpion-like pedipalps but a tail with a caudal sting at the end is lacking. Silk glands are present in the cephalothorax, opening near the end of the chelicerae. The silk is used to construct nests in which they molt or pass the winter. They live

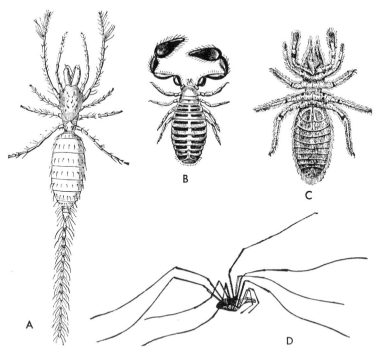

Fig. 10-48. Arachnida. (A) Palpigrada; *Koenenia mirabilis*. (B) Pseudoscorpiones; *Chelifer cyrneus*. (C) Solifugae; *Rhagodes*. (D) Opiliones; *Phalangium opilio*. (After various authors.)

under stones, in moss, under bark, in the nests of termites, ants, and bees, and in houses, and feed on small insects and mites. Large insects to which they cling often carry them about—a fact that probably accounts for their wide distribution.

FAMILY 1. CHELIFERIDAE.   Ex. *Chelifer cancroides*: book scorpion; about 3 mm long; in books, furniture, and clothing; cosmopolitan.

FAMILY 2. CHTHONIIDAE.   Ex. *Chthonius pennsylvanicus*: about 1.9 mm long; eastern United States.

Order 5. Schizomida.   A small group of small arachnids sometimes united with the Uropygi. They differ from them by their small size, shorter tail, several tergal plates on the cephalothorax, and presence of only one pair of book lungs. The pedipalps are not chelate. Mostly tropical in distribution. Ex. *Trithyreus pentapeltis*: about 1 cm long; southern California.

Order 6. Acarina.   The order Acarina includes the ticks and mites, most of which are of small size. The head, thorax, and abdomen are fused together forming an unsegmented body. At the anterior end, a small part of the head region is usually segmented off and hinged to the body proper to serve as a movable base for the mouth parts. In some mites the chitinous integument is membranous throughout, in others some portions of the integument are thickened into protective plates or shields. The body and legs usually bear regularly arranged hairs or bristles. Acarina usually pass through four stages, egg, larva, nymph, and adult. The larva has only three pairs of legs. When it molts to become a nymph it acquires a fourth pair of legs but still lacks a genital aperture. The nymph, in turn, molts and becomes an adult, with four pairs of legs and a genital aperture.

Mites are extremely numerous both in species and in individuals and are found in all sorts of habitats. Some are ectoparasitic, others endoparasitic on or in all sorts of animals and plants. Some are terrestrial, others live in fresh or salt water. Some feed on decaying animal or vegetable matter, others on stored foods, others on plants, others on minute animals, and the parasitic forms on blood.

There are about 166 families; a few follow.

FAMILY 1. ARGASIDAE (Fig. 10–49, A, B).   Soft ticks. The ticks of this family have much the same habits as bedbugs, hiding in cracks or crevices in houses or in the nests of their hosts and coming out at night to feed on the blood of the host for a short period, usually less than half an hour. Ex. *Argas persicus*: parasitic on fowls; vector of fowl spirochaetosis; tropics and sub-tropics. *Ornithodorus moubata* (Fig. 10–49, B): vector of African relapsing fever or tick fever.

FAMILY 2. IXODIDAE (Fig. 10–49, C).   Hard ticks. In the hard ticks the two sexes are often very dissimilar in appearance because the hard dorsal scutum, which both sexes possess, covers the entire dorsal surface in the male

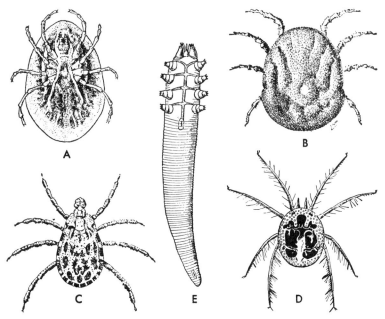

Fig. 10-49. Acari. (A) Argasidae; *Argas reflexus*, female, ventral view. (B) Argasidae; *Ornithodorous moubata*, male, dorsal view; the vector of tick fever. (C) Ixodidae; *Dermacentor andersoni*, male, dorsal view; the vector of certain fevers of man. (D) Hydrachnidae; *Atax alticola*, a fresh-water mite. (E) Demodecidae; *Demodex follicularum*, ventral view; the causative agent of some "blackheads" in the skin of the human face. (Mostly after Brumpt.)

but extends over a small part of the anterior portion of the dorsum of the female. The ticks of this family attach themselves firmly to their hosts and remain upon them, sucking blood, for days or even weeks. Ex. *Margaropus annulatus*: vector of Texas cattle fever. *Haemaphysalis leporispalustris*: rabbit tick. *Dermacentor andersoni* (Fig. 10–49, C); vector of Rocky Mountain spotted fever.

FAMILY 3. ERIOPHYIDAE. Gall mites. These mites feed on plant juices and stimulate the formation of galls, the cavities of which open to the outside. *Phyllocoptes pyri*: pear-leaf blister mite.

FAMILY 4. DEMODECIDAE. Mites that live in the sebaceous glands and hair follicles of man and domestic animals. Ex. *Demodex folliculorum* (Fig. 10–49, E): parasite of cattle, hogs, and man causes "blackheads" in skin of human face.

FAMILY 5. DERMANYSSIDAE. A number of parasitic species belong to this family. Ex. *Dermanyssus gallinae* (Fig. 10–50, D): chicken mite; causes dermatitis in man.

FAMILY 6. SARCOPTIDAE. Itch mites. Many parasites of man, mammals, and birds. Ex. *Sarcoptes scabei* (Fig. 10–50, B): human itch mite. *Psoroptes communis ovis* (A): sheep scab mite.

Fig. 10-50. Acari. (A) Sarcoptidae; *Psoroptes communis;* sheep scab mite. (B) *Sarcoptes scabei,* female ventral view; human itch mite. (C) Trombidiidae; *Trombicula akamushi,* larva with six legs; harvest mite. (D) Dermanyssidae; *Dermanyssus gallinae,* female; chicken mite. (A, after Salmon and Stiles; B, after Gudden; C, D, from Brumpt.)

FAMILY 7. TROMBIDIIDAE(Fig. 10–50, C). Harvest mites and chiggers. Ex. *Trombicula* spp. North American chigger or red bug. (See also Siphonaptera.)

FAMILY 8. TETRANYCHIDAE. Red spiders. Ex. *Tetranychus telarius*: lives on house plants, fruit trees, cotton plants, etc.

FAMILY 9. HYDRACHNIDAE (Fig. 10–49, D). Water mites. Ex. *Hydrachna geographica*: adults, dark red; larvae parasitic on aquatic insects; cosmopolitan.

Order 7. Phalangida. The harvestmen or daddy longlegs may be distinguished from spiders by their extremely long legs (Fig. 10–48, D), the

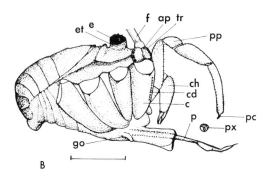

Fig. 10-51. Phalangids. (A) Lateral view of *Leiobunum calcar*, male. (B) Lateral view of *L. politum*, male, with penis exerted. *as*, abdominal segment; *ap*, autotomy plane; *c*, coxa; *cd*, coxal denticle; *ch*, chelicera; *e*, eye; *et*, eye tubercle; *f*, femur; *fs*, spur of femur; *go*, genital operculum; *p*, penis; *pc*, palpal claw; *pf*, femur of palpus; *pp*, patella of palpus; *px*, penis, cross-section, showing sclerotized shaft or nonalate type; *tr*, trochanter. Scale lines are 1.0 mm in length. (From A. L. Edgar. Phalangida of the Great Lakes Region. *Am. Midl. Nat.*, **75**:347–366. Copyright 1966 by the American Midland Naturalist.)

absence of a waist, and their segmented abdomen (Fig. 10–51). Tracheae are present and a single pair of spiracles. There are no silk glands, and hence no web or nest is constructed. Harvestmen are able to run rapidly over leaves and grass. Their food consists of small living insects and the juices of fruit and vegetables. The adults die in the autumn, in the northern part of their range, but their eggs live over winter and hatch in the spring. Ex. *Leiobunum vittatum*: body about 9 mm long; legs from 42 to 90 mm long; in fields and woods; eastern and central America.

Order 8. Solpugida (Solifugae). The Solpugida (Fig. 10–48, C) live in warm countries in sandy regions. Their large chelate mandibles give them a dangerous appearance but they are not poisonous. Tracheae are present opening through a pair of spiracles on the thorax and three pairs on the abdomen. Mostly tropical. Ex. *Eremobates pallipes*: about 13 mm long; southern states west of Mississippi.

Order 9. Amblypygi. Very large nonchelate pedipalps; first leg long with many segments (Fig. 10–52); segmentation evident on abdomen; no spinnerets; no tail. About 60 species, mostly tropical. Ex. *Tarantula whitei*: about 2 cm long; Texas to California.

Order 10. Araneida (Araneae). The spiders; with spinnerets; abdomen unsegmented and joined to cephalothorax by a narrow pedicel; poison glands

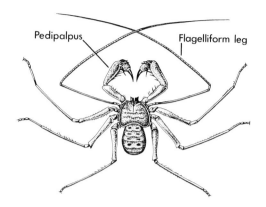

Pedipalpus

Flagelliform leg

Fig. 10-52. Amblypygi. *Admetus pumilio*. (From Sedgwick.)

open on chelicerae. About 70 families. Some commonly encountered spiders are in the following families.

FAMILY 1. AVICULARIIDAE (Fig. 10–53, A). Tarantulas and trapdoor spiders; two pairs of lungs; eight eyes; chelicerae move up and down. Ex. *Eurypelma hentzi*: tarantula; large; southwestern states. *Pachylomerus audonini*: trap-door spider; lives in cylindrical hole in ground that can be closed by hinged earthen door.

FAMILY 2. AGELENIDAE. Funnel-web spiders; legs long; feet with three claws; posterior spinnerets long; eight eyes in two rows. Ex. *Agelena naevia*: grass spider; web concave with funnel-shaped tube at side. *Argyroneta aquatica*: European aquatic spider; lives at bottom of ponds among plants; air carried down from surface.

FAMILY 3. THERIDIIDAE (Fig. 10–53, B, C, I). Comb-footed weavers; tarsi of posterior legs with comb of curved, toothed setae. Ex. *Theridion tepidariorum* (Fig. 10–53, I): common house spider; irregular web in corners, etc. *Latrodectus mactans* (10–53, B): black-widow spider.

FAMILY 4. ARGIOPIDAE (Fig. 10–53, E, F). Orb weavers; tarsi clothed with hairs; three claws on feet; eight eyes; web (Fig. 10–46). Ex. *Epeira foliata*: common on vegetation and fences.

FAMILY 5. THOMISIDAE (Fig. 10–53, D). Crab spiders; short, flat, and crab-like; two claws on feet; eight eyes in two rows. Ex. *Misumena vatia*: frequents flowers; no web; color may change from white to yellow according to color of flower.

FAMILY 6. LYCOSIDAE (Fig. 10–53, H). Running or wolf spiders; body long, hairy; eight eyes in three rows, larger eyes on posterior row; legs long and stout. Ex. *Lycosa helluo*: no web; cocoon attached to female; young carried on mother's back.

FAMILY 7. SALTICIDAE (Fig. 10–53, G, J). Jumping spiders; body short; legs stout; no web; can run or jump forwards, backwards, and sideways; large eyes. Ex. *Salticus scenicus* (Fig. 10–53, J): common on fences and buildings.

Fig. 10-53. Araneida. Species belonging to various families. (A) Aviculariidae; *Chilobrachys stridulans*. (B) Theridiidae; *Latrodectus mactans*. (C) Theridiidae; *Trithena tricuspidata*. (D) Thomisidae; *Thomisus*, a crab spider. (E) Argiopidae; *Epeira angulata*. (F) Argiopidae; *Argiope aurelia*. (G) Salticidae; *Attus*, jumping spider. (H) Lycosidae; *Lycosa fabrilis*. (I) Theridiidae; *Theridion tepidariorum*. (J) Salticidae; *Salticus scenicus*. (From Warburton.)

Order 11. Ricinulei. A rare order, less than 500 living individuals have been collected of about 14 species with a general resemblance to spiders. There are no spinnerets; the mouth and chelicerae can be covered by a hood; eyeless. Ex. *Ricinoides sjostedti* from the Cameroons.

Fig. 10-54. Pycnogonida. *Nymphon stromii;* male carrying egg masses on his ovigerous legs. (From Thompson.)

10 / Class X. Pycnogonida

The Pycnogonida (Fig. 10–54) are marine arthropods, sometimes called sea spiders, with very small bodies and disproportionally long legs. They live among algae and hydroids, on which they feed, and range from one millimeter to several centimeters in length. They are of uncertain systematic position sometimes being placed in a separate phylum. The cephalothorax is segmented and the abdomen much reduced; the appendages consist of a pair of long chelate mandibles, a pair of slender pedipalps, a pair of slender ovigerous legs and four pairs of very long legs usually with nine segments each; four eyes are present; long diverticulae extend from the intestine into the legs; the sexes are separate; the eggs are carried on the ovigerous legs of the males and give rise to larvae with three pairs of legs; they are cosmopolitan in their distribution. Ex. *Pycnogonum, Pallene, Nymphon.*

11 / Class XI. Tardigrada

The Tardigrada, or water bears (Figs. 10–55 and 10–38, B), are minute animals that are often included with the arachnids although they may not even be arthropods. Here they are given the value of a class for the sake of convenience. They live in damp moss or sand and in fresh water or salt water. The head is more or less distinct and the body consists of four segments fused together. Each body segment bears a pair of short, thick legs, which are unsegmented but terminated by from four to nine sharp claws. No circulatory, respiratory, and excretory systems are present. The nervous system, however, is well developed. The sexes are separate. The eggs are large and the young that hatch from them sometimes possess only three pairs of legs. Tardigrades are able to live for several years in a dessicated condition. Two orders are common.

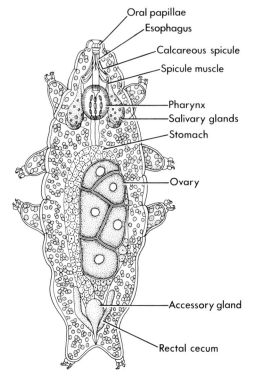

Oral papillae
Esophagus
Calcareous spicule
Spicule muscle
Pharynx
Salivary glands
Stomach
Ovary
Accessory gland
Rectal cecum

Fig. 10-55. Tardigrada. *Macrobiotus schultzei*, showing internal anatomy. (From Shipley, after Greeff.)

Order 1. Eutardigrada. Head without cirri; legs not retractile telescopically; claws united into one branched pair. Ex. *Macrobiotus hufelandi*: 0.7 mm long; one pair strong teeth; fresh-water ponds. *Hypsibius, Milnesium.*

Order 2. Heterotardigrada. Head with two pairs of cirri; legs somewhat rectractile telescopically; claws separate. Ex. *Echiniscus testudo*: 0.3 mm long; one pair long teeth; two red eyes; body reddish, opaque; frequent in damp moss on roofs.

12 / Class XII. Pentastomida (Linguatulida)

The wormlike animals in this subclass are all parasitic. They were formerly grouped with the worms but the morphology of the adults and young indicate they may be arthropods allied to the arachnids. The body is unsegmented although the body wall consists of many rings. No circulatory, respiratory, and excretory systems are present. The alimentary canal is straight and close to the mouth is a pair of horny hooks. The sexes are separate. The larvae have two pairs of legs and are mitelike in shape. Ex. *Reighardia sternae*: genital opening anterior; hooks posterior to mouth; parasitic in gulls and terns. *Linguatula serrata* (*Pentastomum taeniodes*, Fig. 10–38, A): female about 8 cm long; male 2 cm long; adult in nasal cavities of dog, wolf, and fox; eggs discharged with mucus, when swallowed by rabbits, domesticated animals, or man, hatch in stomach, migrate to lungs, kidneys, etc., and encyst; excyst if host devoured by a carnivore and migrate to nose. *Porocephalus* (*Armillifer*) *armillatus*: adult in lungs of snakes; eggs swallowed by various animals, hatch and larvae migrate into the liver and body cavity.

13 / Arthropods in General

The characteristics of each group of arthropods have been presented in the preceding pages, hence it will suffice here to point out in what respects these various groups differ from or resemble each other.

Anatomy. *Divisions of the Body.* The ancestors of the arthropods were probably annelid-like, as in *Peripatus*, which has a muscular body wall and a body that is not divided into well-defined regions. In the Crustacea, Insecta, Chilopoda, and Diplopoda there may be three distinct divisions, head, thorax, and abdomen, or the head and thorax may be united into a cephalothorax. The Chelicerata usually possess a cephalothorax or prosoma and an abdomen or opisthosoma consisting of the mesosoma and metasoma combined. The size of and number of segments in each of these divisions of the body differ widely within the groups and are correlated with the environment and activities of each species.

Appendages. The paired, jointed appendages, from which the term Arthropoda is derived, are of almost infinite variety. Typically each segment bears one pair of appendages but in many species appendages are lacking on many segments. Those that are present were probably derived from a primitive type which has become modified for the numerous functions performed by them. The accompanying table (Segments and Appendages of Arthropoda) indicates in general the appendages of the larger divisions of the phylum.

Cuticle. The exoskeleton of arthropods consists of chitin often hardened by lime salts. The chitin is inelastic and hence increase in size is impossible except during the period when the exoskeleton is cast off (molting or ecdysis). The new chitin secreted by the hypodermis then allows a certain amount of expansion. The chitin is rigid except between certain segments and joints where it is thin and allows the movement of the adjoining parts.

Digestive Tract. The alimentary canal consists of three divisions united end to end. The fore gut or stomodaeum and the hind gut or proctodaeum are of ectodermal origin, and are lined with chitin which is shed when molting occurs. The mid gut is derived from mesoderm. The length, diameter, and sections into which the various parts of the alimentary canal are divided are correlated with the food habits of the species and vary greatly in the different groups.

Segments and Appendages of Arthropoda

Segment	Crustacea (Malacostraca)	Chilopoda	Arachnida	Insecta
1*	embryonic	embryonic	chelicerae	embryonic
2	antennules	antennae	pedipalpi	antennae
3	antennae	embryonic	1st pair of legs	embryonic
4	mandibles	mandibles	2d pair of legs	mandibles
5	maxillules	1st maxillae	3d pair of legs	1st maxillae
6	maxillae	2d maxillae	4th pair of legs	2d maxillae (labium)
7	1st maxillipeds	maxillipeds	embryonic	1st pair of legs
8	2d thor. append.	1st pair of legs	genital operc. ♀ ♂	2d pair of legs
9	3d thor. append.	2d pair of legs	pectines	3d pair of legs
10	4th thor. append.	3d pair of legs	1st abd. seg.	1st abd. seg.
11	5th thor. append.	4th pair of legs	1st lung books	2d abd. seg.
12	6th thor. append. ♀	5th pair of legs	2d lung books	3d abd. seg.
13	7th thor. append.	6th pair of legs	3d lung books	4th abd. seg.
14	8th thor. append. ♂	7th pair of legs	4th lung books	5th abd. seg.
15	1st abd. append.	8th pair of legs	no appendages	6th abd. seg.
16	2d abd. append.	9th pair of legs	1st seg. metasoma	7th abd. seg.
17	3d abd. append.	10th pair of legs	2d seg. metasoma	8th abd. seg.
18	4th abd. append.	11th pair of legs	3d seg. metasoma	9th abd. seg. (styles) ♂ ♀
19	5th abd. append.	12th pair of legs	4th seg. metasoma	10th abd. seg.
20	6th abd. append.	13th pair of legs	5th seg. metasoma	11th abd. seg. (cerci)
21	....	14th pair of legs	....	....
22	....	15th pair of legs	....	....
23	....	16th pair of legs	....	....
24	....	17th pair of legs	....	....
25	....	18th pair of legs	....	....
26	....	19th pair of legs	....	....
27	....	20th pair of legs	....	....
28	....	21st pair of legs	....	....
29	....	genital append. ♀ ♂	....	....
postsegmental region	telson	telson	telson	embryonic

Source : L. A. Borradaile and F. A. Potts. 1932. *Invertebrata*, Cambridge Univ. Press, Cambridge, England.

*Eyes and frontal organs belong to a presegmental region which may have a mesoblast of its own. ♂ indicates the position of the male opening, ♀ that of the female.

Circulatory System.   There is, among the arthropods, no complex series of large blood vessels nor fine capillaries that come into direct contact with the tissues; but the circulatory system is of the so-called open type. The blood is contained largely in sinuses and bathes the tissues directly. Blood enters the heart through ostia and is pumped through arteries to the sinuses.

Respiratory System.   This differs widely in the several divisions of the phylum. In aquatic species respiratory exchanges occur through the general body wall or through well-developed gills or branchiae. Terrestrial species breathe by means of tracheae, or, as in the arachnids, by book lungs or both book lungs and tracheae.

Coelom.   The "body cavity" of arthropods is not a coelom but is filled with blood and known as a hemocoel. The coelom is represented in the embryo by cavities in the mesodermal segments and in the adult is restricted to the cavities of the reproductive organs and certain excretory organs.

Excretory System.   There are no true nephridia among the arthropods. Malpighian tubules are present in insects, chilopods, diplopods, and arachnids and some arthropods possess coelomoducts.

Nervous System.   This is probably derived from an ancestral condition in which a double ventral nerve cord with a pair of ganglia in each segment was present. In the arthropods of to-day there is a brain and more or less shortened ventral nerve chain. The brain consists of several pairs of ganglia fused together, and may exhibit several divisions known as the fore brain, mid brain, and hind brain (Fig. 11–13). The ventral nerve cord likewise usually consists of a reduced number of masses of nervous tissue each comprising several pairs of ganglia.

Eyes.   In *Peripatus* the eyes are a pair of simple, closed vesicles with a lens derived from the wall and a thickened, pigmented posterior complex. In all other arthropods the lens is derived from the cuticula; beneath the lens are cells known as retinulae, in each of which is a vertical rod called the rhabdom; and in and around the retinulae is pigment which may migrate toward or away from the surface according to the intensity of the light. The simple eyes of insects (ocelli) consist of a single vesicle with several retinulae. In chilopods and diplopods a number of vesicles lie close together in a group. The compound eyes of crustaceans and insects are very complex structures, the units of which are known as ommatidia. The arachnids possess eyes that resemble the ocelli of insects but may be degenerate compound eyes.

Phylogeny and Interrelations.   The arthropods no doubt evolved from the same ancestors as the polychaete annelids. The development of a rigid exoskeleton with joints brought about a change in the distribution of the muscles from the continuous type forming a muscular body wall, as in the annelids, to the discontinuous type in which the muscles are separately and diversely developed for the movement of special segments.

The Onychophora resemble most closely the ancestral condition, with a thin cuticle, a continuous and muscular body wall, no joints, one pair of jaws, appendages on the first segment, and a series of coelomoducts of which one pair are ciliated oviducts.

The Crustacea, Insecta, Chilopoda, and Diplopoda have become modified in many ways. The Crustacea differ from the others in the possession of a second pair of antennae and in their aquatic habit. The Insecta have only three pairs of legs and usually wings. Both Crustacea and Insecta possess compound eyes. The Arachnida have anterior appendages modified into chelicerae and lack true compound eyes.

History of Our Knowledge of the Arthropoda.   The term Arthropoda was proposed by von Siebold in 1845 for a group of animals including the Crustacea, Insecta, and Arachnida. This group resembled the Articulata of Cuvier except that the Annelida were removed and placed with the Vermes. Linnaeus employed Insecta as a term for all of the arthropods; but separate classes later were recognized, the Myriapoda by Latrielle in 1796, the Crustacea by Cuvier in 1800, and the Arachnida by Lamarck in 1881. Many changes of comparatively minor importance have taken place since that time and are still being made, a condition that indicates both our lack of knowledge of certain sections of the phylum and the fact that we are making progress.

Embryology and the Biogenetic Law.   Studies of the embryology of arthropods has furnished some of our best evidence in favor of what is known as the biogenetic law or the *recapitulation theory*. Organic evolution, that is, the evolution of one organism from another, is accepted as an established fact by practically all zoologists at the present time. Evolutionists do not claim that the more complex forms have evolved directly from the simpler animals, but that their ancestors were related. Beginning with the simplest animals we find that a single cell performs all the necessary processes of life, e.g., *Amoeba*. Within the lowest phylum, the Protozoa, there are animals consisting of a number of cells more or less intimately bound together into a hollow spherical colony, e.g., *Volvox*. Passing to the next higher group of organisms we are introduced to animals that possess two layers of cells, surrounding a single cavity, e.g., *Hydra*. All animals above the coelenterates have three layers of cells forming their body walls, i.e., they are triploblastic. Four stages in the evolution of animals are represented in the groups just mentioned—(1) the single cell, (2) a ball of cells, (3) a two-layered sac, and (4) a three-layered organism.

Early in the past century it was noticed that these stages correspond to the early stages in the embryology of the Metazoa; in other words, that the development of the individual recapitulates the stages in the evolution of the race, or *ontogeny recapitulates phylogeny*. These stages contrasted appear as follows:

Phylogenetic Stage	Ontogenetic Stage
1. Single-celled animal	egg cell
2. Ball of cells	blastula
3. Two-layered sac	gastrula
4. Triploblastic animal	three-layered embryo

Later other zoologists became interested in the recapitulation theory, and enlarged upon it. Of these Fritz Müller and Ernst Haeckel are especially worthy of mention. The latter expressed the facts as he saw them in his "fundamental law of biogenesis." The ancestor of the many-celled animals was conceived by him as a two-layered sac something like a gastrula, which he called a *Gastraea*. The coelenterates were considered to be gastraea slightly modified.

Fritz Müller derived strong arguments in favor of biogenesis from a study of certain Crustacea belonging to the Malacostraca. Many members of this group do not emerge from the egg so nearly like the adult as does the crayfish.

Fig. 10-56. Four stages in the development of *Penaeus*, a shrimp. (A) Nauplius. (B) Protozoea. (C) Zoea. (D) Mysis. (After Muller and Claus.)

The lobster, for example, upon hatching resembles a less specialized prawn-like crustacean, called *Mysis* (Fig. 10–27, C), and is said to be in the *Mysis* stage. The shrimp, *Penaeus*, passes through a number of interesting stages before the adult condition is attained. It hatches as a larva, termed a *Nauplius* (Fig. 10–56, A), possessing a frontal eye and three pairs of appendages; this Nauplius molts and grows into a *Protozoea* stage (B) which bears three more pairs of appendages and the rudiments of segments III–VIII. The *Protozoea* stage grows into the *Zoea* stage (C). The cephalothorax and abdomen are distinct at this time; eight pairs of appendages are present (I–VIII) and six more are developing. The *Zoea* grows and molts and becomes a *Mysis* (D) with eight pairs of appendages (I–VIII) on the cephalothorax. Finally the *Mysis* passes into the adult shrimp, which possesses the characteristic number of appendages (I–XIX) each modified to perform its particular function. The *Nauplius* of *Penaeus* resembles the larvae of many simple crustaceans; the *Zoea* is somewhat similar to the condition of an adult *Cyclops* (Fig. 10–23, A); the *Mysis* is like the adult *Mysis* (Fig. 10–27, C); and finally the adult *Penaeus* is more specialized than any of its larval stages, and belongs among the higher Crustacea. The above facts have convinced some zoologists that *Penaeus* recapitulates in its larval development the progress of the race; that the lobster has lost many of these stages, retaining only the *Mysis*; and that the crayfish hatches in practically the adult condition. The *Nauplius* stage of the latter is supposed to be represented by a certain embryonic phase (Fig. 10–11, E).

The law of biogenesis should not be taken too seriously, since it has been criticized severely by many prominent zoologists, but it has furnished a hypothesis, which has concentrated the attention of scientists upon fundamental embryological processes, and has therefore had a great influence upon zoological progress.

References to Literature on the Arthropoda

AGRAWAL, V. P. 1965. Feeding appendages and the digestive system of *Gammarus pulex*. *Acta Zoologica*, **46**:67–81.

BAKER, E. W., and G. W. WHARTON. 1952. *An Introduction to Acarology*. Macmillan, New York. 465 pp.

BARNARD, J. L., R. J. MENZIES, and N. BACESCU. 1962. *Abyssal Crustacea*. Columbia Univ. Press, New York. 223 pp.

BARNWELL, F. H. 1966. Daily and tidal patterns of activity in individual fiddler crab (genus *Uca*) from the Woods Hole Region. *Biol. Bull.*, **130**:1–17.

BRINTON, E. 1962. The Distribution of Pacific Euphausids. *Bull. Scripps Inst. Oceanog.*, vol. **8**, no. 2, 219 pp.

BROOKS, J. L. 1957. The Systematics of North American Daphnia. *Mem. Conn. Acad. Arts and Sci.* XIII, 180 pp.

——, and S. I. DODSON. 1965. Predation, body size, and composition of plankton. *Science*, **150**:28–35.

Brooks, M. A. 1963. Symbiosis and aposymbiosis in arthropods. pp. 200–231. In *Symbiotic Associations*. 13th Symp., Soc. for Gen. Microbiol. Cambridge Univ. Press. 356 pp.

Butt, F. H. 1960. Head development in arthropods. *Biol. Rev.*, **35**:43–91.

Cloudsley-Thompson, J. L. 1958. *Spiders, Scorpions, Centipedes, and Mites*. Pergamon Press, New York. 228 pp.

———. 1964. Terrestrial animals in dry heat: arthropods. pp. 451–465. In *Handbook of Physiology*. Section 4: Adaptation to the Environment. Am. Physiol. Soc., Washington, D.C.

Cooper, W. E. 1965. Dynamics and production of a natural population of a fresh-water amphipod, *Hyalella azteca*. *Ecol. Mon.*, **35**:377–394.

Curtis, H. 1965. Spirals, spiders, and spinnerets. *Am. Scientist*, **53**:52–58.

Edgar, A. L. 1966. Phalangida of the Great Lakes region. *Am. Midl. Nat.*, **75**:347–366.

Eisner, T., H. E. Eisner, J. J. Hurst, F. C. Kafatos, and J. Meinwald. 1963. Cyanogenic glandular apparatus of a millepede. *Science*, **139**:1218–1220.

Florey, E., and E. Florey. 1965. Cholinergic neurons in the Onychophora (*Opisthopatus costei*): A comparative study. *Comp. Biochem. Physiol.*, **15**:125–136.

Galun, R., and S. H. Kindler. 1965. Glutathione as an inducer of feeding in ticks. *Science*, **147**:166–167.

Green, J. 1961. *A Biology of the Crustacea*. Witherby, London. 180 pp.

Grice, G. D., and A. D. Hart. 1962. The abundance, seasonal occurrence and distribution of the epizooplankton between New York and Bermuda. *Ecol. Mon.*, **32**:287–309.

Hartland-Rowe, R. 1965. The Anostraca and Notostraca of Canada with some new distribution records. *Can. Field-Nat.*, **79**:185–189.

Hessler, R. R., and H. L. Sanders. 1966. *Derocheilocaris typicus* Pennak & Zinn (Mystacocarida) revisited. *Crustaceana*, **11**:141–155.

Judd, W. W. 1965. Terrestrial sowbugs (Crustacea: Isopoda) in the vicinity of London, Ontario. *Can. Field-Nat.*, **79**:197–202.

Kaston, B. J. 1953. *How to Know the Spiders*. Brown, Dubuque. 220 pp.

———. 1965. Some little known aspects of spider behavior. *Am. Midl. Nat.*, **73**:336–356.

Kinne, O. 1964. Animals in aquatic environments: crustaceans. pp. 669–682. In *Handbook of Physiology*. Section 4: Adaptation to the Environment. Am. Physiol. Soc., Washington.

Maguire, B. 1965. *Monodella texana* n. sp., an extension of the range of the crustacean order Thermosbaenacea to the Western Hemisphere. *Crustaceana*, **9**:149–154.

Manton, S. M. 1960. Concerning head development in the arthropods. *Biol. Rev.*, **35**:265–282.

Paris, O. H. 1963. The ecology of *Armadillidium vulgare* (Isopoda: Oniscoidea) in California grassland: food, enemies, and the weather. *Ecol. Mon.*, **33**:1–22.

Puglia, C. R. 1964. Some tardigrades from Illinois. *Trans. Am. Microsc. Soc.*, **83**:300–311.

Sanders, H. L. 1957. The Cephalocarida and crustacean phylogeny. *Syst. Zool.*, **6**:112–129.

SAVORY, T. H. 1960. Spider webs. *Sci. Am.*, **202**(4):114–124.

——. 1962. Daddy longlegs. *Sci. Am.*, **207** (Oct.):119–128.

——. 1964. *Arachnida*. Academic Press, New York. 291 pp.

SHAROV, A. G. 1966. *Basic Arthropodan Stock*. Pergamon Press, Oxford. 271 pp.

SNODGRASS, R. E. 1952. *A Textbook of Anthropod Anatomy*. Cornell Univ. Press, Ithaca.

TAPPA, D. W. 1965. The dynamics of the association of six limnetic species of *Daphnia* in Aziscoos Lake, Maine. *Ecol. Mon.*, **35**:395–423.

WATERMAN, T. H. 1960–1961. *The Physiology of Crustacea*. Vols. I and II. Academic Press, New York.

WITT, P. N., and C. F. REED. 1965. Spider-web building. *Science*, **149**:1190–1197.

Chapter XI

Class Insecta

I NSECTS form the most important class of invertebrates in many ways. The class contains a greater number of species than all other living species combined. They are an extremely abundant group in terrestrial and freshwater environments as well as having the only winged invertebrates. Although many are harmful insects, many others are useful in control of pests and pollination of plants.

1 / Phylum Arthropoda / Class II. Insecta

(1) Dissosteira carolina—A Grasshopper

The grasshopper is a favorable representative of the class Insecta, because it is less specialized than many of the other common insects and, therefore, exhibits insect characteristics in their more generalized condition.

External Features (Figs. 11–1 and 11–8). *Exoskeleton.* As in the crayfish, the grasshopper is covered by an exoskeleton that protects the delicate systems of organs within. This exoskeleton is the *cuticule*, which consists of chitin and is divided into a linear row of *segments*. The cuticule is mostly hard and rigid; some of the segments are firmly fastened together, but it is softer between other segments, thus allowing movements of the abdomen, wings, legs, antennae, etc. These softer regions are known as *sutures*. The body wall consists of the cuticule beneath which is a layer of cells, the *hypodermis*, which secretes it and under this a *basement membrane*. Each segment is made up of separate pieces known as *sclerites*; usually some of the sclerites of a typical segment cannot be distinguished and the sutures are therefore said to

471

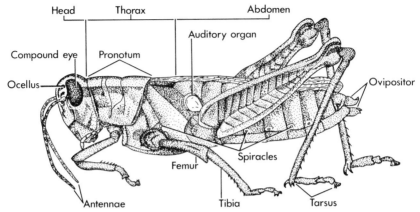

Fig. 11-1. Diagram of a female grasshopper with wings removed on left side. (After Walden, from Wellhouse.)

be obsolete. In the grasshopper the body is divided into three groups of segments that constitute the head, thorax, and abdomen.

Head. Six segments are fused together to form the head (Fig. 11–2). These are not visible in the adult but may be observed in the embryo and are indicated by the paired appendages of the adult. They are as follows: *preoral, antennal, intercalary, mandibular, maxillary,* and *labial.* The exoskeleton of the head is known as the *epicranium*; the front of this is the *frons,* and the sides are the cheeks or *genae.* The rectangular sclerite beneath the front of

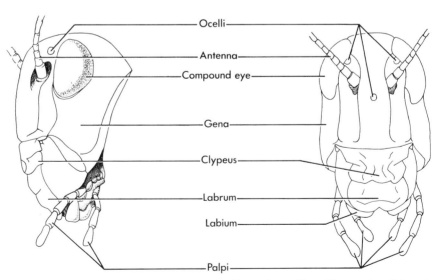

Fig. 11-2. Head of a grasshopper in side and front views. (From Herms, after Folsom.)

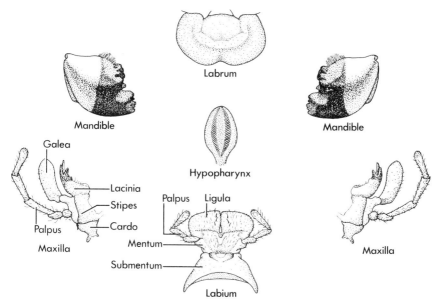

Fig. 11-3. Mouth parts of a grasshopper. (From Herms.)

the epicranium is the *clypeus*. On either side of the head is a *compound eye*, and on top of the head and near the inner edge of each compound eye is a simple eye or *ocellus*. The mouth parts are attached to the ventral side of the epicranium.

Mouth Parts (Fig. 11–3).   The grasshopper is a biting insect, and its mouth parts are therefore *mandibulate*. There is a *labrum* or upper lip attached to the ventral edge of the *clypeus*. Beneath this is the membranous tongue-like organ, the *hypopharynx*. On either side is a single, hard jaw or *mandible* with a toothed surface fitted for grinding. Beneath the mandible are a pair of *maxillae*; each of these consists of the following parts: a basal *cardo*, central *stipes*, a long curved *lacinia*, a long, rounded *galea*, and a *maxillary palp* which arises from a *palpifer*. The *labium* or lower lip comprises a basal *submentum*, a central *mentum*, two movable flaps, the *ligulae*, and a *labial palp* on either side. The labium of the insects appears to have evolved from the lateral union of two appendages resembling the biramous limbs of a crustacean. The *maxillae* have obviously also arisen from this type of appendage. The labrum and labium serve to hold food between the mandibles and maxillae which move laterally and grind it. The maxillary and labial palps are supplied with sense organs that no doubt serve to distinguish different kinds of food.

Ocellus (Fig. 11–4, B).   The simple eyes consist of a group of visual cells, the *retinulae*, in the center of which is an optic rod, the *rhabdome*, and a transparent lenslike modification of the cuticle.

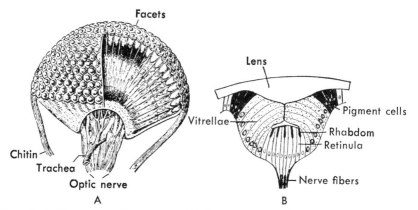

Fig. 11-4. Diagrams of insect eyes. (A) Compound eye. (B) Simple eye or ocellus. (A, from Schmeil; B, from Borradaile and Potts, modified.)

Compound Eye (Fig. 11–4, A). The compound eye is covered by a transparent part of the cuticule, the *cornea*, which is divided into a large number of hexagonal pieces, the *facets*. Each facet is the outer end of a unit known as an *ommatidium*. Such a structure gives mosaic vision as described in the crayfish (Fig. 10–8). Some insects, possibly the grasshopper, are able to distinguish colors.

Antennae. The antennae are filiform in shape and consist of many joints. Sensory bristles, probably olfactory in nature, are present on them and this, combined with the ability of the insect to bend them about, makes them efficient sense organs.

Thorax. The thoracic portion of the body is separated from the head and abdomen by flexible joints and consists of three segments: an anterior prothorax, a middle mesothorax, and a posterior metathorax. Each segment bears a pair of legs, and the mesothorax and metathorax each bear a pair of wings. On either side of the mesothorax and metathorax is a spiracle, an opening into the respiratory system.

Prothorax. A typical segment includes ten sclerites. The dorsal *tergum* (called the *pronotum* in this segment) consists of four sclerites in a row, an anterior *prescutum* followed by the *scutum*, *scutellum*, and *postscutellum*. The lateral *pleura* consist of three sclerites, the *episternum*, *epimeron*, and *parapteron*. The single ventral sclerite is the *sternum*. The *pronotum* of the prothorax is large and extends down on either side; its four sclerites are indicated by transverse grooves. The sternum bears a spine.

Mesothorax. In this segment the tergum (*mesonotum*) is small, but the sclerites of the pleuron are distinct.

Metathorax. The metathorax resembles the mesothorax.

Legs (Fig. 11–5). Each leg consists of a linear series of five segments as follows: the *coxa* articulates with the body; then come the small *trochanter*

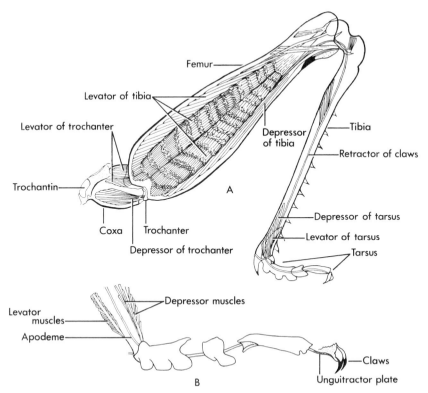

Fig. 11-5. Carolina locust, *Dissosteira carolina*. (A) Musculature of left, metathoracic leg. (B) Tarsus of mesothoracic leg disjointed, showing levator and depressor muscles and tendon-like apodeme of retractor of claws attached to unguitractor plate and extending through tarsus. (After Snodgrass.)

fused with the *femur*, the *tibia*, and the *tarsus*. The femur of the metathoracic legs are enlarged to contain the muscles used in jumping. The tarsus (Fig. 11–5, B) of each leg consists of three visible segments; the one adjoining the tibia has three pads on the ventral surface, and the terminal segment bears a pair of *claws* between which is a fleshy lobe, the *pulvillus*.

Wings (Figs. 11–6 and 11–7).   The wings of insects arise from the region between the tergum and pleuron as a double layer of hypodermis, which secretes upper and lower cuticular surfaces. Between these are tracheae around which spaces occur and the cuticule thickens; they later become the longitudinal wing veins. The *veins* are of value in strengthening the wings. They differ in number and arrangement in different species of insects but are so constant in individuals of any one species that they are very useful for purposes of classification. The mesothoracic wings of the grasshopper, the *tegmina*, are leathery and not folded; they serve as covers for the metathoracic wings which lie beneath them. The latter are thin and folded like a fan.

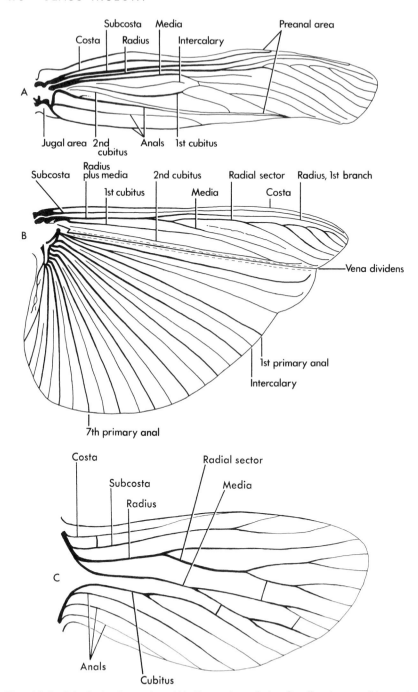

Fig. 11-6. Principal wing veins. (A) Fore wing of the Carolina locust, *Dissosteira carolina*. (B) Hind wing of *D. carolina*. (C) Hypothetical wing of the presumed ancestral insect from which other winged forms are derived. (A and B, after Snodgrass.)

Fig. 11-7. Movement of wings in flight. (A) The wings are elevated on the pleural wing processes by the depression of the tergum due to the contraction of the tergo-sternal muscles. The hind margins of the wings are deflected. (B) The wings are lowered by the elevation of the tergum due to the contraction of the dorsal, longitudinal muscles. Hind margins of wings elevated. (After Snodgrass.)

Abdomen.   The number of segments in the abdomen of the embryo insect is 11 and each of these bears a pair of rudimentary appendages. In the adult of most insects no appendages are present and the number of segments is usually reduced. In the grasshopper segment I is fused with the metathorax; it consists of a tergum only, on either side of which is an oval *tympanic membrane* covering an *auditory sac*. Segments IX and X have their terga partly fused together and their sterna completely fused. Segment XI consists of a tergum only; this forms the so-called *genitalia* consisting in the male of a *subgenital plate*, two *podical plates*, and two *cerci*, and in the female of two podical plates, two cerci, and three pairs of movable plates, which form the *ovipositor* or egg-laying apparatus.

Internal Anatomy (Fig. 11-8).   The systems of organs within the body of the insect lie in the body cavity, which is filled with blood and is a *hemocoel* and not a coelom. All of the systems characteristic of higher animals are represented.

Muscular System (Fig. 11-9).   The muscles are of the *striated* type, very soft and delicate but strong. The number present is very large. They are segmentally arranged in the abdomen but not in the head and thorax. The most conspicuous muscles are those that move the mandibles, the wings, the metathoracic legs, and the ovipositor.

Digestive System (Fig. 11-8).   The principal parts of the alimentary canal are the *fore gut*, *mid gut*, and *hind gut*. The fore gut consists of the *pharynx* in the head into which the *mouth* opens and on either side of which opens a *salivary gland*; next a tubular *esophagus*, which enlarges into a *crop* in the mesothoracic and metathoracic segments; this leads into the *proventriculus*, which is a grinding organ or *gizzard*. The mid gut, which is the *ventriculus* or stomach, reaches posteriorly into the abdomen, and into it eight double, cone-shaped pouches, the *gastric ceca*, pour the digestive juices they secrete. The hind gut is made up of the *large intestine*, into the anterior end of which

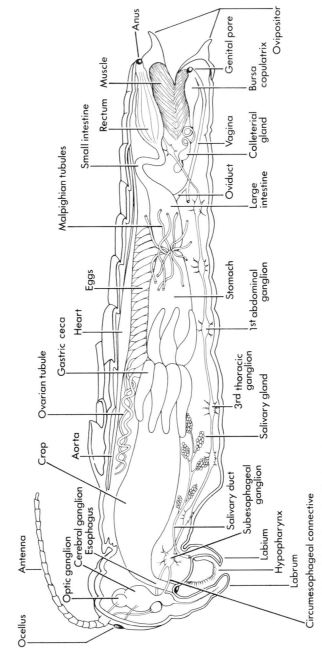

Fig. 11-8. Longitudinal section of a grasshopper showing the internal organs. Diagrammatic. (After Root.)

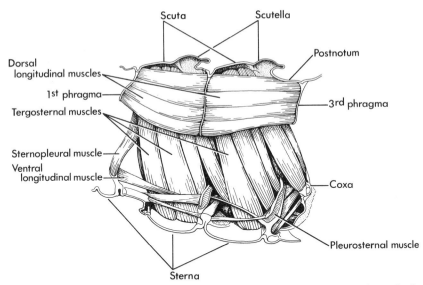

Scuta   Scutella

Postnotum

Dorsal
longitudinal muscles

1st phragma

Tergosternal muscles

3rd phragma

Sternopleural muscle

Ventral
longitudinal muscle

Coxa

Pleurosternal muscle

Sterna

Fig. 11-9. Carolina locust, *Dissosteira carolina*. General view of the musculature in the right half of the mesothorax and metathorax. The dorsal longitudinal muscles, by contraction, arch the tergal plates upward and thereby depress the wings; the tergo-sternal muscles depress the tergal plates, which indirectly elevate the wings. The other muscles are muscles of the legs and of the sterna. (After Snodgrass.)

the delicate *Malpighian tubules* open; and the *small intestine*, which expands into the *rectum* and opens through the *anus*.

Circulatory System (Fig. 11–8). This is not a closed system of blood vessels as in vertebrates and some invertebrates but consists of a single tube located in the abdomen just under the body wall in the middorsal line. The *heart* is divided into a row of chambers into the base of each of which opens a pair of *ostia*. These ostia are closed by *valves* when the heart contracts. The *pericardial sinus* in which the heart lies is formed by a horizontal partition beneath it. At its anterior end the heart forms an *aorta* which opens into the body cavity or hemocoel in the head region. Blood is forced anteriorly through the heart and aorta into the hemocoel where it bathes all the organs. The blood carries nutriment but does not play a large part in respiration as it does in most of the Metazoa because of the highly developed tracheal system. It consists of a *plasma* in which are suspended white blood cells, the *leucocytes*.

Respiratory System (Fig. 11–10). The respiratory system consists of a network of ectodermal tubes, the *tracheae*, that communicate with every part of the body. The tracheae consist of a single layer of cells enclosing a chitinous lining, which, in the larger tubes, forms a *spiral thread* that prevents the trachea from collapsing. The tracheae extend from the *spiracles* (Fig. 11–11) to a longitudinal trunk on either side of the body. The finest tracheae, the *tracheoles*, are connected directly with the tissue to which they supply oxygen

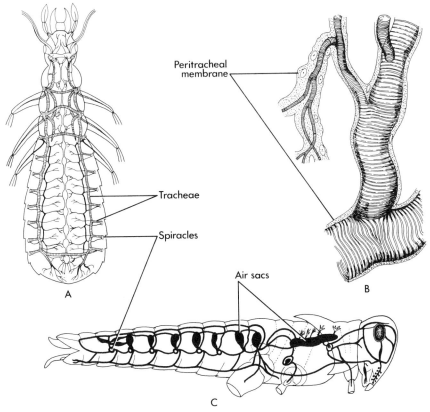

Peritracheal membrane

Tracheae

Spiracles

Air sacs

A

B

C

Fig. 11-10. Respiratory system of insects. (A) Diagram of tracheae in the body of a beetle. (B) Part of a trachea of a caterpillar. (C) Tracheae, air sacs, and spiracles of a grasshopper. (A, after Kolbe; B, after Leydig; C, after Vinal.)

and from which they carry away carbon dioxide, thus assuming the function performed in other animals by the circulatory system. The small blind endings of the tracheoles, on the muscles and other organs, are filled with fluid. During activity of the muscle the concentration of substances in the body fluid around the tracheoles increases. This causes diffusion of water from the tracheole into the surrounding area, thus bringing oxygen into closer proximity to the site where it is being used as the air moves farther down into the blind tip of the tracheole. After activity stops, the metabolic products that changed the osmotic pressure are disposed of and the water returns to the tracheole. In the grasshopper and certain other insects some of the tracheae become expanded into thin-walled air sacs, which are easily compressed and thus aid in the movement of air. Contraction and expansion of the abdomen draw air into and expel it from the tracheal system. In the grasshopper the first four pairs of spiracles are open at inspiration and closed at expiration, whereas the other six pairs are closed at inspiration and open at expiration.

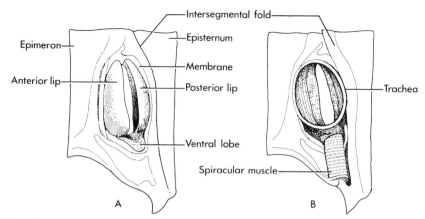

Fig. 11-11. Carolina locust, *Dissosteira carolina*. (A) Left spiracle of mesothoracic segment, outer view. (B) Right spiracle of mesothoracic segment, inner view. (After Snodgrass.)

Excretory System.   The organs of excretion are the *Malpighian tubules* that are coiled about in the hemocoel and open into the anterior end of the hind gut. Uric acid is the principal nitrogenous end product of protein metabolism in insects. It is of very low solubility. The ability of the Malpighian tubule to excrete uric acid with very little water loss in the process is an important factor in the success of insects in terrestrial environments. Potassium ions from potassium carbonate in the body fluid combine with uric acid under alkaline conditions to form the soluble potassium urate. Potassium urate diffuses into the Malpighian tubule and moves with the fluid in it toward the lumen of the intestine. Near the intestine the pH in the tubule shifts to acid and insoluble uric acid and soluble potassium carbonate are reformed. The latter and water are returned to the body fluid while the uric acid is carried on into the gut with a portion of the fluid. Further uptake of water may occur in the gut leaving the feces quite dry with crystals of uric acid included.

Nervous System (Figs. 11–8, 11–12, and 11–13).   There is a *brain*, dorsally located in the head, consisting of three pairs of ganglia fused together (Fig. 11–13). These ganglia supply the eyes, antennae, and labrum. The brain is connected by a pair of *circum-esophageal connectives* with a *subesophageal ganglion*. This ganglion consists of the three anterior pairs of ganglia of the ventral nerve chain fused together and supplies the mouth parts. The *ventral nerve chain* continues with a pair of large ganglia in each thoracic segment. The ganglia in the metathoracic segment are particularly large and represent the ganglia of this segment and of the first abdominal segment fused. Five pairs of ganglia are present in the abdomen. The pair in the second abdominal segment comprise the pairs from the second and third abdominal somites fused together and the pair in the seventh segment represent the ganglia of the

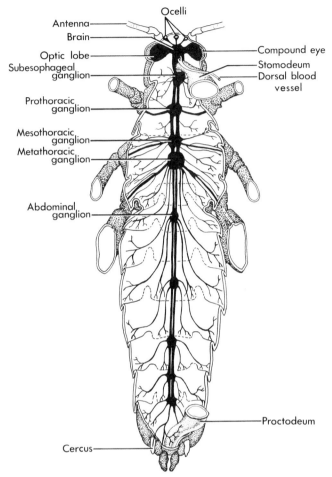

Fig. 11-12. Carolina locust, *Dissosteira carolina*. Dorsal view showing nervous system. (After Snodgrass.)

seventh to the eleventh somites combined. Connected with the brain are ganglia of the *sympathetic nervous system*, which supplies the muscles of the alimentary canal and spiracles.

Sense Organs. Grasshoppers possess organs of sight, hearing, touch, taste, and smell. The *compound eye* and *ocellus* have already been noted. Vision by means of the compound eyes has been described in the crayfish. The ocelli probably do not perceive objects but are merely organs of light perception. The pair of *auditory organs* (Fig. 11–14) are located on the sides of the tergite of the first abdominal segment. They consist of a *tympanum* stretched within an almost circular chitinous ring. The *antennae* (Figs. 11–15 and 11–16) are supplied with the principal organs of smell. Organs of *taste*

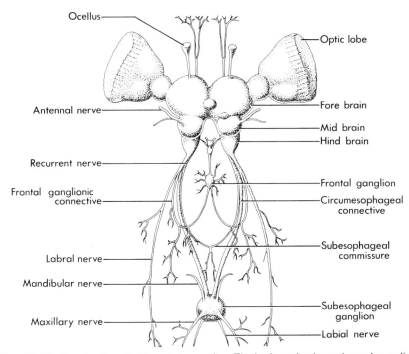

Fig. 11-13. Carolina locust, *Dissosteira carolina*. The brain and subesophageal ganglion and their nerves, as seen after removal of the facial wall of the head. (After Snodgrass.)

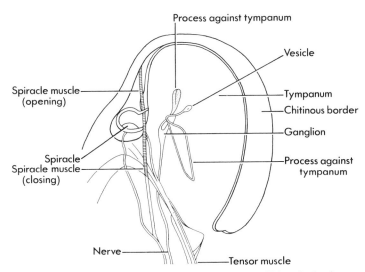

Fig. 11-14. Auditory organ of a grasshopper. (After Graber.)

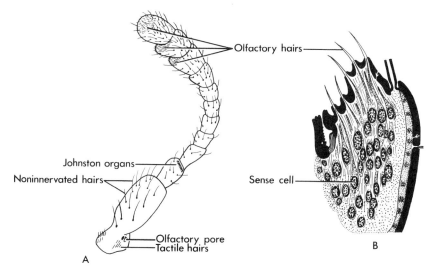

Fig. 11-15. Sense organs of insects. Mexican bean weevil. (A) Antenna, dorsal surface. (B) Antenna, section through tenth segment. (After McIndoo.)

are located on the mouth parts. The hairlike organs of *touch* are present on various parts of the body but particularly on the antennae.

Reproductive System. Female grasshoppers can easily be distinguished from males because of the presence of the *ovipositor* (Fig. 11-8). The female has two *ovaries*. Each consists of a number of filaments usually called *ovarian tubules* which, however, do not possess a lumen (Fig. 11-17). The ovarian filaments contain *oogonia* and *oocytes* arranged in a linear series, *nurse cells*, and other tissue cells. The oocytes grow as they proceed posteriorly down the filament, hence the filament becomes gradually larger toward the posterior end. The filaments of each ovary are attached posteriorly to an *oviduct* into which the eggs are discharged. The two oviducts unite to form a short *vagina*, which leads to the *genital opening* between the plates of the ovipositor. A tubular *seminal receptacle*, or spermatheca, which opens dorsal to the vaginal pore, receives the *spermatozoa* during copulation and releases them when the eggs are fertilized. In the male are two *testes* in which spermatozoa develop (Fig. 11-18). These are discharged into a *vas deferens*. The two vasa deferentia unite to form an *ejaculatory duct*, which opens on the dorsal surface of the *subgenital plate*. *Accessory glands* are present at the anterior end of the ejaculatory duct, which apparently secrete a fluid that aids in the transfer of spermatozoa to the female.

Embryonic Development and Growth. The eggs are fertilized at the time they are deposited, by the entrance of spermatozoa through an opening in one end of the egg shell called the *micropyle*. One sperm nucleus unites with the nucleus of the mature egg; a *blastoderm* is formed around the periphery

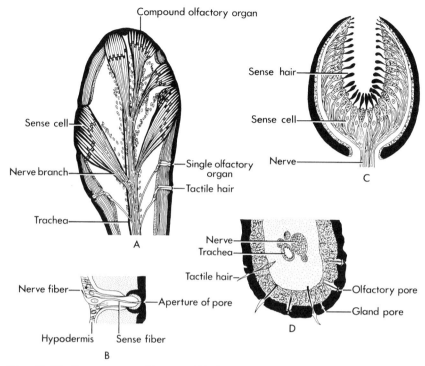

Fig. 11-16. Sense organs of insects. (A) Antenna of larva of a beetle, *Cotinis nitida*, longitudinal section of tip. (B) Single olfactory organ from antenna of *Cotinis*, cross-section. (C) Sense organ, probably static or balancing, in labial palp of codling moth. (D) Antenna of Mexican bean weevil, cross-section of first segment. (After McIndoo.)

of the egg from which an *embryo* develops. The young grasshopper that hatches from the egg is called a *nymph* (Fig. 11–19). It resembles its parent but has a large head compared with the rest of the body and lacks wings. As it grows its body becomes too large for the inflexible chitinous exoskeleton and the latter is shed periodically. Wings are gradually developed from wing buds and the adult condition is finally assumed. This type of development is called *simple metamorphosis* in contrast to the *complex metamorphosis* of many insects which involves larval and pupal stages.

(2) Other Insecta

The Insecta are air-breathing Arthropoda with bodies divided into head, thorax, and abdomen. The head bears one pair of antennae and the thorax three pairs of legs and usually one or two pairs of wings in the adult stage. Insects are more numerous in species than all other animals taken together; over 700,000 species have been described and no doubt a few hundred thousand remain to be discovered. They live in almost every conceivable type

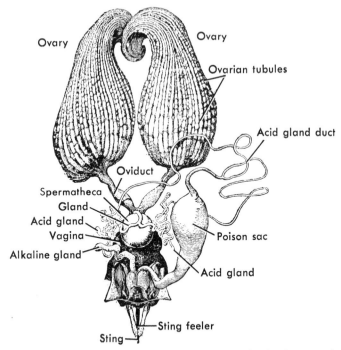

Fig. 11-17. Reproductive organs, sting, and poison gland of queen honeybee. (From Snodgrass.)

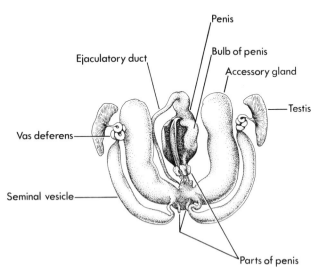

Fig. 11-18. Reproductive organs of drone honeybee, dorsal view, natural position. (From Snodgrass.)

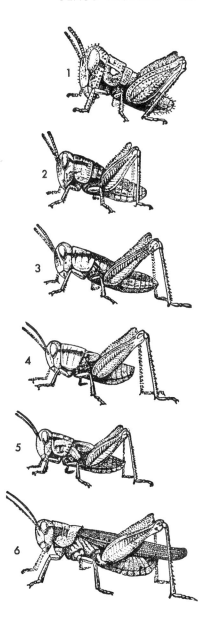

Fig. 11-19. Metamorphosis of a grass-hopper, *Melanoplus femur-rubrum*, show-ing the five nymph stages and the gradual growth of the wings. (From Packard, after Emerton.)

of environment on land and in the water and their structure, habits, and life cycles are correspondingly modified. Nevertheless, it is possible to separate this vast assemblage into orders, families, etc., although there is no unanimity of opinion with respect to the number of these that should be recognized and to the names that should be applied to them. The following classification into subclasses and orders is one commonly used by entomologists in this country.

SUBCLASS 1. APTERYGOTA. Ametabolous: no metamorphosis. Usually included in this subclass is an order of small eyeless insect-like invertebrates that lack antennae, the Protura. They are whitish, up to 1.5 mm long, and live in soil and decaying vegetation.

ORDER 1. THYSANURA. Bristletails, silverfish, etc.

ORDER 2. COLLEMBOLA. Springtails.

SUBCLASS 2. EXOPTERYGOTA. Hemimetabolous: simple metamorphosis.

ORDER 3. ORTHOPTERA. Cockroaches, crickets, grasshoppers, locusts, etc.

ORDER 4. ISOPTERA. Termites or white ants.

ORDER 5. ZORAPTERA. Zorapterans.

ORDER 6. EPHEMEROPTERA. Mayflies.

ORDER 7. ODONATA. Dragonflies.

ORDER 8. PLECOPTERA. Stoneflies.

ORDER 9. PSOCOPTERA. Book lice, etc.

ORDER 10. MALLOPHAGA. Bird lice.

ORDER 11. EMBIOPTERA. Web-spinners.

ORDER 12. THYSANOPTERA. Thrips.

ORDER 13. ANOPLURA. Sucking lice.

ORDER 14. HEMIPTERA. Bugs.

ORDER 15. HOMOPTERA. Plant lice, cicadas, etc.

ORDER 16. DERMAPTERA. Earwigs.

SUBLASS 3. ENDOPTERYGOTA. Holometabolous: complete metamorphosis.

ORDER 17. NEUROPTERA. The dobson, aphis-lions, etc.

ORDER 18. COLEOPTERA. Beetles.

ORDER 19. STREPSIPTERA. Stylopids.

ORDER 20. MECOPTERA. Scorpionflies, etc.

ORDER 21. TRICHOPTERA. Caddisflies.

ORDER 22. LEPIDOPTERA. Moths, skippers, and butterflies.

ORDER 23. DIPTERA. Flies.

ORDER 24. SIPHONAPTERA. Fleas.

ORDER 25. HYMENOPTERA. Bees, wasps, ants, etc.

Structural Modifications. Before discussing the characteristics of these orders it seems desirable to point out certain structural modifications that may be encountered in the various groups. The antennae, mouth parts, legs, and wings are among the most interesting external features of insects.

Wings. The mesothorax and metathorax bear each a pair of wings in most insects. Certain simple species (Thysanura, Fig. 11–24) do not possess wings; others (lice and fleas, Figs. 11–38 and 11–69) have no wings, but this is because they are degenerate. The flies (Diptera, Fig. 11–61, B) have a pair of clubbed threads, called balancers or halters, in place of the metathoracic wings. Attached to each thoracic segment is a pair of legs. Wings enable their owners to fly rapidly from place to place and thus to escape from enemies and to find a bountiful food supply. The success of insects in the struggle for existence is in part attributed to the presence of wings. Wings are outgrowths of the skin strengthened by a framework of chitinous tubes, called veins or nerves, which divide the wing into cells. The veins vary in distribution in different species, but are quite constant in individuals of any given species; they are consequently used to a considerable extent for purposes of classification. From comparisons of various wings a hypothetical ancestral wing was derived with the following principal longitudinal veins in sequence from anterior to posterior. (1) *Costa*: unbranched and at, or near, the leading edge of the wing. (2) *Subcosta*: with a terminal fork, near the basal end it may be connected to the costa by the *humeral* crossvein. (3) *Radius*: with two branches, the first branch unbranched, the second is called the *radial sector* and forks twice (Fig. 11–6). (4) *Media*: forks twice to produce four branches. (5) *Cubitus*: forks to produce two or three branches. (6) *Anal*: unbranched veins numbered 1st, 2nd, etc. from anterior to posterior. Crossveins occur as indicated in (Fig. 11–6, C). Modifications come about by reduction or by addition. In the beetles (Coleoptera) the fore wings are sheathlike and are called elytra. The fore wings of Orthoptera (grasshoppers, etc.) are leathery and are known as tegmina.

Legs. The legs of insects are used for various purposes and are highly modified for special functions, for example, those of the honeybee (Fig.

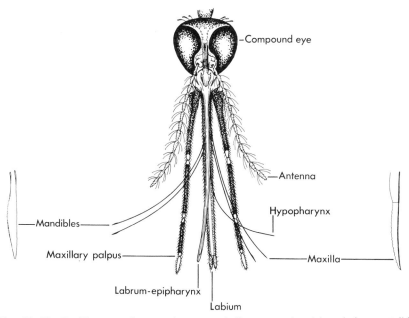

Fig. 11-20. Sucking mouthparts of an anopheline mosquito (*Anopheles costalis*), female. (After Carter.)

11–77). A typical leg consists of five parts—coxa, trochanter, femur, tibia, and tarsus. The tarsus (Fig. 11–5) is usually composed of five segments and bears at the end a pair of claws, between which is a fleshy lobule, the pulvillus. Running insects possess long, slender legs (Fig. 11–47); the mantis has its fore legs fitted for grasping (Fig. 11–26); the hind legs of the grasshopper are used in leaping (Fig. 11–5); the fore legs of the mole cricket are modified for digging (Fig. 11–29, C); and the hind legs of the water beetle are fitted for swimming (Fig. 11–48, A). Many other types could be mentioned.

Mouth Parts.   The mouth parts of insects are in most cases fitted either for biting (mandibulate) or sucking (suctorial). The grasshopper possesses typical mandibulate mouth parts (Fig. 11–3). The mandibles of insects that live on vegetation are adapted for crushing; those of carnivorous species are usually sharp and pointed, being fitted for biting and piercing. Suctorial mouth parts are adapted for piercing the tissues of plants or animals and sucking juices. The mouth parts of the honeybee (Fig. 11–76) are suctorial, but highly modified. In the female mosquito (Fig. 11–20) the labrum and epipharynx combined form a sucking tube; the mandibles and maxillae are piercing organs; the hypopharynx carries saliva; and the labium constitutes a sheath in which the other mouth parts lie when not in use. The proboscis of the butterflies and moths is a sucking tube formed by the maxillae.

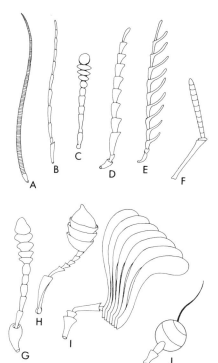

Fig. 11-21. Different forms of antennae of insects. (A) Bristle-like antenna of a grasshopper, *Locusta*. (B) Filiform, of a beetle, *Carabus*. (C) Moniliform, of a beetle, *Tenebrio*. (D) Dentate, of a beetle, *Elater*. (E) Pectinate, of *Ctenicera*. (F) Crooked, of honeybee. (G) Club-shaped, of beetle *Silpha*. (H) Knobbed, of beetle, *Necrophorus*. (I) Lamellated, of beetle, *Melolontha*. (J) With bristle, from fly, *Sargus*. (From Sedgwick, after Burmeister.)

The mouth parts of insects are of considerable importance from an economic standpoint, because insects that eat solid food can be destroyed by spraying the food with poisonous mixtures, whereas those that suck juices must be smothered with gases or have their spiracles closed with emulsion.

Antennae.   The antennae of insects are usually tactile, olfactory, or auditory in function. They differ widely in form and structure (Fig. 11–21). Often the antennae of the male differ from those of the female.

Alimentary Canal.   Of the internal organs of insects the alimentary canal and respiratory systems are of particular interest. The alimentary canal is modified according to the character of the food. An insect with mandibulate mouth parts (Fig. 11–8) usually possesses (1) an esophagus, which is dilated to form a crop in which food is stored, (2) a muscular gizzard or proventriculus, which strains the food and may aid in crushing it, (3) a stomach or ventriculus into which a number of glandular tubes (gastric ceca) pour digestive fluids, and (4) an intestine with urinary or Malpighian tubules at the anterior end. Suctorial insects, like the butterflies and moths (Fig. 11–22), are provided with a muscular pharynx which acts as a pumping organ and a sac for the storage of juices.

Respiratory System.   The respiratory system of insects is in general like that of the grasshopper (Fig. 11–10), but modifications occur in many species, especially in the larvae of those that live in water. Aquatic larvae, in many cases, do not have spiracles, but get oxygen by means of threadlike or leaflike cuticular outgrowths at the sides or posterior end of the body, termed tracheal gills (Fig. 11–34, B). Damselfly larvae possess caudal tracheal gills, and the larvae of dragonflies take water into the rectum which is lined with papillae abundantly supplied with tracheae.

Other structural modifications, peculiar habits, and life cycles are noted in the discussion of the orders.

Embryonic Development (Fig. 11–23).   The embryonic development of insects is a fascinating study. Eggs of the potato beetle, for example, consist

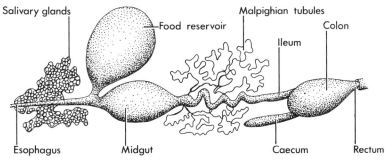

Fig. 11-22. Alimentary canal of a sucking insect, a moth, *Sphinx*. (After Wagner, modified.)

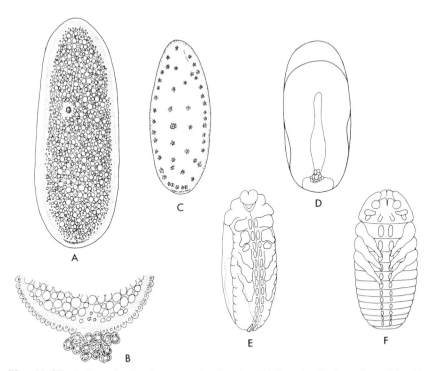

Fig. 11-23. Embryonic development of a beetle. (A) Longitudinal section of freshly laid egg showing fusion nucleus, yolk globules, peripheral layer of cytoplasm, and, at the lower, posterior end, the pole disk of granular "germ-cell determinants." (B) Blastoderm stage at end of twenty-four hours. The primitive germ cells have become extruded at the posterior end. (C) Preblastoderm stage at end of twenty hours showing cleavage nuclei at periphery. (D) Germ band with ventral groove; primitive germ cells near the posterior end. (E) Embryo with segmentation in progress and appendages of head and thorax growing out. (F) Older embryo with mouthparts and legs further developed. (From Hegner.)

largely of yolk globules with a superficial layer of cytoplasm and thin cyto-plasmic strands among the yolk (Fig. 11–23, A). The single fusion nucleus lies in a small island of cytoplasm. Nuclear division is not followed immedi-ately by cell division but hundreds of nuclei are produced before cells are formed (C). Most of these nuclei migrate to the periphery and fuse with the superficial layer of cytoplasm; cell membranes appear and a blastoderm of a single layer of cells (D) covers the entire egg. The rest of the nuclei remain behind among the yolk globules which it is their duty to dissolve. The blasto-derm thickens on one side of the egg forming the germ band in which appears a ventral groove (E). This groove is grown over by the amnioserosal fold and the germ band then becomes divided into segments. Appendages that are destined to become mouth parts and legs grow out from the cephalic and thoracic segments (E, F). The insect egg is very highly organized; certain parts of the potato-beetle egg are destined to produce certain definite parts of the embryo even before the blastoderm is formed as can be demonstrated by killing parts of the fresh egg with a hot needle and allowing the rest of the egg to develop. At the posterior end of the eggs of certain insects, especially Diptera, Coleoptera, and Hymenoptera, is a mass of granules that stain deeply with haematoxylin and appear to play an important part in the origin of the primordial germ cells; for this reason they are known as germ-cell determinants (A). These granules have been traced into the germ cells (B) and the latter have been followed from one generation to the next, illustrating very clearly the theory of the continuity of the germ plasm.

Growth and Metamorphosis. The eggs of insects are of various shapes and sizes. Some of them are colored; others are marked with polygonal areas or ridges. Three types of insects may be distinguished with respect to the method of their development: (1) ametabola, (2) hemimetabola, and (3) holometabola.

The ametabolic insects are essentially like the adult, except in size, when they hatch from the egg; they develop to maturity without a metamorphosis. The Thysanura (Fig. 11–24) and other Apterygota are ametabolic.

The hemimetabolic insects hatch from the egg and develop into adults as in the grasshopper without passing through a true pupal period. Many of the species belonging to the hemimetabolic orders change considerably during the growth period, but are all more or less active throughout their development and are said to undergo simple metamorphosis.

Holometabolic insects, such as the butterflies (Fig. 11–60), pass through both a larval and a pupal stage in their development and are said to undergo complete metamorphosis. The majority of insects belong to this type.

A. Subclass 1. Apterygota

These wingless insects have no metamorphosis. Immature individuals in the early intermolt stages (instars) resemble the adults.

Order 1. Thysanura. Bristletails (Fig. 11–24, A, B). Primitive wingless insects; ametabolic; chewing mouth parts; 11 abdominal segments; usually two or three long, filiform, segmented, caudal appendages; less than 20 species known from the United States. The pair of caudal appendages, or the outer two, if three are present, are cerci; the antennae are long, filiform, and contain many segments; in some the compound eyes are degenerate or absent; in many the jaws are sunk into a cavity in the head; a few possess appendages of two segments, the styli, on the ventral abdominal segments, which may be remnants of legs of the many-legged ancestors of insects.

The silverfish or fishmoth, *Lepisma saccharina* (Fig. 11–24, A), is a common species in houses, especially in the warmer parts of the country. It is covered with beautifully marked, shining scales, and often damages books, clothing, etc., because of its fondness for starch. *Campodea staphylinus* (Fig. 11–24, B) is a delicate, whitish species that lives under stones and leaves, and in rotten

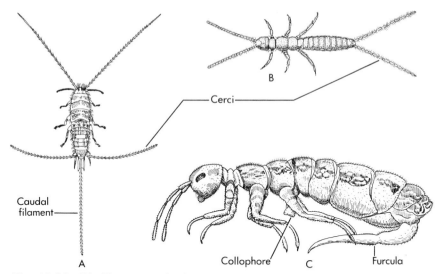

Fig. 11-24. (A) Thysanura. *Lepisma saccharina,* the silverfish. (B) Thysanura. *Campodea staphylinus.* (C) Collembola. Spingtail. (A, from Wellhouse, after Kellogg; B, after Lubbock; C, after Miall.)

wood and other damp places. The firebrat, *Thermobia domestica,* prefers a very warm environment such as the vicinity of stoves and fireplaces. *Japyx* has pincer-like caudal appendages and *Machilis maratima* is a type that bears abdominal appendages.

Order 2. Collembola. Springtails (Fig. 11–24, C). Primitive wingless insects; ametabolic; chewing or sucking mouth parts; four to six segments in the antennae; usually no tracheae; compound eyes absent; Malpighian tubules absent; tarsi absent; six abdominal segments; a springing organ present in most species on the ventral side of the fourth abdominal segment. The springing organ, or furcula, propels the insect into the air when it is released from a catch, the hamula, on the third abdominal segment; mandibles are often overgrown by the cheeks; in some the mandibles and maxillae are modified into piercing organs; on the ventral surface of the first abdominal segment is a tubelike projection, or collophore, which holds the insects to the undersurface of an object with a sticky secretion from the labium.

Collembola are very small insects, often microscopic in size. They are to be found in the crevices of bark, in moss, under stones, leaves, and wood where they feed on decaying matter. The snowflea, *Archorutes nivicolus,* sometimes occurs in winter on the snow in large numbers and is often a nuisance in maple sugar camps. The garden flea, *Bourletiella hortensis,* may become a pest because of its fondness for young vegetables, such as cabbage, cucumbers, turnips, and squashes.

B. Subclass 2. Exopterygota

These winged insects have a simple metamorphosis. Late nymphal instars of winged species show wing buds developing externally.

Order 3. Orthoptera. Grasshoppers, crickets, cockroaches, katydids, locusts, walking sticks, and mantids. Hemimetabolic; chewing mouth parts; typically two pairs of wings, the fore wings often thickened and parchment-like and called tegmina (singular, tegmen), the hind wings folded like a fan beneath the fore wings; in some, wings are vestigial or absent. Six families in this order contain most of the familiar orthopterans.

FAMILY 1. PHASMIDAE (Fig. 11–25).   Walking sticks and leaf insects. These are herbivorous insects. Some of them are wingless and have a slender body, and long legs and antennae, which give them a sticklike appearance. They are not active and move slowly. Their resemblance to the twigs on which they rest and their habit of feigning death, furnish an example of mimicry. *Diapheromera femorata* (Fig. 11–25, A) is the common walking stick of the northern United States. *Aplopus mayeri* is our only winged phasmid; it occurs in Florida. In the tropics are many species with expansions of the abdomen and leg segments and with wings that give them a close resemblance to leaves.

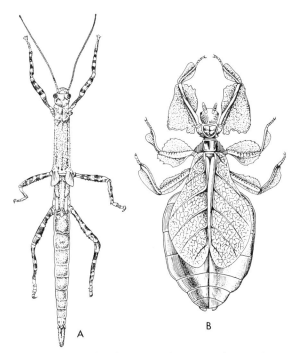

Fig. 11-25. (A) Phasmidae. *Diapheromera femorata*, the northern walking stick. (B) Phasmidae. *Phyllium scythe*, a leaf insect. (A, after Davenport; B, after Westwood.)

Fig. 11-26. Mantidae. *Stagmomantis carolina,* the praying mantis. (After Packard.)

FAMILY 2. MANTIDAE (Fig. 11–26). Mantids. The mantids are carnivorous, feeding on other insects. The prothorax is much elongated and the prothoracic legs are modified as grasping organs. Spines are present on the tibiae and femora and the former can be bent back so as to hold any insect grasped by them. As they lie in wait for their prey, the fore legs are raised in an attitude of prayer, hence the common name, praying mantis. *Stagmomantis carolina* (Fig. 11–26) is a species that occurs as far north as Maryland and southern Indiana. Other species live in the southern United States; many of those that live in the tropics have wings that resemble the leaves of plants in shape and color.

FAMILY 3. BLATTIDAE (Fig. 11–27). Cockroaches. These are omnivorous insects with dorso-ventrally flattened body, head bent down beneath the thorax, long antennae, and legs adapted for running. They are often a nuisance in houses. In nature, they live under stones, sticks, and other objects. The eggs are enclosed in capsules, the oothecae. Some forms are wingless. Three species that occur in the United States are *Periplaneta americana* (Fig. 11–27, A), the American cockroach; *Blattella germanica* (C), the croton-bug, which was introduced from Europe; and *Blatta orientalis* (B), the oriental cockroach, which probably reached America from Asia.

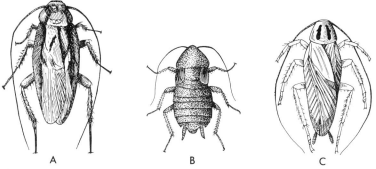

A   B   C

Fig. 11-27. Blattidae. (A) *Periplaneta americana,* the American cockroach. (B) *Blatta orientalis,* the "black beetle"; nymph. (C) *Blattella germanica,* the "croton bug." (A, B, from Herrick; C, from Essig.)

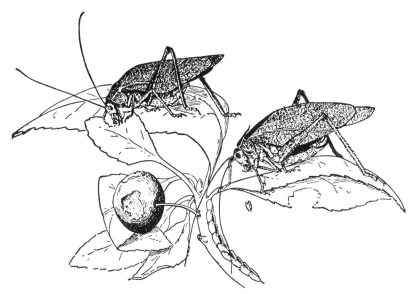

Fig. 11-28. Tettigoniidae. *Microcentrum rhombifolium,* a katydid; male and female are shown feeding on apple leaves; eggs are deposited along stem. (From Essig.)

FAMILY 4. TETTIGONIIDAE (Fig. 11–28).   Long-horned grasshoppers. The antennae of this group are very long and slender; the tarsi have four segments; the ovipositor is long and sword-shaped; the body is often green and is hence inconspicuous; the auditory organs are located in the base of the tibiae of the prothoracic legs. In many species the males have certain veins and cells of each wing-cover near the base so modified that when rubbed together they vibrate and produce a sound. The katydid, *Pterophylla camellifolia,* owes its name to its rasping call notes. Meadow grasshoppers, such as *Conocephalus,* are light-green forms that live among the grass in meadows. In a related family, Gryllacrididae, are certain cricket-like species, such as *Ceuthophilus,* known as cave crickets or camel crickets; they live in dark, moist places in caves, cellars, under stones and wood, etc. The shield-backed grasshoppers are mostly wingless or nearly wingless species, such as the genus *Atlanticus,* and also resemble crickets somewhat in appearance. They live in grassy fields or open woods.

FAMILY 5. GRYLLIDAE (Fig. 11–29).   Crickets. Most crickets have long antennae, metathoracic legs for leaping, and a spear-shaped ovipositor. The males have a highly differentiated stridulating apparatus consisting of a file on the base of one tegmen and a scraper on the other. When the wings are held up over the body, the file is rubbed over the scraper as the wings vibrate and produce the characteristic chirp. Many of the tree-crickets are light green and live in trees. *Oecanthus niveus,* the snowy tree-cricket, is a common

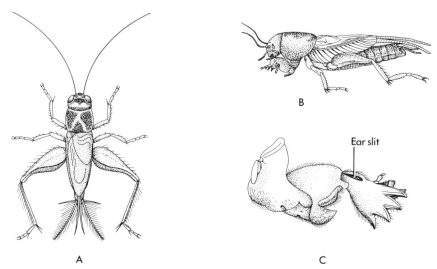

Fig. 11-29. Gryllidae. (A) *Acheta domesticus*, the house cricket. (B) *Scapteriscus didactylus*, a mole cricket. (C) Leg of a mole cricket, showing ear slit. (A, from Herrick; B, after Barrett; C, from Sedgwick.)

species. When a number of individuals are close together they chirp in unison. Field crickets are brown and are abundant in fields where they usually hide in the daytime under stones, etc., or in burrows in the earth but are active at night. Some of them enter houses including the house cricket of Europe, *Acheta domesticus* (Fig. 11-29, A), which has been introduced into the northeastern United States. Mole-crickets (*Gryllotalpa*) are likewise nocturnal. They burrow in the ground and have the tibiae of the prothoracic legs broadened and provided with stout spines well adapted for digging (Fig. 11-29, C).

FAMILY 6. ACRIDIDAE (LOCUSTIDAE) (Fig. 11-1). Locusts or short-horned grasshoppers. Here the antennae are not as long as the body and consist of less than 26 segments; the ovipositor is composed of several short plates; and the first abdominal segment bears a tympanum on either side. Locusts are vegetarians and often cause great damage to crops. The males produce sounds either by rubbing the row of spines on the inner surface of the femur of the metathoracic leg against the outer surface of the tegmina, or while flying, by rubbing the upper surface of the anterior edge of the hind wings against the undersurface of the tegmina. Common species are the red-legged locust, *Melanoplus femur-rubrum*, the Carolina locust, *Dissosteira carolina*, the American locust, *Schistocera americana*, the lubber grasshopper, *Brachystola magna*, and the Rocky Mountain locust, *Melanoplus spretus*, which has been so destructive to crops in Kansas, Iowa, and Nebraska during its migrations. The locusts that were responsible for the plagues of the Pharaohs belonged to this family. In one of the closely related families are certain small active pigmy locusts, such as *Acrydium*, characterized by the

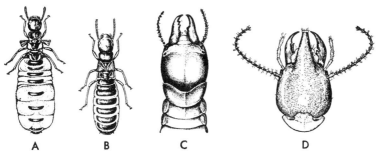

A   B   C   D

Fig. 11-30. Isoptera; termites. (A) *Reticulitermes flavipes.* Mature egg-laying female or queen with abdomen distended. (B) *R. flavipes.* Mature male. (C) *Kalotermes occidentis.* Anterior end of soldier showing large mandibles, and wing pads. (D) *Armitermes intermedius.* Anterior end of soldier showing large biting mandibles, and nasus. (After Snyder.)

presence of a pronotum that extends back over the dorsal surface of the abdomen, sometimes beyond the posterior end of the body.

Order 4. Isoptera (Fig. 11–30). Termites or white ants. Hemimetabolic; chewing mouth parts; two pairs of long, narrow wings laid flat on the back when at rest, or wingless; abdomen joined directly to thorax. These social insects live in colonies much like ants, and are especially abundant in the tropics. They live mostly under cover and the cuticle is light in color and delicate. The adult sexual males and females after their nuptial flight shed their wings near the base where there is a transverse, humeral suture. The castes of termites are more numerous than those of other social insects, such

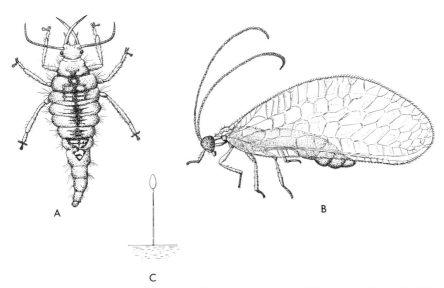

A   B

C

Fig. 11-31. Neuroptera. *Chrysopa californica,* a lacewing. (A) Larva. (B) Adult. (C) Stalked egg. (After Quayle.)

as the bees, wasps, and ants. The species differ with respect to the number of castes present, but each caste contains both males and females. Four castes are usually present: (1) the first reproductive caste, with wings that are shed after the nuptial flight; these are known as king and queen or the primary royal pair; (2) the second reproductive caste, sexually mature but nymphal in form, and known as substitute or supplemental king and queen; (3) sterile workers, which carry on the various activities necessary for the maintenance of the colony, are wingless and usually blind; and (4) sterile soldiers, which are supposed to protect the colony, are wingless, and possess very large heads and mandibles. *Reticulitermes flavipes* is the common species in the northeastern United States. As in many other species, its food consists of dead wood, and it works in the dark, hence, the inside of timbers in buildings are often eaten away without evidence of damage until nothing but a shell remains. Huge nests in the form of mounds over 10 feet in height are built by certain species that live in the tropics. Termite nests are often inhabited by other species of insects; these are called termitophiles. Over 100 species of termitophiles have been recorded. The relation between termites and their intestinal protozoa has already been described.

Order 5. Zoraptera. Zorapterans. A small order of less than two dozen species of tiny, termite-like, colonial insects. Probably feed on animal material. Ex. *Zorotypus hubbardi*; southern United States.

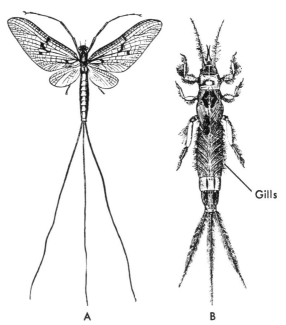

Fig. 11-32. Ephemeroptera. *Ephemera*, a mayfly. (A) Adult. (B) Nymph. (From Kennedy.)

Order 6. Ephemeroptera (Ephemerida) (Fig. 11–32). Mayflies. Hemimetabolic; mouth parts of adult, vestigial; two pairs of membranous, triangular wings, the fore wings larger than the hind wings; caudal filament and cerci very long. The family, Ephemeridae, belonging to this order contains a number of species of delicate insects known as mayflies. The larvae live in the water and breathe by means of tracheal gills (Fig. 11–32, B), usually located in a row on either side of the abdomen; these are outgrowths of the integument containing tracheal branches. Oxygen is obtained by them from the water. The adults live only a short time, hence the derivation of the name Ephemeroptera from the Greek word *ephemeros*, meaning lasting but a day. Frequently large numbers of adults emerge from the water at about the same

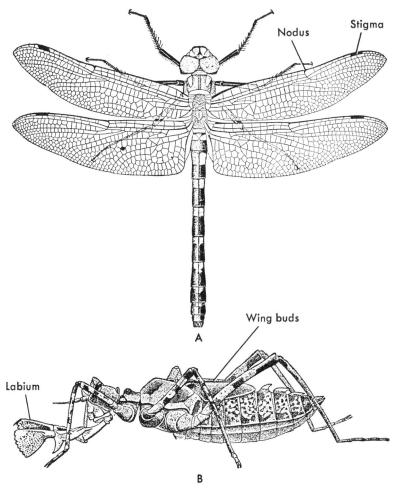

Fig. 11-33. Odonata. *Macromia magnifica*, a dragonfly. (A) Adult. (B) Nymph. (From Kennedy.)

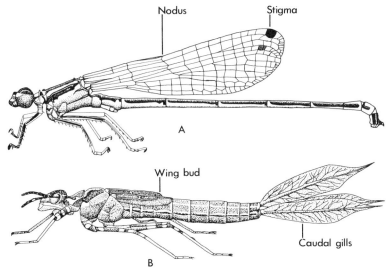

Fig. 11-34. *Ischnura cervula*, a damselfly. (A) Adult, male. (B) Nymph. (From Kennedy.)

time and huge swarms of them suddenly appear; for example, *Ephemera simulans*, around the lakes of the northern United States. The adults when they leave the water are called subimagos, because they molt within a few minutes to 24 hours after they acquire functional wings; they are the only insects that molt in the adult stage.

Order 7. Odonata (Figs. 11–33 and 11–34).   Dragonflies and damselflies. Hemimetabolic; chewing mouth parts; two pairs of membranous wings, the hind wings as large as or larger than the fore wings; large compound eyes; small antennae; nymphs aquatic; both nymphs and adults, predacious. The dragonflies (suborder Anisoptera, Fig. 11–33) are large insects. The wings are usually held in a horizontal position when at rest and the eyes may be made up of larger facets above and smaller ones below. The nymphs breath by means of rectal gills, which line the enlarged posterior end of the alimentary canal, and extract oxygen from the water that is drawn in and expelled from this cavity. The labium of the larva is much elongated and can be extended rapidly from its folded resting position beneath the head so as to impale its prey on the hooks at the end. *Anax junius* is a common, widely spread species of the family Aeschnidae. The damselflies (suborder Zygoptera, Fig. 11–34) are smaller. The wings are parallel with the abdomen when at rest, and are delicate compared with those of the dragonflies. *Agrion maculatum* is a common, dark-colored species partial to streams in woods.

Order 8. Plecoptera (Fig. 11–35).   Stoneflies. Hemimetabolic; chewing mouth parts, often undeveloped in adults; two pairs of wings, the hind wings

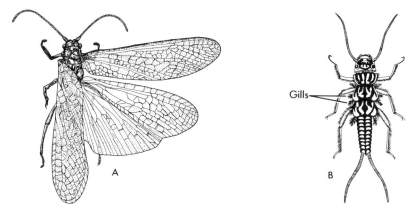

Fig. 11-35. Plecoptera. Stonefly. (A) Adult. (B) Nymph showing tracheal gills. (A, after Comstock; B, after Sharp.)

usually larger and folded beneath the fore wing; tarsus with three segments; nymphs aquatic, usually in flowing water under stones, often with tufts of thoracic tracheal gills. Ten families have representatives in this country. *Allocapnia pygmae* is a common species that may appear on the snow in winter and hence is known as the snowfly. *Taeniopteryx pacifica*, the salmon-fly, is a pest in parts of the state of Washington because it destroys the buds of fruit trees.

Order 9. Psocoptera (Corrodentia) (Fig. 11–36, A).   Psocids and book lice. Hemimetabolic; chewing mouth parts; wingless or with two pairs of membranous wings that have few, prominent veins, the fore wings larger than the hind wings; wings, when at rest, held over body like the sides of a roof. Two

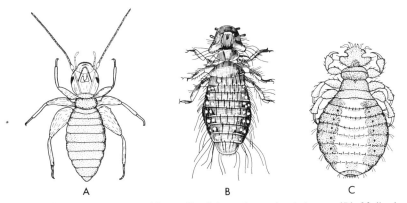

Fig. 11-36. (A) Psocoptera. *Liposcelis divinatorius*, a book louse. (B) Mallophaga. *Menopon pallidum*, a chicken louse. (C) Mallophaga. *Gyropus ovalis*, a guinea-pig louse. (A, from Herrick; B, after Piaget; C, after Osborn.)

families occur in the United States. The family Psocidae contains winged species that live on trees, feeding on dry vegetable matter. They are known as psocids or bark-lice. The Liposcelidae are wingless and called book-lice because they are often observed in old books. *Liposcelis divinatorius* is a species of this type, which feeds on the starch in bookbindings (Fig. 11–36, A).

Order 10. Mallophaga (Fig. 11–36, B and C).   Bird lice. Hemimetabolic; chewing mouth parts; wings absent; eyes degenerate. The Mallophaga are ectoparasites of birds and, less frequently, of mammals. They feed on hair, feathers, and dermal scales. Those that live on mammals usually possess tarsi with one claw adapted for grasping hair; whereas those that live on birds possess tarsi with two claws which aid them in moving among feathers. Representative species are *Menopon pallidum* (Fig. 11–36), the common chicken louse, *Chelopistes meleagridis*, the large turkey louse, and *Bovicola bovis* that lives on cattle.

Order 11. Embioptera (Fig. 11–37, A).   Web-spinners. Hemimetabolic; chewing mouth parts; wingless or with two pairs of delicate, membranous wings, containing few veins, and folded on the back when at rest; and cerci of two segments present. The males are usually winged and the females wingless. Embiids live in warm countries and have been reported from the southern states. They live under stones and other objects in tunnels formed of silk produced by tarsal glands, and some of the 60 or more species known are gregarious. *Anisembia texana* is a species discovered in Texas, and *Oligotoma california* (Fig. 11–37, A) a species from California.

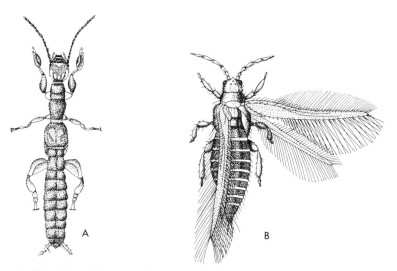

Fig. 11-37. (A) Embioptera. *Oligotoma california*, the California embiid. (B) Thysanoptera. A thrips. (A, from Essig; B, from Moulton.)

Order 12. Thysanoptera (Fig. 11–37, B). Thrips. Hemimetabolic; piercing mouth parts; wingless or with two pairs of similar, long, narrow, membranous wings with few or no veins, and fringed with long hairs; prothorax large and free; tarsi with two or three segments terminating in a bladder-like, protrusible vesicle. Some species of thrips are injurious to cultivated plants; others are carnivorous and feed on aphids, red spiders, etc. Two suborders are recognized. The Terebrantia contains many injurious species, the females of which lay their eggs in the tissues of plants with their sawlike ovipositors. Here belong the onion thrips, *Thrips tabaci*, the greenhouse thrips, *Heliothrips haemorrhoidalis*, the pear thrips, *Taeniothrips inconsequens*, the strawberry thrips, *Frankliniella tritici*, and many others. The members of the suborder

Fig. 11-38. Anoplura. (A) *Pediculus humanus capitis,* the human head louse. (B) *Pediculus humanus corporis,* the human body louse. (C) *Phthirius pubis,* the human crab louse. (D) *Linognathus vituli,* the long-nosed ox louse. (A–C, from Herrick; D, after Osborn.)

Tubulifera are not so injurious, and the females do not possess a sawlike ovipositor. Common species are the mullein thrips. *Haplothrips verbasci*, and the camphor thrips, *Liothrips floridensis*.

Order 13. Anoplura (Fig. 11–38). Sucking lice. Hemimetabolic; piercing and sucking mouth parts; wingless; ectoparasites on mammals; eyes poorly developed or absent; tarsus with one segment bearing a single, large, curved claw adapted for clinging to the hair of the host. The eggs of Anoplura are fastened with a gluelike substance to the hairs of the host and are known as

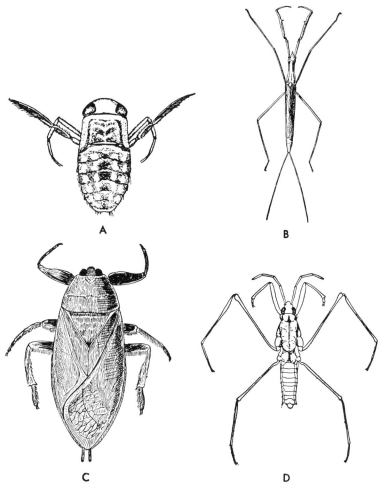

Fig. 11-39. Hemiptera. (A) Corixidae. *Artocorixa alternata*, a water boatman. (B) Nepidae. *Ranatra linearis*, a water scorpion. (C) Belostomatidae. *Lethocerus*, an electric-light bug. (D) Gerridae. *Gerris remigis*, a water strider. (A, after Hungerford; B, after Sharp; C, from Herrick; D, after Woodworth.)

nits. Two species occur on man, the head and body louse, *Pediculus humanus* (Fig. 11–38, A and B), and the crab louse, *Phthirius pubis* (Fig. 11–38, C). Several important diseases are transmitted from man to man by the body louse, including typhus, relapsing, and trench fevers. Among the Anoplura of domestic animals are *Linognathus setosus*, the dog louse; *Haematopinus suis*, the hog louse; and *L. vituli*, the ox louse (Fig. 11–38, D).

Order 14. Hemiptera (Figs. 11–39 to 11–41).   True bugs. Hemimetabolic; piercing and sucking mouth parts; wingless or with two pairs of wings, the fore wings thickened at the base (hemelytra). The labium forms a jointed beak into which the slender, piercing maxillae and mandibles move. This order contains many families of interesting and economically important species, a few of which are as follows. The water boatmen, Corixidae (Fig. 11–39, A), have long, flat, fringed metathoracic legs adapted for swimming; they carry a film of air about the body while under the water. The back swimmers, Notonectidae, likewise have oarlike hind legs, but swim on their backs. The water scorpions, Nepidae (Fig. 11–39, B), obtain air through a long caudal tube that is thrust through the surface; a common long, slender species is *Ranatra americana*. The giant water bugs, Belostomatidae (Fig. 11–39, C), are sometimes called electric-light bugs; their hind legs are also adapted for swimming; some tropical species reach a length of four or five inches; common species are *Lethocerus americanus*, which has a femoral groove on each front leg into which the tibia fits, and *Belostoma flumineum* the female of which fastens her eggs on the back of the male. The water striders, Gerridae (Fig. 11–39, D) have long, slender middle and hind legs, which do not break through the surface film as they skim about over the water. The leaf bugs, Miridae, are very numerous and often injurious to plants, and include such

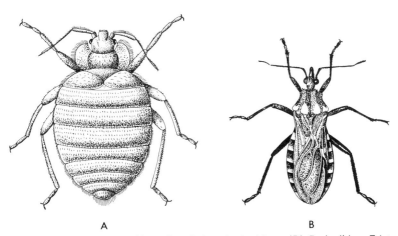

A   B

Fig. 11-40. (A) Cimicidae. *Cimex lectularius,* the bed bug. (B) Reduviidae. *Triatoma megista,* a kissing bug. (From Brumpt.)

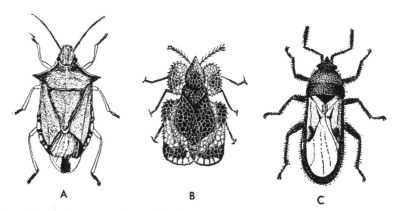

Fig. 11-41. (A) Pentatomidae. *Podisus spinosus,* a stink bug or soldier bug. (B) Tingidae. *Corythuca arcuata,* a lace bug. (C) Lygaeidae. *Blissus leucopterus,* a chinch bug. (A, after Lugger; B, after Comstock; C, after Webster and Riley.)

common species as the tarnished plant bug, *Lygus lineolaris,* and the apple red bug, *Lygidea mendax.* The bed bugs, Cimicidae, are nocturnal insects that live on warm-blooded animals; the human species, *Cimex lectularius* (Fig. 11-40, A), has been accused of transmitting various diseases but has not been definitely incriminated. The assassin bugs, Reduviidae, form a large family that contains among others, certain species known as kissing bugs; several of these, especially *Panstrongylus megistus* (Fig. 11-40, B) and species of *Triatoma,* are responsible for the transmission of the Protozoa (trypanosomes) responsible for the human disease of South America known as Chagas disease. The lace bugs, Tingidae (Fig. 11-41, B), have front wings, or hemelytra, of lacelike structure, as well as expansions of the prothorax and are hence easily recognized. The chinch bugs, Lygaeidae, belong to a large family, the most notorious species being the common chinch bug, *Blissus*

Fig. 11-42. Cicadidae. Six stages in the emergence of an adult harvest fly, or cicada, from the nymph. (After Snodgrass.)

leucopterus (Fig. 11–41, C), that has been so destructive to grain, especially in the Mississippi Valley. The squash bug family, Coreidae, also contains many species, a good example of which is the common squash bug, *Anasa tristis*. The stink bugs, Pentatomidae (Fig. 11–41, A), secrete a fluid with a nauseous odor, hence their name; the harlequin bug, *Murgantia histrionica*, is destructive to garden vegetables, but another species, *Perillus bioculatus* is beneficial because it destroys potato beetles.

Order 15. Homoptera (Figs. 11–42 to 11–45). Cicadas, leafhoppers, aphids, scales. Hemimetabolic; mouth parts for piercing and sucking; usually two pairs of wings of uniform thickness held over the back like the sides of a roof. Many economically important insects belong to this order. Several of the families are as follows. The cicadas, and harvestflies, Cicadidae (Fig. 11–42), are large, noisy insects; the best-known species is the periodical cicada, or seventeen-year locust, *Magicicada septendecim*, the nymphal stages of which live in the ground for seventeen years before the imago emerges. The spittle insects, or frog hoppers, Cercopidae (Fig. 11–43, A), live in a mass of froth elaborated from matter voided from the anus and mixed with a gluelike secretion from abdominal glands. The tree hoppers, Membracidae (Fig. 11–43, B), have a prothorax that extends back over the body and sometimes forms hornlike projections, as in the buffalo tree hopper, *Stictocephala bubalus*, or a hump-back, as in *Telamona ampelopsidis*. The leaf hoppers,

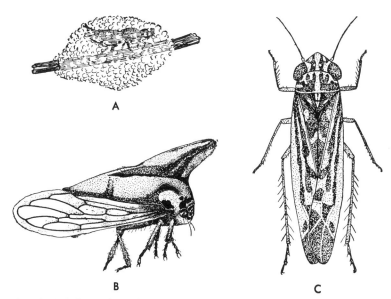

A

B

C

Fig. 11-43. (A) Cercopidae. *Aphrophora*, a spittle insect. (B) Membracidae. *Platycotis vittata*, an oak-tree hopper. (C) Cicadellidae. *Empoasca mali*, the apple-leaf hopper. (A, after Morse; B, after Woodworth; C, from Essig.)

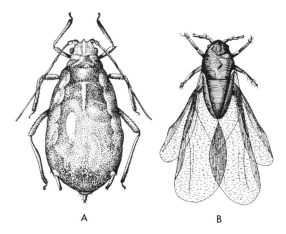

Fig. 11-44. (A) Aphididae. *Rhopalosiphum prunifoliae,* the apple-grain aphis, wingless form. (B) Phylloxeridae. *Phylloxera vitifoliae,* the grape phylloxera. (A, from Wellhouse; B, from Sedgwick.)

Cicadellidae (Fig. 11–43, C), are small and abundant on grass; some are destructive, such as *Euscelis exitiosus* on grain, *Erythroneura comes* on grape leaves and *Empoasca fabae,* on potatoes. The plant lice or aphids, Aphididae (Fig. 11–44, A), are mostly small, green insects with or without wings, that suck juices from plants; they pass from the anus a sweet substance, known as honeydew, which is attractive to ants, bees, and wasps, sometimes bringing about a sort of symbiotic relationship between the aphids and other insects. The life cycle of aphids is of great interest. Females that are parthenogenetic and viviparous hatch from eggs that have lived through the winter. Their offspring are wingless, parthenogenetic females. These give rise to wingless parthenogenetic females, but after a time produce winged females, which

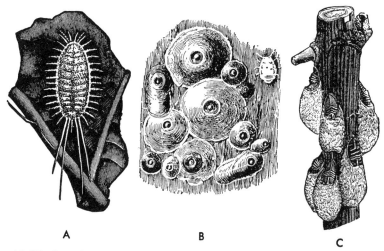

Fig. 11-45. Coccoidea. (A) *Pseudococcus longispinus,* the long-tailed mealy bug. (B) *Aspidiotus perniciosus,* the San Jose scale. (C) *Pulvinaria innumerabilis,* the cottony maple scale, females with egg sacs. (After Comstock.)

migrate to other plants and produce several wingless female generations. As fall approaches, winged males and winged viviparous females appear, they return to the original plant host, mating occurs, and fertilized eggs are laid that remain dormant over winter and give rise to parthenogenetic females in the spring. Among the aphids are the green bug, *Toxoptera graminum*, a pest on wheat and oats, the corn-root aphis, *Anuraphis maidiradicis*. In the related family, Eriosomatidae, are the woolly apple aphid, *Eriosoma lanigera*, and a number of species that produce plant galls, such as the witch-hazel cone gall aphid, *Hormaphis hamamelidis*. The phylloxerids, Phylloxeridae, are also destructive to vegetation, especially the grape phylloxera, *Phylloxera vitifoliae* (Fig. 11–44, B). The white flies, Aleyrodidae, are covered with a whitish powder, hence their name; the greenhouse white fly, *Asterochiton vaporariorum*, is an important pest. The scale insects and mealy bugs, superfamily Coccoidea (Fig. 11–45), are the most serious pests of horticulturists; they include the San Jose scale, *Aspidiotus perniciosus* (Fig. 11–45, B), the cottony maple scale, *Pulvinaria innumerabilis* (C), the cottony cushion scale, *Icerya purchasi*, and the mealy bug, *Pseudococcus longispinus* (A); several species are useful to man, such as the lac insect, *Laccifer lacca*, the cochineal insect, *Dactylopius coccus*, and the China wax insect, *Ericerus pe-la*.

Order 16. Dermaptera (Fig. 11–46).   Earwigs. Hemimetabolic; chewing mouth parts; wingless or with one or two pairs of wings, the fore wings small, leathery, and meeting in a straight line along the back, the hind wings, large, membranous, and folded lengthwise and crosswise under the fore wings; forceps-like cerci at posterior end of abdomen. The earwigs are nocturnal insects that feed principally on vegetation. The European earwig, *Forficula auricularia*, has been introduced into this country; the seaside earwig, *Anisolabis maritima* (Fig. 11–46), occurs along the Atlantic and Pacific coasts;

Fig. 11-46. Dermaptera. *Anisolabis maritima*, the seaside earwig. (From Davenport.)

and little earwig, *Labia minor*, introduced from Europe, has become widely distributed in the United States.

C. Subclass 3. Endopterygota

These winged insects have a complex metamorphosis. The larval stage is followed by an inactive pupal stage from which the adult eventually emerges. No wing buds develop externally in the larvae of winged species.

Order 17. Neuroptera (Fig. 11–31). The Dobson, aphis lions, ant lions, and others. Holometabolic; chewing mouth parts; four similar membranous wings, usually with many veins and cross veins; no abdominal cerci; larvae carnivorous, some with suctorial mouth parts; tracheal gills usually present on larvae that are aquatic. Thirteen of the 20 families have representatives in North America. Among the interesting or common species are the horned corydalus, *Corydalus cornutus*, of the family Corydalidae, whose larvae (used for bait by fishermen) are known as dobsons or hellgramites; the lacewing flies of the family Chrysopidae (Fig. 11–31), such as *Chrysopa oculata*, whose larvae are called aphis lions because they feed on aphids; and the ant lions, larvae of members of the family Myrmeleontidae, such as *Myrmeleon immaculatus*, which live at the bottom of a small pit in the sand and grasp with their strong suctorial jaws any insects that may chance to slide down the precipitous sides.

Order 18. Coleoptera (Figs. 11–47 to 11–53). Beetles, Holometabolic; chewing mouth parts; wingless or with two pairs of wings, the fore wings being hard and sheathlike (elytra) and the hind wings being membranous and folded under the elytra; the prothorax large and movable. The Coleoptera are so numerous and separated into so many families that they are difficult to discuss in a short space. The plan adopted here is to list some of the more important groups and point out their more interesting and important characteristics.

Suborder 1. Adephaga. Carnivorous beetles; first abdominal sternite divided by hind coxae.

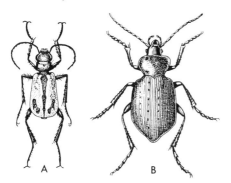

Fig. 11-47. Coleoptera. (A) Cicindelidae. A tiger beetle. (B) Carabidae. A ground beetle. (After Bruner and Howard.)

FAMILY CICINDELIDAE (Fig. 11–47, A). Tiger beetles. Predacious; diurnal; usually metallic green or bronze, banded or spotted with yellow; legs adapted for running; larvae in vertical burrows in ground. Ex. *Cicindela dorsalis, C. punctulata, Tetracha carolina.*

FAMILY CARABIDAE (Fig. 11–47, B). Ground beetles. Predacious, nocturnal; usually black and shiny; legs adapted for running. Ex. *Calosoma scrutator, Poecilus lucublandus, Harpalus caliginosus.*

FAMILY DYTISCIDAE. Predacious diving beetles. Aquatic; antennae threadlike; hind legs adapted for swimming; tarsi of fore legs of some species with suckers; air held under elytra while under water; larvae are "water tigers." Ex. *Dytiscus fasciventris, Colymbetes sculptilis, Cybister fimbriolatus.*

FAMILY GYRINIDAE. Whirligig beetles. Aquatic; social in habit; eyes divided into lower and upper halves; middle and hind legs adapted for swimming; secrete ill-smelling whitish liquid. Ex. *Dineutus vittatus, Gyrinus borealis.*

Suborder 2. Polyphaga. Herbivorous beetles; first abdominal sternite not completely divided by hind coxae.

FAMILY HYDROPHILIDAE. Water scavenger beetles. Aquatic; antennae club-shaped; carry film of air underneath the body. Ex. *Hydrophilus obtusatus, H. triangularis* (Fig. 11–48, A).

FAMILY SILPHIDAE. Carrion beetles. Antennae club-shaped; legs adapted for running; feed mostly on decaying animals. Ex. *Necrophorus marginatus* (burying beetle), *Silpha noveboracensis.*

A   B

Fig. 11-48. (A) Hydrophilidae. *Hydrophilus triangularis*, the giant water-scavenger beetle. (B) Staphylinidae. *Creophilus maxillosus*, the hairy rove beetle. (From Essig.)

Fig. 11-49. Elateridae. A click beetle turning over in the air to its normal position. (From Schmeil.)

FAMILY STAPHYLINIDAE. Rove beetles. Small, slender; elytra short; abdominal segments movable; legs adapted for running. Ex. *Staphylinus maculosus, Creophilus maxillosus* (Fig. 11-48, B).

FAMILY LAMPYRIDAE. Fireflies. Antennae sawlike; prothorax expanded over head; nocturnal; emit light; larvae and wingless females are "glow worms." Ex. *Photinus scintillans, Photuris pennsylvanica.*

FAMILY MELOIDAE. Blister beetles and oil beetles. When dried and pulverized produce blister on skin; European species called "Spanish fly"; undergo hypermetamorphosis. Ex. *Epicauta vittata, Meloe angusticollis.*

FAMILY ELATERIDAE (Fig. 11-49). Click beetles. Antennae serrate; body flattened; larvae are wireworms; leaps (clicks) by means of action of prosternal process in metasternal groove. Ex. *Alaus oculatus, Elater nigricollis.*

FAMILY BUPRESTIDAE (Fig. 11-50, A). Metallic wood borers. Antennae serrate; body hard, inflexible, flattened; bronze or metallic in color; larvae mostly "flat-headed" borers. Ex. *Chalcophora virginica, Chrysobothris femorata, Agrilus ruficollis* (causes raspberry gouty gall).

FAMILY DERMESTIDAE. Dermestids. Small; elytra cover abdomen; adults feign death; feed on furs, wool, household goods. Ex. *Dermestes*

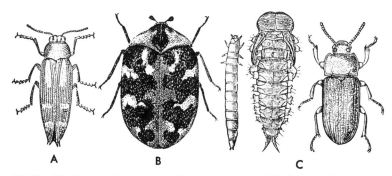

Fig. 11-50. (A) Buprestidae. A metallic wood borer. (B) Dermestidae. *Anthrenus scrophulariae*, the "buffalo bug" or "buffalo moth." (C) Tenebrionidae. *Tenebrio molitor*, the meal worm; larva, pupa and adult. (From various authors.)

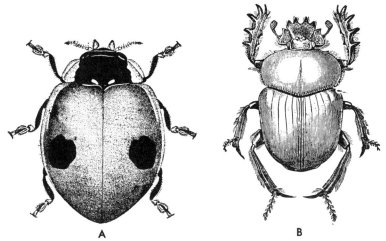

Fig. 11-51. (A) Coccinellidae. *Adalia bipunctata*, the two-spotted ladybird beetle. (B) Scarabaeidae. *Scarabaeus sacer*, the sacred beetle of the Egyptians. (A, from Essig; B, from Sharp.)

lardarius (larder beetle), *Anthrenus scrophulariae* (carpet beetle, Fig. 11–50, B), *Anthrenus museorum* (museum pest).

FAMILY TENEBRIONIDAE. Darkling beetles. Black; fore and middle tarsi with five segments, hind tarsi with four segments; food, dry vegetable matter. Ex. *Tenebrio molitor* (meal worm, Fig. 11–50, C), *Bolitotherus cornutus* (fungus beetle).

FAMILY COCCINELLIDAE. Ladybird beetle. Mostly predacious; some feed on scale insects; hemispherical in shape; red, yellow, or black with black, white, red, or yellow spots. Ex. *Rodolia cardinalis*, *Adalia bipunctata* (Fig. 11–51, A).

FAMILY SCARABAEIDAE. Scarabaeids or lamellicorn beetles. Club of antennae lamellate. Ex. *Scarabaeus sacer* (Egyptian scarab, Fig. 11–51, B), *Canthon laevis* (tumble bug), *Phyllophaga fusca* (June bug), *Macrodactylus subspinosus* (rose bug), *Dynastes tityrus* (rhinoceros beetle), *Euphoria inda* (bumble flower beetle), *Popillia japonica* (Japanese beetle).

FAMILY LUCANIDAE. Stag beetles. Large, sometimes branched, mandibles; club of antennae of flattened plates. Ex. *Lucanus dama*, *Dorcus parallelus*.

FAMILY PASSALIDAE. One species, *Passalus cornutus*, is common in the United States.

FAMILY CERAMBYCIDAE (Fig. 11–52, A). Long-horned beetles. Antennae often longer than body, of 11 segments; tarsi with four segments, third bilobed, fourth very small; larvae, wood-boring grubs. Ex. *Prionus laticollis*, *Megacyllene robiniae* (locust borer), *Tetraopes tetraophthalmus* (milkweed beetle).

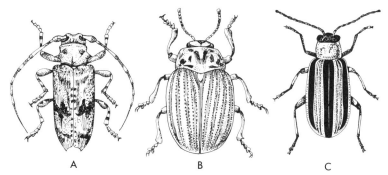

Fig. 11-52. (A) Cerambycidae. *Acanthoderes decipiens*, a long-horned beetle. (B) Chrysomelidae. *Leptinotarsa decemlineata*, the potato beetle. (C) Chrysomelidae. *Acalymma vittata*, the striped cucumber beetle. (After various authors.)

FAMILY CHRYSOMELIDAE (Fig. 11–52, B and C).   Leaf beetles. Body, oval; antennae and legs short; feed on leaves. Ex. *Leptinotarsa decemlineata* (potato beetle, Fig. 11–52, B), *Altica chalybea* (flea beetle), *Cassida nigripes* (tortoise beetle).

FAMILY CURCULIONIDAE. Snout beetles. Head prolonged into snout. Ex. *Anthonomus grandis* (cotton-boll weevil, Fig. 11–53, A), *Curculio rectus* (acorn weevil).

FAMILY SCOLYTIDAE (Fig. 11–53, B, C).   Engraver and ambrosia beetles. Some live on fungus (ambrosia); others are called timber beetles. Ex. *Scolytus multistriatus* (European elm bark beetle, transmits fungus causing Dutch elm disease), *Dendroctonus punctatus* (spruce beetle).

Order 19. Strepsiptera (Fig. 11–54, A).   Stylopids. Hypermetamorphosis; mouth parts vestigial or absent; endoparasitic in other insects; male with club-shaped fore wings and large membranous hind wings; female, wingless

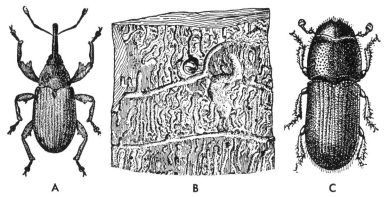

Fig. 11-53. (A) Curculionidae. *Anthonomus grandis*, the cotton-boll weevil. (B) Scolytidae. Galleries of an engraver beetle under the bark of a tree. (C) Scolytidae. *Dendroctonus frontalis*. the southern pine beetle. (After Felt and Hopkins.)

Fig. 11-54. (A) Strepsiptera. A twisted-winged insect. (B) Mecoptera. *Panorpa*, a scorpionfly. (A, after Packard; B, after Sharp.)

and legless, nutrition by absorption; life cycle complex. The stylopids live principally in bees, wasps, and homopterous bugs. Ex.*Xenos wheeleri*, a parasite of the wasp, *Polistes metricus.*

Order 20. Mecoptera (Fig. 11–54, B). Scorpionflies. Holometabolic; chewing mouth parts; antennae long and slender; head prolonged into beak; wingless or with two pairs of long, narrow, membranous wings; males with clasping organ at caudal end resembling the sting of a scorpion; food, fruit, and dead insects. Ex. *Panorpa rufescens, Bittacus strigosus.*

Order 21. Trichoptera (Fig. 11–55). Caddisflies. Holometabolic; vestigial mouth parts in adult; two pairs of membranous wings clothed with long, silky hairs; the aquatic larvae build portable cases of sand grains or vegetable matter fastened together with silk secreted by modified salivary glands. Members of the genus *Hydropsyche* construct nonportable nets in moving water. Ex. *Phryganea interrupta* (case of pieces of leaves), *Molanna cinerea* (case of sand).

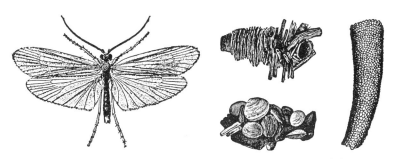

Fig. 11-55. Trichoptera. An adult caddisfly, with wings spread, and three types of larval cases. (After several authors.)

Fig. 11-56. Lepidoptera. (A) Tineidae. *Tinea pellionella,* a clothes moth. (B) Noctuidae. *Heliothis,* the cotton-boll worm or corn earworm. (From Herrick.)

Order 22. Lepidoptera (Figs. 11–56 to 11–60).   Butterflies, skippers, and moths. Holometabolic; sucking mouth parts; wingless or with two pairs of membranous wings covered with overlapping scales. The sucking apparatus, which is coiled underneath the head, consists of the two half-round maxillae fastened together so as to form a tube. The larvae are called caterpillars. They sometimes spin a cocoon in which they pupate. The pupa is often called a chrysalis. It is customary to divide the Lepidoptera into two groups, the moths (Heterocera) and butterflies (Rhopalocera). One family of butterflies, the Hesperiidae, are often set apart and called skippers. Moths are mostly nocturnal and their antennae are usually threadlike or feather-like and without a terminal knob. Butterflies are diurnal; the antennae are threadlike and have a knob at the end; and the wings are held vertically over the back when at rest. Skippers are diurnal; the antennae are threadlike and have a subterminal knob and a terminal recurved hook; and they have a skipping mode of flight. Space allows listing of only a few families.

FAMILY PRODOXIDAE.   Ex. Yucca moth, *Tegeticula alba.* The flowers of the genus *Yucca* depend upon this species for their cross-pollination. The moth visits the flowers in the evening, scrapes some pollen from a stamen, holds it underneath its head, and carries it to another flower. It clings to the

Fig. 11-57. Eucleidae. Larva of a slug caterpillar. Larvae possess irritating bristles. (Photo courtesy of the *Kalamazoo Gazette.*)

pistil of this, and, thrusting its ovipositor through the wall of the ovary, lays an egg. It then mounts the pistil, and forces the pollen it has brought down into the stigmatic tube. Another egg is laid in another part of the ovary, and more pollen is inserted into the stigmatic tube. These processes may be repeated half a dozen times in a single flower. The advantage to the flower is, of course, the certainty of being cross-pollinated and of producing seeds. These seeds provide a supply of food required by the larvae that hatch from the eggs laid by the moth in the ovary. The seeds are so numerous that the few eaten by the larvae may well be spared. Plant and insect are so inter-dependent that natural reproduction of the plant occurs only where the insect occurs and the insect only lives where the yucca is found.

FAMILY EUCLEIDAE. Slug caterpillars (Fig. 11–57). Medium-sized moths; larvae often unusually shaped and with stinging hairs which are skin irritants. Ex. Saddleback caterpillar, *Sibine stimulea.*

FAMILY TINEIDAE. Clothes moths. Ex. *Tinea pellionella* (Fig. 11–56, A).

FAMILY GELECHIIDAE. Ex. Angoumois grain moth, *Sitotroga cerealella*; Pink boll worm, *Pectinophora gossypiella.*

FAMILY TORTRICIDAE. Ex. Spruce budworm, *Choristoneura fumiferana.*

FAMILY OLETHREUTIDAE. Ex. Codling moth, *Carpocapsa pomonella.*

FAMILY PYRALIDIDAE. Ex. European corn borer, *Pyrausta nubilalis*; bee moth, *Galleria mellonella*; Mediterranean flour moth, *Anagasta kuhniella.*

Fig. 11-58. Sphingidae. A hawk moth. (A) Adult. (B) Larva. (C) Pupa. (From U.S. Dept. Agric.)

FAMILY SPHINGIDAE (Fig. 11–58). Hawk moths. Ex. White-lined sphinx, *Celerio lineata*; tomato hornworm, *Protoparce quinquemaculata*.

FAMILY GEOMETRIDAE. Measuring worms. Ex. Fall canker worm, *Alsophila pometaria*.

FAMILY LIPARIDAE. Tussock moths. Ex. White-marked tussock moth, *Hemerocampa leucostigma*; gipsy moth, *Porthetria dispar*; brown-tail moth, *Nygmia phareorrhoea*.

FAMILY NOCTUIDAE. Owlet moths. Ex. Cotton leaf-worm, *Alabama argillacea*; army worm, *Pseudaletia unipuncta*; cotton-boll worm, *Heliothis obsoleta* (Fig. 11–56, B).

FAMILY ARCTIDAE. Tiger moths. Ex. Fall webworm, *Hyphantria cunea*; banded woollybear caterpillar, *Isia isabella*.

FAMILY CITHERONIIDAE. Ex. Regal moth, *Citheronia regalis* (larva in hickory trees); Imperial moth, *Eacles imperialis*.

FAMILY SATURNIIDAE. Giant silkworm moths. Ex. Polyphemus, *Antheraea polyphemus*; luna, *Actias luna*; promethea, *Callosamia promethea*; cecropia, *Hyalophora cecropia*.

FAMILY BOMBYCIDAE. Silkworm moths. Ex. Silkworm, *Bombyx mori*.

FAMILY HESPERIIDAE (Fig. 11–59). Skippers. Silver-spotted skipper, *Epargyreus clarius*; cloudy wing, *Thorybes pylades*.

FAMILY PAPILIONIDAE. Swallow-tailed butterflies. Ex. Tiger swallow-tail, *Papilio glaucus*. The adults occur in two forms, *Papilio glaucus turnus* and *Papilio glaucus glaucus*. *Papilio polyxenes* is known as the black swallow-tail (Fig. 11–60).

FAMILY PIERIDAE. Ex. Cabbage butterfly, *Pieris rapae*; clouded sulphur, *Colias philodice*.

FAMILY DANAIDAE. Milkweed butterflies. Ex. *Danaus plexippus*, the monarch, adult distasteful to birds; "migratory."

FAMILY NYMPHALIDAE. Ex. Spangled fritillary, *Speyeria cybele*; mourning cloak, *Nigenphalis antiopa*; viceroy, *Limenitis archippus* (mimics the monarch, Fig. 11–60, D, E).

FAMILY LYCAENIDAE. Gossamer-winged butterflies. Ex. Banded hair streak, *Thecla calanus*; American copper, *Lycaena phleas*; spring azure, *Lycaenopsis argiolus* (very polymorphic, over a dozen forms named from North America).

Order 23. Diptera (Figs. 11–61 to 11–68). Flies. Holometabolic; piercing and sucking mouth parts forming a proboscis; wingless or with one pair of membranous fore wings, the hind wings being represented by knobbed threads called *halters*; larvae known as maggots; larval skin sometimes serves as a cocoon and called a puparium. The labium usually serves as a guide for the slender, piercing mandibles and maxillae, and for the sucking tube, consisting of an elongated epipharynx from the roof of the mouth and an elongated hypopharynx from the floor of the mouth, which is thrust into the

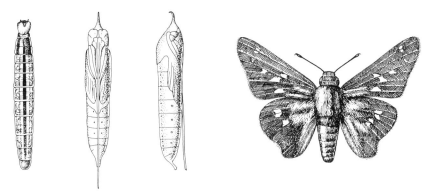

Fig. 11-59. Hesperiidae. *Calpodes ethlius*, a skipper; larva, pupae, and adult. (After Chittenden.)

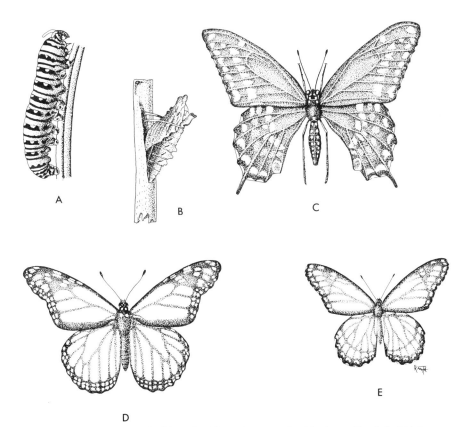

Fig. 11-60. A–C, Papilionidae; *Papilio polyxenes*, the black swallowtail. (A) Larva. (B) Pupa. (C) Adult. (D) Danaidae; *Danaus plexippus*, the monarch. (E) Nymphalidae; *Limenitis archippus*, the viceroy. (A–C, after Webster.)

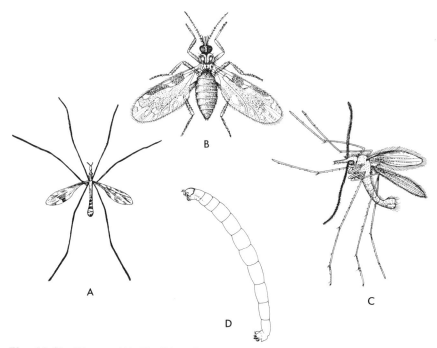

Fig. 11-61. Diptera. (A) Tipulidae. *Tipula,* a crane fly. (B) Ceratopogonidae. *Culicoides guttipennis,* a punkie or "no-see-um." (C) Psychodidae. *Phlebotomus papatasi,* a sand fly. (D) Tendipedidae. A midge larva. (A, after Weed; B, after Pratt; C, after Newstead.)

wound and through which juices are sucked up by means of a pharyngeal pump in the head. Many variations exist in the mouth parts of Diptera.

Suborder 1. Nematocera. Larva with well-chitinized head capsule; pupa enclosed in pupal skin; adult escapes from pupa by longitudinal slit in thoracic region; flies with antennae of more than five segments and usually long and slender.

FAMILY TIPULIDAE (Fig. 11–61, A). Crane flies. Slender body; narrow wings; long legs; transverse V-shaped suture on dorsal surface of mesothorax. Ex. *Tipula abdominalis.*

FAMILY TENDIPEDIDAE (CHIRONOMIDAE). Midges. Larvae (Fig. 11–61, D) important members of aquatic bottom communities. Some are tolerant of organic pollution. Adults do not bite. Ex. *Tendipes decorus* in shallow water with low oxygen content. *T. plumosus* in deep lakes.

FAMILY CERATOPOGONIDAE. Biting midges. Ex. *Culicoides guttipennis,* a punkie or "no-see-um" (Fig. 11–61, B).

FAMILY PSYCHODIDAE. Moth flies. Ex. *Psychoda alternata.* Sand flies of the genus *Phlebotomus* (Fig. 11–61, C) transmit pappataci fever, oriental sore, and oroya fever from man to man.

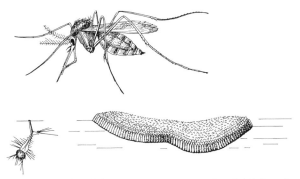

Fig. 11-62. Culicidae. *Culex pipiens*, a common mosquito. Adult female, egg mass on surface of water, and young hanging from surface of water. (From Howard.)

FAMILY CULICIDAE.   Mosquitoes. Ex. *Culex pipiens*, house mosquito (Fig. 11–62); *Anopheles quadrimaculatus* (transmits malaria, Fig. 11–63, A); *Aëdes aegypti* (transmits yellow fever, Fig. 11–63, B). Mosquitoes also transmit dengue and filariasis.

FAMILY CECIDOMYIDAE.   Gall gnats. Ex. *Rhabdophaga strobiloides* (causes willow-cone gall, Fig. 11–64); Hessian fly, *Phytophaga destructor*.

FAMILY SIMULIIDAE (Fig. 11–65, A).   Black flies. Ex. Adirondack black fly, *Prosimulium hirtipes*; buffalo gnat, *Cnephia pecuarum*. These are bloodsucking pests of man and animals. *Simulium damnosum* transmits the human filarial worm, *Onchocerca volvulus* of Africa.

Suborder 2. Brachycera.   Flies with short, thick antennae containing five or less segments; larvae with well-chitinized head capsule.

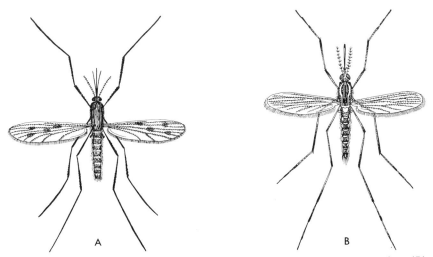

Fig. 11-63. Culicidae. (A) *Anopheles quadrimaculatus*, a malaria mosquito. (B) *Aëdes aegypti*, the yellow-fever mosquito. (After Herrick.)

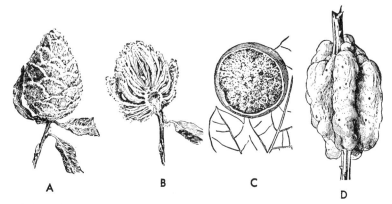

Fig. 11-64. Plant galls due to the presence of insects. (A) Willow-cone gall caused by a fly of the family Cecidomyidae. (B) Same, cut open to show the maggots within. (C) Oak-apple gall caused by a hymenopterous insect, *Amphibolips confluens*, of the family Cynipidae. (D) Blackberry-knot gall due to member of the family Cynipidae. (A, B, after Washburn; C, D, after Beutenmuller.)

FAMILY TABANIDAE. Horse flies. Ex. *Tabanus atratus*; *Chrysops silacea* (transmits human filarial worm, *Loa loa*); *Chrysops discalis* (transmits tularaemia from jack rabbits to man, Fig. 11-65, B).

FAMILY BOMBYLIIDAE. Bee flies. Ex. *Bombylius major* (Fig. 11-65, C). Adults resemble bees; larvae feed on egg sacs of Orthoptera and on hymenopterous and lepidopterous larvae.

FAMILY ASILIDAE (Fig. 11-65, D). Robber flies. Ex. *Erax aestuans*; *Asilus notatus*.

Suborder 3. Cyclorrhapha. Pupa enclosed in last larval skin strengthened with chitin (puparium); head of larvae not sclerotized; adult with five or fewer antennal segments.

FAMILY SYRPHIDAE. Flower flies. Ex. Drone fly, *Tubifera tenax* (larva known as rat-tailed maggot); *Syrphus perplexus*.

FAMILY TEPHRITIDAE. Ex. Mediterranean fruit fly, *Ceratitis capitata* (Fig. 11-66, A); goldenrod gall fly, *Eurosta solidaginis*.

FAMILY PIOPHILIDAE. Ex. Cheese skipper, *Piophila casei* (Fig. 11-66, B, C).

FAMILY EPHYDRIDAE. Ex. Petroleum fly, *Psilopa petrolei* (larva lives in crude petroleum).

FAMILY DROSOPHILIDAE. Pomace flies. Fruit fly, *Drosophila melanogaster* (Fig. 11-66, D), employed more extensively than any other animal for the study of genetics.

FAMILY GASTEROPHILIDAE. Bot flies. Ex. Horse bot fly. *Gasterophilus intestinalis*.

FAMILY OESTRIDAE. Bot and warble flies. Ex. Sheep bot fly, *Oestrus ovis*; heel fly, *Hypoderma lineatum*.

Fig. 11-65. (A) Simuliidae. *Simulium pictipes*, a black fly. (B) Tabanidae. *Chrysops discalis*, the vector of tularemia. (C) Bombyliidae. *Bombylius major*, a bee fly. (D) Asilidae. *Asilus cabroniformis*, a robber fly. (A, from Herrick; B, D, from Brumpt; C, from Essig.)

FAMILY CALLIPHORIDAE.   Ex. Blow fly, *Calliphora vomitoria*; green-bottle fly, *Lucilia caesar*; screwworm fly, *Callitroga hominivorax* (*Cochliomya hominivorax*), larvae parasitic in cattle, ruins hides, eradicated in Florida by release of many sterile males. Stubborn cases of osteomyelitis have been treated successfully with the aid of blow fly maggots.

FAMILY SARCOPHAGIDAE (Fig. 11-66, F).   Ex. *Sarcophaga haemorrhoidalis* (may cause intestinal myiasis in man); *Wohlfahrtia vigil* (may cause cutaneous myiasis in man). Several species live on dead insects in the cups of pitcher plants.

FAMILY TACHINIDAE.   Ex. *Trichopoda pennipes*. This and other species are important parasites of injurious insects.

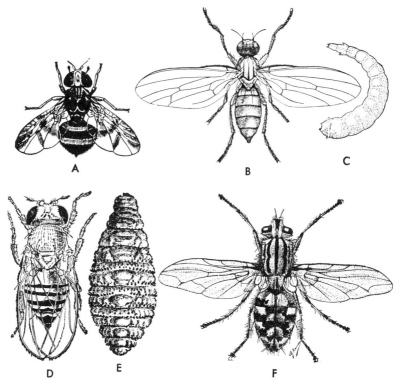

Fig. 11-66. (A) Tephritidae; *Ceratitis capitata*, the Mediterranean fruit fly. (B) Piophilidae; *Piophila casei*, the cheese skipper. (C) Cheese skipper, the maggot of *P. casei*. (D) Drosophilidae; *Drosophila melanogaster*, a fruit fly. (E) Cuterebridae; *Dermatobia cyaniventris*, larva of a bot fly. (F) Sarcophagidae; *Sarcophaga carnaria*, a flesh fly. (A, after Fuller; B, C, after Herrick; D, after Bridges; E, after Blanchard; F, after Brumpt.)

FAMILY MUSCIDAE. Ex. House fly, *Musca domestica* (Fig. 11-67); stable fly, *Stomoxys calcitrans*; tsetse fly, *Glossina palpalis* (Fig. 11-68, A, B, transmit the protozoan parasite of sleeping sickness in Africa, see *Trypanosoma*).

FAMILY HIPPOBOSCIDAE. Louse flies. Ex. Sheep tick, *Melophagus ovinus* (Fig. 11-68, D).

FAMILY BRAULIDAE. Bee lice. Ex. *Braula caeca*, a parasite of the honeybee (Fig. 11-68, C).

Order 24. Siphonaptera (Fig. 11-69). Fleas. Holometabolic; piercing and sucking mouth parts; wingless; body laterally compressed; head small; no compound eyes; legs adapted for leaping; ectoparasites of mammals, a few of birds. Ex. Cat flea, *Ctenocephalus felis* (also attacks dog and man); dog flea, *C. canis* (also attacks cat and man); human flea, *Pulex irritans*; rat flea, *Xenopsylla cheopis*, (transmits bubonic plague); sticktight flea, *Echidnophaga*

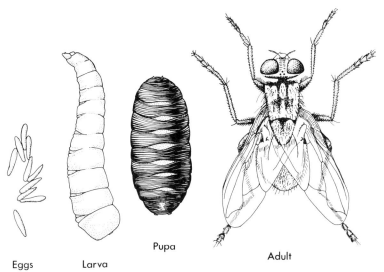

Eggs   Larva   Pupa   Adult

Fig. 11-67. Muscidae. *Musca domestica*, the house fly. (From Woodruff.)

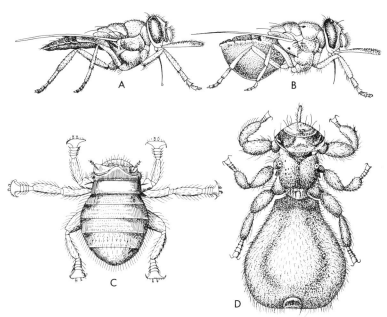

Fig. 11-68. (A, B) Muscidae; *Glossina palpalis*, the vector of African sleeping sickness, (A) before and (B) after a meal. (C) Braulidae; *Braula caeca*, a bee louse parasitic on the honeybee. (D) Hippoboscidae; *Melophagus ovinus*, a sheep tick. (A, B, D, from Brumpt; after Meinert.)

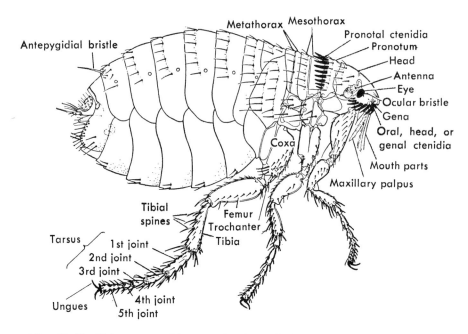

Fig. 11-69. Siphonaptera. Diagram showing principal external features of fleas. *Pulex irritans*, the human flea, and *Xenopsylla cheopis*, the oriental rat flea and vector of bubonic plague; both lack pronotal and genal ctendia. (From Herms.)

gallinacea (serious pest of poultry); chigoe or jigger, *Tunga penetrans*. (See also Acarina, Family Trombidiidae.)

Order 25. Hymenoptera (Figs. 11-70 to 11-78). Holometabolic; chewing or sucking mouth parts; wingless or with two pairs of membranous wings, fore wings larger, venation reduced; wings on each side held together by hooks (hamuli); females usually with sting, piercer, or saw; some parasitic on other insects.

FAMILY TENTHREDINIDAE. Sawflies. Ex. Currant worm, *Nematus ribesii* (Fig. 11-70, A, B); rose slug, *Cladius isomerus*.

FAMILY BRACONIDAE (Fig. 11-70, C). Ex. *Microgaster facetosa* (parasitic on moths); *Aphidius rosae* (parasitic on aphids).

FAMILY ICHNEUMONIDAE (Fig. 11-70, D). Ichneumon flies. Ex. *Megarhyssa lunator* (parasitic on larva of pigeon horn-tail, *Tremex columba*); *Ophion bilineatum* (parasitic on skippers).

FAMILY CYNIPIDAE. Gall wasps and others. Ex. Oak hedgehog gall, *Andricus erinacei*; oak apple, *Amphibolips confluens* (Fig. 11-64, C); mossy rose gall, *Diplolepis rosae* (Fig. 11-71, A, B).

FAMILY EULOPHIDAE. Ex. *Aphelinus jucundus*, parasitic on aphids. This family and a number of closely related families in the superfamily

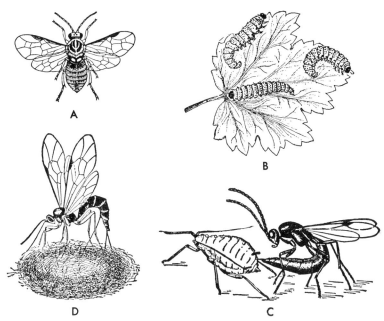

Fig. 11-70. Hymenoptera. A and B, Tenthredinidae; *Nematus*. (A) Adult sawfly. (B) Larva or currant worm. (C) Braconidae; *Lysiphlebus*, a parasite on aphids. (D) Ichneumonidae; *Itoplectis conquisitor;* female laying eggs in cocoon of tent caterpillar. (After various authors.)

Chalcidoidea contain many tiny chalcid wasp species. Most are parasites of other insects, a few are plant pests or seed eaters. *Blastophaga psenes* (Fig. 11–71, C) develops in a gall in wild fig flowers in California. When it emerges covered with pollen it visits other flowers and in the process insures pollination of the cultivated Smyrna fig.

FAMILY FORMICIDAE. Ants. Ants are all social insects and each colony contains several castes as in termites. Ex. Red ant, *Monomorium pharaonis* (Fig. 11–72, B, a household nuisance); agricultural ant, *Pogonomyrmex barbatus*; fire ant, *Solenopsis saevissima richteri*; shed builder, *Crematogaster lineolata* (builds sheds for aphids); fungus-growing ant, *Atta texana*; Argentine ant, *Iridomyrmex humilis* (Fig. 11–72, C, a household and orchard pest); carpenter ant, *Camponotus herculeanus pennsylvanicus* (Fig. 11–72, A); mound-building ant, *Formica exsectoides*; slave maker, *Formica sanguinea*; honey ant, *Myrmecocystus melliger* (certain individuals, repletes, serve as storage reservoirs).

FAMILY VESPIDAE. Wasps. Ex. Solitary jug builder, *Eumenes fraternus*; social polistes, *Polistes fuscatus pallipes*; white-faced hornet, *Vespa maculata* (Fig. 11–73, B); yellow jacket, *Vespa maculifrons* (Fig. 11–73, A).

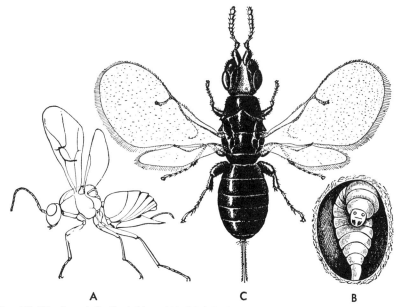

A   C   B

Fig. 11-71. A and B, Cynipidae. (A) *Diplolepis rosae,* causative agent of the mossy rose gall. (B) Larva of same in its cell. (C) Chalcididae. *Blastophaga psenes,* adult female fig insect. (A, B, after Sharp; C, from Essig.)

FAMILY SPHECIDAE. Digger wasps. Ex. Mud dauber, *Trypoxylon albitarsis*; tool-using wasp, *Sphex urnaria* (Fig. 11–74, A).

FAMILY ANDRENIDAE. Ex. Mining bee, *Andrena vicina* (Fig. 11–74, B).

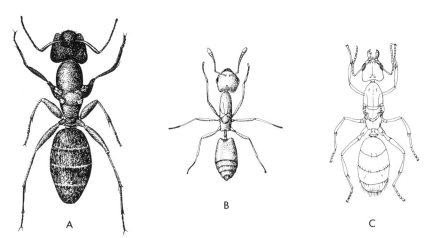

A   B   C

Fig. 11-72. Formicidae. (A) *Camponotus herculeanus pennsylvanicus,* the large black carpenter ant. (B) *Monomorium pharaonis,* the red ant. (C) *Iridomyrmex humilis,* the Argentine ant queen. (From Herrick.)

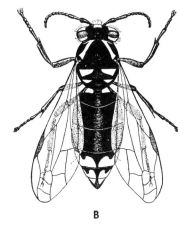

A   B

Fig. 11-73. Vespidae. (A) *Vespa maculifrons*, the yellow jacket. (B) *Vespa maculata*, the bald-faced hornet. (From Herrick.)

FAMILY XYLOCOPIDAE.   Carpenter bees. Ex. *Ceratina dupla.*

FAMILY MEGACHILIDAE.   Leaf-cutter bees. Ex. *Megachile brevis.*

FAMILY BOMBIDAE (Fig. 11–74, C). Bumblebees. Nest-building bumblebee, *Bombus vagans*; usurper bumblebee, *Psithyrus laboriosus* (social parasite of other bumblebees).

FAMILY APIDAE.   Honeybees. One introduced species in the United States, *Apis mellifera* (Fig. 11–75).

The Honeybee.   The mouth parts, legs, and sting of the worker honeybee are so marvelously adapted for various functions that a description of them is presented here and the student is advised to study these structures in detail.

Mouth Parts (Fig. 11–76).   The mouth parts consist of a labrum, or upper lip, the epipharynx, a pair of mandibles, two maxillae, and a labium, or under lip. The *labrum* is joined to the *clypeus*, which lies just above it. From beneath the labrum projects the fleshy *epipharynx*; this is probably an organ of taste. The *mandibles*, or jaws, are situated one on either side of the labrum; they are notched in the queen and drone, but smooth in the worker. The latter makes use of them in building honeycomb. The *labium* is a complicated median structure extending downward from beneath the labrum. It is joined to the back of the head by a triangular piece, the *submentum*. Next to this is a chitinous, muscle-filled piece, the *mentum*, beyond which is the *ligula* (*glossa* or tongue) with one *labial palpus* on each side.   The ligula may be drawn in or extended. It is long and flexible, with a spoon or *bouton* at the end. Hairs of various kinds are arranged upon it in regular rows; these are used for gathering nectar, and as organs of touch and taste. The *maxillae*, or lower jaws, fit over the mentum on either side. Along their front edges are rows of stiff hairs. *Maxillary palpi* are also present.

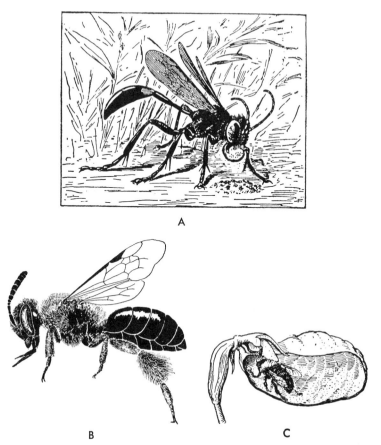

Fig. 11-74. (A) Sphecidae. *Sphex urnaria;* a digger wasp using a stone to pack earth over its nest. (B) Andrenidae. *Andrena*, a mining bee. (C) Bombidae. *Bombus*, a bumble-bee pollinating a flower of the orchid *Cypripedium*. (After various authors.)

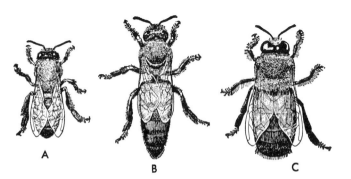

Fig. 11-75. Honeybees. (A) Worker. (B) Queen. (C) Drone. (From Phillips.)

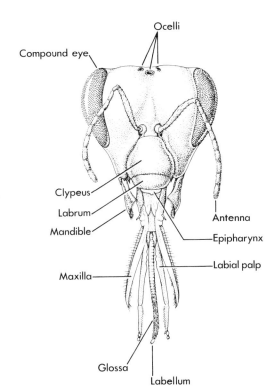

Fig. 11-76. Head of honeybee. (From Woodruff.)

Nectar is collected in the following manner. The maxillae and the labial palpi form a tube, in the center of which the tongue moves backward and forward. When the epipharynx is lowered, a passage is completed into the esophagus. The nectar is first collected by the hairs on the ligula; it is then forced upward by the pressing together of the maxillae and labial palpi.

Legs (Fig. 11–77). The *prothoracic legs* possess the following useful structures. The femur and the tibia are clothed with *branched hairs* for gathering pollen. Extending on one side from the distal end of the tibia are a number of curved bristles, the *pollen brush*, which are used to brush up the pollen loosened by the coarser spines; on the other side is a flattened movable spine, the *velum*, which fits over a curved indentation in the first tarsal joint or metatarsus. This entire structure is called the *antenna cleaner* and the row of teeth which lines the identation is known as the *antenna comb*. On the front of the metatarsus is a row of spines called the *eye brush*, which is used to brush out any pollen or foreign particles lodged among the hairs on the compound eyes. The last tarsal joint of every leg bears a pair of notched claws, which enable the bee to obtain a foothold on rough surfaces. Between the claws is a fleshy glandular lobule, the *pulvillis*, whose sticky secretion makes it possible for the bee to cling to smooth objects. Tactile hairs are also present.

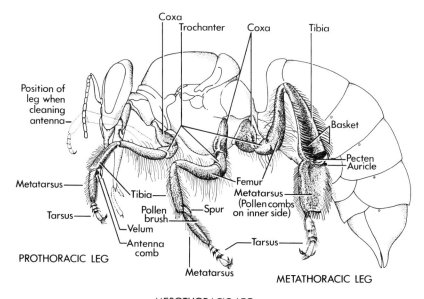

Fig. 11-77. Details of the legs of the honeybee. (From Woodruff.)

The middle, or *mesothoracic legs*, are provided with a *pollen brush*, but, instead of an antenna cleaner, a *spur* is present at the distal end of the tibia. This spur is used to pry the pollen out of the pollen baskets on the third pair of legs, and to clean the wings.

The *metathoracic legs* possess three very remarkable structures, the pollen basket, the wax pinchers, and the pollen combs. The *pollen basket* consists of a concavity in the outer surface of the tibia with rows of curved bristled along the edges. By storing pollen in this basket-like structure, it is possible for the bee to spend more time in the field, and to carry a larger load at each trip. The pollen combs serve to fill the basket by combing out the pollen, which has become entangled in the hairs on the thorax, and transferring it to the concavity in the tibia of the opposite leg. At the distal end of the tibia is a row of wide spines; these are opposed by a smooth plate on the proximal end of the metatarsus. The term *wax pinchers* has been applied to these structures, since they are used to remove the wax plates from the abdomen of the worker.

Sting (Fig. 11–78). The *sting* is a very complicated structure. Before the bee stings, a suitable place is usually selected with the help of the *sting feelers*; then the two *barbed darts* are thrust forward. The *sheath* serves to guide the darts, to open up the wound, and to aid in conducting the poison. The *poison* is secreted in a pair of *glands*, one acid, the other alkaline, and is stored in a *reservoir*. Generally the sting, poison glands, and part of the intestine are pulled out when a bee stings, so that death ensues after several hours, but if

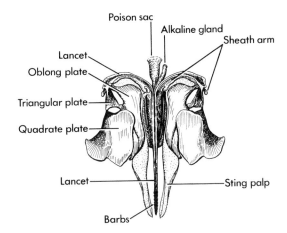

Fig. 11-78. Sting of the worker honeybee. (After Snodgrass.)

only the sting is lost, the bee is not fatally injured. The queen seldom uses her sting except in combat with other queens.

2 / Insects in General

The insects are the largest class of invertebrates. They are also the most important group economically. Enumeration of the general ways they are important will emphasize this point.

A. Positive values and examples.
    1. Pollination of plants. Fruit trees, etc., by honeybee.
    2. Control of insect pests. Cottony cushion scale by ladybird beetle.
    3. Source of food. Honey from bee, roast grasshoppers, etc., for the gourmet.
    4. Source of materials. Beeswax, lac, silk, etc.
    5. Food chain intermediates. Aquatic insects.
    6. Scavengers. Blow flies, ants, dermestid colonies, etc.
    7. Medical use. Fly larvae for burns, etc.
    8. Research tools. Drosophila for genetics, etc.
    9. Aesthetic value. Butterfly collections, inspiration from their sounds, etc.
B. Negative values.
    1. Parasites of man, animals, and plants.
    2. Vectors for diseases of man, animals, and plants.
    3. Destroyers of crops and stored food.
    4. Destroyers of fibers, structures, etc.
    5. Nuisance value of bites, stings, carcasses on windshields, etc.

The positive value of crops which require insect pollination outweighs the combined economic losses caused by insects in this country.

Biological Control. The use of living organisms for the elimination or reduction of pest organisms frequently involves the use of insects. The earliest instance of effective biological control was the introduction of an Australian ladybird beetle, *Rodolia cardinalis*, which effectively controlled a California citrus pest, *Icerya purchasi*, the cottony cushion scale, by feeding upon it.

Perhaps the best method for controlling the Japanese beetle has been the introduction of milky spore disease into soil containing the beetles.

A unique approach to biological control by using sexual competition was successful in eliminating the screwworm fly from Florida. The money invested in the research program and control measures was repaid a hundred-fold or more by the value of the resulting cattle industry in Florida. Control was achieved by the following fortunate circumstances. The female screw-worm fly, *Callitroga hominivorax*, mates once for life. Flies can be sterilized by irradiation during the pupal stage without eliminating the ability of the male to mate. By releasing large numbers of sterile flies among the natural population the wild females often layed sterile eggs because of the large per-centage that had mated with sterile males. The process was continued until the natural population was eliminated.

Attempts to find biological means of controlling other pests are desirable because use of chemical control measures may pollute food and water with compounds of possible danger to man. One encouraging line of research in chemical controls is the effort to develop compounds which mimic hormones, enzymes, etc. in their uptake, effectiveness in very low concentrations, and localization in the cells where they will interfere with vital processes. If these can be tailored to species-specific control compounds, with low or no activity in other organisms, concern about pollution will be less than with compounds of broad spectrum activity and low breakdown rates.

Behavior. In the insects, as in other areas of zoology, behavioral studies are increasing. Among insects we find more highly developed social behavior than in any other invertebrate group.

Communication Among Bees. Scout bees are able to communicate the direction and distance of a food source to other honeybees by a dance. The dance within the hive can indicate the direction of a food source some distance from the hive, a figure-8 dance has a straight run on the face of the honeycomb, the angle of the run from vertical corresponds to the angle of the food from the direction of the sun. Vigor of the dance, odor, and sound give added information.

Construction by Insects. Among the varied things insects make and do, one of the more interesting is the construction of cases by immature caddis-flies. The legs and mouthparts of some larvae assemble a tube of materials held together with silk or secretions. The tube is approximately the length of the larva. When certain sensory receptors at the larval posterior are removed a much longer than normal case is produced which extends far beyond the larval posterior.

Circadian Rhythms. Many insects show peaks of activity at characteristic times of the day. Thus, the cockroach is most active in the early hours of darkness. The compound eyes, not the ocelli, are essential to keep the activity peak entrained on a 24-hour cycle (Roberts, 1965).

Pheromones. Pheromones of insects are secretions that effect other insects of the same species. They are effective in very low concentrations. Thus, pheromones of some female moths may attract males from a mile or more away. The male cockroach responds with changed activity to air-borne pheromones from females. Ants may use them for marking trails. Efforts to chemically identify such substances may yield important bonuses in pest control. Thus, poison containers could be baited with synthesized pheromones of the sex attractant type. This might enable such insects as cockroaches to be controlled without releasing great quantities of insecticide into the environment.

Ecology. Insects have radiated to fill most types of niches in terrestrial and fresh-water environments. Most species have certain requirements that determine their distribution. Thus, in aquatic environments low in oxygen, only those with certain respiratory modifications such as the hemoglobin of some midge larvae or respiratory tubes that reach the air in other dipteran larvae will be found. By using faunal lists of insects from fresh water, it is possible to deduce certain facts about the water quality. In interpreting such information it is necessary to consider many things such as the season at which such information is gathered because some aquatic insects spend only a portion of their life cycle in the water (Fig. 11–79).

The abundance of insects, their prevalence most places, and small size have made them an important food source for many animals and even some plants. Their importance in the food chain or energy cycle is increased by the variety of nutrients they utilize.

The profound effect insects can have on man's use of the earth is illustrated by the slow development of regions where the mosquito and tsetse fly have

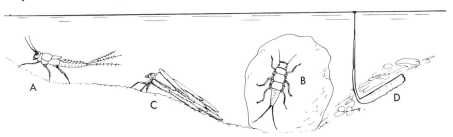

Fig. 11-79. Semiaquatic insects that spend only part of their life cycle in the water. Aquatic larvae. (A) Mayfly. (B) Stonefly. (C) Caddisfly. (D) Rat-tailed maggot. Larvae usually show a strong preference for a particular bottom type.

actively transmitted severe diseases. A more obvious change in this country is the loss of millions of elm trees, which has already occurred in many places due to an insect-borne disease (see Scolytidae).

Physiology.   Among the areas of physiological research on insects where new developments are occurring most rapidly is the field of hormones and neurosecretions. Related to this is one of the most interesting developmental and genetic stories dealing with chromosome puffs (Beerman and Clever, 1964). In midge larvae of the family Chironomidae (Tendipedidae) some morphological events of development have been correlated with production of some hormones and enzymes. Interrelated with this is a sequential puffing of certain chromosomal regions. The puffs are thought to represent an opening up of the DNA helix where messenger RNA is being formed.

The presence of respiratory and excretory tubules, which reach to most parts of the body, have allowed a reduction of the circulatory system in insects. They typically have only a single dorsal vessel, part of which is the heart. The rest of the system is one of spaces.

A wide range of sensory receptors are found in insects. There is considerable variation in their localization. Thus, chemical senses involved in taste may be on the mouth parts in some and on the feet in others. The grasshopper has sound receptors on the abdomen, other insects may have them on their wings. A number of night-flying insects have sound receptors on their wings that are sensitive to sounds of the frequency emitted by bats for echolocating objects.

Many events in insect life cycles are under partial control of the environment. Thus, food, temperature, and photoperiod are some of the things which may regulate events in development. Selection of the proper responses correlated with seasonal events has contributed greatly to the success of insects in terrestrial environments.

References to Literature on the Insecta

ARNETT, R. H., Jr. 1967. Present and future systematics of the Coleoptera in North America. *Ann. Ent. Soc. Am.*, **60**:67–72.

BAKER, J. M. 1963. Ambrosia beetles and their fungi, with particular reference to *Platypus cylindrus* Fab. pp. 232–265 + 2pl. In *Symbiotic Associations.* 13th Symp. Soc. Gen. Microbiol. Cambridge Univ. Press. 356 pp.

BATES, M. 1949. *The Natural History of Mosquitoes.* Macmillan, New York. 379 pp.

BEERMAN, W., and U. CLEVER. 1964. Chromosome puffs. *Sci. Am.*, **210**:50–58.

BELL, R. A., and P. L. ADKISSON. 1964. Photoperiodic reversibility of diapause induction in an insect. *Science*, **144**:1149–1151.

BORROR, D. J., and D. M. DeLONG. 1964. *An Introduction to the Study of Insects.* Holt, Rinehart, and Winston, New York. 819 pp.

CAVILL, G. W. K., and P. L. ROBERTSON. 1965. Ant venoms, attractants, and repellents. *Science*, **149**:1337–1345.

CHAMBERS, D. L., and V. J. BROOKES. 1967. Hormonal control of reproduction— I. Initiation of oocyte development in the isolated abdomen of *Leucophaea maderae*. *J. Insect Physiol.*, **13**:99–111.

CHU, H. F. 1949. *How to Know the Immature Insects*. Brown, Dubuque. 234 pp.

CLEMENTS, A. N. 1963. *The Physiology of Mosquitoes*. Macmillan, New York. 393 pp.

DEMEREC, M. 1950. *Biology of Drosophila*. Wiley, New York. 632 pp.

DERR, R. F., and D. D. RANDALL. 1966. Trehalase of the differential grasshopper, *Melanoplus differentialis*. *J. Insect Physiol.*, **12**:1105–1114.

ESAU, K. 1961. *Plants, Viruses, and Insects*. Harvard Univ. Press, Cambridge. 110 pp.

EVANS, H. E. 1963. Predatory wasps. *Sci. Am.*, **208**(4):144–154.

HERMS, W. B., and M. T. JAMES. 1961. *Medical Entomology*. Macmillan, New York. 616 pp.

JACOBSON, M., and M. BEROZA. 1963. Chemical insect attractants. *Science*, **140**:1367–1373.

JACQUES, H. E. 1947. *How to Know the Insects*. Brown, Dubuque. 205 pp.

JOHNSON, C. G. 1963. The aerial migrations of insects. *Sci. Am.*, **209**(6):132–138.

KAFATOS, F. C., and C. M. WILLIAMS. 1964. Enzymatic mechanisms for the escape of certain moths from their cocoons. *Science*, **146**:538–540.

KETTLEWELL, H. B. D. 1965. Insect survival and selection for pattern. *Science*, **148**:1290–1296.

KNIPLING, E. F. 1960. The eradication of the screw-worm fly. *Sci. Am.* **203**(4):54–61.

LINDAUER, M. 1967. Recent advances in bee communication and orientation. *Ann. Rev. Ent.*, **1967**:439–470.

LINSLEY, E. G. 1963. *The Cerambycidae of North America*. Part IV. Univ. Calif. Publ. in Ent., Vol. 21.

MANI, M. S. 1962. *Introduction to High Altitude Entomology*. Methuen, London. 302 pp.

O'BRIEN, R. D., and L. S. WOLFE. 1964. *Radiation, Radioactivity, and Insects*. Academic Press, New York. 211 pp.

PATTERSON, J. T., and W. S. STONE. 1952. *Evolution in the Genus Drosophila*. Macmillan, New York. 610 pp.

PATTON, R. L. 1963. *Introductory Insect Physiology*. Saunders, Philadelphia. 245 pp.

PFADT, R. E. 1962. *Fundamentals of Applied Entomology*. Macmillan, New York. 668 pp.

PIPKIN, S., R. RODRIGUEZ, and J. LEON. 1966. Plant host specificity among flower-feeding neotropical *Drosophila* (Diptera: Drosophilidae). *Am. Nat.*, **100**:135–156.

RIEMAN, J. G. 1965. The development of eggs of the screw-worm fly *Cochliomya hominivorax* (Coquerel) (Diptera: Calliphoridae) to the blastoderm stage as seen in whole-mount preparations. *Biol. Bull.*, **129**:329–339.

ROBERTS, S. K. 1965. Photoreception and entrainment of cockroach activity rhythms. *Science*, **148**:958–959.

ROCKSTEIN, M. 1964–1965. *The Physiology of Insecta.* Vols. I and II. Academic Press, New York.

ROEDER, K. D. 1965. Moths and ultrasound. *Sci. Am.,* **212**(4):94–102.

SCHNEIDERMAN, H. A., and L. I. GILBERT. 1964. Control of growth and development in insects. *Science,* **143**:325–333.

SMITH, C. F., and J. GRAHAM. 1967. Life history, synonymy, and description of *Neoprociphilus aceris* (Homoptera: Aphididae). *Ann. Ent. Soc. Am.,* **60**:67–72.

WAKELAND, C. 1958. *The High Plains Grasshopper.* U.S.D.A. Tech. Bull. No. 1167. 168 pp.

WEST, L. S. 1951. *The Housefly.* Comstock, Ithaca. 584 pp.

WIGGLESWORTH, V. B. 1956. *Insect Physiology.* Methuen, London. 130 pp.

WILSON, E. O. 1965. Chemical communication in the social insects. *Science,* **149**:1064–1071.

Chapter *XII*
Phylum Echinodermata

THE ECHINODERMS are the starfishes, brittle stars, sea urchins, sea cucumbers, and sea lilies. They are coelomate animals, bilaterally symmetrical in the larval stage but radially symmetrical as adults; usually five antimeres are present. A water-vascular system including organs known as tube feet is characteristic; also a spiny skeleton of calcareous plates. There are five classes of living echinoderms. Four of these are sometimes grouped together in the subphylum Eleutherozoa, because they are able to move about freely; the class Crinoidea together with four classes of extinct species comprise the subphylum Pelmatozoa, which are stalked and attached during all or part of their lives.

The sessile condition was a characteristic of the echinoderms from which unattached forms evolved. Since loss of the sessile habit may have occurred at various times in different groups, it may not indicate a close phylogenetic relationship among the Eleutherozoa. Thus, the concept of Eleutherozoa and Pelmatozoa may be abandoned as there is no strong indication that it is a phylogenetic classification.

CLASS I. ASTEROIDEA. Starfishes. Typically pentamerous; arms usually not sharply marked off from the disk; ambulacral groove present. *Asterias forbesi.*

CLASS II. OPHIUROIDEA. Brittle stars. Typically pentamerous; arms sharply marked off from the disk; no ambulacral groove. *Ophiura sarsi.*

CLASS III. ECHINOIDEA. Sea urchins. Pentamerous, without arms or free rays; test of calcareous plates bearing movable spines. *Strongylocentrotus, Arbacia.*

CLASS IV. HOLOTHUROIDEA. Sea cucumbers. Long ovoid; muscular body wall; tentacles around mouth. *Thyone, Cucumaria.*

CLASS V. CRINOIDEA. Sea lilies. Arms generally branched and with pinnules; aboral pole sometimes with cirri but usually with stalk for temporary or permanent attachment. *Antedon.*

1 / Class I. Asteroidea

(1) Asterias—A Starfish

External Features. The starfishes are common along many seacoasts, where they may be found usually upon the rocks with the mouth down. The upper surface is therefore *aboral.* On the *aboral surface* are many *spines* (Fig. 12–3) of various sizes, *pedicellariae* (Fig. 12–2) at the base of the spines, a *madreporite,* which is the entrance to the water-vascular system, and the anal opening (*anus*). A glance at the *oral surface* reveals a *mouth* centrally situated in the membranous *peristome,* and five *grooves* (*ambulacral*), one in each arm, from which two or four rows of *tube feet* extend.

The Skeleton. The skeleton is made up of *calcareous plates* or *ossicles* bound together by fibers of connective tissue. The ossicles are regularly arranged about the mouth and in the ambulacral grooves and often along

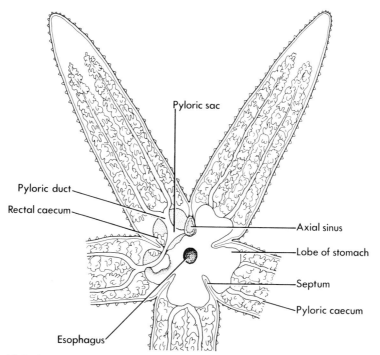

Fig. 12-1. Starfish, *Asterias rubens.* Aboral view with two arms and part of skeleton removed; one lobe of stomach cut away and another lobe turned back. (After Borradaile, modified.)

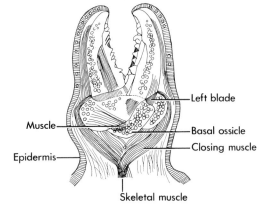

Fig. 12-2. Pedicellaria of a starfish. (After Cuenot.)

Left blade

Muscle

Basal ossicle

Closing muscle

Epidermis

Skeletal muscle

the sides of the arms, but are more or less scattered elsewhere. The *ambulacral* and *adambulacral ossicles* (Fig. 12–3) have muscular attachments and are so situated that when the animal is disturbed they are able to close the groove and thus protect the tube feet. The *spines* of the starfish are short and blunt and covered with *ectoderm* (Fig. 12–3). Around their bases are many whitish modified spines called *pedicellariae* (Fig. 12–2). These are little jaws, which when irritated may be opened and closed by several sets of muscles. Their function is to protect the *papulae* (*dermal branchiae* or *gills*) (Fig. 12–3), to prevent debris and small organisms from collecting on the surface, and to capture food. The skeleton serves to give the animal definite shape, to

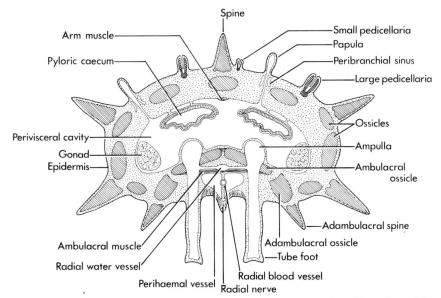

Spine

Arm muscle

Pyloric caecum

Small pedicellaria

Papula

Peribranchial sinus

Large pedicellaria

Ossicles

Periviscetal cavity

Gonad

Epidermis

Ampulla

Ambulacral ossicle

Adambulacral spine

Ambulacral muscle

Radial water vessel

Perihaemal vessel

Adambulacral ossicle

Tube foot

Radial blood vessel

Radial nerve

Fig. 12-3. Diagrammatic transverse section of the arm of a starfish. (From Borradaile and Potts, modified.)

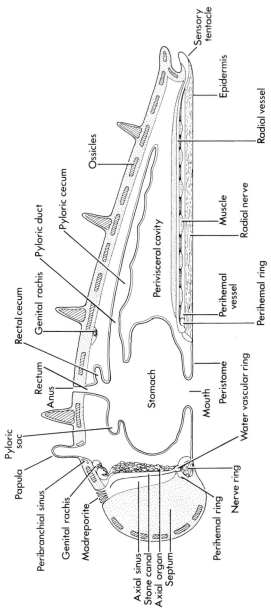

Fig. 12-4. Diagrammatic section through the disk and one arm of a starfish. (From Borradaile and Potts, modified.)

strengthen the body wall, and as a protection from the action of waves and from other organisms.

The Muscular System. The *arms* of the starfish are not rigid, but may be flexed slowly by a few muscle fibers in the body wall (Fig. 12–3). The *tube feet* are also supplied with muscle fibers.

Coelom. The true body cavity of the starfish is very large and may be separated into several distinct divisions. The *perivisceral part of the coelom* (Figs. 12–3 and 12–4) surrounds the alimentary canal and extends into the arms. It is lined with *peritoneum* and filled with sea water containing some albuminous matter. Oxygen is taken into the coelomic fluid and carbon dioxide given off through outpushings of the body wall known as *papulae* or gills. The coelom also has an *excretory function*, since cells from the peritoneum are budded off into the coelomic fluid, where they move about as amoebocytes gathering waste matters. These cells make their way into the gills, through the walls of which they pass to the outside, where they disintegrate.

The Water-Vascular System. The water-vascular system (Fig. 12–5) is a division of the coelom peculiar to echinoderms. Beginning with the *madreporite* the following structures are encountered: the *stone canal* running downward enters the *ring canal*, which encircles the mouth; from this canal five *radial canals* (Fig. 12–3), one in each arm, pass outward just above the ambulacral grooves. The radial canals give off side branches from which arise the *tube feet* (Fig. 12–3) and *ampullae*. The ampullae are bulblike sacs extending into the coelom; they are connected directly with the tube feet, which pass through tiny pores between the ambulacral ossicles. Sea water is forced into this system of canals by cilia, which occur in grooves on the outer surface of the madreporite and in the canals which penetrate it. Arising from the ring canal near the ampullae of the first tube feet are nine vesicles called, after the name of their discoverer, "Tiedemann's bodies." These structures produce amoebocytes, which pass into the fluid of the water-vascular system. *Polian vesicles* (Fig. 12–5) are present in some starfishes, but not in *Asterias*.

The most interesting structures of the water-vascular system are the *tube feet* (Figs. 12–3 and 12–5). They have only longitudinal muscles. A uniform diameter is maintained by circular connective tissue fibers. Fluid forced out of a contracting ampulla causes extension of the tube foot. When the suckered end adheres to an object, contraction of the longitudinal muscles draws the animal forward and returns the fluid to the ampulla. Tube feet are primarily locomotory. They have some sensory and respiratory functions.

Digestion. The *alimentary canal* of the starfish (Figs. 12–1, 12–4) is short and greatly modified. The *mouth* opens into an *esophagus* which leads into a

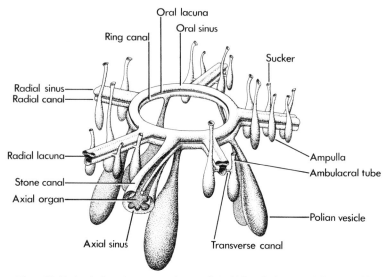

Fig. 12-5. Ambulacral system of a starfish. (After Delage and Herouard.)

thin-walled sac, the *stomach*. Following this is the *pyloric sac*. From the pyloric sac a tube passes into each arm, then divides into two branches, each of which possesses a large number of lateral green pouches; these branches are called *pyloric* or *hepatic ceca*. Above the pyloric sac is the slender *rectum*, which may open to the outside through the *anus*. Two branched brown pouches arise from the rectum and are known as *rectal ceca*.

The *food* of the starfish consists of fish, oysters, mussels, barnacles, clams, snails, worms, Crustacea, etc. When a mussel is to be eaten it is held under the mouth and the arms pull on the valves with a force of up to 1,350 grams. The bivalve can withstand a greater pull for a short time but it eventually yields to sustained pull accompanied by a digestive action of the stomach that has been everted and applied against it. Small bivalves are completely ingested and undigested parts are later expelled through the mouth. Only a very narrow opening is necessary for the starfish to evert its stomach through and begin digestion. Digestive action on the adductor muscles enables the bivalve to be easily opened the rest of the way. Some species of starfish feed on attached microorganisms by everting their stomach over the rock or other materials where they are attached.

The lining of the stomach secretes mucus; that of the pyloric sac and ceca secretes enzymes; these change protein into diffusible peptones, starch into maltose, and fats into fatty acids and glycerine. Thus, digestion is accomplished. Undigested matter is ejected through the mouth, and very little, if any, matter passes out of the anus. The rectal ceca secrete a brownish material of unknown function, probably excretory.

Circulation.   The fluid in the coelom is kept in motion by cilia and carries the absorbed food to all parts of the body.

A number of other spaces and canals have been considered parts of the coelom and some consider them to be a "blood"-vascular system. These are the *axial sinuses* lying along the stone-canal and opening to the outside through the madreporite, the *inner, circumoral perihemal canal,* the *outer perihemal canal* beneath the ring canal, the *aboral sinus,* and the *peribranchial spaces.* The functions of these various cavities are not clear. The homologous structures in echinoids have been shown to have a circulatory function by Boolootian and Campbell (1964). Thus, it is probable that they do have a circulatory function throughout the phylum. A lymphatic or phagocytic function is indicated for these structures also (Ferguson, 1966; Millott, 1966).

Excretion.   Excretion is accomplished by the *amoebocytes* in the coelomic fluid, probably aided by the rectal ceca. The tube feet and papulae, no doubt, serve as areas where soluble waste products diffuse from the echinoderm.

Respiration.   The papulae and tube feet (Fig. 12–3) function as respiratory organs. Cilia covering the papulae as well as those lining their coelomic side circulate seawater and coelomic fluid thus aiding respiratory efficiency

The Nervous System (Fig. 12–4).   Besides many *nerve cells,* which lie among the epidermal cells, ridges of nervous tissue, the *radial nerve cords,* run along the ambulacral grooves, and unite with a *nerve ring* encircling the mouth. The *apical nervous system* consists of a trunk in each arm which meets the other trunks at the center of the disk; these trunks innervate the dorsal muscles of the arms.

Sense Organs.   The *tube feet* are the principal sense organs. They receive nerve fibers from the radial nerve cords. At the end of each radial canal the radial nerve cord ends in a *pigmental mass;* this is called the *eye,* since it is a light-perceiving organ. The papulae are probably sensory, also.

Reproduction.   The *sexes* of starfishes are distinct. The *reproductive organs* are dendritic structures, two in the base of each arm; they discharge the eggs or sperm out into the water through pores in the aboral surface at the interspace between two adjacent arms. Most starfishes have an annual breeding season which seems to be induced by rising spring temperatures. Substances affecting release of gametes have been located in the radial nerves. The *eggs* of many starfishes are fertilized in the water; they are *holoblastic,* undergo *equal cleavage,* and form a *blastula* and *gastrula* similar to those shown in Figure 12–27. The opening (*blastopore*) of the gastrula becomes the anus, and a new opening, the mouth, breaks through. Ciliated projections develop on either side of the body, and a larva called a *bipinnaria* (Fig. 12–28) results. This changes (metamorphosis) into the starfish.

Behavior.   The starfish moves from place to place by means of its tube feet. During the day it usually remains quiet in a crevice, but at night it is most active.

The *responses* of the starfish to *stimuli* are too complex to be stated definitely. When a starfish is placed on its aboral surface it performs the "righting reaction," i.e., it turns a sort of handspring by means of its arms. Professor Jennings taught individuals to use a certain arm in turning over. One animal was trained in 18 days (180 lessons), and after an interval of seven days apparently "remembered" which arm to use. Old individuals could not be trained as readily as young specimens.

Regeneration.   The starfish has remarkable powers of regeneration. A single arm with part of the disk will regenerate an entire body. If an arm is injured, it is usually cast off near the base at the fourth or fifth ambulacral ossicle. This is *autotomy.*

Some species autotomize spontaneously as a method of reproduction and few individuals are found with all five rays of equal size. Because of regenerative ability starfish predators in oyster beds are no longer cut in two and thrown back by the oysterfishermen, but are now completely removed.

(2) Other Asteroidea

The starfishes usually possess five arms that are not sharply marked off from the central disk; in some species, however, as many as 40 arms may be present. The body is flattened. They move about with the oral surface down.

Fig. 12-6. Asteroidea. The cushion star of the Great Barrier Reef of Australia. (Photo by author.)

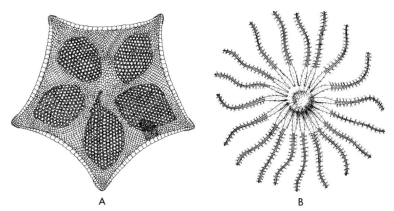

Fig. 12-7. Asteroidea. (A) *Pentagonaster japonicus*, a type with short arms and pentagonal body. (B) *Odinia*, a type with many long arms and small disk. (A, after Sladen; B, after Perrier.)

The viscera extend into the arms and the anus is on the aboral surface. Along the oral surface of each arm is a median ambulacral groove from which project either two or four rows of tube feet. The madreporite is located on the aboral surface between the bases of two of the arms. The outside of the body is covered by a cilated epithelium and characterized by the presence of spines or tubercles, some of which are movable and others modified into pedicellariae. The only special sense organs present are a red eye spot at the end of each arm. There are three orders and about 20 families of living Asteroidea (Figs. 12–6 and 12–7).

Order 1. Phanerozonia. These have one or two rows of large marginal plates along the arms; two rows of tube feet in each arm; and pedicellariae, when present, usually sessile or in pits.

FAMILY 1. ASTROPECTINIDAE. Arms long and slender; paxillae (skeletal tubercles bearing many spines) covering membranous aboral wall; conical tube feet without sucking disks; ampullae bifurcate; usually no anus. Ex. *Astropecten articulatus.*

FAMILY 2. PORCELLANASTERIDAE. Arms short; body more or less pentagonal; paxillae covering membranous aboral wall; no anus; cribriform bodies between certain of the marginal plates; on deep ocean mud bottoms. Ex. *Porcellanaster coeruleus.*

FAMILY 3. OREASTERIDAE. Body thick; marginal plates small; aboral plates arranged in a reticulum. Ex. *Oreaster reticulatus.*

Order 2. Spinulosa. Marginal plates inconspicuous; tube feet with sucking disks; pedicellariae pedunculate, usually absent.

FAMILY 1. ASTERINIDAE. Body pentagonal; aboral plates granular. Ex. *Patiria miniata.*

FAMILY 2. ECHINASTERIDAE. Arms long and slender; no pedicellariae. Ex. *Echinaster spinulosus.*

Order 3. Forcipulata. Marginal plates inconspicuous; pedicellariae stalked; prominent spines.

FAMILY 1. ZOROASTERIDAE. Arms long and slender; disk small; four rows of tube feet; deep sea. Ex. *Zoroaster evermanni.*

FAMILY 2. ASTERIIDAE. Arms tapering and often more than five; medium-sized disk; four rows of tube feet; widely distributed. Ex. *Asterias forbesi, A. vulgaris, Pisaster ochraceus.*

2 / Class II. Ophiuroidea

The brittle-stars and basket stars that belong to this class resemble the starfish in many respects. Although they are not satisfactory for general dissection, species such as *Ophioderma brevispina* can be examined externally for the main features of the class. Only reference to their peculiarities as compared to asteroids is made here.

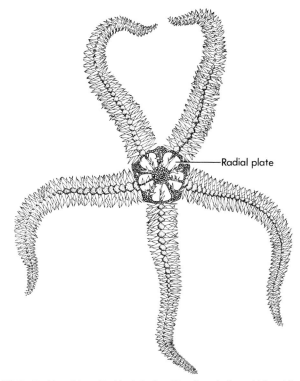

Radial plate

Fig. 12-8. Ophiuroidea. *Ophiothrix fragilis*, aboral view. (After MacBride.)

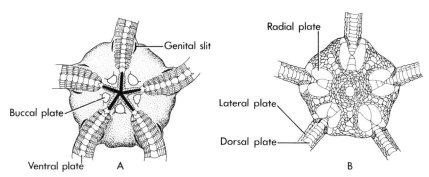

Fig. 12-9. (A) *Ophiura;* oral surface of disk. (B) *Ophioglypha;* aboral surface of disk. (From Woods.)

Skeleton (Figs. 12–8 and 12–9).   The disk in the Ophiuroidea is usually very distinct. The arms are slender and exceedingly flexible. The ambulacral groove is absent, being covered over by skeletal plates and converted into the epineural canal. Each arm is covered by four rows of plates, one aboral, one oral, and two lateral. Spines are restricted to the lateral plates. Within the arm are plates that have fused together and are known as vertebrae. The muscular system of the arm is well developed.

Water-Vascular System.   This differs in several respects from that of the starfish. The madreporite is on the oral surface. The tube feet have lost their locomotor function and serve as tactile organs; the ampullae have consequently disappeared.

Digestive System.   The food of the brittle stars consists of minute organisms and decaying organic matter lying on the mud of the sea bottom. It is scooped into the mouth by special tube feet, two pairs to each arm, called the oral tube feet. The rows of spines that extend out over the mouth opening serve as strainers (Fig. 12–10). The stomach is a simple sac without ceca; it cannot be pushed out of the mouth. There is no anus. The basket star is thought to feed on plankton organisms by trapping them in microscopic hooks on the terminal branches of the rays.

Reproductive System.   The gonads discharge their products into genital bursae which open, one on either side of the base of each arm in most ophiuroids, but in *O. brevispina* the bursae are divided so that two pair appear beside each arm. One species is viviparous. Some deposit large eggs, which develop directly without a planktonic stage. Many produce small eggs, which undergo holoblastic cleavage, eventually developing into a pluteus (Fig. 12–28) larva before metamorphosis to the adult. In *O. brevispina* the arms of the pluteus do not develop even though the larvae are ciliated and planktonic.

Opening of
genital bursa

Arm spines

Tentacle
(modified
tube foot)

Jaw

Tooth papillae

Buccal plate

Tentacle scale

Fig. 12-10. *Ophiopteris papillosa;* mouthparts. (From Johnson and Snook.)

Behavior. The locomotion of brittle stars is comparatively rapid. The arms are bent laterally, and enable animals belonging to certain species to "run," or climb, and probably swim. When pieces of rubber tubing are slipped over the arms the ophiuroids are able to remove them by various methods although they cease trying unsuccessful methods.

Regeneration. The term *brittle star* is derived from the fact that these animals break off their arms if they become injured. This autotomy often allows the individual to escape from its enemies, and is of no serious consequence, since new arms are speedily regenerated. In a number of species the aboral covering of the disk is normally cast off, probably for reproductive purposes.

Classification. Two orders are recognized in the class Ophiuroidea.

Order 1. Ophiurae. Five unbranched arms. Disk usually bearing scales or shields.

FAMILY 1. OPHIODERMATIDAE. Disk covered with granules; oral papillae around mouth. Ex. *Ophioderma brevispina.*

FAMILY 2. OPHIOLEPIDIDAE. Disk covered with plates or scales; oral papillae around mouth. Ex. *Ophiura sarsi.*

FAMILY 3. AMPHIURIDAE. Plates on sides of arms with small, prominent solid spines; oral papillae around mouth. Ex. *Amphipholis squamata* (a viviparous species).

FAMILY 4. OPHIOTRICHIDAE (Fig. 12–8). Plates small on upper surface of arms; no oral papillae; brachial spines project directly from surface. Ex. *Ophiothrix angulata.*

Fig. 12-11. Ophiuroidea. Euryalae. A basket star.

Order 2. Euryalae.   Arms may be branched. Disk usually lacking scales and shields.

FAMILY 1. ASTROPHYTIDAE (Fig. 12–11). Ex. *Gorgonocephalus agassiz* (basket fish).

3 / Class III. Echinoidea

(1) Arbacia—A Sea Urchin

A sea urchin (Fig. 12–12) resembles a starfish whose aboral surface has become exceedingly reduced, being represented by a small area, the *periproct*, and the tips of whose arms have at the same time been bent upward and united near the center of the aboral surface. Both tube feet and spines are used in locomotion. "The spines are pressed against the substratum and keep the animal from rolling over under the pull of the tube feet and also help to push it on."

Skeleton.   The skeleton of the sea urchin is known as a shell or *test*, and is shown in detail in Figure 12–13. The *apical system* of plates contains the madreporite, four other genital plates, with genital pores, and five ocular plates, each with a mass of pigmented cells. There are five pairs of columns of *ambulacral plates*, so called because they are penetrated by tube feet, and five pairs of columns of *interambulacral plates*. On the inside of the test around the peristome in many sea urchins are five arches, often incomplete,

Fig. 12-12. Echinoidea. (A) *Strongylocentrotus*, aboral view, and (B) oral view. (C) *Arbacia*. (D) A cidaroid sea urchin.

called *auricles*. Most of the plates bear spines, which are attached by muscles and move freely on little knoblike elevations called *tubercles*. The *pedicellariae* are more specialized than those of the starfish; they commonly have three jaws. The mouth is provided with five white teeth; these are part of a complicated structure known as "Aristotle's lantern."

Digestive System (Fig. 12–14). The *food* of the sea urchin consists of marine vegetable and animal matter which falls to the sea bottom and is ingested by means of Aristotle's lantern. That sea urchins are capable of capturing fish may be demonstrated by placing specimens in an aquarium with a group of *Fundulus heteroclitus*. The head or tail of the fish is secured by the sea urchin and held against the bottom or side of the aquarium by the spines and ambulacral feet while the body of the fish is gnawed away by the jaws of Aristotle's lantern. The *intestine* is very long; it takes one turn around the inside of the body and then bends upon itself and takes a turn in the opposite direction. A small tube, the *siphon*, accompanies the intestine part

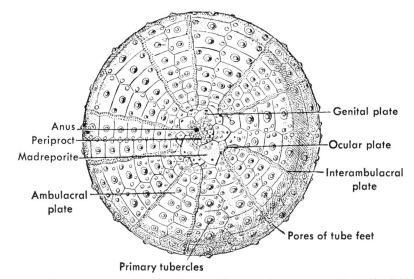

Anus

Periproct

Madreporite

Ambulacral
plate

Genital plate

Ocular plate

Interambulacral
plate

Pores of tube feet

Primary tubercles

Fig. 12-13. Aboral view of the test of sea urchin with spines removed. (From MacBride.)

way opening into it at either end. The *anus* of the sea urchin is near the center of the aboral surface.

Aristotle's lantern (Fig. 12–15) is a complicated apparatus that should command the admiration of every student of nature. The hollow axis of the lantern is formed by the *pharynx*, the body of the lantern, which has the shape of a pyramid with a pentagonal base, is composed of five complicated

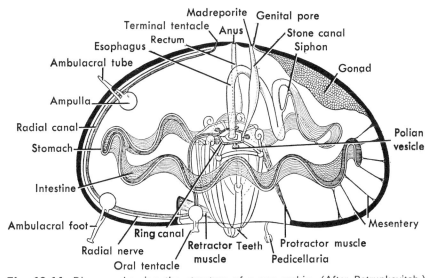

Madreporite   Genital pore

Terminal tentacle   Anus   Stone canal

Esophagus   Rectum   Siphon

Ambulacral tube

Gonad

Ampulla

Radial canal

Stomach

Polian
vesicle

Intestine

Ambulacral foot

Ring canal

Mesentery

Radial nerve   Retractor   Teeth   Protractor muscle
muscle   Pedicellaria

Oral tentacle

Fig. 12-14. Diagram showing the structure of a sea urchin. (After Petrunkevitch.)

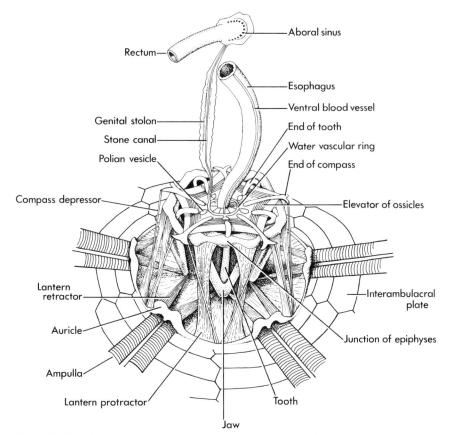

Fig. 12-15. Diagram showing the structure of Aristotle's lantern in a sea urchin. (From MacBride.)

calcareous parts or *jaws* and as many groups of muscles. When isolated each calcareous jaw appears in the shape of a triangular pyramid. The middle portion of the tooth is enclosed between the two halves of an ossicle called the *alveolus*. The elastic free upper end of the tooth is curved over the base of the pyramid and enclosed in a pouch of the oral sinus. The hornlike processes of the alveoli serving for the attachment of the protractors are termed *epiphyses* and, though fused with the alveoli, are in reality separate ossicles. Radiating from the middle of the lantern at its base are five ossicles, the *rotulae*, articulated to the alveoli. Below the rotulae and also radial in position are five *compasses* or Y-shaped ossicles, so-called because of their two diverging ligaments. These long and thin *ligaments* arise, side by side, from the head or distal enlargement of the compass and are attached to the peristomial edge of the two adambulacral plates on each side adjoining the radius to which the ossicle belongs.

The *muscular apparatus* of the lantern is very complicated. It consists of seven sets of muscles consisting of over 60 individual muscles. Among these are the following: (1) Five short interpyramidal (or interalveolar) muscles are attached to the adjoining radial surfaces of the alveoli; hold the alveoli together; and close the teeth. (2) Five pairs of protractors are attached to the epiphysis and the peristomial edge of the test and run to the inside of, and parallel to, the compass ligaments. (3) Five pairs of retractors are attached to the external surface of the alveoli near the teeth and to the auricles. (4) Five muscles bind together the compasses and form the diaphragm surrounding the esophagus. All lantern muscles are composed of smooth fibers. The entire lantern with its muscles is enclosed in the *oral sinus* formed by a part of the peritoneum called the *peripharyngeal membrane.*

The antagonistic action of muscles is readily illustrated by the protractor and retractor muscles of the lantern. Muscles work only by contracting and must have either a hydraulic, elastic, or muscular force to return the part moved so further work may be done by the muscle. By examining a side dissection of the lantern (Fig. 12–15) one can see that the protractors must shorten to move the lantern out while the retractors are lengthened. The reverse happens when the lantern is retracted.

Fig. 12-16. Echinoidea. Diagrammatic view of the axial gland and pulsating vessel complex. 1, cavity of the axocoel. 2, broad flattened compartment. 3, small conspicuous compartment. 4, opening between 2 and 3. 5, slit between axocoel and coelomic cavity. 6, rectal hemal vessel from inner hemal sinus. 7, surface vessels. 8, membrane. 9, axial oral vessel. 10, lumen of axial gland (axial sinus). 11, thickened side of axial gland. 12, pulsating vessel, right branch. 13, stone canal. 14, pulsating vessel. 15, opening between axial gland and stone canal. 16, madreporite. (From R. A. Boolootian and J. L. Campbell. A primitive heart in the echinoid *Strongylocentrotus purpuratus. Science,* **145**:173–175. Copyright 1964 by the American Association for the Advancement of Science.)

Water-Vascular System (Figs. 12–14 and 12–16).   One of the genital plates serves also as a *madreporite*. From the madreporite a *stone canal* leads orally to a *circular canal* surrounding the esophagus aboral to the lantern. From the circular canal arise five *radial canals* and five spongelike bodies called *Tiedemann's bodies* or *Polian vesicles*. Each radial canal leads orally and outward under the radial plates and ends in a terminal tentacle. *Transverse canals* leading to the *ambulacral feet* and *ampullae* are given off by the radial canals. Two pores for each ambulacral foot are present in the ambulacral plates.

Respiratory System.   A large part of the respiration takes place in most echinoids through ten peristomial gills situated on the area surrounding the mouth, one pair in each angle between the ambulacral plates. The tube feet also are respiratory in function.

Nervous System.   A nerve ring encircles the pharyngeal region. From it five radial nerves extend out under the radial canals. Coordinated movements of locomotion depend on these nerves. Localized spine reactions to mild stimuli are coordinated by a subepidermal nerve net, the spines inclining to the direction of the stimulus.

Reproduction.   Sexes are separate and spawning may occur in spring and summer. Fertilization occurs in sea water and development is similar to that described for the starfish in the earliest stages, but the ciliated larva is a pluteus like the larva of a brittle star. The pluteus metamorphoses to become a juvenile urchin. Because eggs and sperm of sea urchins can be taken from urchins, then combined in the laboratory, for successful artificial fertilization, they are important tools of experimental embryology. To apply biochemical techniques to determine sequences of developmental changes in cellular biochemistry, it is much simpler to use quantities of eggs at the same stages of development than to use individual eggs of vertebrates. The earliest experiments involved treatment of eggs with various chemicals to see what aberrations developed. Lithium salts were found to prevent invagination of the endoderm. It would seem that these animals might be useful for preliminary screening of drugs for effects on early development.

Locomotor Organs.   The locomotor organs of an echinoid, the sand dollar (*Echinarachnius parma*), have been studied in detail. *Cilia* on the spines seem to perform feeding, cleaning, and respiratory functions. *Ambulacral feet* aid in moving sand up over the anterior edge of the test. *Spines* are of great importance in locomotion. Long and short ones cover both surfaces. They have a power stroke that passes through a plane perpendicular to the body surface. The spine remains close to the body during the recovery stroke.

Coordinated spine movements are especially prominent on the anterior oral surface.

(2) Other Echinoidea

The Echinoidea are subglobular or disk-shaped and without arms or free rays. The calcareous plates of the skeleton or test are closely fitted together and are usually arranged into five pairs of ambulacral rows and five pairs of interambulacral rows. The surface of the test bears tubercles with which movable spines articulate; these spines are often very long and their tips are in some species poisonous. The pedicellariae are stalked and usually possess three jaws. Nine orders have living species.

Order 1. Stirodonta. Mouth central; anus within apical area; epiphyses separate.

FAMILY 1. ARBACIIDAE. Body subglobular; spines large and solid; aboral tube feet without suckers. Ex. *Arbacia punctulata* (Fig. 12–12, C).

Order 2. Camarodonta. Mouth central; anus within apical area; epiphyses united.

FAMILY 1. ECHINIDAE. Body subglobular; spines solid; periproct with many plates; ambulacral plates with three pairs of pores. Ex. *Tripneustes esculentus.*

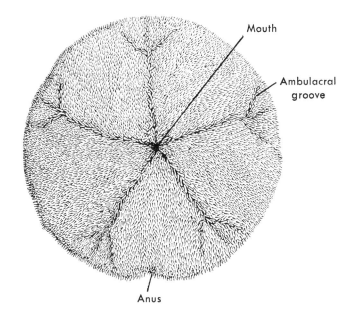

Mouth

Ambulacral groove

Anus

Fig. 12-17. A sand dollar, *Echinarachnius parma*, oral view. (From MacBride.)

FAMILY 2. STRONGYLOCENTROTIDAE. Body subglobular; ambulacral plates with from 4 to 11 pairs of pores. Ex. *Strongylocentrotus dröbachiensis* (Fig. 12–12, A).

Order 3. Clypeastroida. Mouth central; anus outside apical area; body usually flattened.

FAMILY 1. CLYPEASTRIDAE. Body bilaterally symmetrical; shell thick; spines short. Ex. *Clypeaster subdepressus.*

FAMILY 2. SCUTELLIDAE. Body flat; spines very small. Ex. *Echinarachnius parma* (sand dollar, Fig. 12–17).

Order 4. Spatangoida. Body cushion-shaped or heart-shaped; anus, and sometimes mouth, eccentric; no Aristotle's lantern.

FAMILY 1. LOVENIIDAE. Heart-shaped. Ex. *Echinocardium cordatum* (Fig. 12–18).

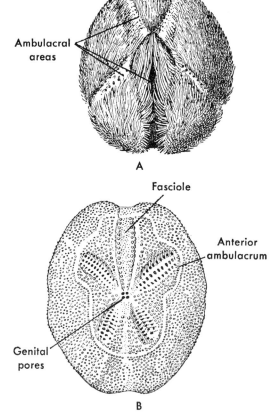

Ambulacral areas

A

Fasciole

Anterior ambulacrum

Genital pores

B

Fig. 12-18. (A) A heart urchin, *Echinocardium cordatum.* (B) Test of a heart urchin, *Schizaster.* (A, from MacBride; B, after Agassiz.)

4 / Class IV. Holothuroidea

(1) Thyone—A Sea Cucumber

To this class belong the sea cucumbers (Figs. 12–19, 12–20, and 12–21). Their most striking external features are the *muscular body wall* almost devoid of large skeletal plates, the *branching tentacles* surrounding the mouth, and the lateral position when at rest or moving about on the sea bottom. The tube feet, when present, are organs of locomotion. They pull the animal along on its ventral, flattened surface. Waves of muscular contraction which travel

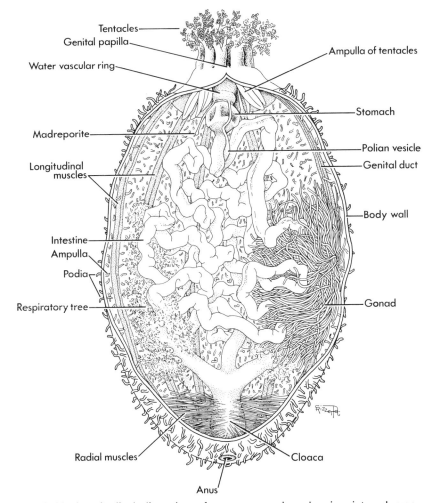

Fig. 12-19. Longitudinal dissection of a sea cucumber showing internal organs. (Modified after Root.)

from one end of the body to the other are important in locomotion, and the tentacles may also assist.

Body Wall. Instead of an articulated calcareous skeleton, the body wall is soft and *muscular* with irregular plates embedded in the dermal layer. Beneath the epidermis and dermis is a thick layer of circular muscles overlying five longitudinal muscles, each of which consists of two bundles. Five retractor muscles are connected with the pharynx and a number of muscles extend from the body wall to the *cloaca* which they are able to dilate. The innermost layer of the body wall is a *ciliated peritoneal epithelium*.

Fig. 12-20. Holothuroidea. Sea cucumbers; (A) extending from hiding place under coral rock; (B) *Stichopus californicus*. (B, from Johnson and Snook.)

Digestive System. The alimentary canal consists of a cylindrical *pharynx*, a short *esophagus*, a small muscular *stomach*, and a long looped *intestine*, the posterior end of which is a muscular enlargement called the cloaca. The pharynx is encircled by a calcareous ring of plates homologous to Aristotle's Lantern of the Echinoidea. The food of most sea cucumbers consists of organic particles extracted from the sand or mud which is taken into the alimentary canal. Some species stretch out their branched tentacles on which many small organisms come to rest. A food laden tentacle is inserted into the mouth, then withdrawn so that the food is wiped off.

Water-Vascular System. This is homologous to those of the other classes of echinoderms. There is a *circular canal* around the esophagus, five *radial canals* which end blindly near the anus, and *tube feet*. The circular canal gives off a *Polian vesicle* and one or more *stone-canals* ending in internal *madreporites*. From 10 to 30 of the tube feet surrounding the mouth are modified as *tentacles* for procuring food.

Respiration. Respiration is carried on by the cloaca, *respiratory trees*, tentacles, tube feet, and body wall. The cloaca and respiratory trees also function as excretory organs. Water flows into the cloaca through the anus and passes into two long branching tubes, the respiratory trees; here part of it probably finds its way through the walls into the body cavity.

Behavior. The common sea cucumbers, *Thyone briareus*, are sensitive to contact with solid objects, and many of them burrow in the sand or mud. They are extremely sensitive to a decrease in the light intensity and will contract the body if an object passes between them and the source of light. They are also negative to light since they move away from the source. *Thyone* remains buried in the mud or covered with debris most of the time. This habit probably affords considerable protection from large predators.

Autotomy and Regeneration. Sea cucumbers possess remarkable powers of autotomy and regeneration. When one is irritated it contracts the muscles of the body wall with such great force that the viscera is extruded through the anus (or sometimes the mouth). The respiratory tree is extruded first. It is of some protective value because some branches (Cuverian organs) of it may swell up into an entangling mass. Parts lost in the process are eventually regenerated.

Autotomy can be induced in *Thyone briareus* in the following manner. When an animal is placed in $7N$ ammonium hydroxide in the proportion of one part ammonia to 800 parts of sea water, they will rapidly eviscerate. More than 90 per cent of specimens eviscerated in this manner live and regenerate lost parts if they are immediately transferred to fresh sea water.

Fig. 12-21. *Cucumaria;* a sea cucumber carrying its young. (After Thomson.)

(2) Other Holothuroidea

Sea cucumbers are elongate cylindrical animals that lie on one flattened side with the mouth at the anterior end and the anus at the posterior end. The muscular body wall contains only small calcareous particles and its external surface is free from cilia, spines, and pedicellariae. There are ten branched oral tentacles around the mouth, and tube feet and ambulacral tentacles may be present on other parts of the body. Among the South Pacific Islands and on the coasts of Queensland and in southern China, dried holothurians are known as "beche-de-mer" or "trepang" and are used for food. Some may be toxic. Holothurian material is said to be used by some south sea natives to stun fish. Five orders are recognized.

Order 1. Dendrochirota. Many tube feet; branching oral tentacles. Ex. *Cucumaria frondosa, Thyone briareus.*

Order 2. Aspidochirota. Many tube feet; peltate oral tentacles. Ex. *Holothuria floridana.*

Order 3. Elasipoda. Tube feet present; no respiratory tree; most are found in deeper regions of the ocean, some are pelagic. Ex. *Kolga hyalina, Pelagothuria natatrix.*

Order 4. Molpadonia. Tube feet absent from most of body; respiratory tree present. Ex. *Caudina arenata.*

Order 5. Apoda. Tube feet and respiratory tree absent.
FAMILY 1. SYNAPTIDAE. Anchor-shaped ossicles in body wall. Ex. *Leptosynapta inhaerens.*

FAMILY 2. CHIRIDOTIDAE. Six-spoked wheel-shaped or sigmoid ossicles in body wall. Ex. *Chiridota laevis.*

FAMILY 3. MYRIOTROCHIDAE. Wheel-shaped ossicles with eight or more spokes. Ex. *Myriotrochus rinkii.*

5 / Class V. Crinoidea

The crinoids are called sea lilies or feather stars (Figs. 12–22 and 12–25). They are attached by the aboral apex of the body throughout life or during the early stages of their development with the oral surface above. Their arms are usually branched and bear pinnules (Fig. 12–23). The tube feet are like tentacles and without ampullae. No madreporite, spines, nor pedicellariae are present. There are over 600 living represenatives of this class belonging to about 150 genera and about 30 families; fossil remains are very abundant in limestone formations. Most of the living crinoids are found at moderate depths, a few are deep-sea forms, and some inhabit shallow water.

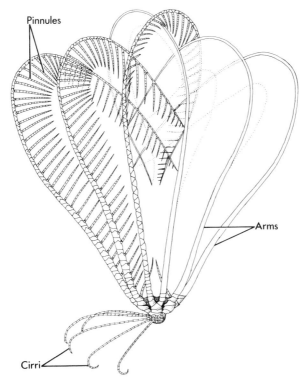

Pinnules

Arms

Cirri

Fig. 12-22. Crinoidea. A feather star, *Antedon adriatica.* The pinnules on three of the arms are omitted. (After Clark.)

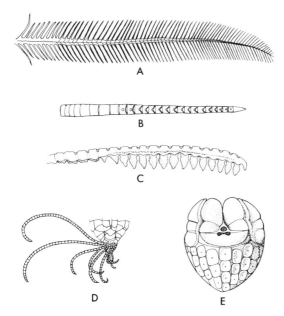

Fig. 12-23. Crinoidea. Details of structure of several species. (A) *Comatula pectinata*, grooved anterior arm. (B) *Capillaster multiradiata*, cirrus with dorsal spines. (C) *Leptonemaster venustus*, terminal cone on oral pinnule. (D) *Nanometra bowersi*, large and small cirri. (E) *Pentametrocrinus japonicus*, centrodorsal and articular faces of the radials. This is the only portion of the body that remains of most fossil feather stars. (After Clark.)

They are abundant both as individuals and as species where satisfactory living conditions exist. Crinoids are often attached by a jointed stalk. Some species break off from the stalk when they become mature, and swim about by means of muscular contractions of the arms.

The arms of crinoids are usually five in number. The apparently greater number is due to branching near the base (Fig. 12–24). The branches may be

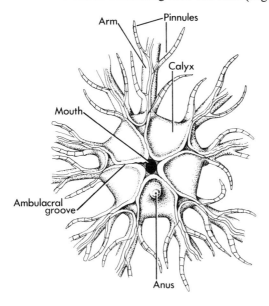

Fig. 12-24. Oral view of *Antedon*. (From MacBride.)

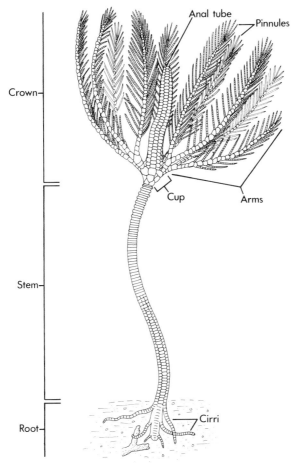

Fig. 12-25. *Botryocrinus decadactylus;* a fossil crinoid. (Brit. Mus.)

equal, or one large and the other small; in the latter case the smaller branch is called a pinnule.

Classification. Living crinoids are included in one order, the Articulata. Three of the more important families are as follows.

FAMILY 1. ISOCRINIDAE. Stalk long, with long cirri; root absent; disk small; arms divided dichotomously up to ten times; pinnules small; about 80 species. Ex. *Cenocrinus asteria* (West Indies).

FAMILY 2. ANTEDONIDAE (Fig. 12–22). Stalk present only in young; cirri at stalk base in adult; arms long, five to twenty in number; pinnules present; over 130 species; cosmopolitan. Ex. *Antedon tenella* (Atlantic coast).

FAMILY 3. COMASTERIDAE. Stalk present only in young; cirri few or absent at stalk base in adult; mouth eccentric; many species in tropical seas. Ex. *Neocomatella alata* (West Indies).

6 / Fossil Echinoderms

Every class of echinoderms with living representatives includes also fossil species except the Holothuroidea of which only isolated ossicles have been found. *Eothuria* was perhaps ancestral to the holothuroideans but is generally considered an echinoid because it was covered with plates. The following groups are known from fossil remains only.

MACHAERIDIA.   The skeleton in this group consists of two or four rows of plates that resemble those of echinoderms. The animals were elongate, probably bilaterally symmetrical, flexible, and possibly attached. Ex. *Machaeridian lepidocelus*.

HETEROSTELEA.   These were stalked forms with bilateral symmetry. The animal probably lay flat on the bottom. No genital pore nor water pore appear to have been present. Ex. *Dendrocystis barrandei*.

CYSTIDEA (Fig. 12–26, B).   Here radial symmetry has developed. The body was attached by a stem and food and water were taken in and genital products expelled from the opposite end. Slender, jointed appendages, the brachioles, usually surrounded the distal end. Ex. *Chirocrinus*.

BLASTOIDEA.   The main skeleton in these consists of thirteen plates arranged in three circlets of radials, orals, and basals. The body was attached by a jointed stem, sometimes with roots. Many brachioles are present. Ex. *Orophocrinus fusiformis* (Fig. 12–26, A).

Fig. 12-26. Fossil echinoderms. (A) Blastoidea. *Orophocrinus fusiformis*. (B) Cystidea. *Lepadocrinus quadrifasciatus*. (Brit. Mus.)

A   B

EDRIOASTEROIDEA. Here the skeleton forms a radially symmetrical circular test of many irregular plates which was attached directly to the sea bottom. Apparently a well-developed water-vascular system was present including tube feet and ampullae. Brachioles are absent. Ex. *Edrioaster.*

OPHIOCISTIOIDEA. Unattached, discoidal bodies enclosed by plates except in the mouth region. No arms, but five ambulacral areas were present. Ex. *Eucladia.*

7 / Echinoderms in General

Anatomy. The echinoderms are unique in the possession of radial symmetry in the adult stage, which is evidently secondary since the larvae are bilaterally symmetrical. The number of radii is usually five.

Body Wall. The epidermis of echinoderms is usually ciliated and contains gland cells and sense cells. The ossicles in the body wall may be few, small, and widely scattered, or large, numerous, and united more or less firmly into a definite skeleton. Certain of the ossicles usually form spines. Pedicellariae are often present.

Coelom. The coelom is complex, consisting of a number of spaces including a perivisceral cavity, a perihemal system, an aboral sinus system, a water-vascular system, a madreporic vesicle, and an axial sinus.

Systems of Organs. The *alimentary canal* may be axial or coiled and may possess diverticulae. *Respiration* is accomplished in many by the tube feet or by a respiratory tree. The tube feet have various other functions, notably locomotion, but probably originated as sensory or food-collecting organs. No *nephridia* are present, excretory matter being taken up by amoeboid wandering cells that pass through the epithelium. The *circulatory system* consists of strands of peculiar lacunar tissue. Probably circulation is rather slow in species having such a system. The *nervous system* is primitive in type, consisting of nerve rings, radial nerves, and nerves to the tube feet, spines, etc. *Sense organs* are not well developed. The general surface of the body is sensitive to touch and the tube feet and terminal tentacles at the end of each radial vessel are especially sensitive to tactile stimuli. At the base of each terminal tentacle in the Asteroidea is an eye spot. Certain holothurians possess statocysts. The sexes are usually separate. The *reproductive organs* are simple and the ova and spermatozoa are shed directly to the exterior without the aid of accessory glands, penis, seminal vesicle, and seminal receptacle.

Development of Echinoderms. In most of the echinoderms, the eggs pass through a ciliated blastula stage (Fig. 12–27), a gastrula stage, and a larval stage, which, in the course of from two weeks to two months, metamorphoses into an adult. The larvae (Fig. 12–28) of the four principal classes of echinoderms resemble one another, but are nevertheless quite distinct. They are

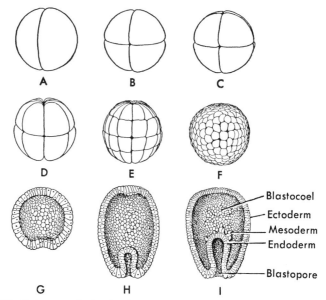

Fig. 12-27. Early stages in the development of the egg of a sea urchin. (From Woodruff.)

bilaterally symmetrical, and swim about by means of a ciliated band, which may be complicated by a number of armlike processes. The alimentary canal consists of a mouth, esophagus, stomach, intestine, and anus. From the digestive tract two coelomic sacs are budded off; these develop into the body cavity, water-vascular system, and other coelomic cavities of the adult.

The larvae of the different classes have been given names as follows: those of the Asteroidea are called *bipinnaria* (Fig. 12–28); Ophiuroidea, *ophiopluteus*; Echinoidea, *echinopluteus*; and Holothuroidea, *auricularia*. The adults which develop from these larvae are, as we have seen, radially symmetrical, although many of them, notably the Holothuroidea, are more or less bilateral in structure. The bilateral condition of the larvae indicates that the ancestors of the echinoderms were either bilaterally symmetrical or that the larvae have become adapted to an active life in the water.

Artificial Parthenogenesis. The eggs of echinoderms pass through a total and equal cleavage, and are easily fertilized and reared to the larval stage in the laboratory. For these reasons they have become classical material for embryological studies and for experimental purposes.

One of the most interesting phenomena discovered by means of experiments with echinoderm eggs is the development of a larva from an unfertilized egg when subjected to certain environmental conditions. This phenomenon is known as artificial parthenogenesis. The eggs of other animals, for example, annelids, are also capable of developing under certain conditions without fertilization, and those of some species, like plant lice and rotifers

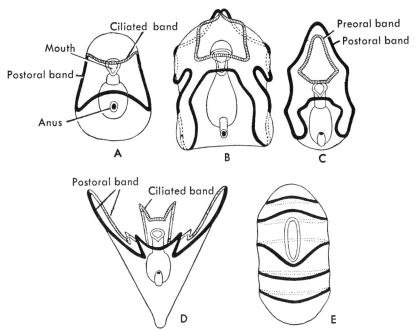

Fig. 12-28. Diagrams of larval echinoderms. (A) Early larval stage. (B) Auricularia. (C) Bipinnaria. (D) Pluteus. (E) Crinoid larva. (From Borradaile and Potts.)

are normally parthenogenetic, but echinoderm eggs have been used for experimental purposes more frequently than any others. Large numbers can be fertilized simultaneously in the laboratory. Since all are then in phase in development, periodic sampling and analysis gives more meaningful data on sequential molecular events than with studies of most other animal embryos.

Interrelations and Phylogeny of the Echinoderms. Echinoderms and coelenterates, because of their radial symmetry, were at one time placed together in a group called Radiata. The anatomy of the adult and the structure of the larvae, however, show that these phyla really occupy widely separated positions in the animal kingdom. The adult echinoderms cannot be compared with any other group of animals, and we must look to the larvae for signs of relationship. The bilateral larva is either a modification for a free-swimming life or an indication of the conditions of its ancestors. The latter view is accepted by most zoologists. The ancestors of echinoderms were doubtless bilateral, worm-like animals which became fixed and were then modified into radially symmetrical adults.

It is interesting to compare the development of echinoderms with that of certain deuterostomes such as *Balanoglossus*. In both, the eggs pass through the indeterminate type of cleavage; the mesoderm arises from the multiplication of cells around the lip of the blastopore; the anus evolves directly from the blastopore; the mouth is formed near the anterior end of the archenteron; the coelom develops from pairs of diverticulae of the archenteron; and the larvae of certain echinoderms are remarkably similar to the *tornaria* larva of *Balanoglossus*. Because of these similarities the echinoderms and chordates appear to be closely related and to have had common ancestors. For this reason these groups are sometimes placed near each other on the phylogenetic tree.

Creatine phosphate is the muscle phosphate of echinoderms as well as chordates. This was once considered strong evidence of a close relationship. However creatine has since been found in a wide variety of other invertebrates. There seems to be a high concentration of the enzyme, creatine phosphatase, in forms with low concentrations of creatine phosphate. Thus, it no longer seems to be strong evidence of close phylogenetic relationship. Apparently it is a case of enzyme-substrate equilibrium, which may be related to food sources of the group.

Echinoderms are a major phylum of special interest because of three ways they differ from other major phyla. One, they are an old, large phylum with no parasitic members. Two, they are an old, large phylum, which has not invaded fresh-water or terrestrial environments. Three, their radial symmetry seems to be of secondary phylogenetic origin.

History of Our Knowledge of the Echinodermata. The name of this phylum was introduced by Klein in 1734 as an appropriate appellation for sea urchins. For many years the echinoderms and coelenterates were included as a class among the Radiata, largely because of the radial symmetry of the adults. The Echinodermata were first recognized as a group distinct from the Radiata by Leuckart in 1847.

References to Literature on the Echinodermata

ALTON, M. S. 1966. Bathymetric distribution of sea stars (Asteroidea) off the northern Oregon coast. *J. Fish. Res. Bd. Canada*, **23**:1673–1714.

ANDERSON, J. M. 1965. Studies on visceral regeneration in sea-stars. III. Regeneration of the cardiac stomach in *Asterias forbesi* (Desor). *Biol. Bull.*, **129**:454–470.

BOOLOOTIAN, R. A., and J. L. CAMPBELL. 1964. A primitive heart in the echinoid *Strongylocentrotus purpuratus. Science*, **145**:173–175.

CHANGEUX, J. 1961. Contribution à l'étude des animaux associés aux Holothurides. *Act. Sci. et Ind.*, No. **1284**. 124 pp.

COCKBAIN, A. E. 1966. Pentamerism in echinoderms and the calcite skeleton. *Nature*, **212**:740–741.

DURHAM, J. W. 1966. Evolution among the Echinoidea. *Biol. Rev.*, **41**:368–391.

FERGUSON, J. C. 1966. Cell production in the Tiedemann bodies and haemal organs of the starfish, *Asterias forbesi. Trans. Am. Microsc. Soc.*, **85**:200–209.

HYMAN, L. H. 1955. *The Invertebrates: Echinodermata.* Vol. IV. McGraw-Hill, New York. 763 pp.

KANATANI, H., and M. OHGURI. 1966. Mechanism of starfish spawning. *Biol. Bull.,* **131**:104–114.

MILLOTT, N. 1966. A possible function for the axial organ of echinoids. *Nature,* **209**:594–596.

NICHOLS, D. 1962. *Echinoderms.* Hillary House, New York. 200 pp.

STEPHENS, G. C., J. F. VAN PILSUM, and D. TAYLOR. 1965. Phylogeny and the distribution of creatine in invertebrates. *Biol. Bull.,* **129**:573–581.

Chapter XIII
Phylum Chordata

THE PHYLUM Chordata contains invertebrate members in addition to the many thousand species of vertebrates. Members of this phylum have the following characteristics, which set them apart from other bilateral, metameric, coelomate animals, with indeterminate cleavage: (1) a hollow dorsal nerve cord, (2) gill slits, or vestiges of them, and (3) a notochord. The characteristics may not be present in the adult but are present some time during the life cycle. The invertebrate species are all marine. The vertebrate members have been most successful in dominating all habitats of the earth although exceeded numerically by many invertebrate groups from other phyla.

Three subphyla of chordates are recognized. The Hemichordata was formerly considered an additional subphylum but have here been recognized as a separate phylum because of the absence of both metamerism and a true notochord.

SUBPHYLUM I. UROCHORDATA. The tunicates. Notochord absent in adult; sessile or planktonic; with a thick body covering of tunicin, a substance related to cellulose. Ex. *Ciona intestinalis.*

SUBPHYLUM II. CEPHALOCHORDATA. The lanclets. Notochord well developed in the adult. Ex. *Branchiostoma.*

SUBPHYLUM III. VERTEBRATA. The vertebrates. With a backbone.

1 / Subphylum I. Urochordata

(1) Ciona intestinalis

Ciona intestinalis (Fig. 13–1) is a widely distributed, solitary tunicate common on both coasts of this country. The body is more elongate than most tunicates. Opposite the attached end are two prominent openings, the *buccal siphon*, or mouth, and the *atrial siphon*. Water passes in the buccal siphon and is

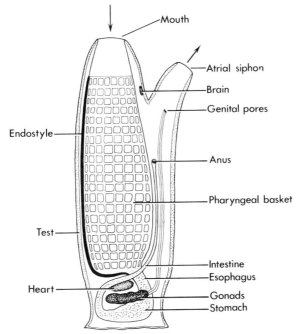

Fig. 13-1. *Ciona intestinalis.* Diagrammatic representation of main internal organs. (Modified after several authors.)

strained through the wall of a very large *pharynx* before passing out the atrial siphon. Planktonic food passing through the openings, or stigmata, in the wall of the pharynx is moved by cilia on the bars to the *endostyle* where it is trapped in mucus and conveyed to the esophagus. Digestion and absorption occurs in the stomach and intestine, and undigested material is ejected through the anus into the atrium where wastes are carried out the atrial siphon.

The mantle or body covering which secretes the test contains muscles that can contract the tunicate and close the siphons. The coelom is not identifiable.

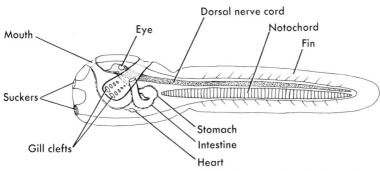

Fig. 13-2. The tadpole larva of a urochordate. (After Van Name.)

The nervous system is poorly developed. The heart is formed from a fold of the pericardial cavity and has the peculiar feature of periodically reversing the direction it pumps the blood. Although there are no excretory organs, less soluble wastes are stored by amoebocytic cells which accumulate along the intestine. Although tunicates are usually hermaphroditic and discharge both eggs and sperm into the water, there is apparently no self-fertilization. A larval stage known as the tadpole larva (Fig. 13–2) develops from the egg. The tadpole has a long tail and shows definite chordate characteristics. It becomes sessile by attaching anterior adhesive papillae and then metamorphoses into the adult.

(2) Other Urochordata

Most tunicates are sessile and abundant along marine shores. They may be transparent or of varying colors. A few are pelagic. Three classes are found.

Class 1. Ascidiacea. Sedentary adults that have lost the tail of the tadpole larva. Many produce colonies by asexual budding. They often form dense carpets on wave washed portions of the intertidal zone. When disturbed they contract and discharge two jets of water through the siphons thus prompting the name *sea squirts*. Ex. *Ciona intestinalis*; *Halocynthia pyriformis*, the sea peach of the East Coast; *Clavelina huntsmani*, transparent, colonial, common in tide pools of the West Coast.

Class 2. Thaliacea. Pelagic. The atrium opens posteriorly. The tail of the tadpole is lost in the adult. Ex. *Salpa*.

Class 3. Larvacea. Planktonic. The adult retains the tail of the tadpole larva. Since these are sexually mature in a larval, or larva-like, stage they are said to exhibit neoteny. Ex. *Oikopleura*.

Fig. 13-3. Lateral view of an amphioxus with part of the body wall removed from the left side to show the general structure. (Reprinted with permission of The Macmillan Company from *College Zoology*, 7th ed. by Robert W. Hegner and Karl A. Stiles. Copyright The Macmillan Company 1959.)

2 / Subphylum II. Cephalochordata

Branchiostoma (*Amphioxus*) (Figs. 13–3 and 13–4) and other lanclets retain the notochord and hollow dorsal nerve cord in the adult. They look fishlike but have no skeletal container for the brain. The fins are fleshy folds with

Epidermis
Fin ray

Myotome
Dorsal root nerve
Nerve cord
Central canal
Ventral root nerve
Notochord
Sclerocoel (coelom)

Dorsal aorta
Hyperbranchial groove
Coelom

Protonephridium

Gill bar
Gill slit
Pharynx
"Liver"
Egg in ovary
Coelom
Transverse muscle

Atrium
Hypobranchial groove
Subendostylar coelom
Ventral aorta
Metapleural fold
Metapleural cavity

Fig. 13-4. Cross-section of an amphioxus in the pharyngeal region, showing various internal structures, including some of the coelomic cavities. (Reprinted with permission of The Macmillan Company from *College Zoology*, 7th ed. by Robert W. Hegner and Karl A. Stiles. Copyright The Macmillan Company, 1959.)

some connective tissue supports. The muscles of the body wall form V-shaped myotomes. A pharyngeal basket filters out food organisms much as the tunicate's does. The pores in the pharynx are slitlike and called gill slits. They alternate with gill bars. A cecum of the intestine projects anteriorly beside the pharynx. The anus discharges to the outside near the caudal fin. The gonads of the separate sexes discharge into the atrium. Primitive nephridial structures similar to those of some polychaetes are present. Pulsations of the ventral aorta circulates blood through arteries in the gill bars, back through the dorsal aorta, then through the other vessels to the ventral aorta. Coelomic cavities are clearly present. Two closely related families occur in most warm, shallow marine areas. The lancelet spends most of its time partially embedded in the bottom sediments.

3 / Chordates in General

The invertebrate members of the phylum Chordata are specialized for filter feeding. They are simple organisms of much less complexity than most mollusks, arthropods, and vertebrates. They are of particular interest because they indicate a clearer relationship, of vertebrates with other animals, than would be evident without them. Closest relationship with other phyla appears to be with the Hemichordata and other deuterostomes.

References to Literature on the Chordata

BARRINGTON, E. J. W. 1965. *The Biology of Hemichordata and Protochordata.* Freeman, San Francisco. 176 pp.

TRASON, W. B. 1963. The Life Cycle and Affinities of the Colonial Ascidian *Pycnoclavella stanleyi. Univ. Calif. Publ. in Zool.*, Vol. **65**, No. 4. 43 pp.

VAN NAME, W. G. 1945. The North and South American Ascidians. *Bull. Am. Mus. Nat. Hist.* **84**. 476 pp. + 31 Pls.

Chapter XIV

Invertebrates—
An Overview

THE INVERTEBRATES present a tremendous array of diverse types of animals with many specializations and peculiar features. A number of common themes may be seen in various groups. Here in a few brief pages, some of the general similarities and points of diversity will be offered as a token summary of a subject that would take many lifetimes to present in detail.

Cellular Biology of Invertebrates. Macromolecules and biosynthetic pathways of invertebrates have much in common within the ranks of invertebrates as well as with other living organisms. Similarities are so great that methods of comparison (Fitch and Margoliash, 1967) are now available that may soon unravel some of the more difficult and intriguing problems of phylogeny. Points of difference, such as formation of unusual compounds, may hold great rewards in searches for new drugs and other materials. An example of their potential value is the use of natural or synthetic pheromones and hormones in pest control with minimal side effects on useful organisms. The invertebrates represent a tremendous resource of varied tissues which may eventually, in tissue culture, biosynthesize needed compounds. Structurally, the cells of protozoans, especially the ciliates, seem to show the most highly evolved forms departing from the "typical cell."

General Morphology. Many aspects of morphology show a close correlation with the physiological function of the structure. Some general correlations with the ecology of the organisms are also present. Thus, larger burrowing forms are typically long and cylindrical in cross-section, a shape that allows a larger biomass of organism to go through small passageways. Because legs or locomotor surfaces from a long linear sequence can all exert

579

eir effect on a small cross-sectional area, they are able to force their way hrough material other organisms could not.

Streamlining and organs of attachment are found on many forms adapted to streams and wave-washed areas. Forms lacking these but found in the same habitats are either good swimmers or actually utilizing protected micro-habitats with less current.

Sedentary forms often show a radial arrangement. This is most noticeable in feeding structures of those species that do not create a strong feeding current but rely on chance arrival of food organisms. Many sedentary and tube-dwelling forms create a feeding and respiratory current with cilia or specialized appendages. Notable examples of predators that lie in wait for prey to be trapped by devices they have constructed are found in the spiders, some net-building caddisflys, and the ant lion.

Planktonic adaptations often include projecting appendages or parts that slow the rate of sinking, high oil content or gas chambers for buoyancy, or swimming devices such as cilia, nectophores, or swimming appendages.

Morphological modifications for protection of soft parts include covering of spines, plates, or shells. Some shelled forms have developed bivalved coverings as exemplified by the brachiopods, ostracods, and pelecypods. Spiraling of a shell into a compact unit has occurred in the Foraminiferida, Gastropoda, and Cephalopoda. The same effect is achieved in the case of the larva of the caddisfly, *Helicopsyche*.

Smaller sized species evolved from larger ancestors often have a reduction or loss of circulatory, respiratory, and excretory structures in comparison to their larger relatives.

The spherical or discoidal shape common in dormant stages and cysts presents less surface to what may be an unfavorable environment.

The cuticle of trematodes and cestodes merits special mention, because this rather thick layer is now known to contain many mitochondria and other inclusions. The mitochondria are an indication that the cuticle is performing an active metabolic function. The outer surface of the trematode cuticle is relatively smooth. That of the cestode is covered with microvilli and pene-trated by tubules which seem to convey some of the surrounding medium to interior.

Feeding and Digestion. Almost any type of natural organic material can be utilized by some invertebrate. Intracellular or extracellular processes may be involved. Food in solution can be utilized by many protozoans and para-sites. Particulate food is utilized by most animals. Small particles are acquired by pseudopodial, ciliary, tentacular, mucoid, or setose mechanisms most commonly. Species feeding on larger particles do so in many ways. In addition to simple ingestion of mud or other material by relatively unspecialized mouth parts, many interesting specializations have developed. Fragmentation of larger food masses by the mandibles of many crustaceans and insects, the radula of mollusks, Aristotle's lantern of *Arbacia*, the valves chelicerae and gnathobases of arachnids, are types used for solid f< the external digestion by eversion of the starfish stomach. Liquid: tissues are utilized by forms with sucking mouth parts or piercing an mouthparts often provided with a muscular pharynx. Among such forms are many leeches, nematodes, suctorians, lepidopterans, and several other arthropod groups.

Internal structural modifications of the digestive tract include the mastax and gastric mill for grinding, various filtering and sorting devices, and folds and cecae for increase of digestive surface or storage capacity.

Secretions of salivary and other glands used include anticoagulants, poisons, many enzymes. Remarkably few invertebrates secrete cellulases for digestion of the very abundant material, cellulose.

Availability of food and frequency of feeding have an influence on growth and rate of development in some species. A most notable example are the ticks.

Water Relationships. The osmotic concentration of body fluids of invertebrates as measured by freezing point depression in degrees centigrade ranges from -0.08 for the fresh-water mussel to -1.85 for marine invertebrates, which have an osmotic concentration near that of sea water. Since marine invertebrates are nearly isoosmotic with sea water, they have few regulatory problems with water balance although they do regulate the ions present in a different balance than that of sea water.

Body fluids of fresh-water invertebrates are hyperosmotic to their environment so the excretory organs and organelles function to eliminate water which diffuses into the organism in addition to eliminating some metabolic wastes. *Artemia*, the brine shrimp, is peculiar in that it is hypoosmotic to its environment. It absorbs water and salt through the gut and excretes salt from special glands in the gills (Copeland, 1966). The glands consist of mitochondria arranged as nested saucers. It is of interest that the contractile vacuole of protozoans is surrounded by many mitochondria. The mitochondria probably provide energy for active transport.

Terrestrial forms are faced with the problem of retaining water for proper functioning of the cells and tissues while still eliminating metabolic wastes. Great losses occur from respiratory surfaces which are not well protected. Thus, the earthworm loses about a third of its body weight if left in dry air at room temperature for about one-half hour. Many insects have negligible losses under similar conditions. Other terrestrial invertebrates that have intermediate losses under such conditions in nature live in humid environments or live with access to water or fluid.

Circulation. Circulation takes place on the cellular level by diffusion and protoplasmic movements. Circulatory systems of larger organisms eliminate most of the restrictive effects of dependence on diffusion over long distances.

They also make possible the localization of physiological functions in organs and a great efficiency through specialization. Extracellular transport may depend on one or more of the following.

1. Movement of the surrounding water. Ex. Sponges and some coelenterates.
2. Gastrovascular-type system. Ex. Coelenterates and flatworms.
3. Transport by body fluids of the coelom or pseudocoelom. Two variations of this type occur. (a) Fluid moved by body movement or activities with a noncirculatory function. Ex. Rotifers, nematodes, and annelids (coelomic fluid). (b) Fluid moved by peritoneal cilia, often in a specific circulatory pattern. Ex. Ectoprocta, Brachiopoda, Chaetognatha, Sipunculida, and Echinodermata.
4. Circulatory, or vascular, system. A great number of variations occur ranging from vessels with peristaltic contractions to well developed chambered hearts with valves and complex systems of vessels. *Open* types have a heart and arteries with blood returning through sinuses or hemocoelic spaces. *Closed* types have heart, arteries, capillaries, and veins which return the blood to the heart.

Blood often contains amoebocytic cells, proteins, and respiratory pigments as well as food, wastes, antibodies, and hormones.

Body fluid or blood is important as a hydrostatic skeleton and in locomotor movements of some groups.

Respiratory Mechanisms. Respiratory surfaces are typically moist, thin walled, and often highly vascularized. There are four general types: the general body surface or surface of appendages, gills, lungs, and tracheae. The Oligochaeta are an example of the body surface type; many mollusks and crustaceans have gills; pulmonate snails have a lunglike mantle cavity, spiders have a lamellated type of lung, holothuroideans a water-lung called the respiratory tree; tracheae of insects and some other arthropods differ from lungs in the extent of penetration of body parts, the tracheal type being less dependent on transport by circulating fluids.

The anthozoan siphonoglyph is probably an aid to circulation of water for respiratory purposes as is the gill bailer, or scaphognathite, of the decapods. The hydrofuge hairs of some aquatic insects are water repellent, thus trapping a plastron of air on the surface of the body for circulation through the trachea. Many other interesting modifications occur in aquatic insects including such things as respiratory tubes in many dipteran larvae and rectal "breathing" in dragonfly naiads.

Respiratory pigments in the blood increase its oxygen carrying capacity. They may facilitate one or more of the following.

1. Proportionally smaller respiratory structures.
2. Greater size.

3. Greater activity.
4. Acquisition of sufficient oxygen at lower oxygen tension.
5. Reduction of the circulatory system.

Respiratory pigments may be red, blue, green, or brown. Hemo᷍
red, iron-containing compound—is one of the more common inve
respiratory pigments. It is found in many annelids, some mollusks,
echinoderms, and some arthropods. Hemocyanin—a green, copper-conｻain-
ing compound—is found in cephalopods, *Xiphosura*, and the Malacostraca.

Respiration may be aided by activity of the animal. As oxygen in the water
decreases, *Tubifex* extends farther from its tube and undulates its posterior
end. Leeches may undulate their body while attached by both suckers when
oxygen is depleted. Many other aquatic forms increase the rate of respiratory
movements as dissolved oxygen decreases until a point near death. This
activity enables them to survive under some suboptimal conditions. The
opposite approach can have survival value too. Cessation of activity minimizes oxygen requirements under conditions of low oxygen. This reaction is
exhibited by *Xiphosura*.

Anaerobic respiration is possible for some invertebrates for short periods
of time. A few, such as the flagellates of termites, must live under anaerobic
conditions. Species that commonly depend on anaerobic processes (many
intestinal parasites are of this type) live in organic rich environments.

Excretion. The elimination of the end products of metabolism is accomplished by a variety of organs. In aquatic forms carbon dioxide and other soluble
wastes are partially eliminated by diffusion from respiratory and other surfaces. Water produced by metabolism as well as water taken in by other
means usually serves as the medium of transport for nitrogenous and other
waste products. Specialized structures for these purposes include contractile
vacuoles (Protozoa), flame cells (flatworms), nephridia (annelids), maxillary
glands (crustacea), and coxal glands (arachnids). Malpighian tubules, of
insects and some other terrestrial arthropods, eliminate uric acid, which can
be excreted with very little water loss. Ammonia is the principal nitrogenous
waste product of most aquatic species. A few species are known to store some
waste products.

Nervous System. Most nervous systems are usually polarized and synaptic although the nerve net of *Hydra* is neither since transmission is in any
direction and contact is apparently made between neighboring cells. The
system is quite diffuse in coelenterates, flatworms, and echinoderms, but in
arthropods and higher mollusks nerve cell bodies are not distributed along
the bundles of their processes forming the nerves. Even in forms without an
obvious head many have cephalization of the nervous system and cerebral
ganglion development. Especially large ganglia may be associated with image
forming eyes. Most zoologists agree that the sponges have no nerve cells.

Sensory receptors are known for a wide variety of stimuli. Many groups have eyes, statocysts responding to gravitational force are common, and some receptors of insects detect sound. Other stimuli responded to include touch, chemical substances in water or air, heat, and humidity. Some snails may respond to magnetism. Response of insects to ionizing radiation is probably not due to a specific receptor.

Neurosecretions are responsible for most of the hormonal activity demonstrated in invertebrates. It seems probable that all invertebrates having nervous systems also produce neurosecretions although only the insects and crustaceans have been intensively studied in this regard. Hormones are also known from the gut of an insect. The most primitive phyla in which neurosecretions have been found are the Coelenterata and Platyhelminthes.

Reproduction. Asexual reproductive phenomena include fission, budding, and regeneration of fragments. Sponge gemmules and bryozoan statoblasts may be considered types of internal buds.

Reproduction from eggs may occur parthenogenetically in some groups. Fertilized sexual eggs are produced by both hermaphroditic and dioecious species. The mechanism of male production varies. Some produce males from unfertilized eggs, females from fertilized eggs. In many, sex is determined by the chromosomes inherited. Sex ratios are sometimes environmentally regulated. *Protandry*, or reversal of the functional sex of a hermaphroditic individual, occurs in several phyla.

Internal fertilization or other types of transfer of sperm by individuals occurs in most parasitic species and species producing small numbers of large eggs. External fertilization may occur in the sea water for many species of marine invertebrates which (more often than fresh-water species) produce great quantities of eggs of small size. In the latter case coordination of release of gametes may be by environmental conditions such as temperature or phase of the moon or by chemical substances released by gamete shedding individuals. Thus, coordination in species not transferring sperm directly minimizes waste of gametes.

Planktonic larvae are common in marine species with small eggs. The enormous numbers enable a few to survive predation and slight chances of reaching favorable environments.

Development. Early cleavage of higher invertebrates are considered to belong to one of two general types, spiral (or determinate) cleavage of the Protostomia, and radial (or indeterminate) cleavage of the Deuterostomia. A trochophore larval type, unequal early cleavage into different sized cells of fixed developmental potential, entomesoderm development from the 4d cell, mouth formation from or near the blastopore, and schizocoelous coelom formation in coelomate groups—these are considered typical of the Protostomia, which includes the flatworms, the pseudocoelomate phyla, lopho-

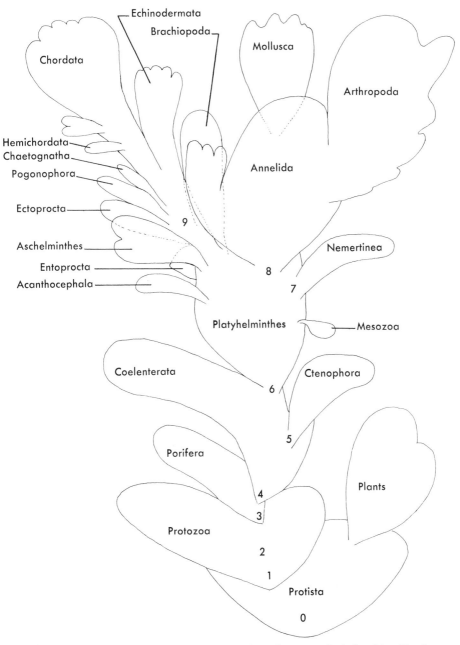

Fig. 14-1. A phylogenetic tree showing one view of suspected relationships. Numbers represent presumed point of origin of the following developments. 0, DNA-RNA. 1, Golgi apparatus, contractile vacuoles, amoeboid movement. 2, flagella and cilia. 3, collagen, spongin, cellular differentiation of multicellular organisms. 4, nerve and muscle cells. 5, biradiality. 6, bilaterality, flame cells, spiral cleavage. 7, blood vascular system. 8, coelom, coelomoducts, metamerism. 9, radial cleavage.

phorate phyla, annelids, mollusks, and arthropods. The Deuterostomia (Chaetognatha, Pogonophora, Echinodermata, Hemichordata, and Chordata) undergo early cleavages into equal-sized cells, which do not have a fixed developmental potential; their mouth does not form in the region of the blastopore; and coelom formation is enterocoelous.

Phylogeny. Speculation on the relationships of the various phyla has been based on a variety of criteria by different authors. For a discussion of some aspects see the introduction to Chapter VII. More detailed discussion of some theories may be found in Chapter 5, Volume I of Hyman (1940); Chapter 9, Volume II of Hyman (1951); Chapter 23, Volume V of Hyman (1959); and throughout Barnes (1963).

Having reviewed all the phyla, it seemed reasonable to the junior author to present a phylogenetic "tree" to represent his concept of phylogeny for the phyla of invertebrates. One fault of the tree as diagrammed in Figure 14–1 is the inability to show proper time relationships. The origins of all the metazoan phyla with living representatives go back millions of years to ancestors of other phyla. Most of the phyla that provided ancestral stock for other phyla have themselves continued to radiate. So it is unlikely that any of the species alive today are unchanged descendants of the ancestral stock. By extension of some ecological principles such as Gause's, it seems likely that during adaptive radiation some of the modified forms would competitively eliminate the ancestral stock, even if it were capable of maintaining its genetic identity unchanged for eons—an unlikely event. Our ignorance of the exact relationship of the multidimensional events that occurred in evolution make it simpler to put what we do see into a two- or three-dimensional representation. If a phylogenetic tree were to be better visualized, it might be imagined as buried with tips of the various branches of all the phyla reaching the surface where the living species are now representative.

Consideration of such a tree may help one to appreciate some facts of living organisms: that for all their tremendous diversity some startlingly basic themes appear and resound through succeeding groups. Study of simpler forms can show many basic facts of life in their most easily demonstrated form.

References for Chapter XIV

BARNES, R. D. 1963. *Invertebrate Zoology.* Saunders, Philadelphia. 632 pp.

CLARK, R. B. 1964. *Dynamics in Metazoan Evolution.* Clarendon Press, Oxford. 313 pp.

COPELAND, E. 1966. Salt transport organelle in *Artemia salenis* (brine shrimp). *Science,* **151**:470–471.

FITCH, W. M., and E. MARGOLIASH. 1967. Construction of phylogenetic trees. *Science,* **155**:279–284.

HYMAN, L. H. 1940–1959. *The Invertebrates.* McGraw-Hill, New York.

JONES, W. C. 1962. Is there a nervous system in sponges? *Biol. Rev.,* **37**:1–50.

PROSSER, C. L., and F. A. BROWN, JR. 1961. *Comparative Animal Physiology.* Saunders, Philadelphia. 688 pp.

THOMPSON, D'ARCY. 1917. *On Growth and Form.* An abridgement by J. T. Bonner, 1961, Cambridge Univ. Press, New York.

Index

Abalone, **361,** 362
Abdomen, 463
  crayfish, 397, 398
  grasshopper, 477
  Insecta, 437
  spider, **448**
Ablastin, 19
Acalymma, **516**
Acanthobdella, 343, 348
Acanthobdellida, 343
Acanthocephala, 252, 257, 263, 286, 288*t.,*
  290–92
Acanthocephalus, **291,** 292
Acanthoderes, **516**
Acanthoparyphium, 248
Acarina, 455–57
Acephala, 393
Acetabulum, 224
Achatina, **366,** 367
Achatinidae, 367
Acheta, **498**
Aciculum, 315
Acmaea, **361**
Acmaeidae, 361
Acnidosporea, 53, **59**–61, 116
Acoela, **220,** 221, 249
Acoelomata, 347
Acontia, 188
Acraspedote, 184
Acrididae, 498
Acropora, 193
Acrothoracica, 429
Acrydium, 498
Actias, 520
Actiniaria, 190–192

Actinobolina, 106
Actinophrys, 45, 108
Actinosphaerium, **27, 45,** 107
Actinozoa, 190
Actinula, 202
Adalia, **515**
Adambulacral ossicles, 543
ADDISON, M. A., 70
Adductor muscles, 379
Adephaga, 512–13
Admetus, **459**
Adruenna, 279
Aedes, **523**
Aeolididae, 365
Aeolis, **364,** 365
Aeolosoma, 335, **336,** 348
Aeolosomatidae, 335, 348
Aeshnidae, 502
Agameris, 271
Agelena, 459
Agelenidae, 452, 459
Aglantha, 177
Agrilus, 514
Agrion, 502
Akeridae, 365
Alabama, 520
Alaria, 231
Alaus, 514
Alcippe, 429
Alcyonacea, 194–96
Alcyonaria, 194–97
Alcyonidium, 300
Alcyonium, 194, **195, 196**
Alimentary canal
  insect, **491**

Note: Numbers in **boldface** indicate pages containing illustrations.

Alimentary canal (*Cont.*)
  Lumbricus, 327
  starfish, 545–46
ALLEE, W. C., 422
ALLEN, R. D., 28
Allocapnia, 503
Alloeocoela, 220, 222
Allogromia, 47–**48**
Allolobophora, 338
Alsophila, 520
Altica, 516
Alveolus, 556
Amblema, 386
Amblypygi, 458, **459**
Ambulacral grooves, 542
Ambulacral ossicles, 543
Ambulacral plates, 553
Ambulacral system, **546**
Ameria, 287
Ametabolous, 488, 493
Amicula, 355
Amitosis, 70
Ammonoidea, 375
Amoeba, 24–42, 70, 103–104, 108, 109
  assimilation, 32
  behavior, 34
  contractile vacuole, 26–27, 31
  cytology, **25**–27
  digestion, 31
  dissimilation, 32
  egestion, 31
  excretion, 32
  food, 26–
  food vacuole, 26, 31
  free-living, 37
  growth, 33–
  habitat, 24
  ingestion, 31, 106
  locomotion, **27**–29
  metabolism, 29
  nucleus, 26
  parasitic, 40
  physiology, 27–34
  protein differences, 39
  reproduction, 33–34–
  respiration, 33
  secretion, 32
Amoeba, 24–37
  discoides, **38**–39
  dubia, **38**
  proteus, 24–**39**, 103–104, 107
  verrucosa, **32**, **38**
Amoebida, 37, **38**, 115
Amoebocytes, 122, 126, 131, 141, 547
Amoeboid movement, 27–**29**, **585**
Amphiblastula, **125**, **128**, 129, 132
Amphibolips, **524**, 528
Amphids, 270
Amphileptus, **90**

Amphineura, 350, 351–55, 390
Amphioxus, **576, 577**
Amphipholis, 552
Amphipoda, 430, **434**
Amphistome, 233
Amphitrite, 313, 320
Amphiuridae, 552
Amphoriscus, 133
Ampullae, 178, 545
Anagasta, 519
Anal, **476,** 489
Anaplasmas, 57
Anasa, 509
Anaspidacea, 430, 431, **432**
Anaspides, 431, **432**
Anax, 502
Ancylidae, 366
Ancylostoma, **276,** 277–**78, 283**
Ancylostomidae, 277
Ancyrocephalus, 232
Andrena, 529, **532**
Andrenidae, 529, **532**
Andricus, 528
Anguillula, 263
Anguispira, 367
Anisembia, 504
Anisolabis, **511**
Anisoptera, 502
Annelida, 286, 288*t.*, 304, 313–49, **585**
  classification, 313, 319–22, 335–38, 343–45
  coelom, 346
  ecology, 348
  literature, 349
  metamerism, 346
  phylogeny, 348
  physiology, 347
  trochophore, 347
Annulus, **11,** 12
  leech, 340
Anodonta, 377–84, 386
  circulation, 380
  digestion, 379
  nervous system, 382
  reproduction, 383
  respiration, 381
  shell, **378**
Anomura, 436
Anopheles, 51, **489, 523**
Anoplophyra, **92**
Anoplura, 488, **505,** 506–507
Anostraca, **425**
Ant, 488, 529, **530**
  lion, 512
  white, 488
Antedon, 323, 542, **565, 566,** 567
Antedonidae, 567
Antenna, **397,** 398, 400*t.*, 422, 474, **484, 490**
Antennules, 398, 400*t.*
Antheraea, 520

Anthomedusae, 173–76
Anthonomus, **516**
Anthozoa, 148, 186–97, 202
Anthrenus, **514,** 515
Antipathes, 193
Antipathidea, 193
Anuraphis, 511
Anus, 479
Aorta, 358, 380, 479
Aphelinus, 528
Aphid, 509, 510–11
Aphididae, 510
Aphidius, 528
Aphis-lion, 488, 512
Aphrodite, **318**
Aphroditidae, 319
Aphrophora, **509**
Apical system, 553, **555**
Apis, 531–35
  communication, 536
  head, 533
  legs, 533–**34**
  mouthparts, 531
  reproductive organs, **486**
  sting, 534–**35**
Apidae, 531–35
Aplacophora, 355
Aplexa, 366
Aplopus, 495
Aplysia, 365
Aplysiidae, 365
Apoda, 564
Apopyles, 124
Aporidea, 243
Apostomatida, 116
Appendages, crayfish, **397,** 398, 399–402
Apseudes, 432, **433**
Apterygota, 488, 493–94
Apus, 425
Arachnida, 396, 448–60, 464*t*., 466
  classification, 452–60
Arachnoidea, 396
Araeolaimoidea, 272
Araneae, 458–**60**
Araneida, 458–**60**
Arbacia, 541, 553–59, 581
  Aristotle's lantern, 555–**56**
  digestive system, 554
  locomotor organs, 558
  nervous system, 558
  reproduction, 558
  respiratory system, 558
  skeleton, 553, **555**
  water-vascular system, 558
Arbaciidae, 559
Arca, **385,** 386
Arcella, **42,** 103–104, 107
Arcellinida, **42,** 115
Archaeocytes, 131, 141

Archaeogastropoda, 361
Archenteron, **334**
Archiacanthocephala, 292
Archiannelida, 286, 313, **338–39,** 348, 355
Architeuthidae, 376
Architeuthis, **374,** 376
Archorutes, 494
Arcidae, 386
Arctidae, 520
Arenicola, 313, **321, 322**
Arenicolidae, 321
Areola, 398
Argas, 455, **456**
Argasidae, 455, **456**
Argiope, **460**
Argiopidae, 459, **460**
Argonauta, **376,** 377
Argonautidae, 377
Argulus, 428–**29**
Argyroneta, 459
Arhythmorhynchus, 292
ARISTOTLE, 145
Aristotle's lantern, 554, 555–**56**
Arm
  crinoid, **565**
  squid, 370
  starfish, 542, **543, 544**
Armillifer, 463
Armitermes, **499**
Artemia, 425, 581
Arteries, crayfish, 405
Arthrobranchiae, 406
Arthropoda, 288*t*., 346, 347, 395–540
  appendages, 464*t*.
  body, 463
  classification, 395–96
  history, 466
  Insecta, 471–540
  literature, 468, 538
  phylogeny, 465, **585**
  physiology, 465
Articulata
  Arthropoda, 466
  Brachiopoda, 303
  Crinoidea, 567
Artocorixa, **506**
Ascaridia, **275**
Ascaris, 264–68, 274, **283**
  germ track, **284**
  life cycle, 267
  morphology, 264
  relations to man, 268
Ascaroidea, 274
Aschelminthes, 252–85, 288*t*., 296, 347, **585**
  classification, 252–53, 254, 260–61, 268–
    81, 282
  ecology, 282
  eutely, 256
Ascidiacea, 576

Ascon sponge, **123**, 138, **139**
Asellota, 433
Asellus, **418**–**22**, 433
Asilidae, 524, **525**
Asilus, 524, **525**
Aspidiotus, **510**, 511
Aspidisca, **101**
Aspidobothrea, 232
Aspidobranchia, 361
Aspidochirota, 564
Aspidogaster, **231**, 232
Asplanchna, **258**, 260
Asplanchnopus, **258**
Astacus, 396, 406
Asterias, 541, **542**–48, 550
    behavior, 548
    circulation, 547
    coelom, 545
    digestion, 545–46
    nervous system, 547
    regeneration, 548
    reproduction, 547
    skeleton, 542–45
    water-vascular system, 545
Asteriidae, 550
Asterinidae, 549
Asterochiton, 511
Asteroidea, 541, 542–50, 570
Astomatida, 91–**92**, 116
Astrangia, 148, **189**–90, 192
Astropecten, 549
Astropectinidae, 549
Astrophytidae, 553
Atax, **456**
Athecanephria, 310
Atlanticus, 497
Atoke, 318
Atoll, 204
ATP, 30, 68
Atria, 353
Atrium, 575
Atta, 529
Attidae, 452; *see also* **Salticidae, 459**
Attus, **460**
Auditory organs, 482, **483**
Auditory sac, 477
Aurelia, 148, 180–84, 186, 197
Auricle, 358, 380
    Arbacia, 554
    Dugesia, 213
Auricularia, 570, **571**
Autogamy, 80, 83, 111
Autolytus, **319**
Autotomy, 294, 416, 548, 552, 563
Autotractea, 37, 44–48, 102, 115
Autotrophic, 4
Avicularia, **298**, 299
Aviculariidae, 459, **460**
Avoiding reaction, 7, 85–**87**

Ax, P., 202
Axenic culture, 61, **67**, 282
Axial cells, 289
Axial filament, 27
Axial gland, **557**
    sinuses, 547, **557**
Axial gradient, 96, 218
Axopodia, **27**, 28, 105, 108
Axostyle, 21

Babesia, **56**–57
Babinka, 391
BAKER, F. C., 393
Balanoglossus, 311, 571
Balantidium, **91**, 104, 107, 113
Balanus, 429, **430**
BARNES, R. D., 320, 586
Basal disk, 149, 155, 188
Basket star, **553**
Basommatrophora, 365–66
Bdelloida, **258**, 259, 260
Bdellonemertini, 296
Bdelloura, 223–24
Bêche-de-mer, 564
Bedbug, **507**, 508
BEERMAN, W., 538
Bees, 488
Beetles, 488, **512**–**16**
    development, **492**
Behavior
    crayfish, 416
    insect, 536
    protozoan, 109
    sponge, 142
Belemnoidea, 375
Belostoma, 507
Belostomatidae, **506**, 507
Beroe, **207**, **210**, 211
Beroidea, 211
Bertramia, 61
Bicosoecida, 115
Biogenetic law, 466
Biological control, 536
Bipalium, 224
Bipinnaria, 570, **571**
Biramous appendage, 398
Bittacus, 517
Bladderworm, **238**, 240
Blastoderm, 413, 484, **492**
Blastoidea, **568**
Blastophaga, 529, **530**
Blastoporea, 547
Blastostyle, **170**, 171, 200
Blastula, 166, **201**
Blatta, **496**
Blatella, **496**
Blattidae, **496**
Blepharisma, 96, 98–**99**, 103
Blissus, **508**

Blood, 329, 358
  circulation, 582
  corpuscles, 329
  crayfish, 404
  plasma, 329
  suckers, 343
  vessels, 329
Bodo, **17**
Bolitotherus, 515
Bombidae, 531, **532**
Bombus, 531, **532**
Bombycidae, 520
Bombyliidae, 524, **525**
Bombylius, 524, **525**
Bombyx, 520
Bonellia, **345**, 346
Book lung, **450**, 451
BOOLOOTIAN, R. A., 547
Bothria, 242
Botryocrinus, **567**
Botryoidal tissue, 341, **344**
Bougainvillia, **174**, 175
Bourletiella, 494
Bouton, 531
BOVEE, E. C., 2, 29, 114
Bovicola, 504
BOYCOTT, B., 390
Brachionus, 258, 259, 260
Brachiopoda, 286, 288*t.*, **301**, 393, 582
Brachycera, 523–24
Brachystola, 498
Brachyura, 436
Braconidae, 528, **529**
Brain, 407
    Dugesia, **214**, 216
    grasshopper, 481, **482**
    Lumbricus, 330, **331**
    Nereis, 317
Branchiae, 381
Branchiobdellidae, 337, 348
Branchiocardiac groove, 398
Branchiopoda, 424–**26**
Branchiostegite, 398
Branchiostoma, 574, 577–78
Branchipus, **425**
Branchiura, 428–**29**
Braula, 526, **527**
Braulidae, 526, **527**
Bristletails, 493
Brittle stars, 550–52
Bryozoa, 297, 298, 347
Buccal cavity, 61, 70–71, 78, 80
Budding, 57, 110, 163, 189, 201, **319**
Buds
    Hydra, 151, 163
    sponge, 122, 142
Buccinidae, 364
Buccinum, 364
Bucephalidae, 233

Bucephalus, 233
Bug, 488, 507–509
Bugula, **298**–99, 300
BULLOCK, T. H., 348
Buprestidae, **514**
Bursaria, 98–**99**
BUSHNELL, J. H., 301
Busycon, **364**
BUTSCHLI, O., 145
Butterflies, 488, 518, 520
Buxtonella, 90
Byssus, **383**
Bythinia, 236

Caddisflies, 488, **517, 537**
Cadulus, 367
Calanoida, 427
Calanus, 427
Calcarea, 121, 122–29, 132–33, 139, 146
Calciferous glands, 328
Callinectes, **435, 436**
Calliobothrium, 242
Calliphora, 525
Calliphoridae, 525
Callitroga, 525, 536
Callosamia, 520
Calsoma, 513
Calpodes, **521**
Camarodonta, 559
Cambarincola, 337
Cambarus, 396, **408**
Campanularia, **176, 177**
CAMPBELL, J. L., 547
CAMPBELL, R. D., 166
Campeloma, **362**, 363
Campodea, 493, **494**
Camponotus, 529, **530**
Cancer, 436
Candona, **427**
Canthocamptus, 428
Canthon, 515
Capillaria, 281
Capillaries, 329, 406
Capillaster, **566**
Caprella, **434**
Captacula, 367, **368**
Capulidae, 363
Carabidae, **512**, 513
Carabus, **490**
Carapace, 397, 431
Carchesium, **94**, 110
Cardo, **473**
CAREY, S. E., 70
Carpocapsa, 519
CARSON, R., 335
Carterius, 137
Caryophyllidea, 243
Cassida, 516
Cassiopeia, 186

Catenula, 222
Catenulida, 220, 221
Caterpillars, 518
Caudal glands, 270
Caudal furcae, 253
Caudina, 564
Cavolina, **364**, 365
Cavoliniidae, 365
Cecidomyidae, 523, **524**
Cecum, 372, 450
Celerio, 520
Cell lineage, **246**, 247
Cellular biology, 579
Cellular metabolism, 30, 68, 105, 112
Cellular respiration, 30
Cenocrinus, 567
Centipedes, 437
Centropyxis, **42**
Centruroides, 453
Cepedea, **23**, 24
Cephalization, 213
Cephalocarida, **424**
Cephalochordata, 574
Cephalodiscida, 311
Cephalodiscus, 311
Cephalont, 53
Cephalopoda, 350, 368–77, 391, 393, 580
Cephalothorax, 463
  crayfish, 397–98
  spider, **448**
Cephalothrix, 296
Cerambycidae, 515, **516**
Cerata, 365
Ceratina, 531
Ceratitis, 524, **526**
Ceratium, **11**, 12
Ceratopogonidae, **522**
Cercaria, **227**, 228, **230**
Cercomonas, **17**, 103
Cercopidae, **509**
Cercus, 477, 493
Cerebral ganglia, 358
Cerebratulus, 294, 296
Cerebropleural ganglion, **382**
Ceriantharia, 193–94
Cerianthus, 193–**94**
Ceritites, **374**
Cervical groove, 397
Cestida, **210**, 211
Cestoda, 212, 238–43, 244
Cestodaria, 242
Cestus, 209, **210**, 211
Ceuthophilus, 497
Chaetae, **316**
Chaetoderma, 355
Chaetogaster, 337
Chaetognatha, 286, 288*t.*, 305–307, 582, **585**, 586
Chaetonotoidea, 254

Chaetonotus, 253–**54**
Chaetopleura, 355
Chaetopteridae, 320
Chaetopterus, **320**, 345
Chalcididae, **530**
Chalcidoidea, 528
Chalcophora, 514
Chalina, **135**, 137, **140**
Chaos, see *Pelomyxa*, **39**
Charonia, **362**, 363
Charybdea, **185**
Cheilostomata, 300
Chelicerae, 449
Chelicerata, 396, 446, 463
Chelifer, **454**, 455
Cheliferidae, 455
Chelipeds, 398, 401*t.*, **419**
Chelopistes, 504
Chiggers, 457
Chilobrachys, **460**
Chilodon, 110
Chilodonella, **90**
Chilomastix, **20**, 21
Chilomonas, **11**
Chilopoda, 396, 437–**39**, 441, 463, 464*t.*, 466
Chinch bug, **508**
Chiridota, 565
Chiridotidae, 565
Chirocrinus, 568
Chironomidae, 522, 538
Chitin, 463
Chiton, 353–55
Chiton, 355
Chlamydomonas, **14**
Chloragogen cells, 327
Chlorohydra, 150, 158, 159, **165**, 173
Chloromonadida, 107, 114
Choanocyte, 122, 124, **127**, 130, 132, 141, 144, 146
  layer, 122, 124, 141, 143, 146
Choanoflagellida, 16, 114
Chonotrichida, 116
Chordata, 288*t.*, 347, 574–78, 586
Choristoneura, 519
Chromadoroidea, 271
Chromatin, 104
  diminution, **284**
Chromatophores, 4, 105, 369
Chromidia, 104
Chromosome, **8**, **23**, 26, 83, 104, 111, 163, 256, 284
  puffs, 538
Chryptomonadida, 114
Chrysalis, 518
Chrysobothris, 514
Chrysomelidae, **516**
Chrysomonadida, **10**, 114
Chrysopa, **499**, 512
Chrysopidae, 512

Chrysops, 280, 524, **525**
Chthoniidae, 455
Chthonius, 455
Cicada, **508**, 509
Cicadellidae, **509**, 510
Cicadidae, **508**, 509
Cicindela, 513
Cicindelidae, **512**, 513
Cilia, 4, **5**, 61–**64**, 71–73, **75**, 105–106, 108, 188, 271, 585
Ciliata, 2, 61–102, 104–105, 106, 108, 110, 116–17
Cimex, **507**, 508
Cimicidae, **507**, 508
Cingulum, **255**, **259**
Ciona, 574–76
Circadian rhythm, 423, 537
Circulation, 108, 581–82
    clam, 380
    earthworm, 329
    echinoderm, 547
    squid, 370
Circulatory system, 582
    closed, 582
    open, 582
Circumesophageal connectives, 407, 481
Circumferential canal, 172, 182
Circumpharyngeal commissure, 317
    connectives, 330, **331**
Cirri, 99, 106, 109, 315, 566
Cirripathes, 193
Cirripedia, 393, 429, **430**, **431**
Cirrus, 226
Citheronia, 520
Citheroniidae, 520
Citric acid cycle, 30
Cladius, 528
Cladocera, **425**
Clam, 377
Clamworm, 314
Clathrina, **132**
Clathrinidae, 132
Clava, 174
Clavelina, 576
Cleavage, 284, 287
    radial, 570, **585**
    spiral, **246**, 247, **585**
CLENCH, W. J., 393
CLEVELAND, L. R., 21
CLEVER, U., 538
Click beetle, 514
Cliona, 136
Clione, 365
Clionidae, 365
Clitellum, 325
Cloaca, 563
Clonorchis, 224
Clothes moth, **518**, 519
Clypeaster, 560

Clypeastridae, 560
Clypeastroidea, 560
Clypeus, 433, 473, 531
Cnephia, 523
Cnidaria, 148
Cnidoblast, 152, **153**
Cnidocil, **153**
Cnidosporea, 53, 58–60, 116
COBB, N. A., 269
Coccida, 53, **55**, 116
Coccinellidae, **515**
Coccoidea, **510**, 511
Coccolithophorida, 114
Cochliomya, 525
Cockroach, 488, **496**
Cocoon, 227, 333, 451, 518
Codling moth, 519
Coelenterata, 144, 148–205, 286, 288*t*., 347, 584, 585
    classification, 148, 173–79, 184–86
    embryology, **201**
    history, 203
    literature, 204
    metagenesis, 198
    morphology, 197
    phylogeny, 202
    physiology, 200
    polymorphism, 199
Coelenteron, 148, 197, 202
Coelom, 267, 287, 316, 325, 346–47, 465, 545, **585**
Coelomata, 347
Coeloplana, 209, 211
Coenenchyme, 194
Coenosarc, 170
Coenothecaleae, 194
Coleoidea, 376
Coleoptera, 488, 493, **512**–16
Coleps, **90**
Colias, 520
Collagen, 140, **585**
Collar cells, 122, 132, 138, 141, 144
Collembola, 488, **494**
Colloblasts, **207**
Collophore, 494
Collotheca, 258, 261
Collothecacea, 259, 261
Collyriclum, 236
Colpidium, 63–**64**, 69, **92**, 103
Colpoda, **91**, 103
Colubotelson, **419**, **422**, 433
Columella, 190
Colymbetes, 513
Comasteridae, 567
Comatula, **566**
Comb jellies, 206
Commensalism, 112
Communication, honeybee, 536
Compasses, 556

Conchostraca, 425
Conductivity, 37
Conjugation, 70, 80–**83, 85**, 110, **111**
Conocephalus, 497
Conochilus, 258, 261
Construction, insect, 536
Contractile vacuole, 104–105, 112, **585**
    Amoeba, 26, 27, 76
    Euglena, 4
    Paramecium, **76**–77
    Tetrahymena, 64–**66**
Conus, **364**
Convoluta, 221
COPELAND, E., 581
Copepoda, 427–**28**
Copromonas, 13
Copulation, 110, 333
    crayfish, 412
Coral, 189–93, **388**
    reefs, 203–204
Corallite, 189
Corallium, 196
Corbicula, 389
Corbiculidae, 389
Coreidae, 509
Corixidae, **506**, 507
CORLISS, J. O., 69
Corn borer, 519
Cornea, 409
Corona, **259**
Coronatae, **185**
Corrodentia, 503
Corydalidae, 512
Corydalus, 512
Corythuca, **508**
Coscinoderma, 138
Costa, **476**, 489
Cotinis, **485**
Cotylurus, 236
Cowry, 363
Coxa, 449, 474, 490
Coxal glands, 451
Crab, 436
    fiddler, **435**
    hermit, **435**
    horseshoe, **447**
    king, **447**
Crago, 436
Crania, 303
Craspedacusta, **176, 177**
Craspedote, 184
Crassostrea, **385**, 386
Crayfish, 396–418
    anatomy, 397–403
    appendages, 398, 399–402
    behavior, 416–18
    circulation, 404–406
    nervous system, 407–10
    physiology, 403–16

regeneration, 415
reproduction, 411–15
Crematogaster, 529
Crenobia, 245
Creophilus, **513**, 514
Crepidula, **362**, 363
Cricket, 488, 495, 497
Criconema, 273
Crinoidea, 541, 542, **565**–67
Crisia, 300, **301**
Cristatella, **299**, 300
Crithidia, **18**, 19
Croton bug, **496**
Crustacea, 393, 395, 396–437, 466, 467
    classification, 424–37
    ecology, 423
Cryptomonadida, **11**
Crystalline cone, 409
    style, 352
Ctenicera, **490**
Ctenidia
    Mollusca, 381
    Siphonaptera, **528**
Ctenocephalus, 526
Ctenophora, 178, 202, 206–11, 286, 288*t.*,
    347
    classification, 209
    morphology, 206
    phylogeny, 209
    physiology, 208
Ctenostomata, 300
Cubitus, **476**, 489
Cubomedusae, **185**
Cucumaria, 541, **564**
Culex, 51, 523
Culicidae, **523**
Culicoides, **522**
Cumacea, 430, 431, **433**
Cunina, 177
Cunoctantha, **177**, 178
Cupelopagis, **261**
Curculio, 516
Curculionidae, **516**
Cuspidaria, **385**, 390
Cuspidariidae, 390
Cuterebridae, **526**
Cuticle, 3, 103, 580
    arthropod, 463
    crayfish, 397
    grasshopper, 471
    Lumbricus, 325, **326**
    Nereis, 315
    Platyhelminthes, 226, 244, **249**
CUVIER, G., 203, 250, 349, 393, 466
Cuvierian organs, 563
Cyanea, 186
Cybister, 513
Cyclophyllidea, 242, 243
Cyclopoida, 427

Cyclops, 156, 279, 427, **428**, 468
Cyclorrapha, 524-26
Cyclosis, 78–79, 108
Cyclostomata, 300
Cydippida, 209
Cylindrolaimus, 272
Cymatiidae, 363
Cynipidae, **524**, 528, **530**
Cypraeidae, 363
Cypris, **427**
Cysticercus, **238**, 240
Cystidea, **568**
Cystobranchus, 343
Cysts, 9, **49**, 54, 240
Cytogamy, 80, 83
Cytoplasm, 103
Cytoproct, 61, 73, 79
Cytostome
   Euglena, 3–4
   Paramecium, 71, 78
   Tetrahymena, 64

Dactyl, **419**
Dactylogyrus, 232
Dactylometra, 186
Dactylopius, 511
Dactylozooids, **178**, 179, 200
DALES, R. P., 348
Dalyellia, 222
Damselfly, **502**
Danaidae, 520, **521**
Danaus, 520, **521**
Daphnia, **426**
Dart sac, 360
DARWIN, C. R., 204, 335
DAWES, B., 250
Decapoda
   Crustacea, 422, 431, 434–**36**
   Mollusca, **374**, 376
DELAGE, Y., 145
Demanian system, 270
Demodecidae, **456**
Demodex, **456**
Demoscolecoidea, 272
Demospongiae, 122, 129–32, **134–38**, 140, 146
Dendrochirota, 564
Dendroctonus, **516**
Dendrocystis, 568
Dendronotidae, 365
Dendronotus, **364**, 365
Dentalium, 367, **368**
Dermacentor, **456**
Dermal branchiae, 543
Dermal layer, 124, 141, 143
Dermanyssidae, 456, **457**
Dermanyssus, 456, **457**
Dermaptera, 488, **511**–12
Dermatobia, **526**

Dermestes, 514
Dermestidae, **514**
Dero, 337
Derocera, 367
Derocheilocaris, 427
Deuterostomes, 288*t.*
Deuterostomia, 584, 586
Deutomerite, 53
Diapheromera, **495**
Diaptomus, 427
Diastylis, 431, **433**
Dibothriocephalus, **241**, 242, 243*t.*
Dibranchia, 376
Dictyocaulus, 278
Dicyema, 290
Dicyemida, 290
Didinium, **5**, **75**–76, 90, 106
Dientamoeba, **40**–41
Difflugia, **27**, **29**, **42**–43, 103, 107
Digenea, 232, 233–37
Digestion, 580
Digestive gland, 380, 403
Dileptus, **90**, 104
Dimorphism 199
Dineutus, 513
Dinobryon, **10**, 11
Dinoflagellida, **11**, 12, 114
Dioctophyme, 281
Dioctophymoidea, 273, 281
Dioecious, 411
Diplocardia, 338
Diplodinium, 99
Diplolepis, 528, **530**
Diplomonadida, 20, 115
Diplopoda, 396, **440–41**, 463, 466
Diplozoon, **231**, 232
Diptera, 488, 493, 520–26
Dipylidium, 243
Directives, 188
Dirofilaria, 280
Discophrya, 96
Disculiceptidea, 242
Dissosteira, 471–85, 498
   abdomen, 477
   circulatory system, 479
   digestive system, 477–**78**
   excretory system, 481
   exoskeleton, 471
   eyes, 473–**74**
   head, **472**
   legs, 474–**75**
   metamorphosis, 485
   mouth parts, **473**
   muscular system, 477
   nervous system, 481–**82**
   reproductive system, 484
   respiratory system, 479–**81**
   sense organs, 473, 482–84
   thorax, 474

Dissosteira (Cont.)
    wings, 475–**77**
Distome, 233
DNA, **9,** 10, 64, 84, 104, 111, 166, 538, **585**
Dobson, 488, 512
Dorcus, 515
Dorididae, 365
Doris, 365
Dorylaimoidea, 271
Dourine, 19
Draconematidae, 271
Dracunculoidea, 279
Dracunculus, 279
Dragonfly, 488, **501,** 502
Drassidae, 452
Drosophila, 524, **526**
Drosophilidae, 524, **526**
Dugesia, **213**–20, 223
    axial gradients, 218
    digestive system, 215
    excretory system, 216
    memory transfer, 219
    morphology, 214
    muscular system, 216
    nervous system, 216
    regeneration, 217, **218**
    reproduction, 217
DUJARDIN, F., 112
Dynastes, 515
Dynein, 68
DYSART, M. P., 111
Dytiscidae, 513
Dytiscus, 513

Eacles, 520
Earthworm, 324–35
Earwigs, 488, **511**
Ebriida, 114
Ecardines, 303
Ecdysis, 415, 463
Echidnophaga, 526
Echinarachnius, 558, **559,** 560
Echinaster, 550
Echinasteridae, 550
Echinidae, 559
Echiniscus, **442,** 462
Echinocardium, **560**
Echinococcus, **241,** 243
Echinodermata, 288*t.,* 347, 541–73, 582, 685
    anatomy, 569
    artificial parthenogenesis, 570
    classification, 541–42
    development, 569–**70**
    history, 572
    larva, **571**
    literature, 572
    phylogeny, 571
Echinoidea, 541, 553–60, 570
Echinopluteus, 570

Echinorhynchus, 292
Echiuroidea, 286, 314, 345–46, 349
Echiurus, 314, 346
Ecology
    Annelida, 335, 348
    Insecta, 537
    Protozoa, 101–103
Ectoderm, 166, 202
Ectoplasm, 3, 26, 28, 62, 71, 73, 103, 105
Ectoprocta, 286, 288*t.,* **298–301,** 582, **585**
Edrioaster, 569
Edrioasteroidea, 569
Edwardsia, 190
Eggs
    Asellus, **421**
    Mesostomum, 245
    Nematoda, **283**
    opsiblastic, 254
    rotifer, 256
    sponge, **125**
    tachyblastic, 254
    trematode, **230**
EHRENBERG, C. G., 112, 250
Eimeria, 54–56
Eisenia, 338
Elasipoda, 564
Elater, **490,** 514
Elateridae, **514**
Electrophoretograms, **39**
Elephantiasis, 279
Eleutherozoa, 541
ELLIOTT, A. M., 64, 70
Elliptio, 386
ELLIS, J., 145
Elysia, 365
Elysiidae, 365
Elytra, 489, 512
Embioptera, 488, **504**
Embryology, 287, 584
    Ascaridia, **275**
    beetle, **492**
    biogenetic law, 466
    crayfish, 413–**14**
    Holoplana, **246**–48
    Hydra, 166
    Lumbricus, **334**
    Mollusca, 392
    sea urchin, **570**
    sponge, **128**
Emerita, 436
Empoasca, **509,** 510
Enchelys, 103
Enchytraeidae, 335, 337
Enchytraeus, 337
Endamoeba, 110; *see also Entamoeba*
Endoderm, 166, 202
Endodontidae, 367
Endolimax, **40**–41
Endoplasm, 3, 26, **28,** 71, 73, 103, 105

Endoplasmic reticulum, **67**, 105
Endopodite, 398
Endopterygota, 488, 512–35
Endosome, 4, **8**
Endostyle, 575
Enoploidea, 270
Ensis, **385**, 389
Entamoeba, **40**–41, 107, 113
Enterobius, 273, **274, 283**
Enteropneusta, 311
Entodiniomorphida, 98–**100**, 116
Entodinium, 99
Entomostraca, 424
Entoprocta, 286, 288*t*., **297**–98, 301
Entozoa, 250
Eoacanthocephala, 292
Eoperipatus, 443
Eothuria, 568
Epargyreus, 520
Epeira, 459, **460**
Ephelota, 104, 110
Ephemera, **500**, 502
Ephemerida, 501
Ephemeridae, 501
Ephemeroptera, 488, **500**
Ephippium, **426**
Ephydridae, 524
Ephyra, **184**
Epicarida, 433
Epicauta, 514
Epicranium, 472
Epidermis, 122, 124, **150**, 151, 166
Epididymus, 342
Epidinium, 98, **100**, 111
Epigynum, 450
Epimera, 397
Epimerite, 53, **54**
Epimeron, 474
Epiphanes, **255**–57, 260
Epipharynx, 531
Epiphragm, 365
Epiphyses, 556
Epipodia, 365
Epipodite, 406
Episternum, 474
Epistome, 300
Epistylis, **94**
Epitheliomuscular cells, 151, **152**
Epitoke, 318
Epsilonematidae, 271
Erax, 524
Eremobates, 458
Ergasilus, 427
Ericerus, 511
ERICSON, D. B., 47
Eriophyidae, 456
Eriosoma, 511
Eriosomatidae, 511
Erpobdella, 345

Erpobdellidae, 345
Errantia, 319
Erythroneura, 510
Esophagostomum, 277
Esophagus, 316, 327, 379, 403, 477, 491
Esperiopsis, **136**
Esterase, 39
Estheria, **425**
Eubranchipus, 425
Eucarida, 431
Eucestoda, 242
Eucladia, 569
Eucleidae, **518, 519**
Eucypris, 426
Eudendrium, 175
Eudorina, 15
Euglena, 2–10, 12, 103, 108, 109
    behavior, 6
    cytology, 2–4
    deses, 12
    gracilis, 2
    locomotion, 5
    nutrition, 4
    piciformis, 12
    reproduction, 9
    sanguinea, 12
    spirogyra, **8**, 12
    viridis, 2
Euglenamorpha, **13**
Euglenida, 12, **13**, 108, 114
Euglypha, **42**, 43
Eukrohnia, 306
Eulamellibranchia, **385**, 386, 389–90
Eulimidae, 363
Eulophidae, 528
Eumenes, 529
Eumetazoa, 288*t*.
Eunice, 319
Eunicidae, 319
Euphausia, 434
Euphausiacea, 431, 434
Euphoria, 515
Euplectella, **133**, 146
Euplexaura, **196**
Euplotes, 100–**101**, 109
Eurosta, 524
Euryalae, **553**
Eurypauropus, 442
Eurypelma, 459
Eurypterida, **447**, 448
Eurypterus, **447**, 448
Euscelis, 510
Eutardigrada, 462
Eutely, 256
Evolution of sex, 14–16
    multicellularity, 14–16
Excretion, 107, 583
Excurrent pore, 124
Exopodite, 398

Exopterygota, 488, 495–512
Exoskeleton, 395, 397, 471
Exumbrella, 172
Eye
  arthropod, 465, **474**
  cephalopod, **373**
  crayfish, **408,** 409
  mollusks, 351, **374,** 375, 391
  Nereis, **317**
  Peripatus, **445**
  Planaria, **217**
  protozoans, 47

Fasciola, **215,** 224, 226, **227, 230, 235, 236,**
  237*t.*
Fasciolidae, 236
Fasciolopsis, 230, 236, 237*t.*
Feather star, **565**
Feeding, 580
Femur, 449, 475, 490
FENNELL, R. A., 65
FERGUSON, J. C., 547
Ferrissia, **366**
Fertilization, *Hydra,* 166
Filariidae, 279
Filarioidea, 279
Filibranchia, **385,** 386
Filopodia, **27,** 105
Firebrat, 494
Firefly, 514
Fishmoth, 493
Fission, **295**
  binary, 109, 111
    Amoeba, **33**
    Babesia, 57
    Difflugia, 43
    Euglena, 9
    Metridium, **188**
    Paramecium, 80
    Stentor, **97**
  multiple, 109
FITCH, W. M., 579
Flabellifera, 433
Flagella, 4–10, 63, 73, 105–106, **125, 141,**
  155, **585**
Flame bulbs, 224
Flame cells, **215,** 216, 221, **585**
Flatworms, 212
Fleas, 488, 526, **528**
  water, 426
Flies, 488, 520–**26,** 527
Floscularia, **258,** 261
Flosculariacea, 259, 261
Flukes, 212, 224–37
Foliaceous appendage, 398
Food vacuole
  Amoeba, **25**–26, 31
  Paramecium, 78–**79**
  sponge, 141

Foot
  Anodonta, 377
  Hydra, 149
  molluscan, 350, **351**
Foraminiferida, 46–**47,** 115, 580
Forcipulata, 550
Forficula, 511
Formica, 529
Formicidae, 529, 530
Fossil
  arthropods, 446–48
  brachiopods, **302**
  coelenterates, 203
  crinoid, **567**
  echinoderms, **568**–69
FOUCART, M. F., 309
Fragmentation, 189
Frankliniella, 505
Fredericella, 300
Frons, 472
Frontonia, **92,** 106
Funiculus, **298**
Funnel, 370
Furcula, 494

Galea, **473**
Galleria, **519**
Galls, plant, 523, **524,** 528, 529, 530
Gametes, 110
Gametocytes, 51, 54
Gammarus, **434**
Ganglion, 331, 372
Garden flea, 494
Gasterodiscoides, 233
Gasterophilidae, 524
Gasterophilus, 524
Gasterostomatidae, 233
Gastraea, 467
Gastric ceca, 477, 491
  mill, 403, 429
  pouch, 182
Gastrodermis, **150,** 151, **154,** 155–56, 166
Gastroliths, 403
  snail, 359
  spider, **449**
Gastropoda, 350, 355–67, 390, 393, 580
Gastrotricha, 252, 253–55
Gastrovascular cavity, 148, **150,** 151, 170,
  172, 188, 197
Gastrozooids, **178,** 179, 200
Gastrula, 202
GAUSE, G. F., 586
GAVIN, M. A., 61
GELBER, B., 89
Gelechiidae, 519
Gemmules, **131,** 137, 142
Genae, 472
Genitalia, 477
Geodia, 135

Geometridae, 520
Geophilidae, 438, **439**
Geophilus, 438, **439**
Gerridae, **506**, 507
Gerris, **506**
Geryonia, 198
Giant fibers
  earthworm, 331, **332**
  squid, 373
Giardia, **20**, 103, 107, 112
GIBBONS, I. R., 68
Gill, 381, 543
  bars, 578
  crayfish, 406, 407*t.*
  Pelecypoda, **379, 381**
  slits, 310, 574, 578
Gipsy moth, 520
Girdle
  Amphineura, 354
  Dinoflagellida, 12
Gizzard, 477, 491
Glair, 412
Glaucoma, 69, **92**
Globigerina, **47**
Glochidia, **383**–84
Glossa, 531
Glossina, 526, **527**
Glossiphonia, 340
Glossiphoniidae, 344
Glottidia, 303
Gnathobdellae, 344
Gnathobdellida, **340, 341,** 344
Gnathopod, **419**
GOLDACRE, R. J., 28
Goldfingia; see Sipunculida
GOLDSTEIN, L., 39
Golgi apparatus, **585**
Golgi bodies, 4, 105
Gonangia, 169, **170,** 171
Gongylonema, **274,** 279
Gonionemus, 148, **171, 172**–73, 177
Gonostomum, 103
Gonothecae, 169, **170**
Gonozooid, 179
Gordiacea, 281
Gordioidea, 282
Gordius, **281,** 282
Gorgodera, **231,** 233
Gorgoderidae, 233
Gorgonacea, 195–97
Gorgonia, 197
Gorgonocephalus, 553
GRAFF, L. VON, 250
Grafting, *Hydra*, **168,** 169
GRANT, R. E., 145
Grantia, 124, **126, 132**
Graptolita, 311
Grasshopper, 471–85, 488, 495, 498–99;
  see also Dissosteira

Gravity, 87
Green gland, 407
Gregarina, 53–**54**
Gregarinida, **49,** 53–**54,** 116
Gromia, **27**
GRUBE, E., 349
Gryllidae, 497–**98**
Gryllotalpa, 498
Gullet, 3, 70
Gumbelina, 47
Gymnoblastea, 173
Gymnolaemata, 300, **301**
Gymnostomatida, **90,** 116
Gyrinidae, 513
Gyrinus, 513
Gyrodactylus, **231,** 232
Gyropus, 503

Habronema, 279
HADZI, J., 202, 209, 249, 287
HAECKEL, E., 467
Haemadipsidae, 344
Haemaphysalis, 456
Haematococcus, **11**
Haematoloechus, 233, **234**–36
Haematopinus, 507
Haemonchus, 278
Haemopis, 344
Haemoproteus, **56**–57
Haemosporida, 53, 57, 116
Halcampa, 192
Haliclystus, 185
Haliotidae, 362
Haliotus, **361,** 362
Halipegus, 233n
Halisarca, 138
Halocynthia, 576
Halteria, 106
Halteridium, 57
Halters, 488, 520
Haminea, **364,** 365
Hamula, 494
Hamuli, 528
HAND, C., 202
Haplosporida, 60–61, 116
Haplosporidium, 61
Haplothrips, 506
Harlequin bug, 509
Harpacticoida, 428
Harpalus, 513
Harringia, **258**
Hartmanella, 103
Hawk moth, **519,** 520
Head, 463
Heart
  branchial, 370
  crayfish, 404
  grasshopper, 479
  systemic, 370

Hectocotylized arm, 374, 392
Hectocotylus, 392
Helicidae, 367
Helicina, 362
Helicinidae, 362
Helicodiscus, 367
Helicopsyche, 580
Heligmosomum, 279
Heliopora, 194
Heliothis, **518**, 520
Heliothrips, 505
Heliozoida, 44–**45**, 115
Helisoma, **366**
Helix, 355–60, 367, 391
   anatomy, 355–58
   circulation, 358
   digestion, 356
   nervous system, **358**
   reproduction, 359
Hellgramites, 512
Helobdella, **343**, 344
Hemelytra, 507
Hemerocampa, 520
Hemichordata, 286, 288*t*., **310–11**, 574, 578,
   586
Hemiclepsis, 344
Hemimetabolous, 488, 493
Hemiptera, 488, **506**, 507–509
Hemocoel, 395, 445, 465
Hemocyanin, 583
Hemoglobin, 107, 583
Hepatic arteries, 405
Hepatic ceca, 546
Hepatic ducts, 403
Hepatozoon, 57
Hermaphroditic, 128
Hermaphroditic duct, 360
Herpetomonas, **18**, 19
Hesperiidae, 518, 520, **521**
Hesperonoe, 345
Heterakis, 17, **274**
Heterocera, 518
Heterochlorida, 114
Heterocoela, **132**, 146
Heterodera, 273
Heteromeyenia, **131**, 137, **140**
Heteromita, 103
Heteromorphosis, 415
Heteronema, **13**
Heteronemertini, 296
Heteronereid, 318
Heterophyes, 237*t*.
Heterostelea, 568
Heterotardigrada, 462
Heterotrichida, 96–**99**, 116
Heterotrophic, 5
Hexactinellida, 121, **133–34**, 140, 146
Hexamita, **20**, 21
Higgens, R. P., 262

Hippoboscidae, 526, **527**
Hippospongia, 138
Hirudinea, 313, 339–45, 348
Hirudinidae, 344
Hirudo, 314, 339–42, 343, 344, 348
Histomonas, 17, 274
Holometabolous, 488, 493
Holophytic, 4
Holoplana, **246**, 247
Holostome, 233
Holothuria, 564
Holothuroidea, 541, 561–65, 568, 570
Holotrichea, 89–92, 116
Holozoic, 5
Homarus, 436
Homocoela, **132**, 146
Homoptera, 488, 509–11
Honeybee, **486**, 531–**35**
Honigberg, B. M., 2, 114
Hookworms, 277
Hoplocarida, 431
Hoplonemertini, 296
Hormaphis, 511
Hormiphora, **207**, **208**
Hormones, 422, 584
Horridge, G. A., 348
Horsehair snake, 281
House fly, **527**
Hutchinsoniella, **424**, 425
Huxley, T. H., 396
Hyalonema, **134**, **140**
Hyalophora, 520
Hydatina, see Epiphanes, 255
Hydra, 148–69, 198, 245, 583
   autoradiograph, 166, **167**
   behavior, 159
   depression, 166
   embryology, 166
   grafting, **168**, 169
   growth, 166
   locomotion, **158**, 159
   morphology, 151
   nematocysts, 152–54, **244**
   nervous system, 156
   nutrition, 156–58
   regeneration, 167–**68**
   reproduction, 162–66
   symbiosis, 158
Hydra, **41**, 94, 101, 148–69, 173, 197
   americana, 173
   carnea, 173
   littoralis, 173
   oligactis, **149**, **152**, 173
   pseudoligactis, 173
Hydrachna, 457
Hydrachnidae, **456**, 457
Hydractinia, **174**, 175
Hydramoeba, **41**, 159
Hydranth, 169, **170**

Hydraulea, 37–44, 115
Hydrocauli, 169
Hydrocorallina, **178**
Hydroctena, 178
Hydroid, 197, 200
  Obelia, **170**
Hydroida, 173–77
Hydroides, 321
Hydrophilidae, **513**
Hydrophilus, **513**
Hydrophyllium, 179
Hydropsyche, 517
Hydrorhiza, 169
Hydrostatic skeleton, 327
Hydrothecae, 169, **170**
Hydrozoa, 148–80, 202, 311
HYMAN, L. H., 202, 250, 282, 586
Hymenolepis, **241,** 243, **249**
Hymenoptera, 488, 493
Hymenostomatida, 91–**92,** 116
Hypermastigida, 21, **22,** 115
Hyphantria, 520
Hypoderma, 524
Hypodermis, 315, 471
Hypopharynx, **473**
Hypostome, 149, 170
Hypotrichida, 99–**101,** 117
Hypsibius, 462

Icerya, 511, 536
Ichneumonidae, 528, **529**
Ichthyophthirius, **92**
Ichthyosporidium, 61
Idothea, **433**
Inarticulata, 303
Incurrent canals, 124
Incurrent pores, 123, 124, 141
Infusoria, 112, 255
Infusorigens, 290
Ink sac, 372
Innkeeper, 345
Insecta, 396, 437, 441, 463, 464*t.*, 466,
    471–540
  antennae, **490,** 491
  behavior, 536
  classification, 488
  control, 536
  ecology, 537
  economic importance, 535
  embryonic development, 491–**92**
  gall causing, **524**
  grasshopper, 471–85
  growth, 493
  legs, 489
  literature, 538
  metamorphosis, 493
  mouthparts, 490
  pheromones, 537
  physiology, 538

  wings, 488–89
Instar, 493
Interambulacral plates, 553
Interstitial cells, 151, 152
Intestina, 250
Intestine, 380, 403, 479, 491
Introvert, 304
Iodamoeba, 40–41
Iota, 273
Iridomyrmex, 529, **530**
Irritability, 36
Ischnura, **502**
Isia, 520
Isocrinidae, 567
Isopoda, 418, 430, 432–**34**
Isoptera, 488, **499**–500
Isospora, **54**–56
Isotricha, **91**
Itoplectis, **529**
Ixodidae, 455–**56**

JACOBS, L., 61
JAHN, T. L., 2, 5, 28, 29, 114
Japanese beetle, 515
Japyx, 494
Jellyfish, 172, 180, 197
JENKINS, M. M., 219
JENNINGS, H. S., 31, 37, 109, 162, 548
JOBLOT, L., 112
Julidae, **441**
Julus, 440, **441**
June bug, 515

Kalotermes, **499**
Kappa particles, **84**
Karyolysus, **56**–57
Karyosome, 4
KATES, J. R., 39
Katydid, **497**
Keratella, 259, 260
Keratosa, **137,** 138, 146
Kerona, 101, 159
KESSEL, R. G., 265
Kidneys, 371
Kinetodesma, 62, **64,** 73
Kinetoplastida, 17, **18,** 115
Kinetosome, 4, 61–**64,** 69, 73–75, 98,
    105
Kinety, 62–**63, 72**–73, 78
Kinorhyncha, 253, **262,** 282
Kissing bug, 19, 508
KLEIN, J., 572
Koenenia, **454**
Koeneniidae, 454
Kolga, 564

Labia, 512
Labial palps, 379
Labium, **473,** 531

Labrinthula, 44
Labrum, **473**, 531
Laccifer, 511
Lacewing, **499**
Lacinia, **473**
Lacinularia, 261
Lacrymaria, **90**
Ladybird, **515**
LAMARCK, J., 349, 466
Lamellae, 381
Lamellibranchia, 384
Lamellisabella, 310
Lampsilis, 386
Lampyridae, 514
Lanclets, 574, 577–78
LANG, P., 250
Lankesterella, **56**
Larva, **467**–68, 493
  actinula, 202
  amphiblastula, **125**, **128**, 129, 132
  bipinnaria, 547
  crustacean, **467**
  cydippid, 209
  echinoderm, 569–70, **571**
  glochidium, **383**
  Muller's, 247, 248
  nauplius, **467**
  pilidium, **294**
  planula, 172
  Pogonophora, **308**
  tadpole, **575**
  tornaria, 311
  trochophore, **338**
  veliger, **392**
Larvacea, 576
LATRIELLE, P. A., 466
Latrodectus, 459, **460**
Laurer's canal, 226
Leaf beetles, 516
Leaf hopper, **509**
Leaf insect, **495**
Lecane, **257**, 260
Lecanicephalidea, 242
Lecquerseusia, **42**
Leeches, 339
LEEUWENHOEK, A. VON, 112
Legs
  honeybee, 533–**34**
  insect, 474, **475**, 489
  Peripatus, **445**
  spider, 449
LEIDY, J., 37
Leidyana, **54**
Leiobunum, **458**
Leishmania, **18**, 19
LEMCHE, H., 353, 393
Lemnisci, 291
Lepadocrinus, **568**
Lepas, 429, **430**

Lepidocaris, **424**
Lepidodermella, 255
Lepidonotus, 319
Lepidoptera, 488, **518**–20
Lepisma, 493, **494**
Leptinotarsa, **516**
Leptodora, **425**, 426
Leptomedusae, **176**–77
Leptomonas, 19
Leptonemaster, **566**
Leptoplana, 224
Leptosynapta, 564
Lernaea, **428**
Lernaeoida, 428
Lethocerus, **506**, 507
LEUCKART, R., 203, 250, 572
Leucocytes, 479
Leucon sponge, 139
Leuconia, **132**, 133
Leucosolenia, **122**–23, **128**, 130, 132, 138, **140**, 146
Leucosoleniidae, 132
Libinia, 436
Lice, 488, **503**
  bird, 504
  book, **503**
  chicken, **503**
  fish, 429
  human, **505**, 507
  sucking 506–507
Ligament sacs, 290
Light, 4, 7, 36, 87, 161, **417**
Ligia, **434**
Ligula, **473**, 531
Limacidae, 367
Limax, **366**, 367
Limenitis, 520, **521**
Limnodrilus, 337
Limnomedusae, **176**, 177
Limnoria, 433
Limpet, **361**
Limulus, 224, 446, **447**
Lineus, 294, **295**, 296
Linguatula, 396, **442**, 462
Linguatulida, 462–63
Lingula, **302**, 303
LINNAEUS, C., 112, 203, 250, 393, 466
Lingognathus, **505**, 507
Liothrips, 506
Liparidae, 520
Liposcelidae, 504
Liposcelis, **503**, 504
Liriope, **177**, 198
Lithobiidae, 439
Lithobius, **438**, 439
Littorina, **362**, 363
Littorinidae, 363
Liver, 371, 380, 403
Lizzia, **181**

Loa, **274**, 280, 524
Lobata, 210
Lobopodia, **27**, 28, 105
Lobster, **396, 399, 404,** 436
Locomotion, 108
Locust, 488, 498
  seventeen-year, 509
Locusta, **490**
Locustidae, 498
Loliginidae, 376
Loligo, 368–74, 376
Lophomonas, 23
Lophophore, 297, 302
LORCH, I. J., 28
Lorica, 12
Loveniidae, 560
Loxoconcha, 427
Loxosoma, 297
Lucanidae, 515
Lucanus, 515
Lucernaria, 185
Lumbricidae, 338
Lumbriculidae, 337
Lumbriculus, 337
Lumbricus, 313, 325–35, 338, 348
  anatomy, **324,** 325–27
  circulatory system, 329–**30**
  digestive system, 327–29
  ecology, 335
  excretory system, 330
  nervous system, 330–**32**
  regeneration, **333,** 335
  reproduction, 332–35
  segments, 325
Lycaena, 520
Lycaenidae, 520
Lycaenopsis, 520
Lycosa, 459, **460**
Lycosidae, 452, 459, **460**
Lygaeidae, **508**
Lygidea, 508
Lygus, 508
Lymnaea, 236, 337, **359, 366**
Lymnaeidae, 366
Lynchia, 57
Lysiphlebus, **529**

MAAS, O., 145
MCALESTER, A. L., 391
MCCULLOUGH, C. B., 159
Machaeridia, 568
Machaeridian, 568
Machilis, 494
MCLEOD, J. A., 250
Macracanthorhynchus, **291,** 292
Macrobdella, 314, 344
Macrobiotus, 396, **462**
Macrodactylus, 515
Macrodasyoidea, 254

Macrogamete, 16, 52, 54
Macromeres, 129, **246,** 247
Macromia, **501**
Macronuclear regeneration, 83
Macronucleus, 61, 64, 70, 73, **80**–85, 89, 96, 104, 111
Macrostomida, 220, **221,** 222
Macrostomum, 222
Macrura, 436
Mactra, **385,** 389
Mactridae, 389
Madreporaria, 192–93
Madreporite, 542, 545, **546, 557**
Maggots, 520
Magicicada, 509
Malacobdella, 296
Malacostraca, 429–37, 464*t.*, 467, 583
Malaria, 51–52, 57–58
Mal-de-caderas, 19
Mallophaga, 488, **503,** 504
Malpighian tubules, 451, 481, 491, 583
Mandible, **397,** 398, 400*t.*, **420,** 422, **473,** 531
Mandibulata, 395
Mantidae, **496**
Mantle, 350, 356, 379
  cavity, 350, 379
Manubrium, 171
Margarites, 362
Margaropus, 456
MARGOLIASH, E., 579
Maricola, 223
Marsupium, 383
MARZKE, F. O., 65
MAST, S. O., 28
Mastax, **255,** 256
Mastigamoeba, **17**
Mastigonemes, 4, 5, **6, 7**
Mastigophora, 2–23, 102, 105, 106, 108, 114–15
Mastigoproctus, 454
Mating type, 70, 81
Maxillae, **397,** 398, 400*t.*, **473,** 531
Maxilliped, **397,** 398, 400*t.*, 401*t.*
Mayfly, 488, **500,** 501–502, **537**
Meal worm, **514,** 515
Mealybug, **510,** 511
Meandrina, 193
Mecoptera, 488, **517**
Media, **476,** 489
Medusa, 173, 197, **198,** 200, 203
  Obelia, **170,** 171
Megachile, 531
Megachilidae, 531
Megacyllene, 515
Megalodiscus, 231, 233
Megarhyssa, 528
Megascleres, 130, 135
Megascolecidae, 338

Megascolides, 338
Melanin, 107
Melanophores, 213
Melanoplus, **487**, 498
Meloe, 514
Meloidae, 514
Melolontha, **490**
Melophagus, 526, **527**
Membracidae, **509**
Membranelles, 63, 73, 78, 80, **106**
Membranes, 105, 112
Membranipora, 300, **301**
Memory, 390
  transfer, 219
Menopon, **503**, 504
Mentum, **473**, 531
Mermithoidea, 271
Merostomata, 396, 446–48
Merozoites, 51, 54
Mesenchyme, 141, 215
Mesenteries, **187**, 188, 190
Mesoblasts, 334
Mesoderm, **334**
Mesodon, 367
Mesogastropoda, **362**
Mesoglea, 122, 135, 148, **150**, 151, **154**, 156, 172, 197
Mesonotum, 474
Mesoperipatus, 443
Mesosoma, 453, 463
Mesosome, 310
Mesostomum, 245
Mesothorax, 474
Mesozoa, 286, 288*t*., **289**–90
Metabolic pathways, 30, 112
Metaboly, 12, 108
Metacercariae, 228
Metagenesis, 198
Metagonimus, **230**, 237*t*.
Metamerism, 287, 346, 352, 585
Metamorphosis, 384, 485, **487**, 488
Metaperipatus, 443
Metasoma, 453, 463
Metasome, 308, 310
Metastrongylidae, 278
Metatarsus, 449
Metathorax, 474
Metazoa, 109, 110–111, 113, 121, 143, **144**, 145, 288*t*., 290, 347
Metoncholaimus, 270–**71**
Metridium, 148, **186**–89, 190
Meyenia, 137
Miastor, 259
Microcentrum, **497**
Microciona, 137, 143
Microfilariae, **274**
Microgametes, 16, 52, 54
Microgaster, 528
Microhydra, 177

Micromeres, 129, **246**, 247
Micromitra, **302**
Micronucleus, 61, 64, 70, 73, **80**–84, 89, **104**
Micropyle, 131, 484
Microscleres, 131, 135
Microsporida, 58–60, 116
Microstomum, **221**, 222, **244**–45
Microvilli, 265, 267
Midge, **522**
Miescher's tubes, 60
Migration, vertical, 423
Millepora, **178**
Milleporina, 178
Millipedes, 440
MILLOTT, N., 547
Milnesium, 462
MINCHIN, E. A., 145
Miracidia, 226–**27**, 229
Miridae, 507
Misumena, 459
Mites, 455–**57**
Mitochondria, 4, 64, **67**, 104, 581
Mnemiopsis, 190, 208, 210
Modiolus, 386
MOHL, H. VON, 113
Molanna, 517
Mollusca, 288*t*., 347, 350–94
  classification, 350, 355, 361–67, 375–77, 384–90
  embryology, **392**
  growth, 393
  history, 393
  literature, 393
  phylogeny, 390–**91**
  reproduction, 391
Molluscoidea, 393
Molpadonia, 564
Molting, 415, 463
Monas, **17**
Monaxonida, **135**–37, 146
Monhysteroidea, 272
Moniezia, 243
Moniliformis, 292
Monocystis, 48–**49**, 53, 110
Monoecious, 127
Monogenea, 232
Monogononata, **258**, 260–61
Monommata, **258**
Monomorium, 529, **530**
Monopisthocotylea, 232
Monoplacophora, 351, 355, 390
Monosiga, 16, **17**
Monostome, 233
Monostyla, 260
Morphology, 287–88, 579–80
Mosaic vision, **409**
MOSES, 279
Mosquito, **523**
Mother-of-pearl, 379

Moths, 488, 518–20
Motion, 108
Motorium, 111
Mouthparts
  grasshopper, 473
  honeybee, 531-**32**
  insect, 490
  mosquito, **489**
Mucous cell, **357**
  gland, 356
MULLER, F., 467
MULLER, O. F., 112, 250
Murex, **364**
Murgantia, 509
Muricidae, 363
Murrina, 19
Musca, 526, **527**
Muscidae, 526, **527**
Muscles, 557
  Arbacia, 557
  Dissosteira, 477
  Dugesia, 216
  Hydra, 152
  Nereis, 315
Mussel, 377
Mutualism, 111–12
Mya, 296, **382**, 389
Mycale, 137
Mycetozoida, 43–**44**, 113, 115
Myidae, 389
Myocytes, 127, 142
Myodocopa, 426
Myonemes, 93, 106
Myotomes, 578
Myriapoda, 441, 466
Myriotrochidae, 565
Myriotrochus, 565
Myrmecocystus, 529
Myrmeleon, 512
Myrmeleontidae, 512
Mysidacea, 430, 431, **432**
Mysis, **467**, 468
Mysis, 431, **432**
Mystacocarida, 427
Mytilidae, 386
Mytilina, 258
Mytilus, 386
Myxidium, **59**
Myxospongida, **137**, 138, 139, 146
Myxosporida, **58**–59, 116
Myzostoma, **323**
Myzostomaria, 286, 322–23

Nacreous layer, 379
Naegleria, 103
Nagana, 19
Naididae, **336**
Nais, 336, **337**
Nanometra, **566**

Nanomia, 179
Narcomedusae, **177**–178
Natantia, 436
Natica, 429
Nauplius, 413, **414, 431, 467,** 468
Nautilidae, 376
Nautiloidea, 375
Nautilus, **375**, 376
Neanthes, 314n.
Nebalia, 431, **432**
Nebaliacea, 430, 431, **432**
Necator, 277
Necrophorus, **490**, 513
Nectonema, 282
Nectonematoidea, 282
Nectophore, 179, 200
Nemathelminthes, 253
Nematocera, 522–23
Nematocysts, 58, 148, 152–54, 197
Nematoda, 252, 253, 263–81
  Ascaris, 264–68
  development, **275**
  free-living, 268
  germ-track, 284
  parasitic, 273, 283
  Turbatrix, 263–64
Nematogens, 290
Nematomorpha, 253, 263, 281–82
Nematus, 528, 529
Nemertinea, **293**–96, 347
Neocomatella, 567
Neoechinorhynchus, 292
Neogastropoda, 363-**64**
Neomenia, 355
Neopilina, 351–53, 355, 391
Neorhabdocoela, 220, 222
Neoteny, 576
Nephridiopore, 317, 325, 330
Nephridium, 316, **317**, 330, **342**, 352, 371
Neophrostome, 330
Nepidae, **506**, 507
Nereidae, 319
Nereis, 313, **314**–18, 319, 347, 348
  coelom, 316
  morphology, 315
  physiology, 316
Nerilla, **339**
Nerve net, **156**
Nervous system
  central, 332
  coelenterate, 197
  crayfish, 407–10
  grasshopper, 481–83
  Hydra, 156
  Lumbricus, 330-**32**
  Nereis, **317**
  peripheral, 332
Neuromotor apparatus, 78, 99, **111**
  fibrils, 109

Neuropodium, 315, **321**
Neuroptera, 488, **499**, 512
Neurosecretion, 348, 584
Nidamental gland, 374
Nigenphalis, 620
Nippotaeniidea, 243
Noctiluca, **11**, 12, 110
Noctuidae, **518**, 520
Nodosaria, **47**
Nosema, **59**
Notochord, 574
Notonectidae, 507
Notopodium, 315, **321**
Notostraca, **425**
Nuclear membrane, 4, 104
   division, **8,** 9, 81–83, 104
Nucleolus, 4
Nucleus, 104
   Amoeba, 26
   Euglena, 4
   Paramecium, 73
Nucula, 385
Nuculidae, 385
Nuda, **210**
Nubidbranchia, 365
Nummulites, **47**
Nutrition, 4
Nyctotherus, 98–**99**
Nygmia, 520
Nymph, 485
Nymphalidae, 520, **521**
Nymphon, **461**

Obelia, 148, 169–72, 176, **198**
Ocellus, 183, 473, **474**
Ochromonas, **6, 7**
Octopoda, **376, 377**
Octopus, 377
Oculina, 193
Odinia, **549**
Odonata, 488, **501, 502**
Odontophore, 352
Odontostomatida, 117
Oecanthus, 497
Oestridae, 524
Oestrus, 524
Oikomonas, **17**, 103
Oikopleura, 576
Olethreutidae, 519
Olfactory pits, 183
Oligochaeta, 313, 348, 349, **582**
Oligomeria, 287
Oligotoma, **504**
Oligotrichida, 116
Ommatidia, **408**, 409, 465
Onchocerca, 280, 523
Oncholaimidae, 271
Onchospheres, 240
Oniscoidea, 433

Oniscus, **433**
Onychophora, 286, 396, **443**–46, 466
Ooecium, 299
Oogenesis, *Hydra*, 164
Ookinete, **50,** 52
Oostegites, 421, 431
Ootype, 226
Opalina, **23**, 24, 104, 107, 233n.
Opalinata, 23, 104–105, 115
Opalinida, 23, 115
Opalinidae, **23,** 24
Operculum, 226, 300
Ophiocistioidea, 569
Ophioderma, 550, 552
Ophiodermatidae, 552
Ophioglypha, **551**
Ophiolepididae, 552
Ophion, 528
Ophiopleuteus, 570
Ophiopteris, **552**
Opiothrix, **550,** 552
Ophiotrichidae, 552
Ophiura, 541, **551**, 552
Ophiurae, 552
Ophiuroidea, 541, **550**–53, 570
Ophryocystis, 110
Ophryodendron, **95**–96
Opiliones, **454;** *see* Phalangida, **457**
Opisthaptor, 232
Opisthobranchia, **364**–65
Opisthogoneata, 442
Opisthopatus, **443**
Opisthopora, 338
Opisthorchidae, 236
Opisthorchis, 224–28, **230,** 236, 237t.
Opisthosoma, 463
Oral disk, 186
Oral groove, 70–71, 73–**74,** 78, 85
Oral lobes, 172, 181
Oral papillae, 444
Oral sinus, 557
Oral sucker, 224
Orconectes, 396, 415, 436
Oreaster, 549
Oreasteridae, 549
Ornithodorus, 455, **456**
Oroperipatus, 443
Orophocrinus, **568**
Orthis, **302**
Orthonectida, 290
Orthoptera, 488, 495–99
Oscarella, **137**, 146
Osculum, **122,** 123, 124, 125, 131, **139, 141,**
   142
Osphradium, 382
Ossicles, 403, 542, 569
Ostia, 123, 124, 131, 138, 381, 479
Ostracoda, 426–**27**
Ostracodinium, 99

Ostrea, 386
Ostreidae, 386
Oviduct, 325
Ovipositor, 477, **478,** 484
Ovotestis, 360
Oxymonadida, 115
Oxyspirura, 279
Oxytricha, 100–**101,** 103
Oxyuris, 257, 259, 273
Oxyuroidea, 273
Oyster, 386

Pachychalina, **140**
Pachylomerus, 459
Pacifastacus, 396
Pagurus, **435,** 436
Palaeacanthocephala, 292
Palaemonetes, 410, 433, **435,** 436
Paleonemertini, 295
Pallene, 461
Pallial groove, 351
Pallium, 379
Palmella formation, 15
Palolo worm, 319
Palpigradi, **454**
Paludicola, 223
Pancreas, 371
Pandorina, **14,** 15, 110
Panorpa, **517**
Pansporoblasts, 59
Panstrongylus, 508
PAPENFUSS, E., 168
Papilio, 520, **521**
Papilionidae, 520, **521**
Papulae, 543, 545, 547
Paraflagellar body, 4
Paragonimus, **230,** 236, 237*t.*
Paragordius, 282
Paramecin, 84
Paramecium, 20, 63, 70–90, 92, 96, **103–104,**
    106, 108, 109, 110, 111
  behavior, 85–89
  binary fission, 80
  cilia, 71–73, **75,** 78
  conjugation, 80–**83,** 85
  contractile vacuole, 73, **76**–77, 80
  cytology, 73
  genetics, 83
  locomotion, **77**–78
  morphology, 70–73
  nutrition, 78
  reproduction, 80–83
  Paramecium aurelia, **80, 82,** 83, 92
    bursaria, 92, 107, 112
    calkinsi, 92
    caudatum, **82,** 92
    multimicronucleatum, **82,** 92
    polycaryum, 92
    trichium, 76, 92

woodruffi, 92
Paramphistomidae, 233
Paramylum, 4
Paraperipatus, 443
Parapodia, 313, **315**
Parapteron, 474
Parascaris, 284
Parasites of frog, 233*n.*
Parasitism, 112, 249
Parazoa, 121, 143, **144,** 145, 288*t.*
Parenchyma, 215, 226
Parthenogenesis, 254, 256
  artificial, 570
Parthenogonidia, 16
Passalidae, 515
Passalus, 515
PASTEUR, L., 59
Patella, 449
Patella, **392**
Patiria, 549
Pauropoda, 396, 441–**42**
Pauropus, 396, **442**
Paxillae, 549
Peachia, **187**
Pebrine, 59
Pecten, 137, **385,** 386, **387–88**
Pectinatella, **299,** 300
Pectinidae, 386
Pectinophora, 519
Pedal laceration, 189
  ganglion, 382
Pedicel, 450
Pedicellariae, 542, **543,** 554
Pedicellina, 297
Pediculus, **505,** 507
Pedipalps, 449
Peduncle, 302
Pelagothuria, 564
Pelecypoda, 350, 352, 377–90
  shell, **378–79**
Pellicle, **32,** 71–**74,** 77
Pelmatozoa, 541
Pelomyxa, **38,** 39
Pen, 376
Penaeus, **467,** 468
Penial setae, 265
Penis, 226, 342
PENNAK, R. W., 259
Pennaria, **174,** 176
Pennatula, **196,** 197
Pennatulacea, **196,** 197
Pentagonaster, **549**
Pentametrocrinus, **566**
Pentastomida, 286, 396, **442,** 462–63
Pentastomum, 462
Pentatomidae, 508, 509
Peranema, 12, **13,** 108
Pericardial cavity, 358
Pericarida, 430

Periderm, 169
Perillus, 509
Periostracum, 379
Peripatoides, 443
Peripatopsis, 443
Peripatus, 396, **443**–46, 463
  characteristics, 446*t*.
Periphylla, **185**
Periplaneta, **496**
Periproct, 553, **555**
Peristomium, 315, 542
Peritoneum, 326, 545
Peritrichea, 89, 93–95, 116
Peritrichida, 93–95, 116
pH, 5
Phacops, **447**
Phacus, 12, **13**
Phagocata, 223
Phakellia, **136**
Phalangida, 457
Phalangium, **454**
Phanerozonia, 549
Pharyngobdellae, 345
Pharynx, 316, 327, 477, 491
Phascolion, 305
Phascolosoma, 304
Phasmidae, **495**
Phasmids, 273
Pheretima, 338
Pheromones, 537
Philodina, **258**, 260
Philomycidae, 367
Philomycus, 367
Phlebotomus, **522**
Phoronidea, 286, 288*t*., **303**–**304**
Phoronis, 303, **304**
Phoronopsis, 303
Phosphatase, **39**, 65
Photinus, 514
Photosynthesis, 4, 5,
Photuris, 514
Phreatoicidea, 433
Phreatoicopsis, 222
Phryganea, 517
Phthirius, **505**, 507
Phyla, outline of, 288*t*.
Phylactolaemata, **299**, 300
Phyllium, 495
Phyllocarida, 430
Phyllocoptes, 456
Phyllodistomum, 233
Phyllophaga, 515
Phylloxera, **510**, 511
Phylloxeridae, **510**, 511
Phylogeny, 286–89, 466, **585, 586**
  Arthropoda, 465
  Coelenterata, 202
  Echinodermata, 571
  Platyhelminthes, 248

Porifera, 144
Physa, **366**
Physalia, 154, **179**, 180
Physidae, 366
Phytomastigophorea, 10–16, 102, 107, 113,
  114
Phytomonas, **18**, 20
Phytophaga, 523
Pieridae, 520
Pieris, 520
Pilidium, **294**
PILSBRY, H., 393
Pinacocyte, 141
Pinnules, **565, 566,** 567
Pinocytosis, 31
Pinworm, 273, **274**
Piophila, 524, **526**
Piophilidae, 524, **526**
Piroplasmas, 57
Pisaster, 550
Piscicola, 343
Piscicolidae, 343
Pisidium, 386
PITELKA, D. R., 5, 62, 112
Placobdella, 56, **343, 344**
Plagiorchidae, 233
Plagiostomum, 222
Planaria, 94, 213, **217**; *see also Dugesia*
Planctosphaeroida, 311
Planes, **419**
Planocera, 224
Planorbidae, 366
Planorbis, 337
Planorbula, 231, 234
Planula, 172
Plasma, 479
Plasma membrane, 57
Plasmagel, 28–29
Plasmalemma, 28–29
Plasmasol, 28–29
Plasmodium, 43, 109
Plasmodium, **50**–51, **56–58**, 110
Plastids, 105
Platelmia, 250
Platycotis, **509**
Platyctenea, 211
Platyhelminthes, 202, 212–51, 252, 288*t*.,
  293, 584, **585**
  classification, 212, 220–24, 232–36, 242–
    43
  embryology, **246**–47
  history, 250
  literature, 250
  morphology, 244
  phylogeny, 248
  physiology, 245
Platyias, 260
Plecoptera, 488, 502–**503**
Pleodorina, 15

Pleopod, 401*t*.–402*t*.
Plesiopora, 335
Plesiothecata, 335
Pleura, 397, 474
Pleurobrachia, **207,** 208, 209
Pleurobranchiae, 406
Pleurocera, **362,** 363
Pleuroceridae, 363
Ploima, 260
Plumatella, **299,** 300, 301
Pluteus, 551, 558
Pneumatophore, 179, **180,** 200
Pneumonoeces; see Haematoloechus, 234
Podical plate, 477
Podisus, **508**
Podobranchiae, 406
Podocopa, 426
Podocoryne, 175
Podophyra, 96
Poecilus, 513
Pogonomyrmex, 529
Pogonophora, 286, 288*t*., **307**–10, 586
Polar cap, 290
Polar capsule, 58
Polar filament, 58
Polian vesicles, 545, **546**
Polistes, 517, 529
Polyarthra, 259, 260
Polycelis, 223
Polychaeta, 313, 314–23
    classification, 319–22
Polycladida, 220, **223,** 224
Polydesmidae, **441**
Polydesmus, 440, **441**
Polygordius, 313, **338,** 339, 347
Polygyra, 367
Polygyridae, 367
Polymastia, 136
Polymastix, **20,** 21
Polymeria, 287
Pollmerurus, 254
Polymorphism, 18, 199–200
Polyopisthocotylea, 232
Polyphaga, 513–16
Polypide, 298
Polyplacophora, **353,** 355
Polyps, **170,** 173, 197, **198,** 203
Polystoma, **231,** 232
Polyxenidae, **441**
Polyxenus, **441**
Polyzoa, 297
Pontobdella, **343**
Popillia, 515
Population growth, **68**–69
Porcellanaster, 549
Porcellanasteridae, 549
Porifera, 121–47, 288*t*., 347
    behavior, 142, 143
    canal systems, 138–**39**

classification, 146
color, 138
freshwater, 137, **140**
gemmule, **131,** 140, 142
histology, 141
history, 145
morphology, 138
nutrition, 141
reproduction, 142
skeletons, 139–**40**
spicules, **140**
Porites, 192
Porocephalus, 463
Porocytes, 141
Porthetria, 520
Portuguese man-of-war, **179,** 180, 199
Portunus, **419**
Postscutellum, 474
Potato beetle, **516**
PRAMER, D., 282
Prescutum, 474
Priapulida, 252, 262, 286, 288*t*. 296–97
Priapulus, 296
Prionus, 515
Prismatic layer, 379
Proales, **258,** 261
Probopyrus, 433
Proboscidiella, **22**
Proboscis
    Acanthocephala, 291
    Dugesia, 215
    nemertine, 293
    Nereis, 316
Procambarus, 396
Procerodes, 223
Procotyla, **216,** 223, 245
Proctodaeum, 463
Productus, **302**
Proglottids, **238**–40
Progoneata, 441
Prohaptor, 232
Proneomenia, **354**
Pronotum, 474
Propod, 419
Prosimulium, 523
Prosobranchia, 361–64
Prosoma, 446, 463
Prosopora, 337
Prosopyles, 124, 138
Prosothecata, 335
Prostoma, 296
Prostomium, 315, 325
Protandry, 584
Proteocephalida, 242
Proteomyxida, **44,** 115
Proterospongia, 144, **145**
Prothorax, 474
Protista, 43, 61, 113–14

Protobranchia, 384–85
Protociliata, 23
Protomerite, 53
Protonephridia, 220, 253
Protoopalina, **23**
Protoparce, 520
Protopodite, 398
Protosome, 310
Protostomes, 288*t.*
Protostomia, 584
Protozoa, 1–120, 141, 144, 288*t.*, 290, 583, **585**
  behavior, 109
  circulation, 108
  classification, 114–17
  colonial, 110
  conjugation, 111
  cytoplasm, 103
  excretion, 107
  food, 106
  form, 103
  habitats, 1–2
  history, 112
  literature, 117
  locomotion, 105–106
  morphology, 103
  motion, 105–106
  neuromotor apparatus, 111
  nuclei, 104
  nutrition, 106
  physiology, 106–110
  plastids, 105
  reproduction, 109–10
  respiration, 107
  secretion, 107
  size, 103
  soil, 102–103
  symbiosis, 111
  types, 1–2
  vacuoles, 104
Protozoea, **467**, 468
Protura, 488
Proventriculus, 477, 491
Pseudaletia, 520
Pseudicyema, **289**
Pseudococcus, **510,** 511
Pseudocoel, 267, 287
Pseudocoelomata, 347
Pseudometamerism, 346
Pseudophyllidea, 242
Pseudopodia, 27–29, 105, 107, 108, **155**
Pseudoscorpionida, **454**
Pseudospora, **44**
Pseudosquilla, 437
Psilopa, 524
Psithyrus, 531
Psocidae, 504
Psocoptera, 488, **503**–504
Psoroptes, 456, **457**

Psychoda, 522
Psychodidae, 522
Pterobranchia, 311
Pteromedusae, 178
Pterophylla, 497
Pteropoda, 365
Pterosagitta, 306
Pterygotus, 448
Pterynotus, 363
Pulex, 526, **528**
Pulmonata, 365–67
Pulsella, 106
Pulvillus, 475, 490
Pulvinaria, **510**
Pupa, 493, 512, **514,** 518, **519, 521, 527**
Puparium, 520
PURKINJE, J. E., 113
Pycnogonida, 286, 396, **461**
Pycnogonum, 461
Pygidium, 346
Pyloric ceca, 546
Pyloric sac, 546
Pyloric stomach, 403
Pyralididae, 519
Pyrausta, 519
Pyrenoid, 4, 5

Quahog, **389**

Radial canals
  Coelenterata, **170,** 171
  Echinodermata, 545, **546**
  Porifera, 124, 138
Radial cleavage, **570, 585**
Radial sector, **476,** 489
Radiata, 203, 571, 572
Radiolaria, 107
Radiolarida, 45–**46,** 112, 115
Radius, **476,** 489
Radula, 352, **354,** 356
Raillietina, 243
Ranatra, **506,** 507
Rat-tailed maggot, 524, **537**
Recapitulation theory, 466
Rectal ceca, 546
Rectum, 479
Red ant, **530**
Red rain, **11**
Red snow, **11**
Red tide, **12**
Rediae, **227,** 228, 230
Reduviidae, **507,** 508
Regeneration, 168, 169
  crayfish, 415
  Dugesia, 217
  Hydra, 168
  Lineus, **295**
  sea cucumber, 563
  starfish, 548

Regulation, 143
Reighardia, 462
Renette, 269, **271**
Renilla, 197
Repletes, 529
Reproduction, 584
  Porifera, 142–43
  Protozoa, 109–10
  crayfish, 411–413
Reptantia, 436
Repugnatorial glands, 440
Reservoir, 4
Reservoir hosts, 237
Respiration, 107, 583
Respiratory system
  adaptations, 347, 582
  insect, 491
  tracheae, 479
Respiratory pigments, 582–83
Respiratory tree, 563
Reticulitermes, **499**, 500
Reticulopodia, 29
Retinular cells, 409, 473
Retortamonadida, 115
Rhabdias, 273
Rhabdiasoidea, 273
Rhabdites, 215, **216**, 221
Rhabditis, **272**, 273
Rhabditoidea, 273
Rhabdocoelida, 220
Rhabdome, 409, 473
Rhabdophaga, 523
Rhabdopleura, 311
Rhabdopleurida, 311
Rhagodes, 454
Rhagon sponge, **139**
Rhizocephala, 429, **431**
Rhizomastigida, 16, 115
Rhizopodia, **27**–28, 105
Rhizostomeae, 186
Rhombogens, 290
Rhopalia, **181**, 182, **183**
Rhopalocera, 518
Rhopalosiphum, **510**
Rhopalura, 290
Rhynchobdellida, 343
Rhynchocoela, 286, 288*t.*, 293–96
Ricinoides, 460
Ricinulei, 460
RINALDI, R. A., 28
Ring canal, 545
RNA, 219, 538, **585**
ROBERTS, S. K., 537
RODALE, R., 335
Rodolia, 515, 536
ROGGEN, D. R., 271
ROGICK, M., 301
ROSS, R., 58
Rossia, 376

Rostrum, 398
Rotalia, **47**
Rotaria, **258**, 260
Rotatoria, 255
Rotifera, 252, 253, **255–61**, 347
Rotulae, 556
Roundworms, unsegmented, 263
ROWE, A. J., 68
RUDOLFI, C. A., 250
RUDZINSKA, M. A., 57
RUSHFORTH, N. B., 161

Sabella, 321
Sabellidae, 321
Saccoglossus, **310**
Sacculina, 429, **431**
Sacks, 255
Sagartia, 192
Sagitta, 305, **306**
Salivary glands, 356, 371, 477, 517
Salpa, 576
Salticidae, 459, **460**
Salticus, 459, **460**
Sand dollar, 558, **559**
SANDERS, H. L., 425
San Jose scale, **510**, 511
Saprophytic, 5
Sarcocystis, **59**–60
Sarcodina, 2, 24–48, 102–103, 105, 107, **112**, 114, 115
Sarcophaga, 525, **526**
Sarcophagidae, 525, **526**
Sarcoptes, 456, **457**
Sarcoptidae, 456, **457**
Sargus, **490**
Sarsiella, 426
Saturniidae, 520
SAVIGNY, M. J. C. DE, 349
Sawflies, 528, **529**
Scale-insects, **510**, 511
Scallop, 386, 387
Scaphognathite, 406
Scaphopoda, 350, 367–**68**
Scapteriscus, **498**
Scarabaeidae, **515**
Scarabaeus, **515**
SCHALIE, H. VAN DER, 393
SCHERBAUM, O., 69
Schistocera, 498
Schistosoma, **230**, **236**, 237
Schistosomatidae, 236
Schizaster, **560**
Schizogony, **50**, 53–**55**, 57
Schizomida, 455
SCHOOLEY, C. N., 5
SCHULZE, F. E., 145
Scleractinia, 192–93
Sclerites, 471
Scleroblasts, 124, 126, **127**, 140, 141

Sclerosepta, 190
Scolex, **238**, 242
Scolopendra, 438, **439**
Scolopendrella, 443
Scolopendridae, **439**
Scolopocrytops, 439
Scolytidae, **516**
Scolytus, 516
Scopula, 93
Scorpion, 452–54
Scorpionflies, 488, **517**
Scorpionida, 452–54
Screwworm fly, 525, 536
Scutellidae, 560
Scutellum, 474
Scutigera, 438, **439**
Scutigerella, 396, **442**, 443
Scutigeridae, **439**
Scutum, 474
Scypha, 124–29, 130, 131, 132, **133**, 138, 146
　embryology, 128
　morphology, 124–27
　nutrition, 127
　physiology, 127
　reproduction, 127, 143
Scyphistoma, 183, **184**
Scyphozoa, 148, 180–86, 202
Sea anemone, 186–89
Sea cucumbers, **561**–65
Sea fan, 197
Sea feather, **196**
Sea lilies, 565–67
Sea squirts, 576
Sea urchins, 563–60, **570**
Sea walnuts, 206
Secretion, 32, 107
Sedentaria, 320
Segments, 313, 325
　crayfish, 397
Segmentation, 326; *see also* Metamerism, 287
Seison, **258**, 260
Seisonida, **258**, 260
Semaeostomeae, 185–86
Seminal receptacle, 332
Seminal vesicle, 226, 333
Sensory receptors, 584
Sepia, 376
Sepiidae, 376
Sepiolidae, 376
Septa, **187**, 188, **193**, 313, 316, 326
Septibranchia, **385**, 390
Serpulidae, 321
Sertularia, 176, 198
Setae, **315**, 325, **326, 419**
Setaria, 280
SHAPEERO, W., 296
Shell, 103, 302, 553, 580
　clam, **378**–79

snail, **361**
　see also Carapace, Lorica, Test, Valves
Shrimp, 436
Sibine, 519
Siboglinum, **307**, 308, 310
SIEBOLD, C. T. E. VON, 113, 466
Silicoflagellida, 114
Silk glands, 451
Silkworm, 520
Silpha, **490**, 513
Silphidae, 513
Silverfish, 493, **494**
Simocephalus, 426
Simuliidae, 523, **525**
Simulium, 523, **525**
Sinantherina, 261
Sinus, 406
Sinus gland, 422, **423**
Siphon
　Anodonta, 378
　Arbacia, 554
　atrial, 574
　buccal, 574
Siphonaptera, 488, 526, **528**
Siphonodentalium, 368
Siphonoglyph, 188
Siphonophora, **179–80**, 199
Sipunculida, 286, 288*t*., 304–305, 345, 582
Sipunculus, 305
Sitotroga, 519
Size, Protozoa, 103
Skeleton, 103, 139, **192**
　exoskeleton, 395
　hydrostatic, 327
　starfish, 542
Skippers, 488, 518, 520, **521**
Sleeping sickness, 19
Slime molds, 43
Slug, 364, 367
Snail, 355
Snowflea, 494
Snowfly, 503
Snout beetles, 516
Social insects, 499, 529, 531
SOLLAS, W., 145
Soldier bug, **508**
Soldier termite, **499**
Solemya, 385
Solemyidae, 385
Solenia, 194
Solenidae, 389
Solenogastres, 355
Solenopsis, 529
Solifugae, **454**
Solpugida, 458
Somite, 313, 325
Sound production, 497, 498
Spanish fly, 514
Spatangoida, 560

Spathebothridea, 243
Spelaeogriphacea, 429
Spermathecae, 332
  Hydra, 163
  Scypha, 128
Spermatophores, 342, 373
Spermatozeugma, 392
Speyeria, 520
Sphaeriidae, 386
Sphaerium, **382, 385,** 386
Sphaerophyra, **95**–96
Sphecidae, 529, **532**
Sphex, 529, **532**
Sphingidae, **519,** 520
Sphinx, **491**
Spicules, 122, 124, 126, **127,** 130–31, 133, 134, 137, 139–41
  birotulate, 137
  flesh, 131
  monaxon, 130, 134, 140
  skeletal, 130
  tetraxon, 134, 140
  triaxon, 133, 140
Spider, **448**–**52,** 458–60
  anatomy, **448**–**50**
  physiology, 450
  red, 457
  web, 451–52
Spines, 543, 558, 559
Spinnerets, **449,** 450, 451
Spinosella, 142
Spinulosa, 549
Spinyheaded worm, 290
Spiracles, 479, **480**
Spirobrachia, 310
Spiromonas, 103
Spirorbis, 322
Spirostomum, 96, 98–**99,** 104
Spirotrichea, 89, 96–101, 116
Spirotrichonympha, **22**
Spirula, **374,** 376
Spirulidae, 376
Spiruroidea, 279
Spondylomorum, **14,** 110
Sponges, 121–47; *see* Porifera.
  bath, **137,** 143
  fresh-water, 137
  glass, 133
Spongia, **137,** 138, 146
Spongicola, 133
Spongilla, **129**–32, 137, **140,** 142, 146
Spongin, 121, 130, 134, 140, 144, **585**
Spongocoel, 122, 124, 125, 131, 132, 133, 138, 139
Sporangium, 43–**44**
Spores, 43, 48, **49,** 52, 54–55, **58**–60
Sporoblast, 49, 55
Sporocyst, 52, 55
  trematode, **227,** 229
Sporogony, **50,** 53–**55,** 57
Sporont, 53
Sporozoa, 2, 48–61, 106, 107, 110, 114, 115–16
Sporozoites, 48–52, 54–**55**
Sporulation, 55
Springtail, **494**
Squash bug, 509
Squid, 368
Squilla, **437**
Stagmomantis, **496**
Stalk, 566
Staphylinidae, **513,** 514
Staphylinus, 514
Starfishes, **542**–50
Statoblast, **299,** 300, 301
Statocyst, 173, 208, 359, 373, **382, 410**
  crayfish, 410
  Obelia, **170**
Statoliths, 359, 373, 410
Stauromedusae, 184–**85**
Stemonitis, **44**
Stenostomum, 221
Stenotrema, 367
Stentor, 96–**98,** 103, 107, 109, 112
Stephanoceros, 257, 258, 261
Stephanoprora, **231**
Stercoral pocket, 450
Sternum, 397, 449, 474
Stichocytes, 271
Stichopus, **562**
Stictocephala, 509
Stigma, 105
  Euglena, 4
Stigmata, Arachnida, 453
Sting, honeybee, 534–**35**
Stink bug, **508,** 509
Stipes, **473**
Stirodonta, 559
Stoichactis, 190
Stoloniferae, 194
Stomach, 379, 403, 491
Stomatoblastula, 129
Stomatopoda, 431, **437**
Stomodaeum, 188, 463
Stomoxys, 526
Stone canal, 545, 557
Stonefly, 488, 502–**503, 537**
Strainer, 403
Streblomastix, **22**
Strepsiptera, 488, 516–**17**
Strigeidae, 236
Strobilization, 184, 239
Strombidae, 363
Strombus, **362,** 363
Strongylocentrotidae, 560
Strongylocentrotus, 541, **554, 557,** 560
Strongyloidea, 276
Strongyloides, 273

Strongylus, 276
Stylaria, 336
Stylasterina, 178
Stylochus, 224
Stylommatophora, 366–67
Stylomurus, 448
Stylonychia, 96, 100–**101**
Stylopids, 516
Stylotella, 142, 143
Subcosta, **476,** 489
Suberites, 136
Subesophageal ganglion, 481, **483**
Subgenital plate, 477
Subimagos, 502
Submentum, **473,** 531
Subpharyngeal ganglia, 317, 330, **331**
Subumbrella, 172
Suckers, 340, 341
Suctorea, 89, **95**–96, 107, 110, 116
Suctorida, 95–96, 104, 116
Sulcus, **11,** 12
Sunderella, **22**
Suprabranchial chamber, **381,** 382
Supraesophageal ganglia, 358
Suprapharyngeal ganglia, 317, 330
Surra, 19
Sutures, 471
Swimmerets, 398, 401*t.*
Swimmer's itch, 237
Sycandra, **128**
Sycon, 124, **128,** 132; *see also Scypha*
Sycon sponge, 138, **139**
Syllidae, 319
Syllis, **319**
Symbiosis, 111, 158, **388**
Symmetry, 287
Sympetrum, 234
Symphyla, 396, 441, **442**–43
Synaptidae, 564
Syncarida, 430
Synchaeta, 259, 260
Syngamidae, 277
Syngamus, 277
Synkaryon, 81–83
Synura, **10,** 11
Syrphidae, 524
Syrphus, 524
Systemic heart, 370
Syzygy, 54

Tabanidae, 524, **525**
Tabanus, 524
Tachinidae, 525
Tadpole larva, **575**
Taenia, **215, 238**–40, 243
Taeniarhynchus, **238, 239,** 243
Taeniidae, 243
Taeniopteryx, 503
Taeniothrips, 505

Tagmata, 395
Talorchestia, 434
Tanaidacea, 430, 431, **433**
Tapeworms, 212, 238–43
Tarantula, 459
Tarantula, 458
Tardigrada, 286, 396, **442, 461**–**62**
Tarsus, 449, 475, 490
TARTER, V., 96
Tectibranchia, 365
Teeth, Pelecypoda, 378
Tegeticula, 518
Tegmina, 475, 489, 495
Telamona, 509
Telestaceae, 195
Telosporea, 53–58, 115–16
Telotroch, **93**
Telson, 398
Temnocephala, **222**
Temnocephalida, 220, **222**
Temperature, 36, 68, 81, 87, 161, 204
Tendipedidae, 522, 538
Tendipes, 522
Tenebrio, **490, 514**
Tenebrionidae, **514,** 515
Tentacles
 Ctenophora, 207
 Helix, 355
 Hydra, 149, 150, **160**
 Loligo, 370
 sea cucumber, 563
 Suctorea, **95**
Tentaculata, **207**
Tenthredinidae, 528, **529**
Tephritidae, 524, **526**
Tercera, **185**
Terebellidae, **320**
Terebrantia, 505
Terebratula, **302**
Terebratulina, 303
Teredidae, 390
Teredo, **385,** 390, 581
Tergum, 397, 474
Termite, 21–23, 488, **499–500**
Terricola, 224
Test, 103, 553, **555**
Testes, **164,** 342
Testicardines, 303
Tethya, **136**
Tetrabranchia, **374,** 375
Tetracha, 513
Tetrahymena, 61–71, 92
 axenic culture, 61, **67**
 contractile vacuole, 61, 64–**66**
 cytology, 61–67
 genetics, 70
 morphology, 61
 physiology, 68–69
 taxonomy, 69

Tetranychidae, 457
Tetranychus, 457
Tetraopes, 515
Tetraphyllidea, 242
Tetraplatia, 178
Tetrastemma, **293**, 296
Tetraxonida, 134–**35**, 146
Tettigoniidae, **497**
Texas fever, 57
Thalassema, 346
Thaliacea, 576
Thecanephria, 310
Thecla, 520
Thalazia, 279
Thelohania, **59**
Thelyphonida, 454
Thenea, **135**, 146
Theridiidae, 459, **460**
Theridion, 459, **460**
Thermobia, 494
Thermosbaenacea, 429
THIELE, J., 393
Thomisidae, 452, 459, **460**
Thomisus, **460**
Thoracica, 429, **430**
Thorax, 437, 463, 474
Thorybes, 520
Thrips, 488, **504,** 505–506
Thrips, 505
Thyone, 541, 561–63, 564
Thysanoptera, 488, **504,** 505–506
Thysanura, 488, 493–94
Tibia, 449, 475, 490
Ticks, 455–**56**
Tiedemann's bodies, 545
Tinea, **518,** 519
Tineidae, **518,** 519
Tingidae, **508**
Tintinnida, 102, 116
Tipula, **522**
Tipulidae, **522**
Tokophrya, **95**
Tooth shells, 367
Tornaria, 311, 572
Tortricidae, 519
Toxocara, 275
Toxoplasma, **60**
Toxoplasmida, **59**–61, 116
Toxoptera, 511
Tracheae, 479, **480**
Tracheoles, 479
Trachylina, 177–78, 202, 209
Trachymedusae, **177**
Tractella, 106, 108
TRAGER, W., 57
Tree hopper, **509**
Trematoda, 212, 224–37, 244
TREMBLEY, A., 112, 203, 250
Tremex, 528

Trepang, 564
Triarthrus, 448
Triatoma, **507,** 508
Trichinella, **274, 280**
Trichites, 90
Trichocera, 259, 260
Trichocysts, **72**–73, **75**–76, 78
Trichodina, **94,** 159
Trichomonadida, 21, 115
Trichomonas, **20,** 21, 233n.
Trichonympha, 21, **22**
Trichophrya, 96
Trichopoda, 525
Trichoptera, 488, **517**
Trichosomoides, 281
Trichostomatida, 90–**91,** 116
Trichostrongylidae, 278
Trichostrongylus, **283**
Trichuris, **274,** 281, **283**
Trichuroidea, 273, 280
Tricladida, 220, 223–24
Tridacna, **388,** 393
Tridacnidae, 389
Trilobita, **447**
Trilobitomorpha, 395, 446
Triodopsis, **366,** 367
Triploblastic, 214, 466
Tripneustes, 559
Trithena, **460**
Trithyreus, 455
Triton, 363
Trochanter, 449, 474, 490
Trochelminthes, 253
Trochidae, 362
Trochophore, 318, **338,** 347
Trochosphaera, 258, 282
Trochus, **255,** 259
Trochus, **361,** 362
Troglotrematidae, 236
Trombicula, **457**
Trombidiidae, **457**
Trophi, 256, **258**
Trophozoite, 21, 48, 51, 53
TRYON, G. W., 393
Trypanorhynchidea, 242
Trypanosoma, **18,** 19, 233n.
Trypoxylon, 529
Tsetse fly, 19
Tube feet, 542, 545, **546,** 547
Tubella, 137, **140**
Tubifera, 524
Tubifex, 313, 337, 583
Tubificidae, 337
Tubipora, 194, **195**
Tubulanus, 296
Tubularia, **175,** 176, **201**
Tubulifera, 506
Tunga, 528
Tunicata, 393

Tunicates, 574–76
Turbatrix, 263–64, 273
Turbellaria, 212, 213–24, **244, 249, 250**
Turrilites, **374**
TUZET, O., 141, 144
Tylenchidae, 273
Tympanum, 482
Typhloperipatus, 443
Typhlosole, **327**

Uca, 423, **435,** 436
Ultraviolet light, 7, 87
Ultrastructure, 112
Umbilicus, 363
Umbo, 378
Uncini, 308
Undulating membrane, 73, 106
  Kinetoplastida, **18**
  Paramecium, 73, 78, 80
  Tetrahymena, 63
  Trypanosoma, **18,** 73
Unio, **378,** 384
Unionidae, 386
Uniramous appendage, 398
Urechis, 345–46
Urnatella, **297,** 298
Urochordata, 574–76
Uroglena, 105
Uroglenopsis, **10,** 11
Uroleptus, 100, **101**
Uropod, 402*t.*
Uropygi, 454
Urosalpinx, 363, **364**

Valves, 378
Valvifera, 433
Vampyrella, **44**
Vas deferens, 325, 333, **342**
Veins, wing, 475, **476**
Velella, **180**
Veliger, **392**
Velum
  Coelenterata, 172
  Protozoa, 95
Vena cava, 380
Veneridae, 389
Ventricle, 352, 358, 380
Ventriculus, 477, 491
Venus, 296, **389**
Venus' flower basket, **133**
Venus' girdle, **210**
Vermes, 250, 349, 393
Vermicularia, **362**
Vertebrata, 574
Vespa, 529, **531**
Vespidae, 529, **531**
Vestibule, 70–71, 91
Vibracula, 299
Vinegar eel, 263

Vinegar roan, 454
Visceral ganglion, 382
Visceral hump, 355, 356
Vitelline duct, 226
Vitelline gland, 226
Vitrellae, 409
Viviparidae, 363
Viviparus, **361**
VOGT, C., 250
Volvocida, **11,** 13–16, 114
Volvocidae, 110
Volvox, **15,** 16, 44, 110, 141
Vorticella, **93**–94, 103, 106, 112
Vulva, 265

Waldheimia, **301, 302,** 303
Walking stick, **495**
WANKO, T., 61
WARDLE, R. A., 250
Wasps, 488, 529
Water bear, 461
Water boatman, **506,** 507
Water relationships, 581
Water scorpion, **506,** 507
Water strider, **506**
Water-vascular system, 545, 558
Web, spider, 451–52
WEBB, M., 308
Weevil, **516**
WEISMANN, A., 111
WELLS, H. S., 277
Whipworm, **274**
White ant, 488
  fly, 511
WICHTERMAN, R., 80
WILLIAMS, L. G., 259
Wing, 475, **476,** 488–89
  movement, **477**
  veins, **476,** 489
WINGSTRAND, K. G., 353
Wireworms, 514
Wohlfahrtia, 525
Wuchereria, **274,** 279

Xenopsylla, 526, **528**
Xenos, 517
Xiphinema, 271
Xiphosura, 446, **447**
Xiphosura, 396, 446, **447,** 583
X-organ, 422
X-rays, 70
Xylocopidae, 531

YAMAGUTI, S., 250
Yoldia, 385
YONGE, C. M., 393
Y-organ, 423
Yucca moth, 518
YUSA, A., 75

Zelleriella, **23**, 24
ZEUTHEN, E., 69
Zoantharia, 190–94
Zoanthidea, **193**
Zoea, **467**, 468
Zonaria, 363
Zonites, 262
Zooanthellae, 12, 112, 190
Zoochlorellae, 92, 97, 107, 112, 137, 158, 222

Zooecium, 298, **301**
Zoomastigophorea, 10, 16–23, 114–15
Zoophyta, 203
Zoothamnium, 94
Zoraptera, 488, 500
Zoroaster, 550
Zoroasteridae, 550
Zorotypus, 500
Zygoptera, 502
Zygote, **14**, 16, 52, 53, 81–82, 110